# CONTENTS

# ILLUSTRATIONS

## MAPS OF NUTTALL'S MAJOR JOURNEYS

For riches vanish, the most stately mansions fall into decay, the most prolific families die out sooner or later; the mightiest states and the most flourishing kingdoms may be overthrown; but the whole of nature must be obliterated before the genera of plants disappear and he be forgotten who held the truth aloft in botany.

— Linnaeus, *Critica Botanica.*

# THOMAS NUTTALL

## NATURALIST

·

## EXPLORATIONS IN

## AMERICA

1808–1841

*Jeannette E. Graustein*

HARVARD UNIVERSITY PRESS

CAMBRIDGE, MASSACHUSETTS

1967

The frontispiece is from a profile of Thomas Nuttall
by his nephew, who was christened Jonas Thomas Booth
but preferred to be called Thomas J. Booth.
It was probably done before Booth sailed for India in June 1849.
However, Booth was back in England from June 1851 to April 1856.
Courtesy of the Gray Herbarium, Harvard University.


Book design by David Ford

Let us as lovers of plants preserve records of our fellow labourers.

— Francis Boott to John Torrey
July 28, 1834

# PREFACE

After living thirty years in America, Nuttall returned to England unwillingly at the age of fifty-six to take over his uncle's estate. Following his death more than seventeen years later, two American obituaries appeared: one was by a casual acquaintance of his last years in the United States, and the other was by an immigrant British gardener who probably had never seen him. Both writers had difficulties in establishing facts concerning the life of a reserved wanderer who was continually taking off on new explorations, but some of Nuttall's associates contributed bits and pieces. The most helpful informant seems to have been Charles Pickering, a trusted friend and confidant of Nuttall during the last half of his stay in America, but, unfortunately for the record, except for one year the two were only occasionally together. Consequently the obituaries are marred by glaring errors and omissions, especially for the early part of Nuttall's career. However, they were accepted without question, and their mistakes were copied and dispersed by earnest botanists and carefree potboilers for three-quarters of a century and are still quoted. Rarely was a search made for more reliable information, such as Jepson's futile effort in 1905–1906 to find Nuttall's notebooks.

In the Gray Herbarium, built on the site of the Garden House where Nuttall had come to live one hundred and one years before, I listened to a famous taxonomist give an animated account of Nuttall's life. Its adventurous aspects aroused my admiration. The story concluded with the statement that, whereas his activities in Philadelphia were fairly well known, little was recorded of his life in Cambridge. I determined, therefore, to trace the activities of his Harvard years and search out his local friends and associations.

Readily available information proved to be limited, yet I found that his publications of thousands of pages contained tantalizing references to memories of childhood, expressions of intense personal feelings, allusions to unrecorded travels and to activities in biological fields not mentioned in the obituaries, evidences of family attachments, friends, and very many acquaintances, as well as frequent errors in his dates and geography. Correspondence of Nuttall and that between some of his friends and acquaintances also proved illuminating and spurred search for further *reliquiae*.

In 1936, Pennell's paper on Nuttall demonstrated how erroneous and inadequate the obituaries were. This new biographical sketch, which utilized the extensive investigations of Willard W. Eggleston (died November 25, 1935), of the United States Department of Agriculture, was based on a study of plant specimens which Nuttall had collected, as well as on his publications, and was molded also by some newly discovered early letters (the Delafield papers). A fresh picture appeared, but little if any light was thrown on the Cambridge years and only Nuttall's botanical activities were stressed; no effort was made to illuminate the years in England — his formative youth when the decision was made to go to America, the changing family situations which maintained a firm hold on the man, and the effective occupations of unwilling old age.

I have included here no bibliographic references to most short sketches of Nuttall for, generally speaking, they are uninformed. Known facts do not sanction a concept of Nuttall at twenty-five as a "spare, stooped, nearsighted fellow" who "saw and thought only botany," or similar ridiculous, disparaging statements. My prolonged searches in America and England have constructed for me a personality different from that which appears in previous accounts.

The number of institutions and persons to whom I am indebted for assistance through the decades I have pursued Nuttalliana is, I fear, beyond enumeration. I have found that Nuttall has many admirers — not limited to North America and Great Britain nor to botanists — who are eager to assist in producing as accurate a record as possible. Collateral descendants of Nuttall who furnished invaluable information and family records include Major and Mrs. William F. Dixon-Nuttall, Mr. and Mrs. Thomas Dixon-Nuttall, Geoffrey Dixon-Nuttall, and the late Samuel Rishworth Booth. The largest collection of Nuttall's own letters is in the voluminous correspondence of Sir William Jackson Hooker at the Royal Botanic Gardens, Kew; I am grateful to the Keeper of the Herbarium for the opportunity of consulting the manuscript collections there and also to the then Librarian, Mr. H. S. Marshall, for his thoughtful anticipation of my every interest. Both the Botanical and Mineralogical Departments of the British Museum of Natural History facilitated study of Nuttall's collections. I am indebted to Mr. O'Grady, General Secretary of the Linnean Society of London, and to the Royal Geological Society. Varied assistance was received at the Liverpool Public Library and Museums, especially from Dr. H. Stansfield of the Department of Botany. Through him I had the valuable help of I. Henry Burkill and F. Ludlow in dealing with Nuttall's Assam plants. Dr. T. C. Barker, economist, was a generous guide to English sources of information. Through the kindness of Richard Saltonstall I was able to consult the files of the Massachusetts Society for Promoting Agriculture. I especially appreciate the great courtesy of Columbia University in extending the facilities of their libraries to me for a long span of time.

For permission to use quotations from letters I am indebted to the courtesy of Mr. H. R. Roberts, Director of the Academy of Natural Sciences of Philadelphia; Mrs. Gertrude D. Hess of the American Philosophical Society Library; the Trustees of the Boston Public Library; Professor Dr. Jacques Miège, Directeur des Conservatoire et Jardin Botaniques, Geneva, Switzerland; Mr. James M. Babcock, Chief, Burton Historical Collection, Detroit Public Library; Mr. Richard H. Hill, Director of The Filson Club, Louisville, Kentucky; Dr. Reed C. Rollins, Director of the Gray Herbarium of Harvard University; Mr. Clifford K. Shipton, Custodian of the Harvard University Archives; Mr. Nicholas B. Wainwright, Director of the Historical Society of Pennsylvania; Sir George Taylor, Director of the Royal Botanic Gardens, Kew, England; The Library Company of Philadelphia; the Massachusetts Historical Society; Dr. George Van Schaack, Librarian of the Missouri Botanical Garden; The New York Botanical Garden; Mr. James J. Heslin, Director of the New-York Historical Society; Mr. Robert W. Hill, Keeper of Manuscripts, New York Public Library; and Dr. W. Stanley Hoole, Librarian of the University of Alabama. Through the kind permission of the Linnean Society of London quotations are made from their manuscripts and records. Individuals who generously permitted me to use letters include Miss Elizabeth Putnam and the late Mrs. Roy A. Hunt. I am grateful to the editors of *Appalachia*, *Bartonia*, and

# PREFACE

*Rhodora* for allowing me to quote from certain articles in these publications. Specific citations of these and other sources are recorded in the notes.

Through this absorbing task, I have been spurred by the interest and assistance of Dr. Frans Verdoorn, Dr. John Francis McDermott of Washington University, Dr. Francis Harper, the late Francis H. Allen, a devoted member of the Nuttall Ornithological Club, Professor Joseph Ewan of Tulane University, Dr. Samuel Wood Geiser of Southern Methodist University, Dr. Richard G. Beidleman of Colorado College, Dr. George W. White of the Geology Department of the University of Illinois, Dr. Reed C. Rollins and Dr. Lily Perry of the Gray Herbarium, and other well-wishers.

For continual reading of manuscript and many suggestions, I am deeply grateful to Professor Fern Yates of Barnard College.

J. E. G.

# CONTENTS

# CONTENTS

# CHAPTER I

# NUTTALL'S AMERICAN RECORD

To converse with nature, to admire the wisdom and beauty of creation has ever been . . . to me a favourite pursuit. — Thomas Nuttall, *Journal of a Journey into the Arkansa Territory*, preface.

Thomas Nuttall emigrated to the United States in the spring of 1808 at the age of twenty-two, already dedicated to the study of its natural history and intending to be an American to the end of his days. His pleasure in first seeing American plants always remained a vivid and cherished memory, and each addition was an exciting experience. His enthusiasm was unbounded when, on his first journey beyond the Appalachians, he began to find species completely unknown. Thereafter botanical exploration became the controlling passion of his life.

He incorporated his early observations into the first taxonomic botanical work of broad scope published in America, two small volumes which received immediate recognition on both sides of the Atlantic as a contribution of great merit. But "he could not rest from travel." Expeditions into frontier country, and beyond, served only to increase his ardor and whet his ambition to go further into the Territories, which abounded in new forms of life and fresh scenes of grandeur. The thrill of collecting natural treasures — floral, faunal, and mineralogical — transcended all considerations of financial expediency and personal safety.

He rejoiced in the fantastic lands of the West, impressive in their undisturbed immensities and fascinating in their revelations of geological history. The Oregon Trail, the Columbia River valley, and the California coast yielded harvests to his eager hands and eyes as had the country along the upper Missouri, the Mississippi, the Ohio, and the Great Lakes, the Arkansas Territory, the Southeast, and the Atlantic States. From observations both wide and intensive, his "keen scientific perception" produced the first correlation of geological formations of two continents. The full expanse of the natural world enticed him, but he always returned to Flora. No other botanist collected as many new kinds of plants within what is now the United States; no other naturalist saw so much of it in primeval condition. He wrote the first ornithology of North America that was priced for general purchase and did it so successfully that three editions of it were brought out at the turn of the century! His field knowledge of the natural history of temperate America was unequaled in his day and has hardly been rivaled. It was not quantity nor scope, however, nor ecological knowledge that most distinguished his work, but a fine discrimination of eye, ear, and scientific judgment and a unique acumen in the field that revealed to him species not found again for decades — in some cases not for over a century.[1] Matching these qualities was his single-minded devotion to nature; this is emphasized in two great American literary classics of the frontier — Washington Irving's *Astoria* and Richard H. Dana's *Two Years before the Mast* — in which Nuttall appears. He is also recognized as "easily the first man of science in Augustan Harvard."[2]

However, Fate intervened in his work on American species and his original hopes of remaining in America; at the close of 1841 he left reluctantly for his native England, breaking abruptly a distinguished and astonishing record of adventurous scientific exploration and of solid accomplishment in advancing the knowledge of American plants, birds and other animal groups, minerals, and geology. While preparing to depart he wrote in rare reflective mood a brief autobiography of his life in America:

Thirty-four years ago, I left England to explore the natural history of the United States. In the ship Halcyon I arrived at the shores of the New World; and after a boisterous and dangerous passage, our dismasted vessel entered the Capes of the Delaware in the month of April. The beautiful robing of forest scenery, now bursting into vernal life, was exchanged for the monotony of the dreary ocean, and sad sickness of the sea. As we sailed up the Delaware my eyes were rivetted on the landscape with intense admiration. All was new! — and life, like that season, was then full of hope and enthusiasm. The forests apparently unbroken, in their primeval solitude and repose spread themselves on either side as we passed placidly along. The extending vista of dark Pines gave an air of deep sadness to the wilderness. . . .

Scenes like these have little attraction for ordinary life. But to the naturalist it is far otherwise; privations to him are cheaply purchased if he may roam over the wild domain of primeval nature. . . .

How often have I realized the poet's buoyant hopes amid these solitary rambles through interminable forests! For thousands of miles my chief converse has been in the wilderness with the spontaneous productions of nature; and the study of these objects and their contemplation has been to me a source of constant delight.

The fervid curiosity led me to the bank of the Ohio, through the dark forests and brakes of the Mississippi, to the distant lakes of the northern frontier; through the wilds of Florida; far up the Red River and the Missouri, and through the territory of Arkansaw; at last over the

> Vast savannas, where the wandering eye,
> Unfixed, is in a verdant ocean lost;

And now across the arid plains of the Far West, beyond the steppes of the Rocky Mountains, down the Oregon to the extended shores of the Pacific, across the distant ocean to that famous group, the Sandwich Islands, where Cook at length fell a sacrifice to his temerity. And here for the first time I beheld the beauties of a tropical vegetation; . . . an elysian land where nature offers spontaneous good to man. . . .

Leaving this favoured region of perpetual mildness, I now arrived on the shores of California, at Monterrey. The early spring (March) had already spread out its varied carpet of flowers; all of them had to me the charm of novelty, and many were adorned with the most brilliant and varied hues. . . . The scenery was mountainous and varied, one vast wilderness, neglected and uncultivated; and the cattle appeared as wild as the bison of the prairies. . . .

After a perilous passage around Cape Horn, the dreary extremity of South America, amid mountains of ice which opposed our progress in unusual array, we arrived again at the shores of the Atlantic. Once more I hailed those delightful scenes of nature with which I had been so long associated. I rambled again through the shade of the Atlantic forests, or culled some rare productions of Flora in their native wilds. But the "oft-told tale" approaches to its close and I must now bid a long adieu to the "New World," its sylvan scenes, its mountains, wilds, and plains; and henceforth, in the evening of my career, I return almost an exile, to the land of my nativity.[3]

One of Nuttall's contemporaries called this brief autobiography "a beautiful piece of elocution. In reading it, you feel carried along with him through all his adventurous journeys. . . . He was strongly attached to the United States. Here were almost all his associations; he had friends who were dear to him; and, wherever he went, whether in the valley or on the mountain, by the shores of the sea or the margin of the quiet stream, he felt surrounded by old acquaintances, his dearest flowers; or met, by chance, a new object for his admiration."[4]

3

CHAPTER 2

# YOUTH IN ENGLAND

Only when one knows what were his peculiar endowment, temper and limitations can his conduct be comprehended. — Henry James, *Charles William Eliot*, I, vii.

EARLY YEARS IN YORKSHIRE. The Ribble valley in the Craven District of western Yorkshire was for centuries the home of Thomas Nuttall's maternal ancestors. Bleak high moors of the Pennines dominate the area so that it is suitable only for sheep raising and has thus remained sparsely settled and wild in character.[1] In the settlements in the Dales, as the numerous river valleys are called, the scene is softened: the villages with their few trees and shrubs and the houses, sheltering one another, form pleasant oases in an austere countryside. Such a village is Long Preston where Thomas was born.[2]

The name Long Preston is said to be a corruption of "Long Priests' Town," commemorating the fact that the church services for a once extensive valley parish were conducted by Augustinian canons from Embsay and Bolton Priories[3] before 1234 when Peter de Hedon became the first resident vicar. The compactly built street-village extends today about half a mile along the main road which runs north and south well above the east bank of the Ribble. Closely placed or conjoined houses, severely built of gray stone, cling to the street. The lich gate, leading to the large enclosure around the ancient church of St. Mary the Virgin, is on a side lane at the south of the village, and nearby is the old parish school which Thomas attended.

On January 6, 1785, at the parish church where generations of Hardacres had worshipped, Margaret Hardacre married James Nuttall of Colne, Lancashire.[4] That the marriage was by license, instead of by the usual banns proclaimed on three successive Sundays before

4

the wedding, implies that Richard Hardacre was well to do. Tradition reports that she returned to the home of her parents, Richard and Agnes (Taylor), for the birth of her first child, Thomas, on January 5, 1786.[5] What pursuit James followed is not known, nor where the family lived, but it is recorded that they were not prosperous. Under financial stress, Margaret may have taken her children to stay for protracted periods with her relatives or may have placed Thomas in the care of her parents; in any case, Long Preston is the locus of all the early memories that Thomas wrote of in later years. It is certain that, after James died in 1798, his widow lived in Long Preston with her three children, Thomas, Susan (Susannah), and Elizabeth,[6] "nearly left in poverty through the wastefulness of their unfortunate father." [7] Various tablets in the church and entries in the parish register bear witness that the Hardacres were a family widely dispersed through the area, some of them, at least, well to do and well connected. Their forebears had perhaps lived there from remote antiquity: on a fragmentary list of Craven men who fought with the long bow at Flodden Field in 1513 under Lord Henry Clifford, one-third of those from the parish of Long Preston were Hardakers.[8] Margaret continued to live in her native village among her kinsfolk until her death in her eighty-first year. For Thomas, Long Preston was the home of his youth to which he always remained attached and frequently returned.

The low rectangular church of St. Mary the Virgin, with "an aspect of heavy, substantial endurance and long, long decay," [9] is set in a great, walled churchyard shaded by lofty trees that dwarf its Norman tower. In the stonework of the small entrance porch, a child's sarcophagus dating from the previous Saxon edifice is half concealed.[10] The interior is large, serene, and comforting. The great hewn beams and the random stonework of the walls invite the eye to endless roving, as do the windows of the north aisle which look out on steeply rising moors. Here Thomas attended regularly the services of the Church of England.

East and north of the village the treeless slopes of sheep pastures climb to the high plateau of the Pennines. Their division by drystone walls, built narrow and high of flat gray stones, forms a conspicuous, irregular pattern on the slopes. The country is spacious and elevated; over it the winds blow unimpeded, increasing the exhilaration of a fair day or the chill of the frequent rains. Autumn comes early. Spring is slow and cold with the yellow flowers of the lesser celandine brightening the grass for weeks in March and April. Young Thomas must have enjoyed the changing aspect of the fells through the seasons, the clear-running becks, and also the river valley to the west of the village where extensive marshes then lined the Ribble. Pendle Hill looms in the south, its symmetrical form familiar to Thomas "from infancy"; by it "all the good wives in the surrounding country could foretel[l] the weather better than by the almanac." [11]

Today the population of six hundred odd is less than that of Nuttall's childhood. No appreciable changes in the village are apparent, although the green may have been larger since it seems that the western end of the green may have been taken for the site of a Methodist church. The maypole which gave its name to the small inn facing the green is gone, and one looks in vain for the old hawthorn whose fragrant white blossoms falling "like a shower of snow" on the sward were connected with Nuttall's "earliest recollections of the joyful arrival of spring — a delightful era in the distant reminiscences of the writer, when yet the simplest boon of nature gave delight." [12] Thomas learned Nature's alphabet along with his schoolroom abc's and never finished reading in her book nor exhausted its problems and fascinations.

The local folk stories which he continually heard had the appeal for him that fairy tales have for children. Thus in middle life he recalled:

A superstitious legend prevails in the north of England, that Pharaoh's daughter was transformed into an Owl, and the common distich, which I have often heard when a child, and while the Owl was screaming on a winter's night, ran thus:

Oh, 'ŏŏ̆ oō —
I once was a king's daughter and sat on my father's knee,
But now I'm a poor Hoolet, and hide in a hollow tree!

an invention that might do credit to the genius of Ovid. . . .

And of the magpie he wrote:

As might have been anticipated from his sagacity, the Pie has been considered as a messenger of fate in the north of Europe, and I have myself, when a boy, been often delighted or vexed, by the augural destiny of their appearance in certain lucky or unlucky numbers. The antiquity of this superstition, still in existence, goes back probably to the time of the Romans.

"As quarrelsome as Quails in a cage," a phrase that he recalled from childhood, is rich in its implications of a rural culture influenced by the natural environment. We know that Margaret Hardacre Nuttall was keenly aware of the animal life around her and speculated about it.[13]

It is improbable that during his school days, which ended when he was fourteen, Thomas got far afield from the village or saw the picturesque natural formations a few miles away that give special interest to this section of the Pennines. It is perhaps unlikely that as a child he appreciated the ancient history of his native village and its environs: that its very street was a portion of a Roman road with remains of Roman camps beside it; that the lower Ribble in Lancashire offered an entrance to the region used by invaders and traders long before and after the Romans arrived and founded Ribchester; that the fine wool of the Pennine sheep was exported to the continent through centuries of blurred political and social history. However, there is no doubt that in later years the historic aspects of Ribblesdale and the discoveries of prehistoric artifacts and fossils in its soil and caves engaged his interest.

Immediately before him at fourteen lay the common lot of the ordinary English boy of the time, the sound vocational training of seven years' apprenticeship in a trade. To this he carried the Yorkshire characteristics of seriousness, independence, thoroughness, and perseverance — qualities that he never lost — and also individual gifts of devotion, acute perception, and an ardent and sensitive spirit that were to build for him an enduring memorial far from his native soil. In Long Preston his accomplishments were never recognized and his name is forgotten.

APPRENTICESHIP IN LIVERPOOL. Free to some extent to choose the trade in which he would serve his apprenticeship, Thomas, endowed with an active, clear intellect and a reflective mind, demonstrated the trend of his nature by electing to learn the printing business with his father's younger brother Jonas. The Nuttalls stemmed from an ancient Lancashire family. Jonas, after serving his own apprenticeship with John Ferguson in Liverpool, was first established in business in Blackburn in the lower valley of the Ribble where he was a partner of J. Hemenway.[14] They were an enterprising pair with a fine reputation and are credited with perhaps the largest book printed in Lancashire before 1800, *An Impartial History of England*, "an astonishing production for so young a press, being well printed in double columns. It was apparently published in 60 × 4 periodical parts." [15]

By 1800 Jonas had started in business for himself in Liverpool, a rapidly growing port with a population of about 75,000.[16] Through the years he entered into various partnerships, the most enduring of which was that of Nuttall, Fisher, and Dixon. Francis Dixon was related by marriage to Jonas, and the son of Henry Fisher married one of Francis Dixon's granddaughters, so the firm was more or less a family affair. Thomas lived with his childless Uncle Jonas and Aunt Frances throughout the seven years of his training, which began in 1800.

Jonas's first business location in Liverpool was at the western edge of the city on Denison Street which commanded a view of the Mersey where the billowing canvas of the sailing vessels created an ever fascinating scene. The Fort nearby on the riverbank was a public recreation spot where the evening drill and the relief of the guard were popular daily events. A short distance away lay St. George's Dock, the resort of West India ships that carried Negro slaves from Africa in their triangular voyages — of all shipping the most spectacular.[17] Thomas probably often walked among the docks and may have then acquired a longing to sail to distant lands. After a few years, Jonas moved the printing shop to Duke Street and his home to nearby Wolstenholme Square where a view of the waterfront was not an around-the-corner matter.

In contemporary directories Jonas's business was listed as "printers and periodical publishers." It is said to have been the first in Liverpool to issue publications to subscribers in monthly or quarterly parts, the cost of which was within the means of small farmers and workingmen; illustrated Bibles, works on religion, biography, travel, and miscellaneous literature were printed in this form. Canvassers covered most of the northern counties to extend this highly profitable business. Reprints in book form were produced also — histories, sermons, dictionaries, and literary masterpieces — as well as new publications.[18] In after years Thomas mentioned that he set the type for a reprinting of the works of Joseph Priestley.[19] The company, which called itself the Caxton Press, occasionally issued on the wrappers "a spirited cock-crow defiance against rival publishers." [20]

Jonas's best-known author was Dr. Adam Clarke, a famous Wesleyan preacher, biblical commentator, and scholar. That he was selected by the Records Commission to reedit Rymer's *Foedera* (the record of England's transactions with foreign powers) attests his reputation for learning. Thomas doubtless assisted in setting the type of the first three volumes of Clarke's *Bibliographical Dictionary*, which appeared in 1802 and 1803 from his uncle's press. The subtitle suggests how Thomas was extending his education:

Containing a chronological Account, alphabetically arranged, of the most curious, scarce, useful, and important *Books*, in all Departments of Literature, which have been published in *Latin, Greek, Coptic, Hebrew, Samaritan, Syriac, Chaldee, Aetheopic, Arabic, Persian, Armenian*, etc. From the Infancy of Printing to the Beginning of the Nineteenth Century with Biographical Anecdotes of Authors, Printers, and Publishers, etc., etc. . . . To which are added, *An Essay on Bibliography.* . . .

In this impressive compendium the entries of Aesop's *Fables* occupy nine pages.

The hours of labor were from dawn to dusk, but Sunday was a day for the Lord and oneself. Thomas always remained attached to the Church of England,[21] although his Aunt Frances was a zealous Methodist, active in the charitable work started by Wesleyans among the wretched poor of the city, and his Uncle Jonas enthusiastically abetted her. Conscious of the deficiencies of his schooling, Thomas devoted all possible time and opportunity to self-education. He concentrated his attention on Latin, Greek, and French and profited from the guidance of a fellow apprentice, a nephew of Dr. Adam Clarke. The cultivation of a small garden was a hobby, but unfortunately this supplied only seasonal exercise and diversion. He spent such long hours at his studies that in his late teens his health began to suffer, and a vacation at his home in Long Preston was arranged for him.

There he happily met with activity physically restorative and mentally stimulating. In the company of John Windsor of nearby Settle, an enthusiastic and keen young botanist of his own age, he collected and studied plants in the region of Craven, incidentally saw some of its spectacular scenery, and learned something about its geology.[22]

The Pennines, a broken irregular chain of high hills extending from Derbyshire to Northumberland, are crowned by carboniferous sediments of varying composition. In the Craven district the youngest, coal-bearing, strata have been completely denuded leaving exposed the underlying millstone grit or, where that also has been eroded, mountain limestone. Some of the higher summits lie in upper Ribblesdale: Whernside (2414 ft.), Ingleborough (2373 ft.), and Penyghent (2273 ft.); and to the south just over the border in Lancashire stands the isolated symmetrical dome of Pendle Hill (1831 ft.). The sides of the hills are steep and the summits flat or broadly domed. Some aspects of the striking scenery for which the region is famous are due to faulting in the mountain limestone: colossal breaks and dislocations that extend roughly east and west for twenty miles form high vertical cliffs which at Gordale Scar display a foaming cascade on precipitous walls and at Malham Cove are carved into a great amphitheatre from the base of which the full-fledged River Aire issues. The faults gave the name "Craven" to the region (from Old French and Middle English usage). The gray millstone grit is turned to practical use in constructing dwellings, outbuildings, and drystone walls throughout the district.

With John Windsor, Thomas followed ancient tracks to Penyghent's summit and to Arncliffe Clouder and other heights of the Craven Hills where such rarities as roseroot stonecrop (*Sedum Rosea* (L.) Scop.), yellow and purple mountain saxifrages (*Saxifraga aizoides* L. and *S. oppositifolia* L.), mountain avens (*Dryas octopetala* L.), and baked-apple berry (*Rubus Chamaemorus* L.) could be found. Perhaps Nuttall's marked ecological interest was awakened here through noting the difference in kind between the plants on the rich limestone slopes and those of the siliceous summits. On the windswept crests, Thomas experienced a delightful feeling of freedom and exhilaration. When he stood on these heights, he found that the emptiness of the far-spread moors below was relieved by the curving courses of the becks and by an occasional tarn; the deep silence was broken by the ringing songs of soaring curlews, the piping trills of pipits, and the lonely bleating of moorland sheep. The great scarps of the Craven displacements, dramatically sheer and majestic, the bubbling underground streams which suddenly find an exit to the surface, intermittent springs, sinkholes of terrifying depth, caves adorned with stalactites and stalagmites, waterfalls and cascades— all these gave to the youth an inkling of the marvels which the world might afford to him who searched. Here on his native hills, in company with his "earliest botanical friend," [23] Thomas's lifelong passion for Flora was born and a keen interest in geology and mineralogy stimulated. This experience was the decisive factor of his life.

He returned to his work in the fast-growing city on the Mersey with a new purpose and a new outlook on the future. To the study of languages he must have added whatever of natural history he could find in the diverse offerings of Liverpool. His small garden would have greater interest. Largely through the efforts of William Roscoe, a private Botanic Garden had been opened in 1803 with John Shepherd as curator; probably Thomas managed to visit this occasionally as a guest.[24] Its five acres, large conservatory, and aquatic sites had been planted with striking exotics of the world's flora. The beautiful planting of palm trees was especially effective[25] in creating a junglelike background for such tropical plants as bananas, coffee and orange trees, sugar cane, gourds, and quantities of elegant orchids.[26]

Although many museums at that time were largely unclassified accumulations of oddities and monstrosities the Liverpool Museum, developed by William Bullock (fl. 1808–1828) from 1801 to 1809, had exhibits of historic and scientific merit, such as objects brought back from Cook's voyages. The fifth edition of the descriptive guide to the museum, printed in 1805 by Jonas Nuttall, lists numerous specimens of plants and the conspicuous animal groups, arranged according to the Linnaean system and differentiated instructively.[27] Benjamin Silliman, who visited the exhibits in May 1805, considered them "well worth seeing."[28] Indeed the excellence of the collection is attested by Bullock's election as a Fellow of the Linnean Society and to membership in the Horticultural, Geological, and Wernerian Societies.[29] There was no public library to supply volumes on natural history, exploration, and travels but Jonas may have belonged to the Lyceum or some other subscription library. Public lectures on botany were given from time to time in Liverpool by James Edward Smith, President and Founder of the Linnean Society of London and the purchaser for Britain of Linnaeus's effects.

As the apprenticeship drew to its end early in 1807, a clash of interests between Jonas and his nephew came to the surface, if indeed it had not previously become apparent. The childless Jonas was probably already anticipating his early retirement to a country estate, and he had doubtless long since settled in his mind that his intelligent and industrious nephew would take his place in the printing business and in his turn become financially successful. But Thomas apparently refused to concur with Jonas's plans because his inclinations drew him strongly to the natural sciences, and he had decided to cast his lot in the United States.

Thomas's life was so single in its dedication to the natural history of America and his ambition such a singular one for a Liverpool printer's apprentice to embrace that the source of his early resolution arouses curiosity. How did an English youth before he reached his majority become committed in his heart to so unlikely a project? His writings give no clue, so speculation may be confined only by probabilities.[30]

John Windsor remarked on the botanical opportunities of the western hemisphere in telling Thomas about one of his botanical friends, Thomas Williams Simmonds, a young graduate of the famous Giggleswick Grammar School near Settle, which Windsor had attended.[31] Simmonds had been one of Windsor's earliest tutors in the study of local plants. After obtaining medical training and a reputation in England as a brilliant natural scientist, he had gone in 1803 as naturalist in the suite of Lord Seaforth, Governor of Barbados; unfortunately in a few months, "while busied in the exploration of Trinidad," death closed his promising career.[32] This account may have given Thomas the idea of studying New World flora on the North American continent, an undertaking which offered scope for a life's work in a genial climate. The names of these three botanists are linked together in the genus *Simmondsia,* which Nuttall established for a California shrub in 1844 at Windsor's request.

Other possible sources of Thomas's fixed notion may have been in such reading as François André Michaux's *Travels to the Westward of the Allegheny Mountains in the States of Ohio, Kentucky and Tennessee*, which was published in English translation in London in 1805, or Alexander von Humboldt's "Essai sur le géographie des plantes." Or, more probably, since he himself made no known statement about it, a fusion of such influences may have played on his imagination.

Thomas's determination to forsake an assured livelihood to go to a distant country, which his uncle considered highly dangerous, resulted in a quarrel and a break between them that persisted for about a year. Tradition reports that during this time Thomas came near to starvation in London, where he tried vainly to find an opening in

biological work. He himself related that he was sometimes "so destitute of money as to be uncertain, on going to bed, where he would
get his breakfast next morning." [33] He would not live for bread alone,
but he found that he could not live without it. Either the breach with
Jonas was healed — and there were plenty of intercessors to achieve
that — or money was supplied from other sources, for Thomas to set
out for America. On March 13, 1808, he sailed from Liverpool for
Philadelphia on the *Halcyon*.[34] He expected to support himself as a
journeyman printer; his cherished objective of studying the natural
history of the new world would have to be subservient to earning a
living. Jonas probably hoped that the young man would learn a good
lesson and return to Liverpool glad to take a permanent place in a
moneymaking business.

For Thomas, 1807 was a lost year in a life otherwise filled with
accomplishment. This may have been the basis for his annoying
tendency to date events of his career a year too early; one might
venture to surmise that these errors resulted from an unconscious
wish to wipe from his memory a period of futile suffering.

# CHAPTER 3

# TRANSPLANTATION

Those that love their owne chimney corner and dare not go farre beyond their own townes end shall never have the honour to see these wonderfull workes of Almighty God. — Francis Higginson, 1629.

THE UNITED STATES IN 1808. Twenty-five years after the close of the Revolution, the thirteen original states on the Atlantic shore had been increased to seventeen by the addition of Vermont, Kentucky, Tennessee, and Ohio, and the Territories east of the Mississippi River were in various degrees of settlement. The trans-Appalachian country was steadily receiving colonists who were going from the North down the Ohio and from the South across the mountains, but even a decade later primitive forest still clothed the lower Ohio valley. Small country towns, like Cincinnati, Ohio, and Louisville, Kentucky, did not grow appreciably until steamboats began to ply in numbers on the Ohio in the 1820s. The new country was an invitation to pioneers of two extremes of disposition, the ambitious and the shiftless. Many hoped by hard work to make permanent comfortable homes on rich virgin soil and were assisting to develop civilized communities such as they had left behind the mountains; others, intent on avoiding work and caring nothing for refinements, lived slovenly and meagerly by hunting and moved westward as the forests were gradually cut and the game retreated.

The Louisiana Purchase in 1803 doubled the territory of the United States, carrying it from the Mississippi to the Rockies. The region, however, was vast and remote. By reason of the native inhabitants, who had not subscribed to the Purchase, the land was so dangerous that, save for some of the nearby banks of the great rivers, it was of immediate interest only to trappers and fur traders.

# TRANSPLANTATION

Politically the United States under the presidency of Thomas Jefferson was developing a less conservative tendency except in New England where the *status quo* favored entrenched financial interests. The national capital had been moved from Philadelphia, Pennsylvania, in the summer of 1800 to the newly created center on the Potomac. Philadelphia's prestige still persisted, however, as the leading city of the country, although it was being eclipsed commercially and in population by New York with its magnificent harbor.

Economically the wealth of the nation was in its land and its carrying trade. Although the population of about seven million was overwhelmingly rural, drawing its living from the soil, greater opportunities were provided by shipping and trade, especially in the north. Every little town on a stream navigable to small ships was a port — Middletown on the Connecticut, Kingston on the Hudson, Alexandria on the Potomac. The Napoleonic Wars impeded shipping, but the profits were sufficiently great to encourage the risks involved. In 1807 Robert Fulton demonstrated that steamboats might before long speed communication and commerce, for a trial run of the *Clermont* from New York City to Albany was made in the astonishing time of thirty-two hours! Manufacturing was carried on in a small way in scattered centers: paper and spinning mills and the making of iron, glass, hats, rifles, clocks, and other small articles were yielding profits. Shipbuilding and printing, well established from early colonial days, were widespread, as were gristmills and sawmills.

Travel was by water wherever possible, for the only first-class road in the country was the sixty-two-mile macadamized turnpike from Philadelphia to the Pennsylvania capital of Lancaster. The few, poor roads, most bearable on horseback, did not encourage journeys for pleasure. Even business trips, when possible, were timed to avoid the deep mud of spring and the dust of dry seasons. William Hamilton called the roads "villainous" and riding on them comparable to being "chin deep in hasty pudding." Stagecoaches had neither springs nor upholstery. The inns were generally indifferent and, beyond the Appalachians, usually crude, noisy, and forbiddingly uncomfortable. To go a hundred miles or so entailed two or three or more strenuous days of discomfort; more distant trips required the careful planning of a major event.

There was no rapid transit of intelligence. The mail was generally carried on horseback by leisurely daytime service only. News of

European events did not arrive for weeks, and adverse weather often subjected it to further delay.

Religion had a strong hold on the thoughts and activities of most of the people. Sunday was devoted to worship, and the morning sermon was the chief mental fare of the week for many of the population. To experience conversion was the pious hope of adolescents; collegians wrote to their parents serious letters about the state of their souls. Missions were established to send trained and sober preachers to the frontiers; itinerant preaching by fanatical revivalists developed later.

It is not easy to keep in mind the inconvenience of daily living in 1808 unless one is steeped in social history. The leisurely pace and the habit of patiently taking time and pains in every activity were in the greatest contrast to our times. Sending a package to a distant point, and sometimes even a letter, might necessitate personal arrangements with a traveler or a ship's captain. Such simple matters as getting a light, or obtaining heat for cooking, hinged on a series of time-consuming chores. The use of gas for lighting was a novelty on exhibit at Peale's Museum in Philadelphia. Oil laboriously gathered at Oil Creek on the Alleghany was valued only as an embrocation, a use adopted from the Indians as suggested by its name of "Seneca Oil." The ingenuity of America was already at work in inventing and improving mechanical processes but chemical knowledge was in its infancy, electricity was a mysterious, uncontrolled force, and the automatic amenities of present-day life were undreamed of.

The population was independent, busy with efforts and plans to improve in economic affairs, generally ambitious, alert and resourceful, and perhaps somewhat smug in its growing prosperity. Money was scarce, and the value of the dollar was high. Cultural activities were more or less confined to the larger towns of the seaboard. Philadelphia's American Philosophical Society (1769), Boston's American Academy of Arts and Sciences (1780), and the Massachusetts (1791) and New York (1804) Historical Societies denote the existence of groups concerned with intellectual interests and rational speculations. These societies produced irregular publications, and there were also a very few periodicals, notably the *Port Folio* (1801–Dec. 1827) in Philadelphia and Dr. Mitchill's *New York Medical Repository*, which found enough support to appear regularly for more than two decades (1797–1824). Such publications furnished an outlet for literary efforts and scientific papers. In 1808 America showed promise of a bright future in all fields of man's endeavor.

Although intellectual activity bore fruits in Newport, Rhode Island, New Haven, Connecticut, Charleston, South Carolina, and larger centers, Philadelphia led the country in all branches of thought — art, science, and literature — through the number of those who devoted their time and efforts to learning. Symmetrically laid out by Penn in large blocks between the Delaware and the Schuylkill Rivers, it had become a busy metropolis along the Delaware wharves, Front Street, and Second Street. West of Fourth Street, which was at the edge of the commercial section, public buildings and residences intermingled to give the pleasant impression of a prosperous and beautiful town. There was a felicitous uniformity in the appearance of the houses, for they were generally constructed of red brick with white marble stoops, washed every morning by the servants. The doors and woodwork were painted white but the shutters were usually dark green. "Every house had its garden, in which vines twined over arbours, and the magnolia, honeysuckle and rose spread rich perfume of summer nights." Lombardy poplars, introduced from England after the Revolution, were fashionable but great native trees shaded most of the city.

The High Street (now Market Street), extending between the rivers, led to a bridge over the Schuylkill. It was wide enough to accommodate a market down its center stretching from Second Street to Eighth. Although most of the blocks in the western part of the city were not yet utilized, the bridge gave access to many outlying farms and estates on the western bank of the Schuylkill, and a considerable suburban area had developed to the north of the town along the road to Germantown, where Pastorius had settled in 1683, the year following Penn's arrival. The city was supplied with banks, private libraries, theatres, a university, a long-established hospital, many newspapers, bookshops and printers' establishments, learned societies, an Academy of Fine Arts, an active port, and regular stage service to New York City, Pittsburgh, Pennsylvania, and nearer towns by the numerous roads radiating from the city through an arc of 180°. Such was the Philadelphia which Thomas adopted as his American home.

# THOMAS NUTTALL, NATURALIST

TWO YEARS IN PHILADELPHIA. The "boisterous" passage of the *Halcyon* from Liverpool to Philadelphia at the end of the winter of 1808 took about five weeks. The tedium of the voyage was relieved when the ship entered Delaware Bay and the forests and marshlands of the shores appeared in spring brightness, a promise of fulfillment to the young botanist. In the morning paper of the twenty-third of April the *Halcyon* was reported as "below in the Delaware River."[1]

The city was a welcome sight to Thomas: he admired its "neatness and appearance of opulence." According to the family tradition, he did not linger even to find a lodging; his eagerness to see American flora led him directly along High Street, across the Schuylkill and out on the Lancaster Turnpike where one unfamiliar plant after another entranced him. However, the American accounts record that his first reconnaissance of the countryside occurred the next day. In either case, when a darkening thunderstorm finally drove him back to the city, his mind was full of questions; he was especially puzzled by a greenbriar (*Smilax rotundifolia*) the anomalous veining of which masks its affinity to the lilies, and he speculated that it might be a passion flower, a genus largely American.[2] He had been unable to obtain a flora of the United States in Liverpool, and the only help he could get from his fellow boarders was the information that Benjamin Smith Barton, who lived nearby on Chesnut Street, had published a botanical textbook. After he had failed to find a copy of *Elements of Botany* at a bookstore, he applied directly to the author and thus initiated a most momentous association.[3]

Barton, Professor of Materia Medica, Natural History, and Botany at the University of Pennsylvania and a practicing physician, was a prodigiously busy man but Nuttall received an explanation for his difficulty as well as encouragement to continue his studies and to bring further problems for solution. Barton had, indeed, a special interest in enterprising young plant enthusiasts, who were never numerous. He was planning to write floras of considerable scope, which necessitated the collecting and drying of plant specimens, arduous and tedious work, for which his many obligations had never left him sufficient time. Only the autumn before, he had lost the services of a capable botanist, Frederick Pursh, who had collected for him for two seasons (1806 and 1807) and put his herbarium in order.[4] When a possible replacement knocked at his door Barton, quickly noting his promising qualities and "ardent attachment to . . . botany," fostered his zeal by continuing to give him every assistance; he allowed him to use his library and instructed him in fundamentals of the science.

It happened that Professor Barton was commencing his yearly course of botanical lectures at the University on Tuesday, April 26, at 12 o'clock.[5] The opportunity was timely, and Meehan's sketch states that Thomas embraced it and that it was at the close of a lecture that he first met Barton.[6] Such a course would be, however, an uncharacteristic indulgence for he could master botany, as he had acquired all but his elementary schooling, by digging it out for himself with whatever help he might be able to enlist, taking every opportunity to see and study the plants of the neighborhood.

Through Professor Barton, Thomas soon became acquainted with William Bartram (1739–1823), then delicate and aging, but with a glorious record of pioneer plant collecting in the remote south. In his prime, he had been unsurpassed in his field knowledge of American plants and animals — he had compiled a list of 215 native birds — but withal he was most modest and retiring. In 1782 he declined a professorship at the University of Pennsylvania because of impaired health. He was gifted as an artist and drew the greater number of the plates for Professor Barton's *Elements of Botany* and illustrations for other of his publications. From Bartram the youth heard much about the luxuriant and varied endemic flora of the southeast and got impressions of the great tracts of wilderness — forests, streams, savannahs, and mountains — which lay beyond the settlements, fascinating in undisturbed serenity as well as in botanical riches; and in the Bartram Garden, operated by William's brother, John Junior, he was introduced to southern species. Here was a great stimulus toward botanical exploration. Appreciation of William Bartram's kindness and helpfulness is implicit in the many references to his "venerable friend" which are scattered throughout Nuttall's writings.

As Thomas's friendship with the Bartram household grew, he learned that William had inherited his love of nature from his famous father, John (1699–1777), who about seventy-five years before had begun his "darling garden," being a natural botanist. John began journeying to distant places to collect new plants for his garden and for shipment to correspondents in Europe. Eventually his industrious pursuit of this enterprise made him famous on both sides of the Atlantic. George III appointed him "Botanist Royal for the British

Colonies in America," and Linnaeus called him the greatest natural botanist in the world. At the top of his garden, which sloped gently to the Schuylkill, he built a pleasant and comfortable house from stone quarried on his farm. Although Nuttall made frequent visits to the hospitable house beyond the Schuylkill where a room became known as Nuttall's, there is no record that he ever met William Bartram's protégé, Alexander Wilson. At this time Wilson was busily writing his *American Ornithology*, a work suggested by Bartram, or traveling about the country soliciting subscriptions at $120 for the proposed nine-volume work.

Nuttall quickly made a start as a student of American botany, but he did not find it easy to get a job as a printer. His small funds dwindled away before he finally obtained one.[7] Once he was employed, however, we hear of no further difficulty, and during the year he was able to save money for seasonal botanical journeys. It is likely that he worked for Dennis Heartt who started as a printer and publisher in Philadelphia in 1807; in 1808 he was located at 58 North Fifth Street.[8] A fellow employee of this period reported that Thomas spent any spare moments of the working hours in study or reading.[9] Where and how he lived, no one knows; he collected his mail at the post office and had messages left at one shop or another. He may have slept at the printing establishment or had some other frugal arrangement which satisfied his simple needs. Thrift was never a burden to him for his requirements were Spartan — perhaps a natural inheritance from his bleak homeland.

As Nuttall extended his acquaintance with Philadelphia, he found sources of information and stimulation additional to Barton's library and the Bartram Garden and household, for he had come, by chance or design, to the American city best equipped to foster his interest in natural history.

Popular in some of its attractions, but sound in natural science, was Peale's Museum, "a world in miniature." There Art was united with Science, "rational amusement" with instruction, in displaying lucidly "the Wonderful Works of Nature" in the classical arrangement of Linnaeus's *Systema Naturae*.[10] Charles Willson Peale (1741–1827), a gifted portrait painter and enthusiastic dilettante naturalist, imaginative and mechanically inventive, was a source of pride and amusement to the city. With restless ingenuity, he had assembled an astounding collection which he was then exhibiting on the second floor of Independence Hall, assisted by his sons Rembrandt and Rubens, and later by Titian, who became the naturalist of the family. The carefully prepared exhibits, comprehensive in scope — zoological, paleontological, ethnological and archeological, mineralogical, technological and, unhappily, teratological — were arranged systematically, and Peale's portraits of notable Americans were hung above the cases in the long hall; a physiognotrace (a device for making small silhouettes) and organ music were additional sources of entertainment.

The exhibits at about this time included 250 mounted mammals, over 1800 birds (Peale's special enthusiasm), 150 reptiles, 650 fishes, thousands of insects, shells, and other invertebrates, over 8000 minerals and fossils, hundreds of Indian objects, casts of classical sculpture and of antique gems and about 250 paintings of distinguished persons by Charles Willson and Rembrandt Peale. Habitat settings, an innovation of Peale, increased the effectiveness of the mounted animals; the Reverend Manasseh Cutler of Ipswich, Massachusetts, who visited the museum in its early days questioned "that even Noah could have boasted of a better collection." The most famous item of all was a mounted skeleton of a mastodon, parts of which Peale excavated in the Hudson Valley in 1801.[11] Framed catalogs listed the natural exhibits according to the Linnaean system of classes and orders. So illuminating were the collections that Professor Barton had his classes in natural history meet periodically with him there for demonstrations.

The romance of the expanding West was suggested in the Indian gear brought back by the Lewis and Clark Expedition and deposited in the Museum through President Jefferson's interest. The dominating piece was a wax figure of Meriwether Lewis — the face taken from a life mask — in Indian dress and the ermine robe given him by Comeawhait, the young Shoshone chief, a brother of Sacajawea, who aided the party in crossing the Rockies. A calumet held in his hand was to teach the lesson of peace to visiting Indians and whites. Peale's Museum had top rating with the western Indian chiefs, who were brought to Washington and escorted on tours to centers of American civilization to impress them with the power and the glory of the United States. An eager youth could acquire here a vivid introduction to the animals, minerals, and races of North America, and undoubtedly Nuttall pored over the cases, storing up facts like a Jules Verne hero.

Peale hoped that his creation might become a national museum but his friend, President Jefferson, although sympathetic, doubted that federal money should be expended on an educational project. Most of the collection merited perpetuation. Professor Barton, addressing the local Linnaean Society in 1807, praised it as "a MUSEUM of great value; and which does honor to its founder, and even to the United States; a museum to which every American citizen should endeavor to contribute his mite of support." [12]

The beautiful estate of William Hamilton (1745–1813), "The Woodlands," lay beyond the Schuylkill on the way to the Bartram Garden. Its conservatories and skillfully landscaped grounds displayed the finest collection of woody exotics in America: here in 1784 were planted the first Lombardy poplars and ginkgo trees in the United States. "Every genteel stranger" had ready access to "The Woodlands." Frederick Pursh (Friedrich Pursch, 1774–1820, of Saxony) [13] had been head gardener there for two or three years (1803–1806), not long after he arrived in the United States from Germany and before Professor Barton employed him.[14] Pursh's predecessor at "The Woodlands" was John Lyon, a Scotch gardener.

Lyon, seeing financial possibilities in exporting American species to garden-loving England, left "The Woodlands" to become an explorer-collector in the southern Appalachians. The son of David Landreth, the nurseryman, held him in long remembrance:

> He made extensive journeys, preserving his accumulated gatherings at my father's nursery, until they amounted to a sufficiency to authorize a trip; thus he made alternate journeys of collection and voyages across the Atlantic. . . . the *Magnolias, Halesias, Stuartias, Virgilias, Gordonias, Pinckneyeas,* and other then rare native trees and shrubs, which decorated the old place — were mainly the contribution of Mr. Lyon. . . . Though then but a child, I recollect him well. He was, for years, when at Philadelphia, an inmate of my father's family, and at one period acted as an amateur tutor to the writer of this sketch. . . . Mr. Lyon was an amiable, well bred, intelligent man, of most sterling worth, and a loyal Briton.[15]

Directly and indirectly Lyon was a source of information to Nuttall of the rich flora of the southern Appalachians.[16]

Seedsmen and nurseries always attracted Nuttall. Doubtless, soon after his arrival, he became acquainted with Bernard M'Mahon (ca. 1775–1816) who carried on a large seed business at his store on Second Street, where he displayed books on gardening and botany.

These books, along with the personality of M'Mahon himself, served as a sort of bait — for few books were ever sold — to lure the garden-minded, the botanically inclined, and the scientifically gifted into the store. Chairs were thoughtfully provided for these visitors, a cordial welcome was sure to be accorded, and soon a sort of informal fraternity sprang into existence the members of which might be found at all times within the store, consulting the latest addition to the bookshelf, enjoying the congenial company, arguing, propounding, and appealing to M'Mahon for decisions. . . .[17]

Nuttall was of this "club." Here he met local plant enthusiasts in person and heard of others past and contemporary.

M'Mahon's thorough British training in horticulture and subsequent experience in America lent such value to his *American Gardeners' Calendar* (1806) that it went through eleven editions and saw over fifty years of use. A copy that M'Mahon sent to Thomas Jefferson established a correspondence between them. On Jefferson's recommendation, Meriwether Lewis after he returned from his transcontinental expedition entrusted a principal share of his seed collection to M'Mahon to be raised as secretively as possible.[18] In planning for the publication of the journals of the expedition, Lewis also arranged for M'Mahon to supervise the study of the herbarium specimens of the expedition: after Pursh returned from a northern botanizing trip that he was making for Professor Barton in 1807, M'Mahon was to house him while he prepared technical descriptions of the dried plants and made drawings of each of the new species.[19] These included not only the collections of the return trip but also those sent to Washington from Fort Mandan in the spring of 1805 that Jefferson had ordered to be turned over to Barton for identification;[20] by mid-1807, Barton had done nothing on them but bitterly resented Lewis's retrieval of them.[21] When Pursh became gardener at Dr. Hosack's Elgin Botanic Garden in New York City early in 1809, he left Lewis's herbarium with M'Mahon but took with him descriptions and drawings of Lewis's plants and, surreptitiously, portions of most of the specimens.[22]

In conversations with Nuttall, M'Mahon would have alluded on occasion to the immensities of the western territories and their uncounted treasures of which Lewis and Clark had brought back such encouraging evidence. Nuttall was listening eagerly to all he could hear about the frontiers, his mind full of hopes for the future.

David Landreth, a Scot, erstwhile gardener of Robert Morris at the "Hills," established the first seed house of importance in Philadelphia in 1784. William Hamilton is said to have employed him to grow the seed from the Lewis and Clark Expedition with which Thomas Jefferson had entrusted him. Although Nuttall did not meet Landreth during his first residence in Philadelphia, the Landreth Nurseries later became one of Nuttall's favorite local haunts.

Nuttall was fortunate in making another good friend in Philadelphia of the enduring quality of William Bartram. This was Zaccheus Collins, a prosperous Quaker merchant and philanthropist whose favorite avocations were identical with Nuttall's, botany and mineralogy. His reputation as a sound and critical student of plants was unexcelled although he published nothing and spoke of himself as "only a sort of desultory Botanist." His large correspondence reveals that his scientific opinion was widely sought, for he was most generous in assisting others with opinions, specimens, or information concerning the seed plants. However, concerning the cryptogams, his chosen field, he was "a retentive gulph . . . going into whose cave so many footsteps may be traced & none coming out." His friendship for Nuttall was firm and lasting; in it the youth found sympathetic interest for his activities and projects, botanical guidance, and, on occasion, financial assistance and advice in handling his savings.

Whether or not the young Englishman met any kindred spirits of his own age, there is no evidence although it is possible that his friendship with Thomas Say, the future entomologist, began thus early. Say's relative, William Bartram, encouraged him in his growing interest in insects, and Alexander Wilson urged him to write down his observations. Since the Says had a country home at Gray's Ferry near the Bartram Garden, visits to the Garden by Thomas Say were probably frequent, and it is likely that the two Thomases met there. Both were full of enthusiasm for natural history almost to the exclusion of practical considerations, and they were good friends later if not at this time.

Nuttall, with his life dedicated to Flora and obligated to spend six long days a week in a printing shop, had but a small margin of time and opportunity for making acquaintances. Under the circumstances, it is surprising that in barely two years he achieved lasting rapport with Barton, Bartram, M'Mahon, and Collins.

NORTH AMERICAN BOTANY IN 1808. At this period there were no full-time students of pure botany in the United States because American culture could not yet support scientists in a single field.

In the colleges the study of science very slowly broadened from a half course in natural philosophy (largely astronomy and physics) by the addition of electives in chemistry, natural history, botany, zoology, or mineralogy for upperclassmen. The scientific subjects offered were taught in most of the colleges by a single professor. He might develop a flair for one branch, but the time he could spare for his favorite was too little and sporadic to permit significant contributions toward its advancement. Writing a textbook for a course was often a pressing need and more in the line of duty: Professor Barton's *Elements of Botany* (1803) was used by his students and those of his successor for years, and Parker Cleaveland's *Elementary Treatise on Mineralogy and Geology*, published in the next decade, brought honor not only to himself but to young Bowdoin College.

The earliest teachers of science were usually physicians because only they had received effectual scientific training, often obtained at medical schools in Europe. After the Revolution, as the medical school in Philadelphia gained increasing prestige and others sprang up at scattered points, science grew stronger in the United States, and the custom of going to Europe for medical training was gradually abandoned. Plant study was ancillary to *materia medica*, which dealt with plants used in medication. The pharmacopoeia was supplied by nature, not by chemical laboratories; the country doctor gathered his "drugs" from the fields and woods and needed to recognize the growing plants as well as know their uses. The dominance of physicians in American science continued throughout the first half of the nineteenth century; for instance, John Torrey and Asa Gray had medical degrees, and Benjamin Silliman attended medical school although he did not take a degree. William Dandridge Peck (1763–1822) and Parker Cleaveland (1780–1858) were exceptional among early teachers of science in that they were not trained as physicians. Both were self-taught in their favorite sciences although they each took half courses in natural philosophy as undergraduates at Harvard (and the latter, chemistry also). Cleaveland served at Harvard as Tutor in Mathematics and Natural Philosophy for two years prior to his appointment in 1805 as professor of those subjects at Bowdoin College of which he was "the pride and ornament" for more than thirty years. His achievements in mineralogy were due entirely to his own efforts: he stated that he did not know that there was more than one kind of rock in the world when he graduated from Harvard.[23] Peck was probably equally ignorant of the plant and animal kingdoms when he graduated in 1782; the fascinations of the living world were opened to him by an imperfect copy of Linnaeus's *Systema Naturae* washed up at Kittery from a wrecked ship.[24] Nuttall, with meager schooling and undisciplined in any science but intending to devote his life to American botany, would have had little prospect of making the barest living had he not had a trade and been without false pride.

Some botanists by avocation commanded sufficient leisure and energy to advance the knowledge of plants as did Manasseh Cutler (1742–1823), pastor at Hamilton, Massachusetts, whose "Account of Some of the Vegetable Productions, Growing in This Part of America, Botanically Arranged," printed in 1785 in the *Memoirs* of the American Academy of Arts and Sciences, was the first botanical publication in New England. In similar case was Gotthilf Henry Ernest Mühlenberg (1753–1815), pastor of Trinity Church (Lutheran) at Lancaster, Pennsylvania, who published two lists of the flora of Lancaster County in the *Transactions* of the American Philosophical Society in the 1790s, two papers on some North American trees with Willdenow in Berlin early in the next decade,[25] and sent new species for publication in Willdenow's edition of *Species Plantarum* including a new genus of the *Gentianaceae* named in honor of Barton.

Mühlenberg earnestly regretted that the plants of the United States were being published in Europe and, as a step toward correcting this, he urged the production of local floras which could eventually be welded into a comprehensive flora of American workmanship. "By joining Hands," he often wrote to his American correspondents, "we may do something clever for our science." In 1792 he wrote to Manasseh Cutler:

> You have made the beginning of a Flora Neo Anglica, and all the Lovers of Botany wish you may go on and finish the noble work. Let each one of our American Botanists do something, and soon the riches of America will be known. Let Michaux describe South Carolina and Georgia; Kramsch, North Carolina; Greenway, Virginia and Maryland; Barton, Jersey, Delaware, and the lower parts of Pennsylvania; Bartram, Marshall, Mühlenberg, their Neighborhood; Mitchell, New York, and You, with the northern Botanists, Your States — how much could be done! If, then, one of our younger Companions (I mention Dr. Barton, in particular, whose business it is) would collect the different Floras in one, how pleasing to the botanical world.[26]

On Mühlenberg's periodic visits to Philadelphia, he habitually called on Barton, stopped at M'Mahon's store for the botanical news, and visited M'Mahon's, Bartram's, and Lyon's nurseries and Hamilton's garden to view whatever new plants they might have and obtain herbarium specimens. He frequently complained to his botanical correspondents that he was not permitted the pleasure of a glimpse of Meriwether Lewis's western plants being grown by M'Mahon and William Hamilton. In his own garden, he tenderly raised plants of six new species from seeds which Lewis had sent to him.

Former medical students at the University of Pennsylvania who had shown an aptitude for botany in Professor Barton's classes and were pursuing it as an avocation came to M'Mahon's store when they visited the city: Dr. William Darlington was practising in West Chester, Pennsylvania; the scholarly Dr. William Baldwin was getting started in Wilmington, Delaware; and Dr. William P. C. Barton was following his uncle's interests locally.

Slowly a knowledge of the men who had laid the foundations of American botany was furnished Nuttall by his continued association with Benjamin Smith Barton, William Bartram, and Zaccheus Collins and by chance conversations such as those he heard at M'Mahon's store. Although most of the talk was about contemporary workers, he gradually acquired an appreciation of the contributions of the pioneers.

The *Flora Boreali-Americana*, based on the collections of André Michaux (1746–1802), written by the distinguished botanist Louis Claude Richard and published in Paris in 1803 in Michaux's name, was the latest volume on the American flora and the only comprehensive treatment of the plants of the eastern seaboard. (Despite its title, it undertook to cover only that part of North America included in the United States before the Louisiana Purchase and a small part of Canada.) For eleven years (1785–1796) Michaux collected plants for the French government. The northern range of his collections was the upper Rupert River, where he was forced to forgo a view of James and Hudson Bays by the early freezing of the river and the consequent mutiny of his Indian guides, who insisted on immediately returning to their villages. From there, he collected plants southward through the eastern United States and across the Appalachians to the mouth of the Ohio. His plans to explore beyond the Mississippi were dashed through his involvement with the political schemes fronted by Citizen Genêt. During the last seven years that Michaux was in

America, he received no remittances from France although he maintained a botanic garden near Charleston and traveled during every growing season. He returned home in 1796, wrote a treatise on the oaks of North America (Paris, 1801), and died in Madagascar in 1802. His son François André (1770–1855), who had accompanied his father to America and came back twice to study American forest trees, was on excellent terms with the American botanists, as his father had been before him; both were well and favorably known in Philadelphia, Charleston, and the southern Appalachians. When Nuttall arrived, the younger Michaux was still in the United States on his last visit. He wrote "In 1808, I passed a great part of the summer with Messrs. John and William Bartram at their charming residence at Kingsessing, on the banks of the Schuylkill. . . . The Large Buckeye began to drop leaves about August 15." [27] While it is not impossible that young Nuttall met Michaux, there is no record of such an incident.

Other foreigners had recently studied American plants. One Samuel Constantine Rafinesque-Schmalz (1783–1840), born of French and German stock in Galata, a suburb of Constantinople, had collected avidly in all departments of natural history from 1802 through 1804, making his headquarters in Philadelphia, where he was employed for a time as a shipping clerk. He had gone back to Europe, to Sicily, but was sending papers on American species for publication in Dr. Mitchill's *New York Medical Repository*. Aloysius Enslen, collecting for Count Lichtenstein of Austria, tended his transplants in a garden in Philadelphia.[28] Mathias Kinn (d. 1825), an uneducated and rather eccentric German of gigantic frame, ranged the southern wilderness seeking botanical rarities and reared them in the adjoining Germantown, Pennsylvania, gardens of his friends Henry Kurtz and John Melchior Meng pending shipment of the plants to dealers in continental Europe.[29] The two English John Frasers, father and son, and also John Lyon collected in the South where they were especially successful in the Appalachians; but most of their plants went to England. On the sixth of his seven expeditions to North America, which spanned thirty years (1780–1810), the senior Fraser collected also for Czar Paul of Russia. As late as 1835, Moses A. Curtis, who collected in North Carolina, wrote, "Everybody knows Michaux & Fraser up in the mountains." [30] The Frasers established a nursery in London (Chelsea) for the sale of their plants and were not widely known in Philadelphia.

# TRANSPLANTATION

Among the academic botanists, old Dr. Adam Kuhn (1741–1817) of the medical faculty of the University of Pennsylvania held the unique honor of having studied with Linnaeus for he had been Linnaeus's only American student (1762–1765); the aging master, cherishing Kuhn therefor, rather than for any botanical flair, perpetuated his name in *Kuhnia*, an American genus of the *Compositae*.[31] He bore the additional honor of holding the first professorship in botany in the United States but, as he did not love plant study, he soon abandoned the professorship, and it was open for Benjamin Smith Barton when he returned from his medical studies in Europe.

Nuttall learned that American botanical books were mortifyingly few. William Bartram never wrote scientific analyses of the many interesting new southern species which he described casually in his *Travels through North and South Carolina, Georgia, East and West Florida*, etc. (1791) and which grew in his garden for all to see. Nor had his father, John, published anything on plants although he corresponded with Linnaeus and several English enthusiasts for decades. However his cousin, Humphry Marshall (1722–1801), who cultivated an arboretum in Marshallton, Chester County, Pennsylvania, had published *Arbustrum Americanum* in 1785, an alphabetical catalogue of the forest trees and shrubs, the first botanical book entirely American. In 1788, *Flora Caroliniana* by Thomas Walter (1740–1788), an English planter settled on the Santee River in South Carolina, was published in London through the assistance of John Fraser, Sr., who had stayed at Walter's plantation. Before the Revolution, Dr. Alexander Garden (1730–1791), a physician practicing in Charleston, a Fellow and later a Vice-President of the Royal Society, had sent many specimens of plants and animals to Linnaeus and other correspondents in Europe; he had been rewarded by having the superb genus *Gardenia* named for him. About fifty years before Walter's work appeared in London, Gronovius published *Flora Virginica* in Leyden (1739 and 1743) from specimens and descriptions of plants which John Clayton (1686–1773) had sent to him from Virginia; Linnaeus, then a medical student in Leyden, studied the Clayton Herbarium with Gronovius. James Greenway, working on a flora of Virginia toward the end of the eighteenth century, complained that the way Clayton did the drudgery and Gronovius reaped the credit was typical of all botanical work done in Virginia.[32] Greenway evidently was looking as far back as the first century of the Virginia Colony when the plant collections of the Reverend John Banister (fl. 1672), missionary in Virginia, were published in England by John Ray (1628–1705), whose classification of flowering plants (1682) was epochal through its stress on the fundamental importance of the number of cotyledons in the embryo. Mark Catesby (1683–1749), after about fifteen years spent in the new world, published *Natural History of Carolina, Florida, and the Bahama Islands* (1731–1743), two magnificent folio volumes of over a hundred plates which he drew and etched. About a hundred years previously, "imperfect and limited" accounts of North American plants were written by Cornutus, Wood, and Josselyn.

From the earliest times, common plants of the Atlantic coast had been sent to Europe and were included with all other known plants in Linnaeus's *Species Plantarum* (1753). His student, Peter Kalm (1716–1779), a Swedish naturalist who traveled in the eastern United States and Canada for several years (1748–1751) studying agricultural methods as well as the flora, swelled the known species from North America for Linnaeus's second edition. In later editions, the number of known American species continued to increase.

But there were pockets of rare plants on the coastal plain and others in the Piedmont and the mountains awaiting a discoverer and untold new species in the trans-Appalachian forests and prairies extending to the Mississippi; what treasures grew in the great Louisiana Territory, the Rocky Mountains, and the country on the Pacific coast, it would take decades to determine. It was a good land for an ambitious botanist for there was much to be done and very few who were interested and qualified to do it.

It should be recalled that this early period in the development of the natural sciences was concerned largely with description and classification, that is, systematics or taxonomy, the *sine qua non* of progress. The first necessity was to recognize the distinguishing qualities of an element or mineral, a plant, or animal and to assign to each a name of its own. Experiments with unknowns led nowhere. Linnaeus stated the situation emphatically: *Nomina si pereunt, perit et cognitio rerum.* This was the most important aspect of Linnaeus's work: to each kind of known plant and animal he assigned a binomial — a generic name followed by a specific name, a combination which gave a unique designation to each species and which indicated by the common generic name the species most closely related. Before this was done, botany had been in a quagmire.

# TRANSPLANTATION

Linnaeus's system of classification was a different matter. As he well knew, it was an artificial and temporary expedient, but it furnished a basis for achieving order out of hodgepodge by supplying clearly marked pigeonholes into which units from a chaotic mass could be readily placed and readily found. His twenty-four classes of plants, based on the number and arrangement of the stamens, and the subdivisions of each class, based on the number and structure of the carpels, readily guided a student to the correct area of a Linnaean flora for the identification of any plant. He recognized that there were natural groups of plants of distinct lineage which cut across his filing system. He named many of them. He offered his mechanical system to fill the gap until an arrangement based on inherent relationship should be worked out. Antoine Laurent Jussieu (1748–1836) soon made a beginning at setting up such a "natural system." [33]

For years after Linnaeus's death, naturalists generally were occupied with studying the new forms which the rapidly expanding world revealed, placing them in appropriate relation to known species and naming them. It was this kind of systematic work that Nuttall was to strengthen by corrections and to amplify by profuse and important additions.

CHAPTER 4

# INITIATION TO AMERICAN FLORA

Speak to the earth and it shall teach thee — Job, xii, 8.

FIRST COLLECTING TRIPS. On June 4, 1809, Nuttall set out from Philadelphia on a collecting trip sponsored by Professor Barton. At seven on Sunday morning he took a coastal vessel which arrived at Lewes, Delaware, on Tuesday afternoon.

On Monday evening we harboured in the mouth of Duck-Creek [which divides the island of Bombay Hook, Delaware, from the mainland] & went on shore on the lower side of the creek, on a marsh about 10 miles long taking in both sides of the creek, and about 5 in breadth. I found here abundance of what they call samphire [*Salicornia*], *Baccharis halimifolia*, called *kinks bush,* a species of *Aster* with very broad leaves, but I believe nothing uncommon. With the Baccharis I found a lucid red stalkᵈ plant with longish narrow leaves recently sprung up from seed. On the beech [*sic*] lay in great abundance what is called the *King Crab* [*Limulus polyphemus*].[1]

Lewes is located just inside Cape Henlopen where Delaware Bay meets the open Atlantic. Hereabouts Nuttall had first seen American land from the *Halcyon*. He never forgot his first night in Lewes: the persistent calls of the whippoorwills, strange indeed to English ears, "occasioned such a confused vociferation, as at first to banish sleep."[2]

From Wednesday through Saturday he visited salt marshes, sand dunes, the beach at Cape Henlopen, and woods, ponds, and swamps near Lewes. It is probable that Barton had shown him the herbarium specimens of plants that might be in the area.[3] Nuttall got several species new to him, which he identified with the help of Michaux's *Flora.* Through letters of introduction that Barton had given him, he had the help of local men. Dr. Harris accompanied him to salt marshes on Wednesday, and on Friday Judge Rodney[4] undertook

32

to show him the coral honeysuckle (*Lonicera sempervirens* L.) but failed to find it. ". . . it had either been all taken up to supply gardens, or has been buried in the advancing & almost perpendicular sand hills, which skirt the wood on the side next the sea." His solitary walks were far more successful than those for which he had local guides. On the sands he found *Cakile edentula* (Bigel.) Hook. (sea rocket) and *Hudsonia tomentosa* Nutt., called locally heath; in dry woods he got *Smilax laurifolia* L. (goatbriar), *Myrica pensylvanica* Loisel. (bayberry), *Ilex glabra* (L.) Gray (inkberry), and *Vaccinium stamineum* L. (deerberry).* Wet woods and ponds yielded *Habenaria blephariglottis* (Willd.) Hook. (white fringed orchis), *Phoradendron flavescens* (Pursh) Nutt., *Proserpinaca palustris* L., *Chionanthus virginicus* L. (fringe tree), *Gratiola aurea* Muhl., *Diodia virginiana* L. (buttonweed), *Utricularia inflata* Walt.[5] and *U. purpurea* Walt. In swamps he collected *Tofieldia racemosa* (Walt.) BSP. (false asphodel), *Lachnanthes tinctoria* (Walt.) Ell. (redroot), *Sarracenia purpurea* L. (pitcher plant), *Polygala ramosa* Ell., *P. corymbosa* Michx., and *Kalmia angustifolia* L. (sheep laurel). Common about Lewes was a curious wanderer from the subtropics, *Proboscidea louisianica* (Mill.) Thell.; "the singular form of its large fruit has obtained it the name of Cuckold's Horns." [6]

On Sunday he did not collect.[7] The next day he set out on foot for the Great Cypress Swamp near Dagsboro about twenty miles to the southwest. In skirting the head of Indian River Inlet, stagnant water filled with half-dead trees and aquatic plants, he spent considerable time searching vainly for *Illicium parviflorum* Michx. (star anise), evidently at the special request of Professor Barton. "I am persuaded it has never been found here" was Nuttall's conclusion concerning this species which we now know grows no further north than Georgia. That night he spent at the house of Mr. Waples, "proprietor of the head of the swamp."

On Tuesday morning leaving Mr. Waples, within a mile of the entrance of the swamp I met with an old man who usually conducts strangers into

---

* Except in quotations, plant names printed in italics are the presently accepted scientific names, whereas Latin names in Roman type were synonyms employed by Nuttall. (The eighth edition of Gray's *Manual* is used as authority so far as possible.) Specific names of which Nuttall was the author are either immediately preceded by an asterisk or followed by "Nutt.," the standard taxonomic abbreviation for his name; his new generic names are preceded by an asterisk.

the swamp. Near his house but in the woods & evidently wild grew the *Yucca* but very small. The old man went with me and in about a mile from the house we began to enter one of the most frightfull [*sic*] labyrinths you can imagine  it was filled with tall tangling shrubs thickly matted together almost impervious to the light  among the shrubs was the *ilex* already mentioned *smilax, &.* It was very wet; knee deep in sphagnum if you step$^t$ off the bridges or wooden causeways. There were some open places called savannahs, but were literally ponds at this time of the year, but are dry in summer . . . and on the edges . . . grew the *cupressus disticha* [*Taxodium distichum,* for which the swamp is named]. In a shady part of the swamp the old man pointed out to me what they here call the Bay-bush which they use for dying yellow, it was not in flower; I suppose it must be the *Hopea* [*Symplocos tinctoria* (L.) L'Hér.]. I saw nothing else new that I remember, & I proceeded to Dagsbury where I was very kindly entertained by Mr. Wells . . . proprietor of nearly all the swamp.[8]

William Hill Wells (c. 1760–1829) had married Elizabeth Dagsworthy Aydelott, the ward and heiress of General John Dagsworthy whose important services in the French and Indian Wars had been rewarded by grants of many tracts of land, among them one of three hundred and eighty acres called the Cypress Swamp. Wells's only daughter married William D. Waples, presumably Nuttall's host on Monday night. Wells, a lawyer and United States Senator, occupying the capacious house built by General Dagsworthy, dispensed liberal hospitality. He had entertained Rafinesque several years before.[9] (Rafinesque mistakenly called the area the Dismal Swamp.) At the time Nuttall was there, General Mitchell of Broadkill, a former Governor of Delaware, was a guest.

On Wednesday I went across the swamp about 7 miles without meeting with one extraordinary vegetable except the *Bartonia* but which of the species I could not tell, about the place where I found this solitary specimen there had last year been abundance but appeared to have been destroyed before it had come to seed, nearly all this part of the swamp I passed through appeared too wet for herbaceous vegetation being covered with little else but *Sphagnum, fern, Magnolia, ilex dahoon, &.* There are no cranberrys, in the swamp at all where I passed thro and the people living on the edge of this part of the swamp scarcely knew what I meant by cranberrys when I described them, neither did I see the *Drosera* having passed thro the swamp and coming to higher ground I met with abundance of the *Hopea* as I take it — some trees 20 foot high & ½ a foot diam. In this part of the swamp there are bears not unfrequently met with as many as 7 having been caught not many months back.[10]

The plants of *Kalmia latifolia* (mountain laurel) were of enormous size, "not inferior to stout Peach Trees." He also got red bay, *Persea Borbonia* (L.) Spreng. (Nuttall's Laurus carolinensis), a small southern tree that was not found again in Delaware, its northernmost station, until one hundred and thirty years later when the Delaware State Forester collected it.[11]

By Wednesday evening he was so bitten by mosquitoes that, at a house where he sought lodging, his swollen face aroused suspicion of smallpox. The next day he walked back to Lewes. During the journey he collected *Iris prismatica* Pursh, *Nuphar advena* Ait., *Nymphaea odorata* Ait., *Diospyros virginiana* L. (persimmon), *Diodia teres* Walt., and noted several familiar trees and shrubs. This gave him a total of at least five undescribed species for the Delaware excursion; he was still able to become sole author of one of these nine years later.[12]

Friday he sent off a long, detailed letter and two boxes of specimens to Barton; the plants, totaling forty-three species, still exist in the herbarium of the Academy of Natural Sciences of Philadelphia. The letter begins naively:

Honor$^d$ Sir,
I fear you have been anxiously expecting to hear from me before this time but as I could not communicate any thing with certainty respecting the subject in hand at an earlier period you will perhaps excuse the delay.

He acknowledged receiving a letter from Barton which enclosed a letter of introduction to Col. Hale; Nuttall had presented the letter and received the promise of an introduction to a General Bull who lived in the direction he was going to travel.

From Lewes, Nuttall set off on foot for Nanticoke River (on the Chesapeake Bay watershed of the Del-Mar-Va peninsula). Unfortunately we have no further information about the June trip, but there is a strong implication in the family account of his travels that he did not go appreciably further.[13]

The southern journey was successful for pupil and patron; for Nuttall it meant a satisfying increase of his floral acquaintance and for Barton welcome data on the geographic distribution of species for his proposed floras. Nuttall reported to his family that the hospitality of the countryside made the tour so inexpensive that he refused Barton's assistance in defraying expenses.

In midsummer Nuttall set out on a northern pedestrian excursion the first part of which followed the general route Pursh had taken in

1807 to collect for Barton. He wrote to Barton from Wilkes-Barre on August 10, listing or describing the plants he observed on his way from Bethlehem and over Pocono Mountain. He began:

Honor^d Sir

I left Phila ½ after 4 in the morning [of Saturday, August 5] & reached Bethlehem in good time Saturday evening. I spent Sunday in the town, & on Monday went as far as Heller's gap w[h]ere staid all night. . . . I admire the interesting appearance of the country about Beth^m being romantically diversified with high hills covered with grand forests.[14]

Near Bethlehem he found "a fine Orchis," from his description evidently the species on which he based his section *Aplectrum*; soon afterwards he got *Habenaria fimbriata* (Ait.) R. Br.

Tuesday night he "lodged in the gap at White's tavern under the blue mountain where for the first time I saw" *Rhododendron maximum* L. He spent half of the next day "on the Pokono or broad mountain," finding among numerous other species *Clintonia borealis* (Ait.) Raf., *Habenaria orbiculata* (Pursh) Torr., *Dalibarda repens* L., and *Gaultheria procumbens* L. "I . . . could neither see ponds nor lakes, consequently I missed the *Utricularia* from which I was not a little grieved, but intend to give it another looking over."

He spent Wednesday night in Wilkes-Barre. There "on the rocks I found a *campanula*. I believe the identical species so common in the north of England, and well known by the name of Blue-bell [*Campanula rotundifolia* L.]". On the banks of the Susquehanna he got *Arethusa bulbosa* L.[15] From Wilkes-Barre he sent to Barton all the plants he had collected — over thirty-five species — "finding it impractible to carry them any further." As he states that he has decided to omit going to Wyalusing until his return, he perhaps took a more direct route into New York State. Comments in his publications suggest that he may have visited the salt springs of Onondaga, where "the *Salicornia* of the sea marshes" grows,[16] and possibly also Lake Owasco. Not uncommonly he refers to plants growing along the St. Lawrence but it is doubtful that he means the river itself for on one occasion he wrote of "descending the St. Lawrence, or rather its chain of lakes." He studied the Falls of the Genesee.[17] Eventually he reached Buffalo, Niagara Falls, and adjoining Canada.

Barton probably had no further word from him until October, when a letter arrived written on the tenth at Canandaigua. Later some plants arrived for him along with Nuttall's full collection of fossils and minerals, the weight of which had become burdensome. Nuttall wrote in part:

> After seeing the grand cataract of Niagara, the most astonishing production of nature, I proceeded into Canada as far as *Ancaster* at the head of Lake Ontario & 50 miles from Queenstown [*sic*]. I no sooner reached this place than I fell sick of the billious [*sic*] fever there prevalent — hardly recovered from this, I was attacked by the *aigue*, so that I have in all been detained near a month  Consequently to my great mortification, I have entirely lost several fine plants, particularly what I collected in the neighbourhood of *Lake Erie*, and at the Fall; all that still remains of them in my possession are poor dried specimens but even these did not escape, as soon as I was able to examine them, I found them eat up by *mould*.

Following this statement of his "misfortunes & bad success" he gave a long account of some of the plants he had seen, describing those which he had not identified.[18]

He was still becoming acquainted with known eastern species such as *Vallisneria americana* Michx., *Utricularia cornuta* Michx. ("abundant on the Table rock, at the Falls of Niagara"), and *Symphoricarpos albus* (L.) Blake.[19] He also encountered rare or unknown species: *Polanisia graveolens* Raf. "on the sandy shores of Lake Erie, near Buffaloe creek"; his Hedeoma glabra [*Satureja arkansana* (Nutt.) Briq.] on calcareous rocks at the falls of Niagara and "upon the banks of the St. Lawrence and the upper lakes" and *Zigadenus glaucus* Nutt. in similar sites; the highly localized hart's-tongue fern [*Phyllitis Scolopendrium* (L.) Newm. var. *americana* Fern.] near Canandaigua "in the crevices of calcareous rocks, beneath the shade of the Hemlock . . . and accompanying the *Taxus canadensis* or American Yew"; and it seems that he first collected his *Dentaria* *maxima* on this excursion.[20] His study of "a low succulent, dydymenous plant" that he saw growing in great numbers in a thick beech woods west of Batavia resulted in his establishment of the genus *Epifagus* nine years later.[21]

At Canandaigua, Nuttall profited from conversing with Dr. Samuel Dungan, a natural history enthusiast who had been a pupil of Dr. Caspar Wistar in Philadelphia before he started practice in Ontario County in 1797.[22] It is very likely that Barton had given Nuttall a letter of introduction to him, and Nuttall may have first called on him on his way westward.

Again Nuttall informed his family that his own savings covered the expenses of the long walking tour.[23] The continued assurances to them that he was earning enough to pay for botanical expeditions encourage the belief that his uncle's opposition to his plans for emigration had been based partially at least on skepticism that Thomas would be able to succeed in his objectives in America. Through the winter of 1809–1810 he probably set type industriously for in the spring he again had savings on hand.

BARTON'S PROPOSAL. In January 1810, Professor Barton received a call from a distinguished citizen bearing an engaging offer. On the untimely death of Governor Meriwether Lewis the previous autumn, General William Clark, his coleader of the 1803–1806 Expedition, with characteristic courage assumed the responsibility of superintending the publication of an official report of the expedition, although such an undertaking lay entirely outside his own talents. Lewis had expected to publish the report and toward that end had arranged for Pursh to describe the new plants collected; but his heavy duties as Governor of Missouri Territory and the remoteness of his residence delayed the matter. After Lewis's death Clark came East.[24] In Philadelphia he asked Nicholas Biddle to prepare the narrative from the journals and, probably at the suggestion of Thomas Jefferson, Clark made a contract with Barton to describe the animals and plants collected and to list the Indian vocabularies that Lewis had painstakingly secured. Barton's work was to appear in an Appendix within six months of the main account. Arrangements were made that all passages in the journals relating to plants and animals should be copied for Barton's use.[25] The scientific opportunity thus opened to him for a second time evidently rekindled Barton's ambition to make an important contribution to natural science such as he had long dreamed of — a systematic treatise on the flora and fauna of a large part of North America. During the next years, he answered Clark's anxious inquiries with the confident statement that the work would take a very short time, but there is no evidence that he accomplished anything toward the publication. Thus Barton's "hand of inaction" twice thwarted attempts to secure scientific credit for the discoveries in natural history made by Lewis and Clark.

Barton did, however, take very prompt action, as we believe, toward acquiring an assistant for the task: he proposed to Nuttall that he undertake an extensive journey to the great plains of the West for two years' collecting. The two trips that Nuttall had made during the previous summer had sufficiently proved his ability and his cooperative spirit. No hint appears that Barton disclosed any motive for the costly undertaking of sending a collector such a tremendous distance, but the sequence of events strongly suggests that, in sending Nuttall to the West, Barton hoped and expected that he was providing himself with an employee who would be well equipped by his experiences to do or assist with the job to which he himself was committed. That Barton had appraised the young Englishman as artless, confiding, and pliant is shown in a letter of introduction to William Henry Harrison, Governor of Indiana Territory, one of several letters of introduction that Barton supplied, which described him as "a young man, a native of England, brought up in a manner under my own eyes and instruction, and distinguished by his love of science, his integrity, his sobriety, and *innocence* of character." [26]

It seems significant that, shortly after Barton received the 1804 plant collection of Lewis and Clark, he engaged Pursh to work on his herbarium and make collecting trips; and, likewise, when the full Lewis and Clark harvest came into his hands he proposed that Nuttall collect for him in the northwest. Moreover Barton made provision for raising seeds of the specimens by having a greenhouse built — the first private one in Philadelphia — and establishing a garden.[27] There can be no reasonable doubt that he cherished ambitious plans.

Although Nuttall was a British citizen, Barton attempted to secure a United States passport for him with a British visa to assist him in Canada, but Nuttall left without such a document. However, Barton continued his efforts and finally, more than six weeks after his protégé had left Philadelphia, importuned President Madison directly for "some protection, some kind of letter of facility, . . . for Mr. Nuttall." No official record of any endorsement of Nuttall by the government has been found.[28]

Nuttall was to receive a salary of eight dollars a month and all expenses.[29] He was to keep a daily journal of observations for Barton's exclusive use and was restricted from communicating any part to any person without Barton's consent; he was to collect "animals, vegetables, minerals, Indian curiosities, etc.," a portion of which he might retain, but strictly for himself lest "they might otherwise fall into the hands of persons who would use them to my disadvantage." A contract was written out by Barton and signed by both.[30]

Although Barton was so eager to protect his scientific interests, we wonder if he did not give his consent orally to the sale of seeds and plants for horticultural use so that Nuttall might increase his income above the $96 a year the contract guaranteed him. It seems that, if this were not the case or if Nuttall had not understood it to be so, he would hardly have spent so much time and labor as he did gathering and caring for seeds, roots, and living plants. It is unlikely that either man would foresee that sales to seedsmen were scientific risks.

Benjamin Smith Barton (1766–1815) was a cosmopolite of the greatest prestige. His appearance was distinguished and forceful: his mien keenly intellectual — he was thought to resemble Goethe. As a nephew of David Rittenhouse (1752–1796), the leading astronomer of his time in America, and as a protégé of the Penns, scholarly circles at home and abroad made him welcome, and his career was adorned by a succession of honors. He had been appointed Professor of Natural History and Botany on the distinguished faculty of the Medical School of the University of Pennsylvania when he returned from Europe trained in medicine; he was a vice-president of the American Philosophical Society from 1802; he was elected as the first President of the local Linnaean Society; and, from 1808 to 1812, he served as President of the Philadelphia Medical Society. After Benjamin Rush died in 1813, Barton applied for and received his professorship in the theory and practice of medicine.

On intimate acquaintance, however, blemishes of accomplishment and character became apparent behind the imposing facade. He was a prolific writer, but his publications were of a trivial nature, both *ipso facto* and in comparison with the ambitious projects which he publicly announced from time to time. A scholarly production of moderate dimensions, such as a local flora, did not engage his interest for he was goaded by an overly ambitious spirit. His "irritable and even cholerick" nature strained his relations with many of his colleagues and associates. He lacked generosity of spirit to the point of injustice; he was accused of plagiarizing the experiments of a fellow scientist and of appropriating the discoveries of others and was guilty of even more serious dishonorable deviations.[31]

It is a striking fact that Nuttall, who was wont to comment appreciatively on his friends and acquaintances whenever any opportunity offered in his thousands of published pages, expressed neither warmth of feeling nor even indebtedness to Barton. For this omission some commentators have deemed Nuttall ungrateful, but lack of gratitude was a characteristic he did not possess. However, he had penetrating discernment that made him acutely sensitive and bitterly critical of such blemishes of temperament as "affected wisdom and canting lore of age and pretended experience" and the "feeble bucram of self importance."[32] Nuttall should not be condemned for not eulogizing Barton without weighing their disparate personalities and the tangled situations involved in the compact between them.

For Nuttall, the opportunity offered to him in 1810 was the fulfillment of his dearest dreams. With eager anticipation he made preparations to leave. Barton loaned him a double-barreled gun, a pistol, a dirk, five blank books, a steel pen, a thermometer, and one volume of Hoffman's two-volume *Flora Germanica* [!] — probably unintentionally left at Barton's by Pursh. Nuttall bought, at his patron's expense, gunpowder, a powerhorn, a shot belt, a pair of scales, and four quires of paper (for pressing plant specimens).[33] It is doubtful that the adventurer ever put the artillery to the use for which it was designed; but he did find the gun barrel useful in loosening the soil from the roots of plant specimens. That he started out with a trunk on this journey, which, according to the "Directions for Mr. Thomas Nuttall," was to head via Lake Winipeg [*sic*] toward latitude 55° on the Beaver River,[34] is a simple indication of the complete lack of comprehension on both sides of the nature of the undertaking. Blissfully ignorant of the endless obstacles and dangers of the wilderness, Nuttall left Philadelphia at five o'clock on the morning of Thursday, April 12, 1810, to travel by stagecoach to Pittsburgh, "the Gateway of the West."[35]

# CHAPTER 5

# WEST WITH THE ASTORIANS

No Indians existed for Nuttall, there were no interruptions or delays, no possibilities of disaster or death, there was only the flora that no one had seen. — de Voto, *Across the Wide Missouri*

THE GREAT ADVENTURE STARTS. The stagecoach took eight long days to reach Pittsburgh.[1] The first day's journey was over a fine turnpike which extended sixty-two miles to Lancaster. The red maples, skunk cabbage, and whitlow grass (*Draba verna* L.) were in flower along the route. The tree swallows had returned. Bluebirds and meadow larks were singing, and the rocks along the way provided interest. Nuttall's enthusiasm and expectations were attuned to the burgeoning season. The flowery phrasing at the beginning of his diary suggests an elated mood.

Lancaster, the largest interior town of the United States, the temporary capital of Pennsylvania, and the marketing center of prosperous German farming country, was distinguished in the eyes of botanists as the home of Dr. Henry E. Mühlenberg whose preeminent rank and leadership in the study of plants won him the sobriquet of "The American Linnaeus." It is regrettable that Nuttall did not call on him that Thursday evening to make his acquaintance and be introduced to his large herbarium. It is almost certain that the two never met.[2]

After the first day, the roads were dirt, or more probably mud at this time of the year, and incredibly rough. On the second day, while crossing the Susquehanna by ferry at Harrisburg, Nuttall saw bloodroot gleaming on the sheltered banks. Not far west of the river, the road began the alternating ascent and descent of successive ridges of the Appalachians that continued all the way to Pittsburgh. Rains, melting snow, and heavy goods wagons had eroded and gutted the slopes into steep and stony pitches; there was nothing to cushion the impact of the wheels on the rocks nor the passengers' contact with the wooden seats as they were bounced about. On Sunday evening at McConnellsburg after crossing Tuscarora Mountain, Nuttall wrote in his diary, "To-day I had a fit of the ague again, bro't on I had reason to believe by fatigue." The next day the stage arrived early enough in Bedford to permit a two-mile walk to a chalybeate spring where Nuttall drank copiously, hoping for a beneficial effect.

The following day he felt better. The coach started at 3:30 in order to have daylight for the hard climb over Allegheny Mountain, the highest of the ridges. Nuttall crossed the crest on foot so that he could better observe the flora. He was "mortified" that all he found of interest was arbutus in blossom amid patches of snow and several ruffed grouse. On the last two mornings the start was made at four o'clock for crossing Laurel and Chestnut Ridges. As they approached Pittsburgh, the weather became warmer and the plants were further advanced.

Good fortune bestowed on Nuttall a most stimulating companion for the wearisome journey across Pennsylvania in Manuel Lisa of St. Louis, a Spanish fur trader on the Missouri River. His exhaustive knowledge of the far West was tapped by continuous queries from the eager young naturalist, who listened to accounts of the great Missouri and its tributaries and of the surrounding terrain, descriptions of some of the strange mammals — prairie dogs, mountain sheep, and mountain goats — information about Indian tribes from the Osages of the southwest plains to the Crows of the eastern slopes of the Rockies at the headwaters of the Yellowstone, and a critical estimate of Meriwether Lewis's character and achievements. Nuttall wrote to Barton an enthusiastic account of the information he had obtained from Lisa.[3] The two travelers parted at Pittsburgh with no expectation of meeting again.

Nuttall stayed in Pittsburgh for five full days, April 19 to 25. "The younger Dr. Stevenson," to whom he evidently brought a letter of introduction from Professor Barton, spent the greatest part of a day showing him two glass manufactories, the remains of the British fort, and deposits of arrowheads and flints. He advised Nuttall that the Mahoning Salt Springs of Barton's itinerary were too inconsiderable to warrant so great a detour. Most of Nuttall's time in Pittsburgh was occupied in observing the flora and fauna of the vicinity. Opposite the city on the banks of the Monongahela he first found his white dog's-tooth violet growing among the common yellow-flowered species. On Wednesday, April 25, he started on foot for Presque Isle (Erie) on Lake Erie, about one hundred and forty miles to the north, sending his trunk by boat up the Allegheny River and French Creek to the head of navigation at Le Boeuf (Waterford). The vegetation was more backward than around Pittsburgh but observations of the geology and mineralogy beguiled the pedestrian.[4] The next day when the temperature reached 86° in the shade, he suffered the disagreeable surprise of a return of the ague. The third day on the road he made a detour near Butler to visit a salt spring because Barton wanted information on springs of all kinds. During the five following days severe attacks of intermittent fever completely incapacitated him; this and his illness in the late summer of 1809 were evidently malaria, a disease very widespread throughout frontier country. It was May 7 when by gradual stages he reached Franklin whence his route followed French Creek. But first he made a side trip to see the oil springs on Oil Creek, a more eastern tributary of the Allegheny River. The oil was petroleum, which the Indians used as liniment and for which the whites found no better use till half a century later when the area which Nuttall visited became the first scene in the dramatic development of a mammoth American industry. Hampered by attacks of malaria and by wretched footing — "the road in most places was like a continuation of ponds & very obscure" — Nuttall struggled on to Le Boeuf where he received the bad news that, owing to low water in French Creek, his trunk was still in Franklin. "Brooding with a heavy heart" on his "disastrous journey," he immediately started to retrace the watery way. Back at Franklin he suffered the severest attack of the ague that he had ever experienced and again for five days he treated himself in every way he knew;[5] he was almost ready to abandon the whole venture. Twice during his return trip to Le Boeuf, ague delayed him for a day, but thereafter no mention of the disease appears in his diary.[6] Carrying the contents of his trunk on his back and his gun in his hand along the boggy wilderness track, his body weak and his mind full of misgivings, he endured the most arduous and discouraging days of the whole journey. However he did not fail to note and diagnose as best he could the plants and animals along the way and to observe near what is now known to be the boundary of the Pleistocene glaciation "fragments of primitive rock . . . the 1st time I have seen it on this side the mountains." [7]

He received encouragement from his confidence that he had found at least four undescribed species: the running strawberry-bush (*Euonymus obovatus* Nutt.), a toothwort (*Dentaria heterophylla* Nutt.), the white dog's-tooth violet (*Erythronium albidum* Nutt.), and blue-eyed Mary (*\*Collinsia verna* Nutt.).[8] The last, which exhibited new generic characters, remained one of Nuttall's American favorites to the end of his days; he described it in his diary as "very elegant . . . the lower lip is of a bright azure blue which no color can excel." He frequently met with plants new to him which he struggled to identify from the Latin descriptions in Michaux's *Flora Boreali-Americana* or Hoffman's *Flora Germanica*. He was also baffled by unfamiliar birds, amphibians, and reptiles. But the accurate descriptions he recorded in his diary enabled him eventually to name most of them correctly. He saw abundance of orchids, wild turkeys, and porcupines.

At Erie he waited three days vainly hoping to get a boat for Detroit. The best arrangement he could make was to send his excess baggage in care of a captain whose boat was eventually going to that port. He started out on foot on June 7, following the beach or the ridge road, expecting to walk to Detroit, a distance, he reckoned, of 250 miles from Erie. He continued to find small animals, birds, and many plants which he had never before encountered and, along the shore, rocks and minerals of diverse origin. On June 7, he passed through "Painsville" settled five years before and, three days later, "came to a small settlement on *Kioga* called *Cleveland*." He lingered there because the weather was wet and a boat bound for Detroit was hourly expected, but after a couple of days of fruitless waiting he continued his journey along the southern shore of Lake Erie until he reached a settlement on the Huron River where again a boat was hourly expected. By this time Nuttall had learned that the western shore of Lake Erie was so low and swampy that reaching Detroit by land from the south was not practical. He had directions from Barton to visit the Huron Indian town of Sandusky thirty-five miles in the interior, but, having already suffered so many delays, he decided not to risk missing the expected boat by making the journey. It arrived in three or four days but unfavorable winds silted the river mouth and delayed its sailing so he had altogether a week in the area for botanizing,

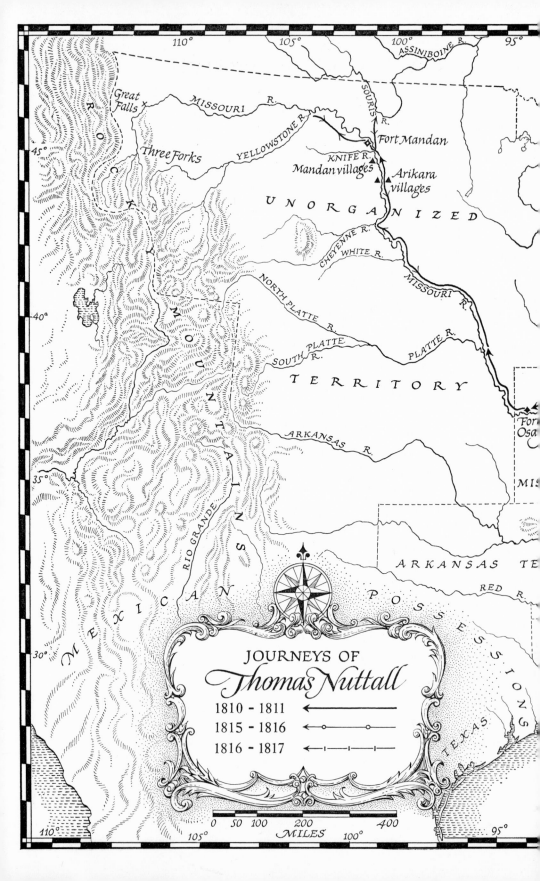

JOURNEYS OF
*Thomas Nuttall*

1810 – 1811  ⟵
1815 – 1816  ⟵∘————∘
1816 – 1817  ⟵|———|———|

0  50  100    200        400
MILES

**Inset (top right):**

Philadelphia to Erie

0  50  100  200 MI.

Erie
Le Bœuf
Franklin
Butler
Pittsburgh
ALLEGHENY R.
SUSQUEHANNA R.
JUNIATA R.
LAUREL MT.
Harrisburg
Lancaster
Bedford
York
Philadelphia
OHIO R.
MONONGAHELA R.
Frederick
Harper's Ferry
Alexandria

**Main map:**

90°   85°

C A N A D A

LAKE SUPERIOR

MICHIGAN TERRITORY

Green Bay
Mackinac Island
Bois Blanc I.
LAKE HURON
WISCONSIN R.
FOX R.
PORTAGE
Le Baye
LAKE MICHIGAN
LAKE ST. CLAIR
Detroit
MISSISSIPPI
rie
hien
buque
Chicago
HURON R.
Cleveland
LAKE ERIE
Le Bœuf
ALLEGHENY R.
Franklin
Butler
Pittsburg
Chambersburg
Harrisburg
Lancaster
Philadelphia
40°
ILLINOIS
INDIANA
OHIO
ILLINOIS R.
Cincinnati
OHIO R.
Portsmouth
Hanover
Alexandria
POTOMAC R.
Shepherdstown
Staunton
BLUE RIDGE
VIRGINIA
St. Louis
Charles
MERAMEC R.
RI TERR.
New Madrid
Lexington
KENTUCKY
The Barrens
CUMBERLAND R.
POWELL R.
CLINCH R.
HOLSTON R.
CUMBERLAND GAP
TENNESSEE R.
Morganton
NORTH CAROLINA
35°
Asheville
CATAWBA R.
Rutherfordton
SOUTH CAROLINA
CAPE FEAR R.
Wilmington
TENNESSEE
ORY
MISSISSIPPI TERRITORY
ansas Post
ALABAMA TERRITORY
Augusta
SANTEE R.
Charleston
GEORGIA
Savannah
LOUISIANA
Natchez
30°
FLORIDA TERRITORY
New Orleans

Gulf of Mexico

90°   85°   80°

S.H. BRYANT

visiting Indian mounds and sulphur springs, collecting marine fossils on the shore, wandering over the first prairie he had ever seen, and writing long, semi-Latinized descriptions of plants in his diary. He was impressed by the luxuriant vegetation of the prairie, the picturesqueness of the occasional islandlike clumps of trees, and the vastness of its extent.

Nuttall began a cash account at the back of his diary when he started on his journey but took little interest in it for he kept it for only four weeks (up to his visit to Oil Creek) and never totaled it.[9] The entries of assets are somewhat enigmatic although he seems to have started with $30 of his own money, $20 from Barton, and $90 in notes. He credited himself as the owner of $254.00. The expenditures recorded amounted to $40.07. Allowing for the usual $20 fare on the stagecoach to Pittsburgh, his food and lodging averaged about 72 cents a day during the period of the cash account. Because the distance between Franklin and Le Boeuf was covered three times, he had walked more than 400 miles from Pittsburgh to the Huron River. This proved to be the only sustained walking of his expedition for at Detroit he reached a network of great waterways, ready-made routes through the heart of the continent, with no feasible alternative mode of travel.

The old post of Detroit, established by Cadillac in 1701, had been in American hands for only fourteen years, for the British had been reluctant to give up the northern forts after the Revolution as required by the peace terms of 1783. The population of about 1500 was largely French, and the town was frequented by Huron, Ottawa, and Chippeway Indians from nearby villages.

Nuttall reached Detroit on June 26 and stayed there for a little more than a month, busily studying the flora and fauna, springs, the incidence of goiter, the ways of life of the various Indian tribes settled in the area, and the possibilities of proceeding westward. He enumerated in his diary the mammals, fish, and the birds of the region. The sylva was generally similar to what he had been seeing, but with the loss of the persimmon and cucumber trees of Pennsylvania and the buckeye of Ohio.

Nuttall found the priest at Detroit, Father Gabriel Richard, to be "a learned and intelligent observer."[10] He probably pored over the priest's Latin lexicon to increase his botanical vocabulary for beyond Detroit his plant descriptions rarely lapsed into English. The references in his diary at this time to Alexander MacKenzie's *Voyages from Montreal to the Frozen and Pacific Oceans* and to Abbé Molina's *The Geographical, Natural, and Civil History of Chili* suggest the possibility that Father Richard's books enabled him to refresh his memory of works already borrowed from Barton's library. Reflections of avid reading appear in all his writings. Perhaps, as a printer, he was of some assistance to the philanthropic priest whose pioneer printing press was devoted to furnishing the youth of his flock with moral and educational texts.

Barton's directions were that from Detroit Nuttall should go via Chicago to visit the Indian tribes on the west side of Lake Michigan near Green Bay and thence across country to the shore of Lake Superior which he should follow till he reached Grand Portage, the start of the Lake-of-the-Woods route to Lake "Winnipic" (he was asked to learn "the true Indian spelling" of this!); from Lake Winnipeg he was to proceed northwest as far as latitude 55° on the Beaver River.[11] On the route from Detroit to Lake Superior, Barton thought an Indian guide would be necessary and urged caution in selecting one known for integrity and sobriety! The winter was to be passed where most convenient and economical. The return from the Beaver River was to be along a south-southeasterly course via a couple of British fur posts to the Missouri River and then easterly to the upper Mississippi. He was to go down that river and reach Fort Vincennes on the Wabash and thence return to Philadelphia through Kentucky and Virginia. In Virginia "with a proper guide" he was to visit the Peaks of Otter and the Salt Pond Mountain. These fantastic directions close with the admonition, "Always remember, that, next to your personal safety, science, and not mere convenience in travelling, is the great object of the journey. In pursuit of curious or important objects, it will often be necessary to court difficulties in travelling."[12]

The route stipulated for Nuttall from Grand Portage to Lake Winnipeg and thence up the Saskatchewan was used by brigades of the British North West Company, one yearly going up and returning down the Saskatchewan. The ultimate objective of the undertaking, however, and all other routes of the proposed journey were the product of an urban imagination working with a more or less hypothetical map. Moreover no hospitality could be looked for from the two British fur companies who were literally at murderous war between themselves and with the American fur traders. To send a lone unseasoned youth to make his way across such immensities of *terra incognita* infested by hostile British and savage Indians seems an incredible plan. It cannot be maintained that Barton was unaware of the dangers of the undertaking for in seeking a passport for Nuttall he wrote, ". . . I have no doubt, should his life be spared, that he will add much to our knowledge of the geography, the natural history & of the countries through which he is directed to pass." [13] Evidently Nuttall was regarded as expendable. However, Barton obviously knew nothing of the character of the plains Indians, the vastness of the western wilderness, and the threatening situation along the Canadian boundary, which broke into open warfare in 1812.

At Detroit Nuttall began to discover the serious flaws in his patron's instructions. While he was observing the flora and the Indians, he was also learning that in the great northern forests one did not travel directly toward an objective but followed waterways. To reach any point toward the west one started north to Lake Huron, traversing its full length to Michilimackinac on Mackinac Island in the strait between Lakes Huron and Michigan, for from the Great Lakes this was the point of departure for the West. Chance soon favored him with an opportunity for covering this part of the journey. Aaron Greeley, appointed in 1806 as surveyor of the new Territory of Michigan (1805), had to go to Mackinac Island to survey the holdings of the settlers. He started from Detroit on July 29 in a birchbark canoe, and Nuttall accompanied his party.[14]

As they passed up Detroit River, through Lake St. Clair, and up St. Clair River, Nuttall saw few species that he had not met with at Detroit; he mentioned in his diary only buttonweed and bank swallows. However the geological revelations were compensatory: after passing fossiliferous rock on the upper St. Clair, he found, "along the southern coast of the Huron, very intelligible indications of the approaching termination of this secondary formation, in the vast beds, as I may call them, of adventitious granitic rocks, which for more than one hundred miles in succession, continue to line its shores" — valuable light on the general location of great geological units.[15]

Nuttall was quickly initiated into the mode of travel of the Northwest: the large canoe, manned by French-Canadian voyageurs in picturesque garb, the camping sites on islands or mainland, the early morning starts, the monotonous meals of hulled corn boiled and mixed with fat, the songs of the boatmen, all became familiar. As the party advanced, Lake Huron opened before them, vast as an ocean, and the familiar hardwoods — birch, poplars, and maple — yielded to a darker forest with conifers predominating, a wilderness scene completely strange to Nuttall. Even at a distance, the spiring silhouettes of the trees kept him continually aware that he was on a novel adventure, and "the wild cries of the loons echoing over the great northern waters" carried to him the conviction that Nature reigned undisturbed in these remote regions for their weird, echoing calls, "instead of disturbing solitude, only deepen and confirm it."

The nightly camps and the stops for breakfast permitted regular botanizing in new locations where he was often thrilled by finding species he had never before seen growing. For the first time, he met with *Linnaea borealis* L., in fruit, for the lovely fragrance of its delicate twin flowers was long gone by as were the rose-purple blossoms of *Polygala paucifolia* Willd., which formed extensive carpets in the spruce forests. He saw a prostrate species of juniper, a European coltsfoot (*Tussilago Farfara* L.), and a *Calypso,* not in flower; on Bois Blanc Island he was delighted to see *Primula farinosa* L. He found several species unknown to science including *Iris *lacustris, Coreopsis *palmata, Cirsium undulatum* (Nutt.) Spreng., *Tanacetum *huronense,* and what proved to be a new variety of *Habenaria hyperborea* (L.) R. Br., although Nuttall published it as Orchis huronensis. He was greatly exhilarated by the journey into the north. Greeley's party arrived at Michilimackinac on August 12, two weeks and three hundred miles from Detroit.

Nothing can present a more picturesque or refreshing spectacle to the traveller, wearied with the lifeless monotony of a canoe voyage through Lake Huron, than the first sight of the island of Michilimackinac, which rises from the watery horizon in lofty bluffs imprinting a rugged outline along the sky. . . . A compact town stretches along the narrow plain below the hills, and a beautiful harbour . . . Indian canoes rapidly shooting across the water in every direction. There is no previous elevation of coast to prepare us for encountering the view of an island elevated more than three hundred feet above the water.[16]

The Jesuits who founded a mission at Mackinac in 1670 would have been amazed by the activity in that area one hundred and forty years later and aghast at the riotous celebrations for which it was notorious. As the rendezvous of much of the fur trade and the field headquarters of John Jacob Astor's fur company, its waterfront streets and taverns periodically swarmed with roistering French Canadian voyageurs spending their last sou before setting out on a new season of paddling and portaging through the forests of the northwest. Greeley and Nuttall found the little town gay with music and populous with gaudily capoted Canadiens, their hats adorned with bright feathers, the emblem of the Pacific Fur Company, who were enjoying the gregarious pleasures of the taverns before tackling a voyage that was to prove the longest, most arduous, and dangerous of their careers.[17]

Nuttall promptly discovered that there was no possibility of reaching any of his Canadian objectives; the British North West Company controlled the entrance to Lake Superior and the Grand Portage and permitted no encroachments on their territory.[18] But he met with a magnificent substitution. The expedition then equipping at Michilimackinac was planning to follow the Lewis-and-Clark route from St. Louis to the mouth of the Columbia River in order to establish a trading post there for Astor interests incorporated as the Pacific Fur Company. The overland leader, Wilson Price Hunt, invited Nuttall to accompany the brigade, which was then about ready to leave for St. Louis in order to ascend the Missouri in the spring.

Nuttall was able to stay some days at Michilimackinac and there he discovered the salmonberry, *Rubus *parviflorus*. He was pleased with a gift of specimens of fibrous gypsum from the Ottawa River and also received some of "the softish, brown-red argillaceous stone so much esteemed and employed by the Indians in the manufacture of their pipes [catlinite]." [19]

The route to St. Louis crossed Lake Michigan, led up Green Bay and the Fox River, and, after a short portage, followed down the Wisconsin River to the Mississippi. The trip from Mackinac to Le Baye near the mouth of the Fox River took about a week or ten days for an experienced party. Nuttall had excellent opportunities for collecting at the camping and cooking sites which were usually on thickly forested islands. He had been delighting in plants new to him since reaching Pittsburgh, and now he was finding an increasing number of species completely unknown. Whenever his boat touched shore he hurriedly alighted in eager anticipation and lost himself in the vegetation. This habit occasioned exchanges of witticisms among the voyageurs, who suspected the sanity of a person who dug up "weeds" with such devotion and excitement. Nor was Nuttall enamored of the Canadiens; he found in them the twin blights of superstition and intolerance, which placed them far below the vegetable kingdom in interest.

Soon after leaving Detroit, Nuttall either neglected to write in his diary for a period or started a new notebook, but at Le Baye on the Fox River and later he made a few entries to fill up some of the empty pages of the first notebook of the trip — the only one which has been found. So we have the entry:

Arrived at LeBay 26th Aug
Sept.[r] 9th Sunday Left LeBay in the afternoon and passed up Fox R.

These dates, being in conflict with those given by Washington Irving in his account of the Astoria party, bring to light some factual errors in that classic volume not previously recognized. However no quantity of minor inaccuracies can ever impair the fascination of Irving's *Astoria*.

The two weeks spent at Le Baye gave Nuttall a chance to get information for Barton from Menominee Indians and probably also from Winnebagos, Sauks, and Foxes. He jotted down a few Indian words but his interest turned to their harvesting of maple sugar and wild rice, their manitous and medicine men. A Menominee chief showed him nuggets of pure copper "collected near the outlet of R. Croix." Hereabouts he first saw *Smilacina trifolia* (L.) Desf. and his own Artemisia gnaphalodes, now regarded as a variety of the *A. *ludoviciana* that he got soon afterwards near St. Louis. On the way up Fox River Nuttall was impressed, as Captain Jonathan Carver had been forty-four years before, by the great quantity of wild rice and the abundance of wildfowl. On September 10 the party reached the portage where Nuttall made the last *dated* entry in his first notebook, concluding with the description in Latin of a new species, *Amorpha canescens* Pursh.[20] The swift current of the Wisconsin quickly brought the party to the Mississippi. Nuttall observed that the Wisconsin had cut its banks to reveal veins of lead ore in the great "calcareous platform" he had been tracing from Lake Erie westward.[21] ". . . Mr. Dickson received from the Indians a grant of these lead-mines, which Mr. Dickson informed me, promised to be no less productive than those they gave to Monsieur Dubuque, situated on the western side of the Mississippi. . . ."[22] Before descending the great river, the brigade paddled two miles above the confluence to visit Prairie du Chien, a gathering and trading place of Indian tribes from immemorial time, where the warwhoop was taboo in the interests of trade, where wampum drilled from shells of Atlantic quahogs was exchanged for the long claws of the grizzly of the Rockies or for Minnesotan stone for the red peace pipes. Nuttall got there his *Dalea* \**enneandra, Penstemon* \**grandiflorus,* and *Artemisia* \**serrata,* local productions never before found to be of value. He also saw for the first time *Lithospermum incisum* Lehm. (Batschia longiflora Nutt.), and *Castilleja sessiliflora* Pursh (Euchroma grandiflora Nutt.). In his diary Nuttall mentioned about two hundred and twenty species of plants that he collected between Philadelphia and St. Louis.

From Prairie du Chien, both southward and westward, he occasionally found in the river gravels water-rounded "varieties of fine calcedony . . . carnelian, sard, &c. . . . possessing every requisite beauty for the lapidary," and strikingly distinct from anything he had seen to the eastward. The origin of these pebbles of various sizes perplexed him.[23] When the brigade stopped at the Dubuque Lead Mines, forty miles below Prairie du Chien, Nuttall collected many invertebrate fossils in limestone from the mine dumps — *Terebratulites, Alcyonites,* and *Encrinites.*

The party arrived in St. Louis before the end of September. In October, Hunt conducted the unruly crew of engagés 450 miles up the Missouri to the mouth of the Nodoway River for winter encampment where they could be self-sustaining. Nuttall remained in St. Louis until into March.

ST. LOUIS. The formal ceremony of the transfer of Upper Louisiana Territory to the United States had taken place in March 1804 at St. Louis, the chief settlement. Its site, a prominent outcrop of limestone on the western bank of the Mississippi about eighteen miles below the mouth of the Missouri, had been carefully selected in the winter of 1763–1764 by Pierre Laclede Liguest who had come up from New Orleans hoping to monopolize the trade with the Indians of the Missouri. His heirs, the Chouteau family, still held a large share of the trade although the profits had attracted many competitors, among whom the most energetic and able was Manuel Lisa, the man with whom Nuttall had traveled across Pennsylvania.

The town in 1810, with a population of about 1400, extended for over a mile along the river bluff. The three principal thoroughfares, parallel to the water, were cut at right angles by shorter streets. The river landings were the centers of activity where the motley residents and visitors of the frontier town mingled — French and Spanish, Creoles, Indians, Kentucky backwoodsmen, New England Yankees and French-Canadian voyageurs. North, south, and west from the town spread the vast, undulating prairies undisturbed save for a few widely scattered, struggling French settlements.

In 1808 a post office had been established. (It took six weeks for the mail to come from Pittsburgh.) Joseph Charless (1772–1834), an Irish printer, started a weekly newspaper, the *Missouri Gazette*.[24] The financial success of the venture may be judged by an early subscription list of 170 names and by two items which appeared in the paper in the spring of 1810: first, an appeal for payment of subscriptions, whether it be in corn, flour, beef, or pork, and shortly thereafter an advertisement generously spiked with capital letters stating that Charless "receives Boarders by the day, week or month . . . on the most moderate terms." One is tempted to surmise that Nuttall, who had to provide for himself until the spring, may have boarded with Charless in exchange for labors at the printing press. The printer's advertisement for an apprentice about three months after Nuttall's departure shows that he had enough work to use an extra hand.

Charless's generous and friendly nature appears in some of the stories of the time. He kept a comfortable spot at his shop where copies of eastern newspapers were available. The Indians who visited the town discovered that they might there enjoy the novel experience of sitting in chairs, and Charless always made them welcome by handing each an old newspaper which they perused solemnly whether held correctly or upside down, nor did they fail to turn the pages in concert with other readers.

Indians were increasingly frequent visitors to St. Louis; many came from curiosity but some had business with the Territorial Agent for Indian Affairs, General William Clark, or "Redhead," as he was called by all the tribes. Their name for St. Louis was "Redhead's Town." The first judgment of him by the Missouri River tribes in 1804–1805 never suffered modification — he was "a great chief, fair and honorable in his dealings, and a man of his word"; their full confidence was never extended to another white man. Perhaps Nuttall talked with this amiable gentleman about the memorable expedition to the Pacific and the plants along the way.

Since Manuel Lisa spent this winter at home in St. Louis, he and Nuttall must have met from time to time and renewed their stage-coach acquaintance.[25] The hospitable Spaniard perhaps entertained the young Englishman in his home occasionally. Lisa was worried by lack of news from one of his partners in the Missouri Fur Company, Andrew Henry, who the previous June had retreated with a small band of trappers across the Rockies before the assaults of the Black-foot Indians; if no word came, Lisa planned to go up the Missouri in the spring to hunt for the party.

By curious coincidence another botanist was in St. Louis; a settlement which had not sheltered a naturalist in its forty-six years now entertained two. John Bradbury (1768–1823), an Englishman in his early forties, a member of the Linnean Society of London, had come to the United States under the auspices of a committee of members of the Liverpool Botanic Garden to collect living plants for the Garden.[26] He was engaged for three years at £100 a year. Since he had recently been working for William Bullock on the bird exhibits at the Liverpool Museum, he had received an additional commission from Lord Stanley to collect skins of birds and other vertebrates. From his most active patron, William Roscoe, he brought a letter of introduction to Thomas Jefferson whom he visited at Monticello for more than two weeks in August 1809, promptly after his arrival in America. Jefferson persuaded him to go to the unexplored country beyond the Mississippi as the richest center of new species with horticultural appeal. As Bradbury leisurely proceeded westward, gathering specimens and viewing the country, he was delayed a month by the ague and did not reach St. Louis until the last day of the year. Until the vegetation became active, he collected birdskins and prepared a nursery plot where plants could be accumulated for later shipment to Liverpool by way of New Orleans. Recurrent attacks of the ague interfered with his field work during the growing season but he sent off a large collection in the autumn of 1810. He was down the Mississippi at Ste. Genevieve occupied with this work when the Astoria Expedition arrived in St. Louis. By that time Bradbury had a wide acquaintance in the little settlement. His genial, sympathetic nature, broad experience, and wide interests gave him a ready approach to all manner of men and he was generally liked and respected. One of his favorite companions was Henry Marie Brackenridge (1786–1871), the son of Judge Hugh Brackenridge of Pittsburgh, a young lawyer of unusual ability, who was writing articles for the *Missouri Gazette* while he considered starting practice in the town.

On Bradbury's return from Ste. Genevieve he met the leaders of the Astoria Expedition, Hunt, Ramsay Crooks, and Donald McKenzie, who impressed him as uniting "the manners and accomplishments of gentlemen . . . with the hardihood . . . of . . . backwoodsmen." He recorded in his *Travels* that he gladly accepted the invitation which he promptly received from Hunt to accompany the expedition as far as suited him; he considered the opportunity so unusual that he abandoned then and there the idea he had been entertaining of going to the Arkansas. Yet late in November he wrote to William Roscoe that he planned to spend the next summer on the Arkansas River.[27] It was not until a couple of weeks before the Astorians started that he wrote to his patron that he had decided to go up the Missouri with a "Hunting party enroute to the Pacific" and spend the summer collecting on the upper Missouri, for, although he still preferred the Arkansas as a richer botanical region, he found that he could not finance the trip.[28] Was this intended as a rebuke to his backers? Neither side was satisfied with the fruits of the agreement. Bradbury with a wife and eight children to support in Britain was short of funds, and the contributors, not allowing for the distance involved and the dormant seasons, prematurely judged his shipments as inadequate.

Nuttall probably learned a good bit about mineralogy from the more experienced Bradbury, who gave him "very fine specimens of white, blue and amber" fluorite that he had collected at a lead mine "at the Rock and Cave in the vicinity of the Ohio" (Cave-in-Rock, Illinois Territory).[29] In November, Bradbury and Nuttall made an excursion together to the lead mines on the Meramec River south of St. Louis — possibly including those of Moses Austin at Mine à Breton, accounted the richest.[30] Nuttall observed that the deposits of galena here were in line with those on the Wisconsin River and at Dubuque and heard that they extended southwestward to the White River.[31]

As Bradbury had botanized on the Meramec during the summer, he was able to point out to Nuttall on high hills in the vicinity of the mines a number of unfamiliar plants which concealed their attractions in dormancy, among them a small tree, *Bumelia lanuginosa* (Michx.) Pers. var. *oblongifolia* (Nutt.) R. B. Clark, and the herbaceous *Mentzelia oligosperma* Nutt.[32] Nuttall collected great quantities of seeds wherever they were available and later grew many of them successfully. It was an *Oenothera* raised from Nuttall's seed collection of which Sims became author: the beautiful *O. missouriensis* under cultivation in England produced flowers six inches in diameter! In writing of various plants, Nuttall referred four times to the Meramec River and spelled the name differently each time, but not once did he hit on the form used today.

In spite of their common interests and months of association, Bradbury and Nuttall did not form a warm friendship. This seems to have been due rather to lack of mutual attraction than to rivalry in their objectives. Nuttall may have explained that he was not free to publish his findings. Bradbury seemed to have regarded the youth as naive and narrow in his interests. In his writings, Nuttall made several acknowledgments of information received from Bradbury and named a western species of *Castilleja* for him.

Nuttall saw the United States Army garrison at Fort Belle Fontaine and we have a diary record of his observations at the Cantine mounds six miles east of St. Louis in Illinois:

100 ft. high, in the American bottom n^r St. Louis are perhaps the largest & most perfect specimens of Indian fortification. the largest of which is about 2500 ft. circumfer. the area of some of them are now occupied as gardens by the monks of La Trappe, they are like all others which I have heard of strewed with fragments of earthen ware & human bones.[33]

His subsequent writings indicate that he spent many hours wandering about the countryside noting the terrain, the birds and their migrations, trees, and dried fruiting stalks of flowering herbs. Near St. Louis he found new species of plants of which he ultimately became the author, for example, *Artemisia* \*ludoviciana, *Baptisia* \*leucophaea, *Psoralea* \*Onobrychis, and the species of poppy on which he based his genus \*Stylophorum. Others strange to him were either already known or published by rivals before he was free to make public his findings; one of the most splendid of these was *Silene regia* Sims, a tall plant bearing abundant scarlet blossoms.[34] In the garden of Mr. Chouteau he carefully observed an Osage orange tree, a monotypic species from the southward which he subsequently named \*Maclura in honor of William Maclure.

The most exotic birds he saw were Carolina parakeets (now extinct) which darted in screaming flocks through dense forests on the river banks, feeding on fruits of the sycamore.[35] A graphic description of two whistling swans which he observed in domestication he recorded twenty-three years later.

> In the winter of 1810, I saw two of these graceful birds in a state of domestication near St. Louis (Missouri) which were obtained with several others at the same time, in consequence of the extreme cold. The thermometer falling to 15° below zero, they were unable to bear the cutting severity of the weather, and fell disabled, accompanied by several Wild Ducks, into an adjoining field, where a few survived and became tame.[36]

As Nuttall became acquainted with the region, he realized that the location of the town was superb from a scenic as well as a practical view: the country was a rich, rolling prairie dotted with groves of oaks, hickories, and black walnut which, being free of bushy undergrowth, presented an elegant, parklike appearance. Many small clear streams carried "limpid and transparent waters to the yellow and turbid Mississippi." From the summits of hills to the northward, Nuttall found a splendid panorama spread before him. The great Missouri hid its muddy waters in a heavy border of woods but the Mississippi, flowing between treeless banks could be traced far to the north; the little hills of Illinois completed the view to the northeast whereas to the northwest, as far as the eye could reach, the grassy prairies extended like a quiet sea studded with islets of trees. The seemingly unlimited reaches of this great West, grand and awesome, and Nature's unmatchable landscaping roused Nuttall's eager anticipation of the coming expedition up the Missouri.

UP THE MISSOURI. In January, Hunt came down to St. Louis from the wintering camp to make final arrangements for the journey to the Pacific.[37] He needed more hunters, not only to secure meat for the party but also to increase its fighting strength, because the Sioux were reported to be aggressively hostile. The Canadian voyageurs were exclusively boatmen and would be little if any help in an Indian attack. Hunt also wanted to engage as interpreter Pierre Dorion, a half-breed whose French-Canadian father had lived many years with the Yankton Sioux; the Lewis and Clark Expedition had employed both father and son as interpreters on the middle Missouri. However there was competition for Dorion's services. Manuel Lisa, who was preparing to go up the river, claimed Dorion's services on the basis of money owed the Missouri Fur Company for quantities of whiskey he had consumed at their Mandan post during the preceding season. This infuriated Dorion who, having no understanding of the great expenses of a middleman in the wilderness, thought he was being robbed by the charge of $10.00 a quart, so he determined to join the Astorians, and he made the most of the favorable market by exacting large wages and, at the last moment, refusing to embark without his squaw and two children.

Hunt's boat left St. Louis on March 11 to go up the Mississippi and enter the Missouri. Nuttall and Bradbury, who wished to wait for the mail that was expected the next day, were to walk across country and meet the boat at St. Charles.[38] However Bradbury heard that Lisa had arranged to have a writ of indebtedness served on Dorion at St. Charles, a procedure that he had used in 1806 to collect a debt from the interpreter of Pike's Expedition. Local feeling, which sympathized with the "underdog," persuaded Bradbury and Nuttall to set out during the night to give warning so that the Dorion family might take to the woods before the boat reached the village and rejoin the party later beyond the danger point. When Dorion returned to the boat west of St. Charles, he was without his goods and squaw, whom he had alienated by a beating. A searcher was sent out to find her but, as he had no success, the party soon camped on Bon Homme Island. Before dawn the squaw hailed the camp from the shore, and, with the high-spirited family united, the expedition was able to proceed.

A few small and poor French settlements lay west of St. Charles, and further up the river some immigrants from the United States had taken up land. Daniel Boone had come in the 1790s when he lost his Kentucky land to titleholders; he said he needed more elbow room. As he stood on the bank at La Charette watching the Astorians, Bradbury conversed with him and learned that he had lately returned from his spring hunt with nearly sixty beaver skins.

The next day another celebrity joined them for some miles. This was John Colter of the Lewis and Clark Expedition who had by special permission separated from that party on the upper Missouri during the return in 1806 in order to join two trappers. The next year he acted as a guide on the Yellowstone waters for Manuel Lisa. During the winter of 1807–1808, while going as Lisa's envoy to visit the mountain tribes, he discovered "Colter's Hell" on the Shoshone River and the Teton and Jackson Hole region. He had also crossed the area now known as Yellowstone National Park and become acquainted with the topography of a vast wilderness never before visited by a white man. His findings were luckily preserved on William Clark's valuable map published in 1814.

When Colter learned that the Astorians proposed to follow the Lewis-and-Clark route to the Pacific, he made every effort to persuade them to change their plans and cross the mountains at a more southerly point, not only that they might profit by the easy passes which he had found through the Wind River Range, but, more vital, to avoid the deadly Blackfeet. No white man knew the ferocity of this tribe so well as Colter. He narrated his experiences hoping to convince the Astorians of the soundness of his advice.[39]

In the spring of 1808 when he was traveling with Crow Indians near the Three Forks of the Missouri, the Blackfeet made a sudden attack. Since both sides were armed only with bows and arrows, Colter's rifle was an important factor in routing the foe in a hard-fought battle, an event the Blackfeet never forgave. Only once before had any of the band seen a white man from the United States. Seven adolescent braves had encountered Meriwether Lewis and three of his men on a reconnoitering trip and, in an attempt to steal the rifles and horses of the whites, two of the Indians had been killed, the only catastrophe of the kind in the course of the Lewis and Clark Expedition. The Blackfeet lived for warfare; they were scourges of their Indian neighbors and became enemies of the Americans at their first meetings. Some years afterwards they stated that they considered Lewis justified in protecting his possessions but that Colter had been guilty of aggression in aiding the Crows. In that encounter Colter received a severe leg wound but got back to Lisa's post unaided.

In the battle between the Crows and the Blackfeet, the decision had been so close that neither side collected its dead. Some months later, Colter and a fellow trapper suffered another meeting with a hundred or more Blackfeet. This resulted in the riddling of his provocative companion by scores of arrows and subsequent dismemberment. Colter made the most dramatic escape from blood-thirsty avengers that the long annals of Indian warfare have furnished. He saved himself, stripped of clothes and shoes, in a race before the youngest braves of the band, armed with spears, which would have provided a truly savage form of torture but proved unsuccessful because of Colter's desperate courage and resourcefulness. When he eventually got back to Lisa's post on the Yellowstone at the mouth of the Big Horn, about three hundred miles away, he was so blackened by the elements and emaciated by starvation that his friends did not recognize him until he spoke.

The fascination of the free life in the great plains and mountains held Colter in the regions ranged by friendly tribes, but in the spring of 1810 his job as guide for the Missouri Fur Company again took him into Blackfoot country for the establishment of a new post at the Three Forks. He warned the partners and the trappers of the dangers; their route crossed the old battlefield of the Crows with its whitened bones; he pointed out the perilous path of his miraculous escape and the locale of each horrible crisis; but the business of trapping the beaver was paramount, and nowhere were beaver more abundant and thicker furred than on the headwaters of the Missouri in the hunting grounds of the Blackfeet.

The founding of the new post was in charge of Col. Pierre Ménard and Andrew Henry. Before it was completed, the Indians struck fatally at scattered groups of trappers. Colter was among those who finally got safely back to camp. His mind was made up. Three times God Almighty had preserved him from these redskins, and that was more than was reasonable. With two companions he promptly but cautiously moved out of the area, across to the Yellowstone, and down to the company's post at the mouth of the Big Horn. From there he paddled alone to St. Louis, 2000 miles in thirty days. Henry led several of the survivors at the Three Forks across the Rockies to trap beyond Blackfoot country and had not been heard of since.[40]

If Colter had not recently married he would have joined Hunt's party, and his knowledge of the country on both slopes of the Rockies would have protected the Astorians from many of the horrible sufferings which lay ahead of them. Hunt was deeply disturbed by Colter's account of the dangers on the headwaters of the Missouri.

The boat moved slowly up the mighty river swollen by almost incessant rains. The great velocity of the current, the shoals, the sandbars, and submerged and immersed trees kept the average progress to about ten miles a day despite the good spirits and songs of the oarsmen. When a favoring wind filled the sail, the record was improved. Nuttall and Bradbury chose to walk on shore when conditions were suitable. The trees of tremendous size — predominantly hickory, oak, ash, walnut, and cottonwood — interested them; shadbush and hepatica were already in blossom. After the last of the straggling set-tlements had been passed, about two hundred miles up the river, the bear and deer became abundant. One day Bradbury was pursued by an aggressive skunk, which he shot; he added the pelt to his collection and found that the Canadiens considered the flesh a delicacy. The pedestrians watched a prodigious flock of feeding passenger pigeons which concealed the ground for acres. The first time that they came to an unfordable creek, Bradbury was surprised to find that Nuttall could not swim; as Nuttall refused Bradbury's offer to swim him across on his back they had to walk three or four miles upstream to find a crossing by means of an uprooted tree.

On the eighth evening out from St. Charles, they heard of a mixed war party of Iowas, Potawatomi, Sioux, and Sauks in the neighbor-hood moving against the Osages — "unpleasant news," for a war party's actions were aggressive and unpredictable. "Every one found in the warrior's path is an enemy." From this night the men slept on their arms.

Fort Osage (Fort Clark), a United States Army post about three hundred miles up the Missouri, had been established in 1808 by Governor Meriwether Lewis and built under General Clark's super-vision. The fort was the last link with law and order; there the party was welcomed by Ramsey Crooks who had come down with nine men from the wintering station to meet them.[41] The Osage Vil-lage near the fort was celebrating the return of a war party which had destroyed an Iowan village and taken seven scalps, those of two old men and five women and children abandoned by the fleeing band. The scalps adorned the roof of the chief's lodge. The army doctor took Bradbury on a tour of the village during which he saw the in-teriors of a couple of the lodges and was hospitably regaled with strange food. The Osages were a very tall, well-built race, greasy and filthy, more savage in countenance than the eastern Indians, and openly curious about the whites. Before daybreak the party was awak-ened by howling lamentations, matins peculiar to the Osage nation.

Having fair winds for sailing, they reached the wintering encamp-ment near the Nodaway a week after leaving the Fort. The united party numbered nearly sixty persons: five partners (Hunt, Crooks, Donald McKenzie, Robert McClelland, and Joseph Miller), the two naturalists, Dorion's family, forty boatmen, and some hunters. From the wintering encampment, the party proceeded in four boats furnished with masts and sails. They soon passed the mouth of the Platte, 600 miles from St. Louis, and were on the upper Missouri where the scenery became more spectacular, if less beautiful. The country was entirely open, the grassy plains clothed in "Buffalo grass," *Buchloë dactyloides* (Nutt.) Engelm. Trees were confined to the river bottoms and islands, and the channel of the river was cut deeply between steep banks which often were eroded into miniature mountain ranges or castellated summits. New animals were seen: wapiti, bison, pronghorns, and colonies of prairie dogs. Nuttall collected a hoary bat, a new species, which he took to Europe where it was published as *Nycterus cinerea* (Beauvois).[42]

The herbaceous flora above the Platte was thrillingly unfamiliar. A mallow, *Sphaeralcea coccinea* (Pursh) Rydb., with scarlet flowers in dense racemes often extended "over the plains in such quantities as to communicate a brilliant redness to thousands of acres."[43] The mallow, a small white primrose (*Androsace occidentalis* Pursh), and two handsome *Penstemons*, the small *\*albidus* and the tall *\*grandiflorus* with lilac flowers as large as foxgloves "which they not unaptly resemble" (already seen at Prairie du Chien) grew along the upper Missouri from the Platte northward and into the interior as far as Nuttall explored. He recorded that they "extended to the Mountains." From the White River more species joined the parade: lavender-flowered *Astragalus \*gracilis* on the plains, large white-flowered *Oenothera \*caespitosa* on arid denuded hills, *Atriplex \*argentea* in saline places, and odorous *Artemisia \*longifolia* in rocky situations on the banks of the Missouri. A band of country two or three hundred miles along the Missouri centering at the White River produced a new genus that Nuttall considered "the most splendid plant in the Natural Order of Cruciferae," having large and numerous yellow and orange flowers in a long raceme; he was pleased to name the genus *\*Stanleya* for Lord Stanley, an active naturalist. Other plants were localized: near the White River a little green-flowered milkweed, (*Asclepias \*lanuginosa*) and a white-flowered legume (*Sophora \*sericea*) appeared; at the Great Bend was a ragwort (*Senecio \*integerrimus*) with large yellow blossoms and the low-growing, pungent thorn grass [*Munroa squarrosa* (Nutt.) Torr.] covering thousands of arid acres; in moist places about the confluence of the Cheyenne was a violaceous-flowered phloxlike plant (*\*Collomia linearis*) for which Nuttall established a new genus. Only one violet grew on the upper Missouri, a stemmed yellow one (*Viola nuttallii* Pursh) extending from "the Rock River" to the mountains. Many such beautiful species were gathered by the botanists as well as quantities of less striking plants, not excluding grasses and "weeds." Unfortunately neither of the toilers in the field was destined to garner fitting credit for his labors.

At the upper Missouri, the party had reached the hunting grounds of the plains Indians whose economy centered about the buffalo. These Indians included the Ottos, Omahas, Panis, Poncas, the many nations of the powerful Sioux, and other lesser tribes. Parties of any of these Indians might appear on either bank of the river at any time and in any mood. While trading at the village of the Omahas, Hunt learned that several nations of the Sioux were assembling up the river to oppose the advance of his party. Alarming incidents kept the apprehensions of the men simmering. One night eleven young Sioux with tomahawks in hand rushed into camp but they were instantly surrounded and, after a warning from Hunt, were conveyed across the river.

There were some desertions among the hunters, but through chance meetings on the river the party luckily acquired five highly experienced trappers, three of whom (Hoback, Rezner, and Robinson) had spent the winter with Andrew Henry beyond the Rockies on Henry's Fork of the Snake River. Their information, which corroborated Colter's report, caused Hunt to change his proposed route. He decided to leave the river at the Arikara village, which lay a few hundred miles ahead, and strike westward across country. This decision brought before the botanists the problem of when and how they should return.

The long-dreaded encounter with the Sioux suddenly occurred. Two envoys came to inform Hunt that Yankton and Teton Sioux had been encamped nearby for eleven days to arrest his party's further advance in order to prevent their trading with the Arikaras, Mandans, and Minetarees, against whom the Sioux were waging war. The number of lodges mentioned indicated six hundred warriors, and the messengers said that two more bands of Tetons were expected. Soon afterwards the bluffs ahead on the east of the river were seen to be swarming with Indians, afoot or mounted, all in full warpaint and regalia but armed for the most part only with bows and arrows. A pitched battle impended. The boats put to on the opposite shore to prepare: all arms were put in order; the swivel and two howitzers were fired with powder only, for moral effect, and immediately after were heavily loaded with shot for business. The boats then moved across the river and, when stationed about three hundred feet from the Indians, all of the party seized their arms. After a moment of confusion the enemy signaled for a parley by moving their buffalo robes before them from side to side.

Fourteen of the chiefs came down to the deeply cut bed of the river and seated themselves on the sand in an arc about a fire which was being prepared. The five partners, accompanied by Dorion and Bradbury, went ashore and completed the circle under the protection of the boats. A calumet, the ceremonial peace pipe, with a stem six feet long decorated with tufts of horsehair dyed red, was lighted by an attendant, held toward the sun, the earth, and the compass points, and then handed to the great chief who, after taking a few whiffs, holding the bowl, inserted the stem into Hunt's mouth. Hunt followed his example, and the peace pipe traveled around the circle. After the ceremonial smoking, Hunt explained that his party was not intending to trade with the river tribes but was only passing through the country to see their dear brothers on the great salt lake to the west, and the chiefs, professing to sympathize — they too had brothers at a distance whom they yearned to see — graciously received the gifts of tobacco and corn which were distributed, and the crisis was over.

Preparation for this encounter may have been the occasion when it was discovered that Nuttall's gun had been put to strange uses. One version is that the muzzle was plugged with earth because it had been used as trowel, pick, and shovel to release the roots of plants from the soil, and another is that Nuttall, knowing that the guns would be kept safe and dry, had used the bore as a safe storage place for packages of seeds he had collected.

Another alarm occurred soon after the encounter with the Sioux. While Hunt's boat was hemmed in between the shore and a long sandbar, the bank above was suddenly crowded with Indians in war-paint who were pushed forward by others coming on. Fear gripped the party for it was thought these were the reinforcements of Teton Sioux who had been expected by the main body. Luckily, however, they proved to be friendly Arikaras, Mandans, and Minetarees moving against the Sioux, so friendly that each shook hands with all members of the party. They decided to return to their villages to trade with the Astorians for powder, ball, and knives, deferring their warfare

until they should be better equipped. Brackenridge recorded an anecdote from this encounter which Miller related to him: "The party
was on the point of firing; while every one was in momentary expectation that this would take place, Nuttal, who appeared to have been
examining them very attentively, turned to Miller, 'sir,' said he,
'don't you think these Indians much fatter, and more robust than those
of yesterday.'"[44]

Twelve hundred miles up the river, the Astorians were joined by
the boat of the Missouri Fur Company commanded by Manuel Lisa
which had left St. Louis more than three weeks later and had been
striving to overtake them for mutual protection in passing through
the country ranged by the hostile Sioux.[45] In lieu of Dorion, Lisa had
engaged Charbonneau, the interpreter of the Lewis and Clark Expedition, who was accompanied by his squaw Sacagawea, a Shoshone.
Lisa had with him as a guest Henry Marie Brackenridge, who had a
curiosity to see the country. Like Bradbury, he kept a journal which
was later published, and therein is a paragraph describing Nuttall.

There is in company a gentleman . . . Mr. Nuttal, engaged in similar
pursuits [to those of Bradbury], to which he appears singularly devoted,
and which seem to engross every thought, to the total disregard of his
own personal safety, and sometimes to the inconvenience of the party he
accompanies. To the ignorant Canadian boatmen, who are unable to
appreciate the science, he affords a subject of merriment; le fou is the
name by which he is commonly known. . . . He is a young man of genius,
and very considerable acquirements, but is too much devoted to his favorite pursuit, and seems to think that no other study deserves the attention
of a man of sense. I hope, should this meet his eye, it will give no offence;
for these things, often constituted a subject of merriment to us both.[46]

Unfortunately Dorion's quarrel with Lisa was not the only source
of friction between the two parties. Crooks and McClelland, who had
traded in partnership on the Missouri, believed that, two years before,
Lisa had double-crossed them with the Teton Sioux who pillaged
much of their trade goods, and they roused Hunt's apprehension that
Lisa might influence the Arikaras against the Astorians. Lisa on his
part had been uneasy that Hunt might turn the Sioux against his
smaller group to "secure his own passage," and he blamed the two
erstwhile partners for the present hostility of the Sioux, for they had
saved a portion of their goods by a subterfuge which was keenly resented by the Indians.

The adroit Spaniard was an enigma to many of his contemporaries. His boldness, daring, and energy were likened to that of Cortez or Pizzaro; his superior mind and indefatigable industry swept away difficulties which to others were insurmountable. He had an uncanny understanding of the Indian temperament so that he was highly successful in trading with the tribes and could cajole them when other traders were repulsed; in consequence he acquired a reputation for treachery against the whites although no reliable evidence to support the suspicions has ever been uncovered. On the contrary, during the War of 1812, by fomenting intertribal warfare, manipulating the savages like puppets, he saved the white settlements on the western frontiers from the Indian attacks which the British constantly strove to inspire.

At first the two parties advanced together but, after a violent quarrel between Lisa and Dorion which was smothered by the combined alertness of Bradbury and Brackenridge, a distance was maintained between them. However, after a council was held with the Arikara chiefs, all was pleasantness for, following the ceremonial smoking, almost the first words that Lisa spoke in answer to the chief's words of welcome were a recommendation of Hunt's party to their favorable treatment, and he further said that he would consider any injury done them as done to himself.

At the Arikara village Hunt made preparations for starting on the overland trek. Horses had to be purchased for carrying the baggage and he hoped to get enough from the Arikaras and the Cheyennes so that all the men could ride. In the end the supply proved inadequate to provide mounts except for the partners; the Indians would not part with their best ponies trained for the buffalo hunt but they figured they could easily replace ordinary pack animals by theft or barter. The boats and some trading goods were to be turned over to Lisa in exchange for horses, which the Missouri Fur Company had at their Mandan post two hundred miles further up the river, about one hundred and fifty miles by land.

Nuttall and Brackenridge accompanied Lisa who went up by boat to superintend the transfer of the horses at the Mandan post, and Bradbury joined Crooks's mounted party, which rode overland. The land party, fearing roaming bands of Sioux, made forced marches, riding from dawn till dark and keeping in valleys of creeks and the dips of the prairie as much as possible. Late on the fourth night they arrived at the post, where they were warmly welcomed by Reuben Lewis, a partner of the Missouri Fur Company. Lisa's boat started from the Arikara village on the morning that Crooks left but the river travel took twice as long. After Crooks had come to an agreement with Lisa on the purchase, he drove the horses back to the Arikara village. Bradbury, however, remained at the Mandan Post until Lisa's boat returned; he was finding so many new plants that he could not bear to leave sooner.

AT THE MANDAN POST. The Mandan post of the Missouri Fur Company had been established in the summer of 1809 on a high bank two hundred yards west of the river.[47] It consisted of a triangular palisade fifteen feet high enclosing a square blockhouse and outbuildings. The ground floor of the house was used for furs and the second floor provided living quarters for the trappers. Reuben Lewis (1777–1844), the only brother of Meriwether Lewis and a partner of the Missouri Fur Company, had been at the post from its start and had there received the shocking news of his brother's death on the Natchez Trace. A garden which supplied fresh vegetables was under the care of an Irishman who hospitably made it available for the living plants which Bradbury, and later Nuttall, transplanted from the prairies.

Nuttall immediately started to explore the terrain about the post. Brackenridge reported that one day when he accompanied Nuttall they were delighted to find ripe strawberries, "a pleasing treat." Bradbury was bothered by the myriads of mosquitoes which demanded the constant need of one hand to protect the eyes. Nuttall recorded neither the amenities nor the torments of the country; he was intent on the boundless bounties of nature.

There were five Indian settlements in the vicinity of the post, all on the western side of the Missouri, often called collectively the Mandan Villages. The travelers visited them more than once. One of the Mandan chiefs, She-he-ke, or Big White, from his fair complexion, welcomed them with "Come in house." In 1806 he had accepted the invitation extended by Lewis and Clark to visit the Great White Father in Washington and, accompanied by his squaw, Yellow Corn, little son, White-Painted House, and an interpreter and his family, he went down river with the returning Expedition. His white visitors found him intelligent and sensible and listened sympathetically to his remarks which, Brackenridge wrote, dwelt on "the insecurity, the ferocity of manners, and the ignorance, of the state of society in which he was placed." [48]

The Fourth of July was celebrated by a dinner on Lisa's boat. The Spaniard, who had become a citizen of the United States through the Louisiana Purchase, entertained the two English botanists; his partner Lewis, who was a Virginian; Brackenridge, the son of a Princeton graduate; and two Minetaree chiefs, who paid a timely call at the post, Black Shoe and One-Eyed, a monster of cruelty feared by his own people. The Indians "ate with moderation, and behaved with much propriety, seeming studious to imitate the manners of the white."

Two days later, when Lisa returned to the Arikaras to trade until the end of the season, Bradbury and Brackenridge accompanied him. Soon afterwards the erstwhile guests set off for St. Louis with two boatloads of pelts of the Missouri Fur Company and a great quantity of living plants stowed in *caissettes,* which Bradbury had bought from the Astorian voyageurs who could not take them overland. The descent of the stream was rapid, and they were back in St. Louis by early August.[49]

Nuttall remained at the Mandan post until the autumn and so was able to collect both flowers and fruits of many of the species of the rich western flora which had not yet been introduced to the scientific world, although the Lewis and Clark Expedition had sent back collections in 1805 and taken back more in 1806. He walked great distances over the monotonous plains, cactus infested or pungent with sagebrush, seeking grassy glades or following winding beds of small streams. A trail that struck almost directly westwards from the Mandan villages to the Yellowstone River, near the confluence of the Big Horn, doubtless enticed the naturalist. He was very eager to reach the Rocky Mountains; and, failing completely to comprehend that in that latitude the continental divide lay hundreds of miles further west, he confused westward hills and mountains with the main ranges. Consequently he later gave the distribution of many of his species as extending "to the northern Andes." Another trail that ran north to the British fur companies' posts on the Assiniboine he probably also followed.[50] He got his *Yucca *glauca* "1600 miles up the Missourie, about latitude 49°." [51] On one occasion, with his usual obliviousness to such matters as food, time, and distance, he went so far that his strength failed completely and he collapsed on the open plains. He was more than a hundred miles from the fort (as the story was told in third-hand accounts) without food, and there seemed nothing to do but resign himself to death. Fortunately a roaming Indian spied his passive form and took him back to the post in his canoe.[52] As a collector of herbs, the natives called him "pale-face medicine man." Only a war chief was as highly esteemed as a man who worked magic with plants, and for what else would a man gather miscellaneous weeds? This experience gave Nuttall mixed feelings about the Indians: eventually he came to fear and mistrust them as capricious and sometimes ferocious creatures, but he recognized their skill and ability in their own mode of life and was grateful for kindnesses that he received from some of them. In his various wanderings, which brought him into contact with most of the western tribes, he developed the policy of discreetly avoiding them in the wilderness so far as possible; in their villages their tradition of hospitality usually protected the white man.

Among the most important of Nuttall's activities was the work of drying his herbarium specimens. The preparation of good specimens — and Nuttall made excellent ones even under the most untoward conditions as the thousands now in the British Museum bear witness — is no casual matter but one demanding thought and delicate care in the initial pressing and frequent subsequent attention to the drying, a time-consuming and tedious job.

Among the new plants of his harvest were *Solanum *triflorum,* "a weed in and about the gardens of the Mandans and Minitaree," *Opuntia fragilis* (Nutt.) Haw., and *Mamillaria vivipara* (Nutt.) Haw. on high, gravelly hills — the cacti extending "to the mountains," *Petalostemum *villosum* with roseate August flowers on the sandy banks of the Knife, and, in favored spots on the plains, two beautiful *Penstemons* — the small lavender *gracilis* and the rare azure *angustifolius.* One of his most brilliant species, magenta-flowered *Hedysarum *boreale,* came from arid, denuded soil on the banks of the Missouri; it was not found thereabouts again until a hundred and ten years later when a special effort was made to relocate it to verify Nuttall's site. Abundant about the Fort were two species of *Orobanche* — *ludoviciana* and *fasciculata* — "not apparently parasitic." A new grass, *Schedonnardus paniculatus* (Nutt.) Trel., occupied dry saline areas of the plains; in humid places he got *Lactuca ludoviciana*

(Nutt.) Riddell and a very localized plant of a new genus of the *Scrophulariaceae* with bright yellow flowers, *Orthocarpus luteus*. On the borders of thickets around the fort grew *Dracocephalum *parviflorum* and, "in moist situations on the margins of small streams and valleys, abundant from Ft. Mandan to the mountains," he collected *Lilium philadelphicum* L. var. *andinum* (Nutt.) Ker. A species which especially engaged his interest was an *Eriogonum* (his *E. flavum* of Fraser's 1813 catalog) that grew "on arid denuded argillaceous hills . . . from the Arikara village to the northern Andes"; his first published article consisted of a discussion of this showy western genus.

Some of his observations were geological. Rock and earth grotesquely eroded, strata of coal, petrified wood, and a few other fossils, the occurrence of pumice floating on the river, and the well-exposed strata of the whole region furnished tantalizing suggestions of the geological history of the country. In his fossil collection were specimens of a unique shell from "the ancient alluvium . . . washed out of the banks of the river from White river of the Missouri to the Mandans, but at the same time, locally and not uniformly distributed." In 1820 Thomas Say published this and an identical fossil collected by Lewis and Clark as a new species of Lamarck's *Baculites* (*B. compressa*), a widespread extinct genus of ammonites of the Upper Cretaceous.[53]

In his enthusiasm for the flora and geology of the country his attention was not entirely distracted from Barton's instructions to collect animals, Indian vocabularies and legends, information concerning mineral springs, the incidence of diseases, the medicinal use of plants by the Indians, and so on and on. Bradbury mentions the great number of new snakes and the interesting mammals that he himself collected, but he gives no information concerning Nuttall's zoological activities. It is probable that Nuttall's poor marksmanship prevented his collecting any animals except the smallest. A specimen of a ground squirrel that he took to England was evidently never named, nor was one secured by Lewis and Clark in western Montana. Both these early specimens belonged to the var. *pallidus* (J. A. Allen, 1874) of a species described in 1821 by Dr. Mitchill as "Spermophilus tridecemlineatus" (*Citellus*).[54] Nuttall was said to have often told of his difficulties in keeping his specimens of snakes and lizards from drying out because thirsty Indians were bent on draining off the alcohol in which they were preserved. We know that he collected quantities of insects, for scores of species that he got on the Missouri River were published by Thomas Say from 1817 onwards; most of these were beetles, the least fragile of the insects, and by far the largest order.

Efforts to amass ethnological and hygienic data depended to a considerable extent on the aid of an interpreter. During that summer the Mandan post employed the highly experienced René Jessaume, a French Canadian who had lived many years among the Minetarees after service with the British North West Company and had accompanied Meriwether Lewis to Washington as interpreter for the Mandan Chief She-he-ke. However for practical matters the tribes possessed a common sign language of remarkable clarity. Two Omahas informed Bradbury that they had seen him at Charless's printing shop in St. Louis by the simple expedient of lifting a corner of their buffalo robes and extending them before their faces, then turning them over as a man does a newspaper in reading it, pointing at Bradbury and down the river. Nuttall developed some ability in interpreting sign language. About ten years later he wrote "These Indians [Shawnees] possess the same symbolical or pantomimic language as that which is employed by most of the nations with which I have become acquainted. It appears to be a compact invented by necessity, which gives that facility to communication denied to oral speech."

Nuttall did not neglect the opportunity of observing the agricultural products and methods of the Mandan Indians, the "best farmers" of the western plains. Hedrick in his *History of Horticulture in America to 1860* says that the Mandans

grew some dozen or more varieties of corn, six kinds of beans, one of which, the Great Northern, is still grown by the Whites as a valuable field bean; and an amazing number of pumpkins, squashes, and gourds. To these they quickly added cucumbers and watermelon obtained from the Spaniards, besides which they grew a species of tobacco and several varieties of sunflowers. Through long growing and selection, these crops had been adapted to the heat, drought, and short season of this northern land. . . . this tribe . . . cultivated several plants now considered weeds, such as lamb-quarter and pigweed, and used several wild fruits if they did not actually plant them: the native plums, cherries, June berries, buffalo berries, thornapples, wild grapes, and even rose haws among others.[55]

If Nuttall's divergence from the routes laid down for him in Barton's directions had caused him any concern he was now able to more fully appreciate the fanciful nature of Barton's instructions. At the Mandan villages the American fur traders came into open competition with the British from posts on the Assiniboine, and evidence was abundant that Indian partisans were being encouraged to pillage and destroy American "intruders."[56] In view of what Nuttall had learned of the vastness of the western country, the constant danger from roaming savages, and his own ineptness in the indispensable crafts of the frontier, he should have concluded that he had been inordinately lucky to have arrived so easily and safely in a new and rich floral belt with good prospects of getting his loot back to the civilized world. To transport his baggage he would have to return downstream through New Orleans, a further deviation from Barton's unrealistic directions.

At the close of the summer Andrew Henry arrived safely at the Mandan post with forty packs of beaver skins, and the three partners — Lisa, Lewis, and Henry — took the accumulated peltries down to St. Louis, arriving on October 21. Nuttall accompanied them.[57]

Bradbury, still suffering from the fever which had attacked him ten days after his return to St. Louis in midsummer, was staying four miles out of town with his friend Samuel Bridge who had emigrated from Manchester, England. On August 16, in a letter to William Roscoe, Bradbury enclosed a note to the Committee of the Liverpool Botanic Garden resigning from his undertaking and stating that he had now sent all the plants to which they were entitled under their agreement.[58] In December when he was well enough to travel, he made arrangements to take charge of a boatload of lead consigned to New Orleans. When the great earthquakes which destroyed New Madrid (the worst ever experienced in central North America) started at two o'clock in the morning of December 16, Bradbury's boat happened to be tied up for the night at an island near the epicenter. Bradbury was wakened by a tremendous noise and the terrified cries of the crew. He rushed to the cabin door and saw "that the boat was still safe at her moorings. . . . the perpendicular banks, both above and below us, began to fall into the river in such vast masses as nearly to sink our boat by the swell they occasioned."[59] The shocks which continued throughout the night were felt over a million square miles. They occurred for several days with decreasing frequency and severity and continued sporadically for a year. As the party proceeded they saw wreckage of many boats and often saw banks falling into the river carrying their burden of trees with them. Their boat got safely through the drifting timber. At Natchez the crew had a close view of the *New Orleans,* the first steamboat to descend the Mississippi; she had steamed by their flatboat some 340 miles above, at the mouth of the Arkansas. Bradbury reached New Orleans before mid-January 1812. There he met his friend Bracken-ridge who had left St. Louis in November.

Bradbury shipped his herbarium specimens to his son, John Leigh Bradbury, in Gloucester, England, with instructions "to form a new connection." On January 20, he sailed for New York expecting to leave shortly for England, but the War of 1812 interfered with his plans for a prompt return. Meanwhile his son, feeling that the herbarium belonged to Bradbury's sponsors (although the dried collection seemed to have been an independent enterprise of little interest to the Garden), made plans to turn it over to William Roscoe.[60]

We have a little information about Nuttall's descent of the Mississippi in a trading boat about a month before Bradbury's. He visited Indian mounds near New Madrid, obviously before the settlement was destroyed by the earthquakes.[61] Since he nowhere mentions the stupendous earth tremors which were felt at great distances, he must have been well away before the first quakes occurred. He watched apprehensively with his companions for signs of the river pirates on and near Stack Island. The boat made a stop at Natchez, which enabled Nuttall to collect. He dug roots of a new composite, *Cacalia* *tuberosa,* which Bradbury had pointed out to him growing about St. Louis; the roots produced flowering plants in 1813 in Fraser's garden in London. He also collected *Prunus caroliniana* Ait., a new variety of *Bumelia* that Bradbury had called to his attention at the lead mines and *Hydrangea quercifolia* Bartr. collected in Florida decades before by his aged friend William Bartram.

More than twenty years later he described a curious event of the journey:

In the month of December, 1811, while leisurely descending . . . the Mississippi . . . I had the opportunity of witnessing one of those migra-tions of the Whooping Cranes, assembled by many thousands from all the marshes and impassable swamps of the north and west. The whole continent seemed as if giving up its quota of the species to swell the mighty host. Their flight took place in the night, down the great aërial valley of the river, whose southern course conducted them every instant towards warmer and more hospitable climes. The clangor of these numerous legions, passing along, high in the air, seemed almost deafening; the confused cry of the vast army continued, with the lengthening procession, and as the vocal call continued nearly throughout the whole night, without intermission, some idea may be formed of the immensity of the numbers now assembled on their annual journey to the regions of the south.[62]

It is now believed that this was a migration of sandhill cranes, for whooping cranes were never as abundant as this.[63]

At New Orleans, Nuttall for the first time examined wild palmettos which grew "in troublesome abundance" around the city, saw *Crinum americanum* L., "plentiful in the marshes," the scandent *Brunnichia cirrhosa* Gaertn., and a shrubby *Acacia* (*farnesiana* L.) conspicuous by its fragrant yellow flowers. He collected several fruited legumes, grasses, street weeds, and *Rhamnus lanceolata* Pursh while awaiting embarkation.

As St. Louis and the lower river towns were essentially ports, Nuttall must have heard that Congress had passed a second Nonintercourse Act in March 1811, prohibiting trade with Great Britain. So it was doubtless a happy surprise to find at New Orleans a ship about to sail for Liverpool. The *Columbia* had been in port advertising for a cargo since mid-September. The December 11th issue of the *Courrier de la Louisiané* carried a notice that she was ready to receive shipments to Liverpool, and she evidently sailed within a few days.

No intimation appears of Nuttall's reason for embarking for England rather than for an American port but we surmise that it was reason enough that a ship happened to be sailing for Liverpool. Since leaving Philadelphia and wandering in very strange lands, Nuttall had heard little or nothing from his family and friends, and with war obviously brewing it might be many more years before he would see them or perhaps hear from them if he failed to seize the opportunity of leaving American shores. Before he sailed he sent to Barton herbarium specimens, seeds, and notes of his journey as his contract demanded.[64] Since he never repudiated his agreement, scrupulously refrained from scientific publication, returned to Philadelphia as quickly as he could make arrangements to leave England after the war ended, and evinced no consciousness of wrong doing, there seem no grounds for the suspicions of ulterior motives in his going home which some commentators have expressed. They overlook the eagerness of youth and its warm attachments. Under the circumstances, exoneration of Nuttall's course of action seems superfluous.

Barton was greatly incensed because Nuttall did not arrive in Philadelphia. The contract stipulated that he should return overland through Indiana and Kentucky and collect in Virginia. Such a route with the burden of his collections could have been taken only at great expense, which he could not command. In any case it was an unreasonable route. The frequent impossibility of adhering to the unrealistic terms of the contract must have inured Nuttall to transgressions. Moreover he would have seen no importance in his personal appearance in Philadelphia so long as Barton received the collections. His employer's deep annoyance with him — freely expressed in England in 1815 — supports the impression that Barton had counted on his services in describing and naming not only the plant collections that he himself had made but also those of the Lewis and Clark Expedition.

No record could be found of the arrival of the *Columbia* in England; she may have been seized as a prize of war, a common fate at that time, or her name may have been changed *en route* to one more pleasing in Britain. In any case Nuttall reached home within a few months.

CHAPTER 6

# ENGLAND

## 1812–1815

The wilderness, rough, harsh, and inexorable, — has charms more
potent in their seductive influence than all the lures of luxury and
sloth. — Parkman, *Conspiracy of Pontiac*

FAMILY AFFAIRS. In the year in which Thomas left Philadelphia
for remote western regions, his Uncle Jonas purchased a tract of
land at the edge of Thatto Heath, a coal-mining area in the township
of Sutton, about ten miles east of Liverpool.[1] He built a commodious
Georgian house and proceeded to develop an estate with lawns, gardens, and orchard, greenhouses and an elaborate conservatory, stable,
carriage house and gatehouse, fringed with tenant farms in addition
to the home farm. As the land had been covered with hazelnut bushes,
the estate was named Nutgrove. At this time Jonas discontinued his
business activities although he was scarcely forty, and his partners
Francis Dixon and Henry Fisher assumed the responsibilities of carrying on the printing and publishing company.

Jonas's wife Frances, "a very zealous Wesleyan," was appalled by
the godlessness, ignorance, and squalor in which the coal-mining
families of Thatto Heath lived: no church, school, nor medical care
was readily available to them. She immediately arranged for religious
services to be held on Sunday afternoons in the kitchen of Nutgrove
Hall to which all the villagers were invited.

Usually a preacher from Liverpool attended, but, failing him, Mr.
Nuttall conducted the services himself. Very soon the room became too
small to accommodate those who wished to hear the Gospel, and the services had perforce to be held on the open heath. Some of the greatest
sinners of the neighbourhood — poachers, bull-baiters, cock-fighters, and
pugilists — were converted, and many precious trophies won for Christ.[2]

In 1811 Jonas built Nutgrove Chapel and School in the village. Preachers, supplied regularly by the Liverpool Circuit, arrived Saturday evenings at Nutgrove Hall to remain until Monday mornings. Jonas also built a cottage for the schoolmistress and provided an endowment yielding £30 a year for her salary; she was to be supplied with fresh vegetables from the garden of Nutgrove Hall *in perpetuo*. Frances visited the sick and assisted almost daily in teaching sewing and knitting at the school.

News of the radical changes in his uncle's mode of life may have reached Nuttall through the St. Louis post office. When his ship docked in England, we may assume that his first care was his precious collections, especially any living plants. At the printing shop in Liverpool he would find the Fishers and some of his Aunt Mary Dixon's large family, but as Jonas was *in loco parentis* Thomas would drive as soon as possible to Nutgrove Hall. The gun and powderhorn that he took with him from Philadelphia on a memorable April morning in 1810, were hung on the kitchen wall at Nutgrove where they remained as a symbol of exciting adventures that spellbound the small boys of the family for three generations. Jonas's greenhouses, garden, and gardener provided for prompt cultivation of the American plants and facilities for raising Thomas's large collection of seeds.

After his collections were cared for, Thomas doubtless set out for Long Preston to see his mother and sisters. Tradition reports that he was especially attached to his younger sister, Elizabeth, a general favorite in the family, who was about seventeen at this time. They and numerous other relatives, friends, and neighbors were eager to hear about the strange world across the ocean and his four years of varied adventures. Thomas had attentive audiences for his descriptions of the frontier country, the primeval America which fascinated him: the charm of the deciduous woods with its great variety of trees each with its own features of beauty, the shining white bark of "majestic sycamores leaning their vast trunks and massive limbs" over the streams, the candlelike fruits of the towering tulip trees, the lofty vase-shaped elms, the aspens with their leaves always aquiver; the forbidding appearance of the dark northern forests of pines, pointed spruces, and firs forming dense, interminable walls along the shores of the great northern lakes; the mighty river system which he had followed for thousands of miles through wild scenery of open glades, verdant prairies, and sterile plains — all in all a world of such undisturbed immensities as could not be imagined by an untraveled Englishman. The animals were on the same scale — herds of tens of thousands of buffalo roamed the plains; the passenger pigeons lived in incredible flocks that darkened the sky and took hours to pass by; the streams were full of fish and beaver, the ponds, covered with ducks; deer, bears, wolves, and many smaller creatures ranged everywhere; but most interesting and beautiful of the products of this fabulous land were the new and strange herbaceous plants which adorned the vast country. So little of the flora had been scientifically examined that it was truly a botanist's paradise. He told about all these things but he could give no adequate impression to his listeners of the charm and serenity the scenes held for him.

The second war between Great Britain and the United States which had been building up since the close of the Revolution finally broke out in June 1812 and was not concluded until the end of 1814. In consequence Nuttall remained in England for about three years, making his headquarters at Nutgrove Hall. He felt at home there, having spent his adolescent years with his Uncle Jonas and Aunt Frances in Liverpool. The transplants from Missouri Territory and the new seedlings throve vigorously in gratifying numbers. From them Thomas made some donations of interest. To the Liverpool Botanic Garden he gave plants of his azure *Penstemon* raised from seed[3] and a buffalo berry, a western shrub with edible scarlet fruits which he later named *Shepherdia argentea* in honor of the Director of the Garden, John Shepherd (1764?–1836), "a most scientific gardener and skillful cultivator."[4] In the *Sylva,* Nuttall commented on the fate of this *Shepherdia*: "kept in a greenhouse, it was, I presume, killed with kindness, and was soon lost." He may also have contributed to the herbarium of the Garden but none of his Missouri species have survived among the specimens of Nuttall which are still treasured by the Liverpool Museum.[5] He made many gifts to Aylmer Bourke Lambert and gave seeds to William Anderson, gardener for James Vere at Kensington Gore, and to the nearby gardens at Knowsley, the seat of the Earl of Derby.[6]

Knowsley Park was a pleasant walking distance across the fields from Nutgrove. Nuttall became acquainted with the gardeners there and frequently visited the gardens, greenhouses, and the zoological preserves developed by Lord Stanley, a naturalist of note who succeeded his father in 1834 to become the thirteenth Earl. Lord Stanley became a warm admirer, friend, and advocate of Audubon.

At about this time Thomas's sister Elizabeth frequently resided at Nutgrove where, under the influence of the household, she became an ardent Methodist, a conversion which in later life was to be a daily trial to Thomas. A year or so after Thomas returned to America, Elizabeth married her cousin, Richard Dixon, the son of Jonas's partner, an ironmonger of Burnley, Lancashire. A few months after Thomas arrived in England, the elder of his sisters, Susannah, married Thomas Booth, a farmer of Long Preston.

During the growing seasons Nuttall doubtless went on botanizing jaunts hither and yon, near and far, to specialized habitats. He studied the flora about Long Preston with increased insight; he wrote that *Scheuchzeria palustris* L. is

common to morasses in the north of Europe. From the singularly isolated occurrence of this plant in the milder states of America, I am inclined to believe it on the decrease in such situations. In the turf morasses, or moors as they are called, in the northern parts of Yorkshire, (Craven) in England, I have commonly seen the singular vestiges of this plant inlayed through spongy or more recent turf, obtained where none of the plant exists at the present day.[7]

Excursions were made also to secure geological data, for he observed and collected fossils of the coal measures — "casts of enormous channelled *Culmariae*" — at Bradford in the lower Aire Valley of Yorkshire.[8] In studying his fossils from the far West, Nuttall consulted whatever paleontological publications he could locate. He was amazed to find that the illustrations in William Martin's *Petrificata Derbiensia* (1809) showed brachiopods, corals, and crinoids similar to his American specimens from the limestone at the Dubuque lead mines. A visit to see for himself the stratigraphy of Derbyshire confirmed not only the similarity of the fossils but also of the embedding rocks. The tilted beds of compact "mountain limestone" of Derbyshire showed the same composition as "the great calcareous platform of the Mississippi valley." Moreover the animal and vegetable impressions of the coal beds of both regions were similar. The only marked difference between the two was in the dip of the strata. These strata, so distant from each other, had obviously been formed under similar influences and at the same time in the history of the earth — the period which was to be called the coal-bearing or Carboniferous. No correlation had yet been made between the strata of the eastern and western hemispheres; in fact William Smith (1789–1839) had not yet begun the publication of *Strata Identified by Organized Fossils* (1816–1819). Nuttall's observation was, therefore, momentous. But with characteristic caution he delayed the announcement of it for several years until he had extended his geological observations to southeastern and southwestern areas of the United States.

BOTANICAL ACTIVITIES. There is every indication that Nuttall had been studying his herbarium specimens and preparing Latin analyses of them from the time of their collection. In his first 1810 notebook we see the full evolution of the technique: beginning with descriptions in simple English with rare use of specialized terms, he employed increasingly the Latinized terminology of plant taxonomy with abrupt resorts to English where his Latin vocabulary failed; the last descriptions are consistently in Latin as is expected by botanical usage in the publication of a new species or genus.[9] Doubtless by the time he arrived in England on a sailing vessel he had completed written analyses of all his plants. He still had to compare them with specimens in established herbaria and with descriptions of species already published. In the spring of 1812 he went to London to consult botanical collections and libraries and also to make arrangements for some nurseryman to handle the sale of his new plants and seeds.

Among the many nurseries in and around London, Fraser's Nursery at Sloane Square, King's Road, Chelsea, was especially suitable for marketing Nuttall's new species as it specialized in American introductions. The younger John Fraser and his brother James carried on the business in London after their father's death in 1811. Fraser's Nursery agreed to sell Nuttall's plants and distributed a special advertisement of them for the 1813 season: "A catalogue of New and Interesting Plants, Collected in Upper Louisiana, and principally on the River Missourie, North America."[10] Although Nuttall prepared the list of eighty-nine species, assigning a scientific name to each new species and characterizing briefly about fifteen, his own name did not appear in the catalog; hence he forfeited the authorship of many of the described species as well as the *nomina nuda*. It was common knowledge among botanists and seedsmen that he wrote the catalog, and he himself plainly and frequently asserted his authorship in letters, in the *Genera,* and in other published material especially during his last years in America.[11]

Thomas must have felt handicapped by lack of funds of his own and have been eager to turn his horticultural collections to profit. His actions suggest that he believed Barton was interested only in reserving scientific publication to himself, and he was too inexperienced to foresee that sale of the plants in England and the printing of a catalog would imperil this right. However it soon became apparent that he was in an unpleasant position. Inevitably his most attractive plants at Fraser's Nursery were formally published with colored plates in Curtis's *Botanical Magazine*, which John Sims, M.D., was then editing. As early as August 1, 1812, Bartonia decapetala Pursh was shown on Plate 1487; exactly a year later two more of Nuttall's plants were featured: Scilla esculenta Ker[12] (t. 1574) and *Allium stellatum* Fraser (t. 1576). Two *Oenotheras, missouriensis* Sims and *caespitosa* Nutt. (t. 1592 and t. 1593), appeared November 1, 1813, and Rudbeckia columnaris Sims [*Ratibida columnifera* (Nutt.) Wooton & Standl.] (t. 1601), December 1, 1813. In the next two years, six more species of Fraser's catalog were illustrated and described: one of these (t. 1707) had already been published by Michaux; four others (t. 1667, t. 1672, t. 1673, t. 1706) had by then appeared in Pursh's *Flora*; the last, *Mentzelia oligosperma,* published four months after Nuttall had left England, was credited to Nuttall by his friend A. B. Lambert who grew the plant.

That Nuttall persistently refrained from taking advantage of the opportunities for publication that others were seizing seems sufficient proof that it was not his intention to violate his contract with Professor Barton. As it turned out, the latter lost little from Nuttall's arrangements with the Frasers because Pursh had descriptions or herbarium specimens from other sources of practically all the species which Fraser's Nursery received, and he published them promptly. Unfortunately Nuttall was not financially compensated for his seeds and plants: decades later he wrote that "that rogue Fraser . . . never accounted to me yet!"[13]

In London, which was surfeited with seedsmen and nurseries, two influential centers were fostering botany as a science: the illustrious Sir Joseph Banks (1743–1820) and the Linnean Society of London. Banks, President of the Royal Society for more than forty years (1778–1820), made his splendid library and herbarium accessible to all scientists. The presiding genius was the librarian, Robert Brown, "a miracle of Botanical wisdom and learning." His adoption of Jussieu's natural system of classification was instrumental in displacing the artificial system of Linnaeus in England. Nuttall found in him such botanical acumen that he ever after spoke of him as "the great Robert Brown." [14]

The Linnean Society was started in 1788 by seven men who were dissatisfied with the calibre of an established society of natural history. The most active of the group, James Edward Smith, son of a wealthy wool merchant of Norwich, had purchased Linnaeus's herbarium and other natural history collections, library, and manuscripts, four years earlier. The investment was rewarding: in a few months Smith was elected a member of the Royal Society, and when he went to the continent on a tour and to finish his medical studies he was everywhere ceremoniously honored as the owner of the Linnean Collections. Elected the first president of the Linnean Society of London, he held that office until his death in 1828, although he lived in Norwich from 1796. In 1812, he was knighted as "Institutor and President of the Society" by the Prince Regent, its Patron. There were four categories of members — Honorary, Foreign, Fellows, and Associates. Semimonthly meetings were held from early November through June at the rooms of the Society in Soho Square. Among botanists the membership included Robert Barclay (1751–1830), Robert Brown (1773–1858), James Dickson (1737–1822), Jonas Dryander (1748–1810), William Jackson Hooker (1785–1865), William Kirby (1759–1850) later an entomologist, John Sims (1749–1831), and Aylmer Bourke Lambert (1761–1842).[15] The last named, renowned for his sumptuous monograph on the genus *Pinus*, served as a vice-president from 1796 until his death.

Lambert, with a town house on Lower Grosvenor Street and an immense enthusiasm for botany and horticulture, was most accessible and friendly to botanical travelers, and his herbarium, one of the largest and finest in England, comprising those of Pallas (Russian plants, Asian, etc.), Ruiz and Pavon (South American), and hundreds of lesser collections, was open to scientific visitors on Saturday afternoons.

Through Lambert and Archdeacon Hodgson, Frederick Pursh presented to the Linnean Society a paper containing "descriptions . . . of Plants discovered by Messrs. Lewis and Clarke on their Journey across the Continent of North America."[16] Pursh was present as a visitor when the first unit of the paper was read on January 21,

1812, and attended four of the five additional meetings that the presentation of the paper required.[17] It is ironic to recall how Thomas Jefferson and M'Mahon had schemed and worried to protect Lewis's interests and that William Clark was still expectant that the plants and animals discovered by the party would be introduced to the scientific world in an appendix to the Journals by Benjamin Smith Barton. The main report of the expedition was finally published twelve months after Pursh's *Flora,* but Barton's contribution was conspicuous by its absence.

For two years Pursh was an almost constant visitor at the meetings of the Linnean Society, usually introduced by Lambert, George Anderson,[18] or William Anderson. The latter, after managing James Vere's gardens with signal success, became Curator of the Chelsea Botanic Garden (the old garden of the Guild of Apothecaries) early in 1814. In February 1813, Pursh presented a short paper on a new genus, Hosackia, which honored his latest employer in America, Dr. David Hosack of New York, a Foreign Member of the Linnean Society.[19] At the meetings some of Pursh's American acquaintances were unexpectedly brought to mind. Indeed John Lyon attended two meetings (February 18 and March 18, 1812). Benjamin Smith Barton communicated through John Mason Good, a Fellow, a description of a new species of Proteus or Siren. A letter containing observations on the luminosity of the ocean written by Professor William Dandridge Peck of Harvard College to Sir Joseph Banks was read.[20] Shortly before he sailed for England, Pursh had visited Peck and having seen his alpine specimens from the White Mountains of New Hampshire was adding some new species therefrom to his *Flora.*[21]

John Lyon had brought over with him a very large number of seeds and potted plants of about 400 species, chiefly southern plants, not new but scarce in Britain. Following a procedure somewhat similar to his 1806 auction, he advertised this collection as being on sale off the King's Road, Chelsea, near the end of May 1812.[22] Nuttall probably met Lyon in London and questioned him on the distribution of species of the southern flora, for a few years later he quoted him as saying that the black locust was abundant around Nashville.[23] Thereafter he showed a special interest in him. Lyon was back in the United States by early 1813.[24]

During 1812 and 1813 Pursh compiled the text of his *Flora Americae Septentrionalis,* sending units to the printer as they were completed. At this time there were in England three separate sources of knowledge of plants of upper Louisiana Territory: Nuttall's collections, John Bradbury's which his son destined for William Roscoe in Liverpool, and Frederick Pursh's copies of the descriptions and drawings of the Lewis and Clark specimens which he had made in 1807–1808 for Lewis's proposed publication, together with fragments secretly abstracted from the specimens. Timing and "Weird," who "goeth ever as she must go," determined the honors of authorship of the new species. Bradbury, who found himself prevented by the war from following his collections to England, was eliminated from the race; Nuttall was restrained from publication by his contract with Barton; no considerations hampered Pursh. He had established himself in London as an authority on the Lewis and Clark plants before Nuttall arrived on the scene, and through Lambert he eventually obtained a series of Bradbury's specimens. He published the western discoveries as well as southeastern plants that had come under his observation in the collections of others, although he had never been beyond the Appalachians nor south of Virginia except for a dip into Northampton County, North Carolina. Bradbury complained bitterly and often about his loss of scientific credit after toiling in a far and dangerous country where his health had been ruined, but Nuttall was able to accept the situation more philosophically at the time, perhaps because the loss appeared to be Barton's rather than his own.[25]

However, Nuttall had an immediate quarrel with Pursh on the limited and definite grounds that Pursh had mulcted him of the only treasure to which he held a claim, a supposed new genus which was to honor Barton.[26] When the two exprotégés of Barton met by chance in London, Nuttall enthusiastically showed Pursh a beautiful large-flowered plant of the plains (*Mentzelia decapetala*) which, thinking it represented a new genus, he was on the point of publishing as Bartonia superba. Although his contract with Barton did not permit publication in general, he assumed the privilege of thus honoring his patron and had informed him of his intention. Mühlenberg's *Bartonia,* published by Willdenow in 1801, was based on a very inconspicuous species with small flowers, and Nuttall, all too ignorant of the concept of priority, knew the western plant would be more gratifying to Barton. The new Bartonia appeared in the August 1, 1812, issue of the *Botanical Magazine,* but with Pursh as the author!![27] Nuttall was credited only with supplying the specimen from which the drawing was made for the accompanying plate.

It is difficult to understand how Pursh achieved the authorship of the species even though we have Nuttall's explanation to Barton concerning the publication. He wrote on February 24, 1813, from Sutton, Lancashire:

In the 307 number of the Botanical Magazine, tab. 1487, I did myself the pleasure of giving your name to a very splendid plant, which was figured from a dried specimen; and it afterwards flowered with me from seeds. A Mr. Pursh, with whom I became accidentally acquainted in London has in my absence, as you will perceive, taken his opportunity of advertising himself at my expense, at the close of my [!] communication.[28]

The closing statement to which Nuttall refers, written by John Sims, the editor of the *Botanical Magazine,* reads: "For the above generic and specific characters, and indeed the whole communication, we are indebted to Mr. FREDERICK PURSH, author of a new Flora of North-American plants, now in the press." The simplest explanation would be that Nuttall innocently entrusted his written description of the plant and the specimen to Pursh for delivery to John Sims.

Whatever the exact circumstances were, Nuttall was bursting with indignation over the loss of his one ewe lamb, the failure of his first attempt at scientific publication. Pursh's defence, printed in his *Flora,* was that he had made a drawing and description in 1807 of a flowering specimen of Lewis and he could not "with justice and propriety to the memory of M. Lewis" allow Nuttall to garner "the exclusive credit of discovery. . . ."[29] This seemed hypocritical reasoning to Nuttall for he knew that Pursh's specimen consisted of only an imperfect capsule, an entirely inadequate basis for any description or identification, and he denied that Lewis had brought back a flowering specimen.[30] In any case Nuttall's fond hopes of authorship collapsed in a complete debacle — there was nothing to salvage. However Nuttall was supported by the justice of his cause, and he eventually met sympathy from those who knew Pursh best. Six years later in his own text on North American plants he gave a long review of this controversy as he understood it and a criticism of Pursh's defence in the debate between them and concluded: ". . . It was not surely honorable in Frederick Pursh, whom I still esteem as an able botanist to snatch from me the little imaginary credit due to enthusiastic researches made at the most imminent risk of personal safety!"[31]

Pursh's paper on Meriwether Lewis's plants furnished a nucleus for the flora of North America that he was preparing. The Banksian herbarium was rich in American plants: notably Banks's own collections in Labrador and Newfoundland, Archibald Menzies's plants from the Vancouver Expedition to the west coast of North America (1791–1795), specimens gathered at the Physic Garden at Chelsea from plants received as contributions from John and William Bartram, Humphry Marshall, and Dr. Garden, and Clayton's herbarium, on which Gronovius based his *Flora Virginica* (1739). Pursh also consulted Labrador plants in Dickson's herbarium, Walter's herbarium, which was in the Frasers' hands, Nuttall's western plants in the Frasers' nursery, and Lyon's southeastern plants widely distributed in London nurseries. Moreover he had his own herbarium and notes on many species seen in American herbaria, especially Professor Barton's, which contained contributions from numerous southern correspondents.[32] On September 7, 1812, Lambert sent some seeds from Boyton, his country place in the Wylye Valley, Wiltshire, to Sir James Edward Smith, apologizing for their delay by explaining that he had just received them, "Mr. Pursh being so busy at present printing his Flora Americana he delayed sending the seeds sooner." It was generally accepted that Lambert financed the publication. At some point he had to take Pursh firmly in hand and hold him at the exacting job which he had undertaken, keeping him under supervision, for Pursh had a way of relaxing completely over liters of beer.

In the autumn of 1813, Lambert wrote happily to Nuttall: "I . . . have the pleasure to inform you Mr. Pursh has again begun to work on his Flora which I expect will now go on very fast he has I see mentioned you very often in the sheets that are lately come from the printer."[33] Nuttall was filled with consternation by the realization that Pursh was making use of herbarium specimens that he had given to Lambert[34] and also of plants grown at Boyton from his seeds and perhaps also of illuminating remarks that he himself had made. When the two had met, Nuttall, enticed by Pursh's genuine interest in his plants, may have shown him many of his specimens, giving detailed information about them which Pursh's retentive memory was putting to use. Pursh's *Flora* first mentions Nuttall under *Centunculus lanceolatus* L. (vol. I, p. 97). After stating that a specimen was seen in Nuttall's herbarium, he (Pursh) goes on, "The specimens of Mr. Nuttall's [*sic*] were collected on the Missouri, they are about four inches high; and according to his observations, very obligingly communicated, this species is generally pentandrous.[35] In the next one hundred and eighty pages eighteen further references to Nuttall's herbarium appear. Only five of these dealt with new species that Pursh did not have in Lewis's collection or from other sources, and for one of these, *Viola nuttallii,* he perhaps had Nuttall's cooperation.[36] Nuttall's name is not mentioned again in the main body of the *Flora* except under two species of Bartonia. Nuttall evidently immediately answered Lambert's note insisting that no further use be made of his collections since Barton had sole right to their publication. However Pursh circumvented Lambert's orders by the simple expedient of omitting Nuttall's name when he used Nuttallian material; by this method he harvested about eight more of Nuttall's species. The total number of new species that Pursh owed solely to Nuttall's trusting inexperience was not great, for Bradbury's plants from the Missouri country finally fell into his hands. Nuttall was learning about taxonomic publication through very unpleasant experiences, which could be interpreted to discredit his integrity.

Lambert's note to Nuttall carried more bad news from the point of view of the recipient: "Mr. Bradbury has sent to Mr. Bullock a fine parcel of specimens which are now at Sir J Banks he does not know whose the[y] are as there is no letter with them." That Lambert had the facts of this matter well jumbled appears from the Bradbury correspondence and a letter from William Bullock to William Roscoe written in London on November 4, 1813.

Sir

I laid your Letter before Sir J.[h] Banks who requested me to return his warmest thanks for the very liberal manner in which you have permitted him to take a specimen of each of the duplicates of the Plants sent by Bradbury and that he will consider it his duty and have great pleasure in forwarding to the Liverpool Garden whatever is in his power to add to it. Mr. Brown will make the selection tomorrow when they together with Dr. Roxboroughs shall be forwarded as you request.

Mr. Lambert has just called on me to request me to make a similar request to you on his part that I did for Sr. Josh. which I do only because I promised him not having the same reasons that I had in the other Case he *says* he has 20 new Peruvian Plants living that he will send you in return you will please to determine for yourself in this case. — I would certainly select the duplicates myself were the case mine

I am Sir very truly yours
W. Bullock[37]

Obviously the complete herbarium had reached London through Bullock; the writer believes that, by the request of Roscoe, he had brought it from John Leigh Bradbury. About this time Bullock had business in southwest England securing some bones of an *Ichthyosaurus* exposed on the coast near Lyme Regis in Dorset for his London museum. Time was pressing Lambert, for Pursh's *Flora* must have been almost finished by the date that his request was relayed by Bullock to Roscoe. Whether from Roscoe or from Banks,[38] Lambert secured a set of Bradbury's plants, which Pursh described in a Supplement. This of course included most of Nuttall's Missouri treasures.

It would be gratifying to know more about the beginning of Nuttall's acquaintance with Lambert. They probably first met at Sir Joseph Banks's herbarium and library, and as a matter of course Lambert would invite Nuttall to use the American collections in his large herbarium. Nuttall gave Lambert not only an almost complete set of his western specimens but also a great number of seeds, many of which were successfully grown at Boyton. As early as the summer of 1812 Lambert wrote to Sir James Edward Smith about the quantity of new plants he had growing from foreign seed, many from Mexico (Louisiana Territory); one species, *Psoralea esculenta* Pursh, was raised from seed taken from Lewis's specimen.[39] The others seem to have been donations of Nuttall.

At the first meeting of the Linnean Society of the 1812–1813 season, November 3, Nuttall was proposed for membership as a Fellow and on January 17 was duly elected. His certificate of recommendation reads

Mr. John [!] Nuttall of Sutton Lancashire, a Gentleman who has travelled in many parts of America; and who has discovered many new plants, on the Banks of the Missouri, or the Mississippi; and has brought a rich Herbarium and many living plants to this Country, being desirous of the Honor of becoming a Fellow of the Linnean Society, we whose names are underwritten do from our personal knowledge recommend him as likely to become a useful and valuable member.

> A. B. Lambert
> Jn° Baker
> James Dickson
> Will Bullock

James Dickson, a protégé of Sir Joseph Banks who published on British cryptogams and sold seeds in a "little covert in Covent Garden," like Lambert, was one of Smith's picked group who organized the Society. Smith praised his "powerful mind, spotless integrity, singular acuteness and accuracy." William Curtis facetiously described him, "*Maximus in minimis.*" William Bullock, interested especially in zoology, had moved the private museum that he had been conducting in Liverpool to London where from 1812 his collections attracted great attention at "Egyptian Hall," Piccadilly. He had probably known Nuttall as an apprentice in Jonas's shop where he had printing done. His enthusiasm for natural history is reflected in the name "Bullock's oriole," a brilliant bird of our Southwest, one of many species he collected in Mexico in 1823.[40]

Nuttall did not attend a meeting of the Society to "sign the obligation" in the Members' Book until December 7, 1813, a meeting at which Pursh was a visitor.[41] The next day Lambert reported to Sir James, "We had a good meeting of the society last night, Lord Louvain was proposed; two elections & M Nuttall admitted. . . . *Flora Americana* will finish printing this week."[42]

Although the title page of *Flora Americae Septentrionalis* bears the date 1814, the publication was completed about the middle of December, 1813.[43] Pursh presented a copy to the Linnean Society at its meeting on December 21 and shortly thereafter became a rare visitor. It is important to note that Pursh's Preface gives a series of erroneous dates for his career in America, almost every date mentioned being at least one year too early, and he is two years previous in the time of his employment at Hosack's garden, a date which is well authenticated elsewhere as starting in the spring of 1809. Other of his statements are dubious. A curious deception pervades the text in the form of frequent statements that he has seen plants in their natural habitats — indicated by the symbol *v.v.*, for *vide vivum* (seen living) — which grow only in regions which he never visited. Pursh's collections in both B. S. Barton's and Lambert's herbaria show the limited extent of his botanizing with which his *v.v.*s do not correspond.[44] Hardly a botanist of the time failed to cite cases of his publication of the discoveries of others.[45] These practices led him into some droll errors: for instance he attributed *Ranunculus auricomus* L. to Pennsylvania although no one has found it south of Greenland, and, in figuring Lewis's plants, he combined the flowers of *Berberis aquifolium* Pursh with the leaves of *B. nervosa* Pursh.[46] His *Flora* was not noted for its reliability.

In midsummer of 1813 Lambert wrote to Sir James about a new *Oenothera* which had just flowered from seed collected by Nuttall: "he collected the seed on the borders of Mexico [!] but had never seen the flower or has any person except at Boyton yet it is certainly one of the most splendid & curious plants that has ever been sent to this Country." Twice in the following summer Lambert wrote jubilantly to the president of his favorite society about the quantity of his new plants: "I never had more new plants to show you, nearly *the whole collection* from Nuttall several of which are now just in flower & very interesting." And again, "Nuttall has given me almost the whole of his living plants he brought." [47] He did not mention the herbarium specimens that Nuttall had given him. Lambert presented Nuttall with about two hundred exotic specimens supposedly garnered by Francis Masson (1741–1805/6), the first collector sent out by the Royal Botanic Garden of Kew, who between 1772 and his death in Montreal visited many remote spots, greatly enriching the gardens and conservatories of Britain.[48]

How much time Nuttall spent in London we can only conjecture. He was there in the spring of 1812 but did not attend a meeting of the Linnean Society until late in 1813, eleven months after his election. In the spring of 1814 John Windsor, who was completing medical training in London, was introduced as a guest by Nuttall at two successive meetings — April 19 and May 3. (The Recording Secretary did not name in the Minutes all members present at meetings although he seems to have recorded scrupulously all visitors and their sponsors.) In April 1814, Nuttall signed the certificate proposing Windsor for membership in the Linnean Society, completing a list of endorsers headed by Lambert; Windsor was elected at the first meeting of the following autumn,[49] and the next year he began practicing medicine in Manchester. Nuttall's second recorded attendance was not until January 17, 1815, shortly after the peace treaty between England and America had been signed. Among those present at this meeting were the Reverend William Kirby, the leading British entomologist, and Henry Brooke, a mineralogist of note, both of whom were to name specimens in honor of Nuttall. Kirby received at least two of several brilliantly colored beetles that Nuttall collected up the Missouri: he published Trichodes (*Clerus*) *nutalli* in 1817[50] and a second species, labeled in his cabinet *Lytta nuttalli*, Thomas Say published under that name in 1824.[51] Nuttall's communication of minerals did not occur until his second visit to England.

A less fortunate sponsorship by Lambert, George Anderson, and Nuttall was that of Charles Whitlaw (fl. 1776–1829), a Scotsman who after two years at the Edinburgh Botanic Garden made several visits to the United States and Canada where he delivered botanical lectures in various places.[52] "His portly person, ruby face, and broad Scotch accent with a tone of confident assurance which told of perfect self satisfaction, made an indelible impress."[53] In conversations with him Nuttall obtained information concerning the Canadian distribution of some American species, of which he made use in his *Genera*. Seeds that Whitlaw sold in England at a good price had not produced plants corresponding with his "luminous descriptions."[54] He was not elected.

Nuttall was in London in the spring of 1815, probably to get his affairs in order preparatory to leaving England. He attended the meetings of the Linnean Society on April 4 and May 2 and sailed from Gravesend for America on May 8, 1815.[55]

# CHAPTER 7

# SOUTHERN EXPEDITIONS

Wem Gott will rechte Gunst erweisen
Den schickt er in die weite Welt
Dem will er seine Wunder weisen
In Berg und Wald und Strom und Feld.
— Eichendorff.

RETURN TO AMERICA, 1815. Nuttall's voyage from Gravesend was unhappy and prolonged. The captain was a "knave," the crew, ex-prisoners, the ship a "wreck," but "after a tedious passage of *nine* weeks in a vessel every moment on the point of foundering or shipwreck," it arrived at the port of Philadelphia.[1]

Foremost in Nuttall's mind must have been a conference with Professor Barton concerning the western expedition and the unexpected anticipation of its botanical discoveries by Pursh's publication. There is no record that a settlement of expenses and salary ($8 a month) had been made between the two. But it turned out that Barton was in Europe. His health had failed during the winter to such a degree that he had been forced to give up his work, and in April he had sailed for France hoping to recruit his strength through travel and freedom from the daily round of duties.

Zaccheus Collins still had his father's shop on North Second Street across from Christ Church. He gladly welcomed his young friend after an absence of more than five years. Nuttall was eager to tell about the great Missouri country, so expansive and strange in scenery and so rich in its flora and fauna, and about the English botanists he had met and the species of North American plants in the English herbaria, many of them the type specimens of eastern and western coastal plants.

Collins too had much news to impart. The learned Henry Mühlenberg had died in May, lamented by the parish he had served for thirty-five years and by botanists in America and Europe. Two years earlier he had published "Catalogus Plantarum Americae Septentrionalis" arranged according to the artificial system of Linnaeus. Hopes were entertained that his valuable work on the grasses and sedges might still be published. William Hamilton had died two years before, after suffering several years of failing health, and his beautiful garden was "almost a wilderness." Alexander Wilson had also died in 1813; the eighth volume of his *American Ornithology* was edited and the last volume prepared by George Ord. In Asheville, North Carolina, the previous autumn on September 14, John Lyon had succumbed to typhus fever; Dr. Macbride (1784–1817), A. B., Yale, 1805, Stephen Elliott's botanical collaborator, who vainly traveled a long distance to treat him, thought he had been bled to death through well-meaning solicitude.

A distinguished and learned Portuguese historian, statesman and botanist, the Abbé Corréa da Serra, living temporarily in Philadelphia, had given Barton's course in botany during the late spring. His lectures, open also to the general public, were highly praised for their style, wit, and accurate knowledge. His class used Mühlenberg's catalog but Corréa had changed its arrangement from the Linnaean to the "natural system" of Jussieu which, based on similarities of vegetative and floral structure, brought together in one class only plants naturally related. The use of the modern system in Corréa's lectures was a significant forward step in American botany.

Public lectures were becoming popular: Professor Cleaveland of Bowdoin College gave a course of lectures in mineralogy in Philadelphia in 1814 and in the spring of the same year Dr. John Barnes and Dr. John Fothergill Waterhouse jointly gave a course of botanical lectures which they repeated in 1815. The trend appeared also in Boston where Professor Peck, Massachusetts Professor of Natural History at Harvard, and Dr. Jacob Bigelow gave a popular course in botany in 1813 in aid of the Botanic Garden in Cambridge, and the junior lecturer carried on alone in the two years following. Dr. Bigelow, who got his medical degree at the University of Pennsylvania in April 1810 about the time Nuttall left for the West, had been concerned by the scarcity of texts available for his class and in consequence in 1814 published *Florula Bostoniensis*, the first reputable local flora to appear in the United States, and also an American edition of Sir James Edward Smith's *Introduction to Physiological and Systematic Botany.*

A small group of natural history enthusiasts in Philadelphia had started a society early in 1812 which called itself the Academy of Natural Sciences. Zaccheus Collins had been elected to membership in March.

Dr. David Hosack had sold his Elgin Botanic Garden to the State of New York when he gave up his professorship of botany at Columbia College to teach the Theory and Practice of Physic at the College of Physicians and Surgeons, but he still pursued botany as an avocation. The State granted the garden (which included the land where Rockefeller Center now stands) to Columbia College in 1814. Collins had recently seen Dr. Hosack at Sully's studio in Philadelphia where they started a discussion of some problems of plant identity that was being continued by correspondence. On August 1, Collins wrote to Hosack that Mr. Nuttall had determined the coastal species in question to be *Arenaria peploides* L.[2] Doubtless Nuttall spent many hours with Collins during the heat of the summer studying herbarium specimens and using Collins's microscope to examine the smallest structures.

The war had evidently prevented copies of Pursh's *Flora* from reaching book dealers in the United States at the time of publication for it was a few years before the American botanists obtained copies. Collins eagerly examined Nuttall's copy and the two discussed it in detail. Collins pointed out that Pursh claimed *Schizaea pusilla*, Dr. Caspar Wistar Eddy's rare little find in the New Jersey pine barrens, and Rafinesque's *Drosera filiformis* from the same area of botanical surprises as well as species of others. Collins doubtless regarded Pursh's filching of Nuttall's Bartonia of little importance since Mühlenberg's *Bartonia* predated it and would stand even though it was overshadowed in size and beauty by Nuttall's western plant. Rafinesque changed the faulty generic name to "Nuttalla"[3] but the new species proved to belong in the Linnaean genus *Mentzelia*; this was the first of several ill-fated generic names honoring Nuttall.

Zaccheus Collins lent a sympathetic ear to the problem which was uppermost in Nuttall's mind: how best to place before the botanical world his field knowledge of the new western species which Pursh had published with their habits, habitats, and distributions faultily or inadequately described or omitted.[4] Permission from Barton to write about species already published would be unnecessary. After months of mulling over the matter, he had decided to bring out a new edition of Pursh's publication. The tedium of his prolonged passage across the Atlantic had probably been somewhat alleviated by preoccupation with this plan.

At the Bartram Garden, Nuttall found that William's brother John had died and that Colonel Robert Carr, the husband of John's daughter Ann, had taken over the management of the business. William, old and frail, was delighted by the return of the young botanist and listened with keen attention to his stories of the great West and the plains Indians. He himself had lived for several years deep in the wilderness among the Indians of the southeast, Creeks, Cherokees, and Seminoles, and was well acquainted with their customs, traditions, and languages. It would seem that Nuttall, who was leaving on a southern botanical trip at the end of the summer, asked Bartram's advice concerning promising routes of travel, for he followed a road in Georgia that his venerable friend had taken in his youth and ended his pedestrian tour at Wilmington, North Carolina, where Bartram had lived for some years.

Nuttall visited M'Mahon not only at his store on South Second Street but also at his "Upsal Garden" on the road to Germantown where the most admired planting was a row of native oaks of thirty different species. M'Mahon was especially interested in hearing of Pursh's publication of the plants of the Lewis and Clark Expedition. That the plants collected by the Lewis and Clark Expedition were published in England was a sad reflection on the scholarship of the United States.

During the summer, Nuttall introduced himself to David Landreth, by presenting a letter from Fraser recommending him as a plant collector. David Junior, then not quite thirteen, recorded the visit many years afterwards. "I distinctly remember the first time I saw him, standing beside my father, in the dusk of a summer's evening; a stranger, of quiet manner and careless toilet." [5] Lyon's death the preceding autumn had lost to Landreth his accustomed source of southern plants so he probably was glad to agree to receive shipments from Nuttall.

Nuttall wrote: "Commercial concerns of trifling importance held me in this place [Philadelphia] untill [sic] the close of August." [6] This business perhaps had to do with securing orders and the investment of his funds. He had left some savings in Philadelphia in 1810 when he started on his western adventure, and he probably received a monetary gift from Jonas when he left England in 1815 to finance and ease his return and cover a possible emergency. Jonas must have been proud of Thomas's achievements and his election to the Linnean Society; so charitable to others, he could hardly fail to tender some assistance to such a worthy member of his family and household. There are indications in letters that Thomas kept his funds at interest and that Zaccheus Collins acted for him in small financial affairs when he was away from Philadelphia for prolonged periods. After his return to America in 1815, Nuttall never again earned his living by setting type. Certainly for the next five years he was completely engrossed by botanical studies in the field or the herbarium. How did he support himself? As one source of income he adopted Lyon's and Kinn's mode of selling plants and seeds collected in the free wilderness. A letter that Nuttall received from an English gardener which asked for lilies and roses et cetera but "not a single Botanical plant as I have enough of them already,"[7] indicates that he had solicited orders for American plants and seeds before he left England, and we know that he arranged to collect for seedsmen in Philadelphia. Later, occasional courses of lectures helped to support him, and he probably expected profits from his projected flora.[8]

FIRST SOUTHERN TRIP. Before autumn came, Nuttall set out through Lancaster, York, and Hanover in Pennsylvania and Frederick, Maryland, to view the confluence of the Potomac and Shenandoah Rivers at Harper's Ferry.[9] He described ecstatically "the stupendous scene so elegantly described by the ex-president Jefferson in his Notes on Virginia where the rivers Shenandoah and Potomac uniting, appear to burst their way thro' the Blue Ridge, . . . a landscape of horrible grandeur and wild magnificence, of mingled rocks, roaring rivers, and gloomy forests." Jefferson had written that this scene is worth a voyage across the Atlantic, and Nuttall made it the first objective of his tour. He found there near its northern limit Michaux's Sedum pulchellum on shelving rocks and, not far away on slate rocks on the margin of the Shenandoah, Linnaeus's Achyranthes dichotoma, which Nuttall subsequently transferred to Paronychia Mill.[10] He went up the Potomac at least as far as Shepherdstown where he first got his *Enslenia albida[11] [Ampelamus albidus (Nutt.)

Britt.] and far enough up the Shenandoah Valley to trace the line of the Blue Ridge near Staunton. It is enlightening in this connection to note that Weyer's Cave, then a favorite spot with mineralogists for securing specimens of stalactites and stalagmites, lies less than fifteen miles to the northeast of Staunton. Nuttall did not miss opportunities to add to his collection of minerals.

Before the middle of October he proceeded down the Potomac and got a view of "Washington in its ignominious ruins, the deserted palace of the president and the magnificent wreck of the imaginary Capital!" He wrote that at the "port of Alexandria" he embarked for Savannah.

On the same day that we left Alexandria, the breeze conducted us past the rural seat of the immortal Washington, — the sacred groves of Mount Vernon, the peacefull but forsaken residence of the Father of America! . . .

In ten days we arrived at the port of Savannah in Georgia, a town built in the West India style upon a high bank of moveable sand and surrounded by deep and undrainable swamps, a situation so unhealthy as to be justly dreaded by Europeans who but seldom escape either death or disease.[12]

In Savannah Nuttall sought out Dr. William Baldwin (1779–1819), an ardent botanist who had received his medical degree at the University of Pennsylvania in April 1807 and had practised in Wilmington, Delaware, until late in 1811, when pulmonary weakness forced him to move to a milder climate. There he lost no time in acquainting himself with the flora of large areas of South Carolina and Georgia and in meeting the active botanists of the Southeast — Lewis and John Eatton Le Conte, northerners whose father had a plantation near Riceborough, Georgia; Stephen Elliott of Charleston, South Carolina, with plantations on the Ogeechee River and elsewhere; Dr. Samuel Boykin of Milledgeville; and Dr. Thomas Wray of Augusta.[13] Through correspondence with Dr. George C. Shattuck of Boston, his classmate at medical school, Henry Mühlenberg, and later Dr. William Darlington, Baldwin kept up-to-date on botanical events in the north, personal letters at that time having to serve in lieu of scientific periodicals. When Baldwin became a surgeon in the United States Navy in the War of 1812, he was stationed for over two years at St. Mary's, East Florida, a fruitful location for taxonomic studies. Nuttall found that he was "better acquainted with the plants of America than any other person I have yet met with. For more than

a week together we were engaged in looking over his herbarium re-
plete with new plants, collected in East and West Florida near the
sea coast." Each one of the southern species unfamiliar to Nuttall
was examined and discussed with great interest. Baldwin gave Nuttall
duplicate specimens of some of his new and as yet unpublished
species. There was no dearth of conversation; botanical gossip flowed
freely. Nuttall discussed his plan of publishing an expanded and
corrected edition of Pursh's *Flora*.[14] Baldwin, like most American
botanists, had not yet been able to secure a copy. Nuttall was unable
to get one for him when he returned to Philadelphia but he wrote
to Lambert about Baldwin, initiating a correspondence between the
two, and Lambert sent Baldwin a copy of Pursh's work.[15]

For a month Nuttall remained in Savannah and found in the field
some of the plants which he had seen for the first time in Baldwin's
herbarium. He also received some help from a local druggist, August
G. Oemler, whom Mühlenberg had introduced to Baldwin in 1811;
although Oemler's special interest was the algae he knew the flowering plants and pointed out some distinctive species to Nuttall. Ad-
miring the towering specimens of *Magnolia grandiflora* L., the traveler observed on the branches large quantities of a parasite then called
"Epidendrum Magnoliae [*Phoradendron flavescens* (Pursh) Nutt.];
it appeared to grow on no other tree." Species he found in the vicinity
that he correctly considered new included *Habenaria* *repens, Gerardia* *linifolia*, and *Vernonia* *altissima*. Among the many known
species he collected was Pursh's Solidago retrorsa (S. *tortifolia* Ell.),
noteworthy because, contrary to his habit, Nuttall entered on the
label of his specimen now in the British Museum of Natural History,
the place and date of collection, "Geo Oct 24." He also found an
inodorous variety of yellow jessamine.

From Savannah he sent to William Anderson plants and seeds including the new *Gerardia* and a quantity of specimens of Epidendrum
Magnoliae, some being for Lambert. He also sent collections to John
Shepherd at the Liverpool Botanic Garden and doubtless to M'Mahon
and Landreth in Philadelphia and to other nurserymen.

He wrote to Lambert that he heard of Abbot (ca. 1760–ca. 1840)
in the city "but had not the pleasure of seeing him." Two quarto volumes of John Abbot's beautifully colored plates of insects had been
published in London in 1797 by James Edward Smith under the title
*Natural History of the Rarer Lepidopterous Insects of Georgia*. Abbot

also made drawings of 160 species of birds, which remained unpublished.

When Nuttall left the city he followed up the Savannah River 130 miles to Augusta, Georgia, finding interesting plants all along the way, for the southern flora was new to him. His ecological interest is marked:

In my way thro' these forests of perennial verdure almost exclusively filled with *Pinus australis* [long-leaf pine], in a soil of almost pure sand, I was occasionally gratified by repeated discoverys of new and rare plants. . . . Wherever the sterile platform of sand was diversified by a gravelly hill the southern oaks uniformly made their appearance such as the *Quercus Catesbei, Q. nigra, Q. triloba, Q. cinerea, Q. obtusifolia,* and *Q. coccinea* but the most prevalent of all the species is the *Q. Catesbei* wh. appears often after the prevalence of all the pines to usurp the place of the long leaved Pine.

One of the herbs, Michaux's *Eriogonum tomentosum,* interested Nuttall so greatly that a year and a half later he centered his first botanical paper on it and two other species of the genus that he had collected in the far West. He remarked its habitat and geological limits with great care:

. . . It abounds throughout the sandy and sterile forests of Georgia and South Carolina, always beneath the shade of the *Pinus australis,* . . . to the immediate neighbourhood of Orangeburgh (Orangeburgh county, S. Carolina,) where it suddenly disappears, no where appearing to cross the Santee to the north. . . . it disappears above Augusta in Georgia, where hills of deciduous trees (oaks, hickories, &) and primitive soil commence.[16]

In Nuttall's terms it was restricted to the "ancient maritime alluvium" of the southeast. Such ecological observations were unusual to the point of nonexistence in contemporary botanical writing.

In Baldwin's herbarium Nutall had seen a new genus of the Compositae, collected on the Altamaha. "About 20 mls. from Savannah on my way to Augusta I found a second species of this interesting genus [his *Balduina uniflora] . . . and a beautiful new *purple* flowered species of *Coreopsis*! [C. *rosea].*" On the margins of many sandy springs and ponds he found a plant with violet-blue flowers (*Lindernia grandiflora* Nutt.); a few miles from Augusta he got a new species of grass "with remarkably long awns," *Aristida *tuberculosa.*

"After spending a few days in Augusta in the agreeable company of Dr. T. Wray," he crossed the Savannah River and botanized across central South Carolina to Wilmington, North Carolina. He continued to meet with a gratifying number of plants that he knew only from printed descriptions or herbarium specimens. Of the many *Liatris*like species that he found, he published three as new; of these *L. *tenuifolia* remained valid; *resinosa* has been degraded to a variety of *L. spicata* L., and *corymbosa* proved to belong in a related genus [*Carphephorus corymbosus* (Nutt.) T. & G.]. Other new species from this stretch of the journey included *Danthonia *sericea*, a grass of sandy soils, *Lupinus *diffusus*, a widespread legume, *Chrysopsis *trichophylla*, which was with him along most of the way, and in swamps near Wilmington he got *Tofieldia *glabra*.

On January 26, 1816, he wrote a long letter to Lambert describing his adventures since embarking at Gravesend and listing many of the southern species he had seen. The first and closing paragraphs of the long letter read:

A detail of all my journeys, my adventures, and Botanical discoveries, is much more than I can promise you in this sheet, however happy I might be to indulge my vanity and perhaps tire your patience. If they shall be hereafter deemed worthy by my friends I shall not hesitate to offer my journals to the public, notwithstanding their imperfections. . . .[17]

If no extraordinary disappointment takes place with me I hope to ascend Red River of the Mississippi and examine the adjoining province of Mexico in wh. no doubt I shall meet a rich harvest of Botanical treasure.

Before a boat was available from Wilmington to the North, Nuttall had time to trace the curious and "singularly insulated" Venus's fly-trap (*Dionaea muscipula* Ellis) along the north side of the Cape Fear River for fifty miles and was informed that it continued to occur to Fayetteville.[18] On the banks of the river near the city he got Oenothera *riparia (*O. fruticosa* L.), and he found the outcrop of "floetz limestone" which Maclure had traced discontinuously to the southward. In a shipment of plants and seeds he made from Wilmington to William Anderson was *Pleea tenuifolia* Michx. (*Bot. Mag.*, t. 2051, XLVI, 1819); again some were to be delivered to Lambert. He sent Venus's fly-trap and other living plants to the Liverpool Botanic Garden; *Pinguicula lutea* Walt. (*Bot. Register*, t. 126, II, July 1, 1816) and *Pogonia ophioglossoides* (L.) Ker (*Bot. Register*, t. 148, II, October 1, 1816) to the Coville Nursery in London; and doubtless plants to other nurserymen.

When Nuttall got back to Philadelphia,[19] he learned that Benjamin Smith Barton had died at his home on December 19. He had arrived in New York from England in November so ill and weak that his return to Philadelphia was protracted and uncertain. During this time he gave detailed directions for the disposal of various papers many of which he ordered destroyed. Only three days before his death he dictated a memoir on the new genus Bartonia, addressed to the American Philosophical Society. Zaccheus Collins as a member of the committee to consider its publication (the committee recommended that the article be not published) perhaps possessed a copy of this paper.[20] If Nuttall saw it, he would have read Barton's view of their association with the greatest interest. That he was accused of deviating from the route Barton had laid down — even three years of war on the frontier had not convinced Barton that Nuttall was helpless in that matter — only emphasized Barton's abysmal ignorance of the West. Barton's version of the publication of Bartonia by Pursh was not entirely in accord with the statement that Nuttall had sent him. However, Barton's general intention had been to give credit to Nuttall, for he concluded by saying, "These memorandums . . . afforded me an opportunity of doing some justice to the zeal and services of Mr. Nuttall, who has contributed essentially to extend our knowledge of the North-Western Flora of North-America; and to whom the work of Frederick Pursh is under infinite obligations." Then he added another sentence which was lightly crossed out: "I might say something more in this place, concerning my claims to the collections of these two travelers and botanists; but this is rather a matter which respects the individuals concerned than the Public." What Pursh owed to Nuttall was the opportunity of appropriating Bartonia, of publishing *Viola nuttallii* and a few additional species not in Lewis's or Bradbury's herbaria, and descriptive details of some far western plants.

Barton told botanists in England during the summer of 1815, that he had been deceived by Nuttall as well as by Pursh.[21] Grounds for such an imputation in regard to Nuttall can be found only in his divergence from the impossible routes Barton had laid out for him. Any other offence arose from "the innocence of character" of which Barton had been quick to take advantage. Pursh's case was different: Barton suspected him of publishing many species from his herbarium. Pursh's personal reputation in England had already collapsed. Although his *Flora* was admired there, he had become *persona non grata*.[22] Ungrateful, seldom sober, living on borrowed funds which he made no gesture toward repaying, he had been excluded from all intercourse with the fastidious Sir James Edward Smith. Sir Joseph Banks, more red-blooded and generous, finding him a growing nuisance, provided funds for his return to America whither he departed with a barmaid bride.[23] Rumor soon reached the United States that he was in Canada attached to Lord Selkirk's ill-fated plans for colonization in the valley of the Red River, although he had previously accepted the directorship of a proposed botanic garden at Yale College where a medical school was opened in 1813.

Zaccheus Collins had other surprising news: Rafinesque had recently called on him. His return to America after more than ten years' absence had been made tragic by shipwreck early in November on rocks off Fisher's Island near New London, with the loss of his manuscripts, drawings, natural history collections (fifty boxes of them), and his investment in the cargo. All his scientific work and worldly goods were gone.[24] Although his material situation had been alleviated through Dr. Mitchill's prompt assistance, the crushing loss of the products of years of labor became, in the opinion of some commentators, a cause of possible later mental derangement. He had come down to Philadelphia not merely to see old friends but to support his candidacy for the professorship in botany and natural history at the University of Pennsylvania left vacant by the death of Benjamin Smith Barton. In this effort he was disappointed, for the prize went to Dr. William P. C. Barton (1786–1856), Princeton 1805. The decision was not due to lack of knowledge of Rafinesque's gifts, for he had not been forgotten in Philadelphia and some of his papers, sent from Sicily, on new "Genusses" and species that he had found in the United States in 1803 and 1804 had appeared in Dr. Mitchill's *Medical Repository* from 1805 on.

In the interval between the Savannah trip and his next expedition, Nuttall saw other old friends in Philadelphia. With William Bartram he reviewed his discoveries and experiences in Georgia and the Carolinas. He probably had plants and seeds for Landreth and M'Mahon and would check the condition of any plants which he may have shipped to them. Nuttall was not again to see M'Mahon, who died in September 1816. In the publication that Nuttall had in prospect and of which he doubtless told M'Mahon in their last conversations, he honored his respected friend's memory by the genus *Mahonia* — a most fitting attribution since M'Mahon had raised Lewis's seeds of *Mahonia aquifolium* (Pursh) Nutt. in his greenhouse and cultivated the woody plants for several years.

Barton's death freed Nuttall from the contract which might have prevented him from publishing the few species in his western collections which Pursh had not included in his *Flora*. He widened the scope of his proposed work from a revision of Pursh's *Flora* to a broader treatment. In preparation for this, he decided to continue his exploratory trips, realizing that he needed a greater acquaintance with the plants east of the Mississippi, and especially those of the Appalachians, than he yet possessed. Though he was as eager as ever to enter on unbotanized territory, he deferred his long-anticipated southwestern journey until he had published his eastern and Missouri observations. In the spring he started on a long circuit involving the descent of the Ohio River to Kentucky, wanderings through Kentucky and Tennessee, and return across the southern Appalachians and through North and South Carolina to Charleston.

TRAVELS IN 1816. The first botanical aim of the 1816 expedition was to search in northwestern Pennsylvania for a lost treasure. In mid-May 1810, south of Waterford (Le Boeuf), Nuttall had found a new genus with a striking, irregular flower, the upper lip pure white, the lower "bright azure blue." He was eager to publish it but could not for he had lost the specimens. He had decided that as soon as he again obtained a plant he would name this elegant little genus for Zaccheus Collins — he already spoke of it as *Collinsia verna*. The "quixotic" search up the alluvions of the Allegheny Valley, which added more than a hundred miles to his journey, proved unsuccessful. He arrived at Pittsburgh in June disappointed and behind his time schedule for the whole collecting season.

He sent a box of specimens to Collins from Pittsburgh, but no letter; his youthful enthusiasm for letter writing was fading. However in the autumn he wrote to Collins from North Carolina giving a general account of his experiences. Therein we learn that at Pittsburgh he took passage on a boat going to Portsmouth, Ohio.

The lowness of the Ohio was another source of delay, as I am satisfied I could have walked down to Marietta and Portsmouth in the same time w.h was uselessly sacrificed in descending the current and seeing nothing but muddy water! I, however, stole time, during the descent by walking across the circuitous bends to again discover *Collinsia verna*. . . . As I have obtained ripe seeds I hope we shall have a figure of it however, Dr. Short, of Lexington, who draws extremely well has promised me a figure of it next spring. I think it has hitherto escaped notice from its very early appearance and evanescence. . . .[25]

In his *Genera* Nuttall recorded other interesting species he found while descending the river, including Dracocephalum *cordatum [*Meehania cordata* (Nutt.) Britt.] growing "on the shady islands . . . about 40 miles below Pittsburgh," emitting "an agreeable balsamic aroma."[26] At Portsmouth he made a foray up the Scioto River where he saw *Juglans nigra* L.[27]

Dr. Daniel Drake (1785–1852), a practicing physician of Cincinnati, met almost all the scientists and "notable strangers" who visited the West by the Ohio route. Alexander Wilson had sought him out when he descended the river in the spring of 1810, for, although Drake was then only twenty-five years old, he was already widely known as a local leader in literary, civic, and scientific projects. Drake's family had moved in 1788 to frontier Kentucky where he grew up as the oldest child in a primitive one-room log home. When he was fifteen he started an apprenticeship with his father's friend Dr. William Goforth, the leading physician of Cincinnati, to be "transmuted" into a doctor. His "diploma" secured (written by Dr. Goforth), he set out on horseback for Philadelphia to round out his training with a winter of medical courses at the University of Pennsylvania. After a decade of practice in the West, he returned to Philadelphia for a second winter of lectures and received his medical degree in May, 1816.[28] He devoted as much attention to botany as his duties permitted; in 1810 he had printed a list of the indigenous plants of the area based on his herbarium, which Nuttall had the opportunity of examining. Nuttall collected with Drake and left with him a box of plants to be sent to Collins. It was at this time that Nuttall found his *Seymeria *macrophylla* (mullein-foxglove), a large, yellow-flowered plant, on the shores of the Little Miami River, and the mint on which he established the new genus *Synandra*.[29]

Nuttall had the pleasure of meeting another student of plants who was more constant in his devotion to botany than the civic-minded Dr. Drake. It is in doubt whether Nuttall first heard of Dr. Charles

Wilkins Short (1794–1863) of Kentucky from Dr. Drake or knew of him through one of his numerous friends in Philadelphia, where he had received his medical degree in 1815, or through meeting his older brother, John Cleves Short, who was practicing law in Cincinnati. His maternal grandfather, Judge John Cleves Symmes, had bought 1,000,000 acres on the north of the Ohio between the Little and Great Miami Rivers and his mother's sister married William Henry Harrison, Governor of Indiana Territory, distinguished in warfare and statesmanship. Charles graduated at Transylvania University in Lexington in 1811 and, after studying medicine for a few years with an uncle, attended the Medical School of the University of Pennsylvania. In Philadelphia his bachelor uncle, William Short, an eminent diplomat, introduced his nephew widely and arranged for him to live in the same house as John Vaughan, Secretary and Librarian of the American Philosophical Society, one of the most hospitable, cultured, and engaging men in the city. His class in botany went on excursions with Professor Barton "to the banks of the Schuylkill River and to the New Jersey shore to gather and study plants." Short developed a tremendous and lasting enthusiasm for botany and learned to prepare herbarium specimens so beautifully that the sheets which he donated or exchanged were highly prized.[30]

Nuttall found Short at his home in Lexington in the bluegrass country, "a singularly neat and pleasant town" with "an air of leisure and opulence." As Short had no botanical crony nearer than Dr. Drake, he was delighted by Nuttall's advent and spent many days with him not only botanizing in several directions from Lexington but also assisting him "in taking plans and measurements of an extensive [aboriginal] fortification at the confluence of the great Miami and Ohio rivers, and of another in this vicinity." The mouth of the Miami, not far west of Cincinnati, was about eighty miles from Lexington, but the journey, by carriage, was a familiar one to Dr. Short for his grandfather Symmes had lived at North Bend on the lower Miami on an estate inherited by his son-in-law and executor, William Henry Harrison.[31] Nuttall was happy to learn from the latter of the existence of *Catalpa* [*speciosa* Warder] "in very considerable quantities in the forests of the Wabash" for he himself had never seen it on the banks of the Ohio, Mississippi, or Missouri.[32] John Cleves Short had sufficient interest in plants to join the two botanists on some of their collecting trips. Between Nuttall and Dr. Short a warm friendship developed which found expression in an exchange of occasional letters through more than four decades.

During his stay in Lexington, Nuttall had an opportunity to see the paleontological cabinet of John D. Clifford (d. 1820) who had retired to Lexington, a favorable location for pursuing his avocations, after a successful business career in Philadelphia. From Big Bone Lick and similar sites in Kentucky, he had gathered teeth of the rhinoceros, bones of the mastodon and the mammoth, and, from caves near the Green River, bones of the *Megatherium*.[33] Rafinesque was a favorite of Clifford. They shared many interests; during Rafinesque's first stay in the United States he had been a clerk in Clifford's countingroom, and in 1818 Clifford's influence as a trustee secured him a professorship at Transylvania University in Lexington.

From Lexington the pedestrian Nuttall went southwestward across Kentucky through "the Barrens" in the valley of the Green River system;[34] Short called the area "natural flower-gardens." In the varying habitats Nuttall traversed, he found new species of plants: *Desmodium pauciflorum* in shady forests, *Pycnanthemum *pilosum* in the glades, and *Aster *gracilis* in the savannahs.[35] His route cannot be traced continuously. He saw the very rare *Magnolia macrophylla* Michx. "in Tennessee near the banks of the Cumberland river,"[36] and a flock of adult and young semipalmated plovers was "observed on the shores of the Cumberland, in Tennessee, by the 9th of September."[37] If these statements are geographically correct, he must have made a dip into the western half of Tennessee and returned to Kentucky, for he wrote to Short that it was on the Kentucky River that he "met with the first sempervirent shrubs in my way to Carolina."[38]

To the east of the Cumberland Gap, Nuttall found that "the calcareous rock puts on the appearance of chalk, and even contains nodules of flint," reminiscent of the calcareous cliffs he had noticed near the Maha Village on the Missouri which "more closely resemble chalk than any thing of the kind I have heretofore seen or heard of in North America" and observed that great abundance of nitre, as in the Cumberland Ridge, "is always connected with caverns of calcareous and arenilitic rock."[39] Continuing southeastward from the Gap on the old approach to the Wilderness Road, he crossed the Powell and the Clinch, mountain-born tributaries of the Tennessee River. At Bean Station he diverged from the historic route from the north to continue southeastward across the Holston to the French Broad which he followed through the main ridge of the Appalachians to Asheville. The Smoky Mountains and their luxuriant flora enchanted him. On dry, gravelly hills near the confluence of the Big Pigeon River and the French Broad he got *Houstonia* *tenuifolia.*[40] "On the rocky banks of the French Broad river, Tennessee, near the Warm Springs" (the name was changed to Hot Springs in 1866; it has always been in North Carolina) he found *Philadelphus* *hirsutus* in abundance and *Paronychia argyrocoma* (Michx.) Nutt.[41]

On October 2, from the little town of Rutherfordton, North Carolina, about forty-six miles southeast of Asheville on the edge of the Piedmont plateau, he wrote a long letter to Zaccheus Collins. After apologizing for his remissness in writing and recounting the chief events of his journey, he became more subjective.

The field tho remote and ample is quite meager and uninteresting, and had I not found another object of scientific importance quite sufficient to counterbalance to my disappointment in Botany, I should have placed this entire summer to my large acc't of lost time.

I have enjoyed an uncommon share of health and happiness. I have hardly known any weariness of mind (en[n]ui) — this gentle traveling on foot is, I think, the way to prolong life and health both. I shall never again consent to be cooped up in a city; for what has nature spread around me such a profuse and entertaining variety of objects of skill and wonder, but that I might examine and contemplate them, and be happy. How charmed have I been with the romantic and picturesque mountains of the French Broad. I shall ever remember this awfull [*sic*] chaste but magnificent scenery with pleasure. How many wonderful dislocations of strata — produced without any visible agency — are there for the puerile philosopher and the geologist to account, . . . but the works of Nature are often great, unsearchable, and past finding out! — let us leave things amidst the venerable clouds of mystery, rather than attempt to unravel facts beyond the sphere of our comprehension.[42]

Nuttall stated that he was then occupied with "making up a collection of Magnolias and other ornamental plants." This must have been a commercial project which would aid in defraying the expenses of his long journey. The plants were probably sent to England and also to Landreth and M'Mahon, to both of whom Nuttall sent his respects in a postscript.

The traveler had constantly in mind the plant hunters who had preceded him in the southern Appalachians and the special prizes each had gathered — William Bartram, André and François André

Michaux, the Frasers, Mathias Kinn, and John Lyon. "I am on the ground," he wrote to Collins, "w^h poor Lyons has once travelled with so much assiduity — but, alas, his labors are at an end. He is remembered by several but I have not found the place where he died." [43]

In his letter to Collins he outlined his plans for the rest of the tour: "I mean to have a look at the Basaltic wall of the Yadkin and Catawba creek before I have done with North Carolina." He expected to sail from Charleston about December.

Since Nuttall was heading for the upper waters of the Catawba, the question arises as to why he made such a considerable detour southward to Rutherfordton. The explanation may lie in the other "object of scientific importance" to which he referred in his letter, presumably geology and mineralogy. From 1790 Rutherfordton had been the center of the gold-mining industry of the United States so it offered an unusual opportunity to obtain specimens of the ore, for gold deposits were very rare in the Northeast.[44] Another possibility is that he was searching for "Flat-Rock," where Michaux found his *Sedum pusillum*; there is a place by that name near Hendersonville not far to the west. Although this was not Michaux's Flat Rock, Nuttall may have got information concerning other localities called by the same name.

From Rutherfordton, Nuttall's route to "Catawba Creek" passed not far to the east of the Blue Ridge and the great mass of Mount Mitchell which attains the highest elevation east of the Mississippi (6684 ft.); however its supremacy was not then recognized. The Linville River, the northernmost tributary of the Catawba, cascades down the steep and very deep gorge it has cut between the main Blue Ridge and a long southeastern spur known as Table Mountain Ridge (locally Jonas Ridge), although Nuttall called it the Catawba Ridge. Here in open bushy forests he found Michaux's Baptisia mollis [*Thermopsis mollis* (Michx.) M. A. Curtis] in abundance. The upper part of the ridge was covered with Table Mountain pine (*Pinus pungens* Lambert); on the summit of Table Rock Mountain, at about 4000 ft., he had his first view of *Abies fraseri* (Pursh) Poir., limited to the high altitudes of the southern Appalachians, and saw extensive stands of *Rhododendron catawbiense* Michx., although he did not have the pleasure of seeing the slopes brilliant with its blooms, as the Frasers did when they discovered it on Roan Mountain. *Xerophyllum asphodeloides* (L.) Nutt. was "very abundant on the summit of the

Catawba ridge"[45] and "extensive caespitose patches" of a new *Hudsonia* which he published as *H. *montana*.[46] He also saw on the highest summits sand myrtle, *Leiophyllum buxifolium* (Berg.) Ell., then attributed to *Ledum*; Nuttall remarked that it was "probably a distinct genus, but requires further examination."[47] He stated in the *Sylva* that he also climbed Roan Mountain (6286 ft.), which lies northwest of Table Mountain Ridge.

Nuttall may have had plans of following up the headwaters of the Linville River to the west slope of Grandfather Mountain in order to reach the sources of the Yadkin on the east side. If so, he gave up the idea when he saw the bristling impenetrable density of the vegetation and that "precipices of the Linville may be 1000 feet perpendicular on Grandfather Mountain." No evidence appears in his writings that he made his anticipated visit to the Yadkin.

He botanized on the banks of Laurel Creek near Morganton. Further down the valley of the Catawba, about twelve miles southeast of Lincolnton, he sought out the stand of *Magnolia macrophylla* discovered in 1789 by André Michaux on the banks of a small stream, the only known station east of the Appalachians. The stand of the species that Nuttall had found near the Cumberland River in Tennessee had not fruited; he now eagerly collected seed of this little-known tree for his customers and friends.

His next objective was another attempt to find "Flat Rock." He located it about sixteen miles north of Camden, South Carolina, a granitic outcrop nearly five acres in area, near Hanging Rock Creek. He wrote an account of the event to Charles W. Short, giving the state correctly, but in his *Genera* he inadvertently published it as in *North* Carolina and Short, in referring to it in an article, relied on the *Genera* instead of Nuttall's letter and thus helped to perpetuate the error. However Nuttall did not find a *Sedum*. In shallow, weathered depressions of the granite there were carpets of a puzzling small orpine with fruiting capsules unique in form, for which he set up the new genus *Diamorpha*.[48] In swamps not far away he hunted out Michaux's *Kalmia cuneata*.

Southward from Camden he soon crossed the Santee River as he continued on to Charleston, South Carolina. This area offered a second opportunity to establish the limits of Michaux's interesting *Eriogonum tomentosum*; like the long-leaf pine, it failed to accompany him to the city, being restricted to "the ancient maritime soil."[49]

"In the dry and sandy forests" not many miles from the city he saw occasionally a very low, shrubby Chinquapin, *Castanea *alnifolia*.[50]

The last goal of the long journey was to meet Stephen Elliott (1771–1830), one of the South's most distinguished men, who was working on a flora of South Carolina and Georgia. Although Elliott was not a practising physician like many of the botanists Nuttall had met in America, he had studied medicine after graduating from Yale College. He became active in public affairs and served in the legislature of his native state for twenty years and in 1812 was appointed President of the new State Bank of South Carolina in Charleston. There he took the lead in establishing a Literary and Philosophical Society and in 1828 with Hugh S. Legaré started *The Southern Review,* to which he contributed many articles. Time for botany had to be found at odd moments, but Elliott persevered in publishing sections of his flora until he finished the last part of *A Sketch of the Botany of South Carolina and Georgia* in 1824.[51]

The first section of Elliott's *Sketch* had already been printed but had not been distributed because when Dr. William Baldwin saw the proof he was very upset to find that some new species he had discovered had been written up without his knowledge although credited to him as author; he felt that the descriptions were "mangled" and that publication of his species by another person injured him.[52] Consequently it was agreed between the two that the number should be reprinted so that Baldwin could write the descriptions of his own plants for the *Sketch*. Revised copies of the first part were to be sent out with the second part before spring.

Zaccheus Collins had written to Elliott of Nuttall's pedestrian expedition which was to end at Charleston, and in September he wrote to Nuttall in care of Elliott, enclosing two letters which had come for him from England.[53] So Elliott was anticipating Nuttall's call long before it was paid. Passages in the publications of both show that they shared a close study and discussion of the eastern plants.

Early in February 1817, Lambert received from Charleston "a very interesting letter from Nuttall" giving an account of his long journey, and reported to Sir James Edward Smith that he "has done much." [54] Daniel Drake also received a long letter in which Nuttall wrote of a projected trip down the Ohio in the autumn of 1817 en route to California! [55]

Before the end of January the Delaware River was frozen at and below Philadelphia. The *General Wade Hampton,* the ship by which Elliott always sent his commissions to the north, was the last to get through to the northern city from South Carolina that winter. (It was reported as "below" on Saturday, January 18, 1817.) Later arrivals had to put in at Lewestown Roads near the entrance of Delaware Bay.[56] Nuttall doubtless sailed from Charleston but not as early as he had expected, for there is no record of his presence in Philadelphia until the last of February.

CHAPTER 8

# PUBLICATION

Without system the field of Nature would be a pathless wilderness.
— Gilbert White, *Selborne*, Letter LXXXII.

PHILADELPHIA, 1817–1818. The years 1817 and 1818 were epochal in Thomas Nuttall's career. In 1817 he received local recognition as a naturalist through election to the Academy of Natural Sciences of Philadelphia and to the American Philosophical Society; in 1818 the publication of his *Genera of North American Plants* won him international acclaim.

During his first stay of two years in Philadelphia his job as a printer and his devoted study in every spare moment had effectually isolated him socially from all persons but the few whom he sought out for their kindred interests. Since then seven years had elapsed during which he had made but two sojourns there, about two months in the summer of 1815 and a similar stay in the late winter and early spring of 1816. In 1817 he came to know Philadelphia as a social community. His faithful attendance at the weekly meetings of the Academy drew him into a group with whom he was quickly serving on committees and establishing casual or friendly associations. As his acquaintance with men of scientific interests rapidly increased he found himself a part of a celebrated circle in Philadelphia, albeit on the periphery. He became a not infrequent guest at the Wistar Salons, weekly gatherings of the local intellectual elite to which notable visitors to the city were invited. Dr. Caspar Wistar (1760–1818) initiated these assemblies at his home; after his death, the group continued to meet under the original designation.

Nuttall's election to the Academy of Natural Sciences on January 28 as a Corresponding rather than a Resident Member indicates that he was not then back from his long journey. The earliest date that we have for his return is February 28, when he wrote a long letter from Philadelphia to Charles Wilkins Short which he marked "Favor of George Ord." [1] The first indication of Nuttall's attendance at a meeting of the Academy appears as an entry in the Minutes for March 4, 1817, "Mr. Nuttal [sic] promised to produce a communication at the next meeting." [2] (The names of those attending the weekly meetings were not recorded in the Minutes until 1822.) There is no further reference to the promised paper but Nuttall seems to have been present regularly thereafter whenever he was in Philadelphia.[3] Indeed he spent most of his time working at the Academy.

Those most faithful in attendance at the meetings at this period were Thomas Say, Dr. John Barnes, Dr. Gerard Troost (a chemist), Zaccheus Collins, Reuben Haines (a philanthropic merchant), Dr. Richard Harlan (a mammalogist who later became a warm friend of Audubon), George Ord (a zoologist), Isaac Lea (a publisher and conchologist), and William Maclure (1763–1840) (a prominent geologist), the chief benefactor of the society, president from December 1817 until his death.

Early in 1817, at the urgency of Maclure, a committee was appointed to consider the feasibility of launching a publication; as this was a difficult and expensive undertaking for such a small group, the committee included the most prosperous members. This was an important proposal because the only media then existing in the United States for the publication of scientific papers were irregular volumes of the American Philosophical Society and the American Academy of Arts and Sciences and a few medical journals. At the last meeting in March the decision was made to go ahead with the project and a committee was appointed to produce the first issue. The eight persons given this responsibility — Maclure, Dr. Thomas Cooper, Dr. Robert Patterson, T. Say, Haines, Ord, Nuttall, and J. H. Dallas — expedited the work so efficiently that in May they produced fifty copies of the first thin number of the *Journal* for distribution.

The first volume was in two parts each one consisting of six modest numbers. Part I closed with the December issue of 1817; the six numbers of Part II appeared from May to December of 1818. The numbers of Part I were printed by D. Heartt, but tradition reports that this proved too expensive so the issues of Part II were printed on a secondhand press at Maclure's house by volunteers, Nuttall and Say setting most of the type.

The three articles which composed the initial publication, written by Ord (1781–1866), Thomas Say (1787–1834), and Lesueur, introduced new species to science; these set the standard of admitting only original work to the pages of the *Journal*. Ord named and described the Rocky Mountain sheep as Ovis montana (*O. canadensis* Shaw), and Say described some new shells; Lesueur's paper was on six new species of *Firola* (*Gasteropoda*) collected in the Mediterranean in 1809.

Charles Alexandre Lesueur (1778–1846), a French zoologist and artist who taught drawing and painting, had reached the United States with Maclure in May 1816. His experience of more than three years on the French expedition of *Le Géographe* and *Le Naturaliste*, which explored along the Australian coast, Pacific islands, and the Cape of Good Hope, made him a valuable member of the Academy, which he joined in 1818. He generously contributed scientific drawings for many of the papers which appeared in the *Journal* and commanded the friendship and esteem of all those who knew him.

A paper by Nuttall entitled "Observations on the Genus *Eriogonum*, and the Natural Order *Polygoneae* of Jussieu" was divided into two installments in the June and July issues of the *Journal*. Michaux had found the type species of *Eriogonum* on the southern coastal plain; at that time the genus was regarded in America as monotypic. However Bradbury and Nuttall obtained two more species far up the Missouri. Pursh published these from Lewis's collection, but the name that Nuttall gave one species in Fraser's catalog, *E. flavum*, has been adopted as having priority. While studying in Sir Joseph Banks's herbarium the collections made by Menzies on the west coast of North America, Nuttall ran across two additional species of the genus, which had been named by Sir James Edward Smith, *E. latifolium* and *E. parvifolium*. With characteristic insight Nuttall predicted that "the genus Eriogonum as yet peculiar to North America . . . may probably form a numerous genus, whenever the great plains of *California*, the *Columbia*, the *Missouri* and the *Arkansa* shall be explored." His discussion of the position of *Eriogonum* in Jussieu's natural system is evidence of his appreciation of the importance of the natural classification, an almost inevitable result of his contact with Robert Brown.

In the second number of the *Journal*, Thomas Say presented the first paper of a prolonged series published therein, describing new species of North American insects. Of the eight species considered in the initial paper (on *Coleoptera*), five had been collected by Nuttall on the Missouri River.[4] Others of his collecting appeared as Say studied intensively the different orders and genera to which they belonged. In 1819–1820 Say spent more than a year on the Missouri watershed with the Long Expedition busily gathering zoological specimens of all kinds; although he secured some insects that were in Nuttall's collection, there were still unpublished western species of Nuttall that nobody else had found. At least two species of his 1811 garnerings, *Lestes basalis* of the *Neuroptera* and *Cercaris sexta* of the *Hymenoptera*, were not published until twenty-six and more years after they were caught.[5] In the whole of Say's entomological publications, forty-seven Missouri species are attributed to Nuttall's collection only.

Since his return to the city, Nuttall was giving his main attention to writing a systematic treatment of the North American flora, a laborious and exacting task which occupied most of his time and thoughts for about a year and a half. When the growing season arrived, he could not resist botanizing, but he restricted his excursions to nearby areas. When he first got back to Philadelphia, he had written to Charles Wilkins Short that he expected to be in Kentucky in the summer for an extended stay there and in Ohio, perhaps arriving by June. However, when he became immersed in his big undertaking, he was eager to push it to completion so that he would be free to set out on the southwestern expedition which had been luring him since his return from the Missouri.

Nuttall's field trips in 1817 may have been largely to secure horticultural material to maintain his supply of bread and milk. He wrote of collecting many specimens of *"Isoëtes lacustris"* where it grew abundantly on the banks of the Delaware near Kensington, of finding a species of *Malaxis* on the Wissahickon, of searching the New Jersey woods along the Delaware, and of getting some rarities at Cape May. On one occasion at least he was accompanied by Professor W. P. C. Barton who was writing *Compendium Florae Philadelphicae* (1818), building on his *Prodomus* of 1815. In it he acknowledged considerable assistance from both Zaccheus Collins and Nuttall. He used the generic descriptions of Nuttall, who loaned prepublication sheets of his own text to Barton for this purpose.

A more frequent companion during the summer was W. C. Stüve

of Bremen, a young German chemist working temporarily in Philadelphia who was enthusiastically collecting a herbarium of American plants. Nuttall had met him through Collins to whom he had brought a letter of introduction from Professor Franz Karl Mertens of Bremen. Toward the end of the summer Nuttall and Stüve went northward as far as New York City, the latter armed with a letter from Collins introducing him to Rafinesque.[6] That eccentric botanist was out of town to his own vast regret for he was eager to talk with Nuttall to urge him to include in his publication the botanical names that Rafinesque had published in the *New York Medical Repository* and also to rescue for him three of his discoveries which had been appropriated by Pursh, Allium triflorum, *Drosera filiformis*, and *Asclepias viridiflora*. (He had already written to Collins about these matters asking his intercession with Nuttall.)[7] Nuttall, evidently glad to exact justice from Pursh, referred the three claimed species to the complainant; the last two now stand in Rafinesque's name although the *Asclepias* wandered off for a long period into another genus set up by Elliott. Later Rafinesque made further requests of Nuttall through Collins which were not so well received. In general Nuttall, like most contemporary botanists, ignored Rafinesque's botanical papers as unreliable.

In the spring Stephen Elliott had sent to Collins and Nuttall copies of the first and second numbers of his *Sketch of the Botany of South Carolina and Georgia* and to the latter a list of his northern *disserata*. Stüve evidently took over the commission for in October he wrote to Elliott that he was sending fifty plants, most of which were on Mr. Nuttall's list, and wanted in exchange seeds to plant in Germany on his return.[8] Nuttall sent Elliott "some rare plants" from the Missouri[9] and to the Liverpool Botanic Garden seeds of Pennsylvania and New Jersey plants.

Three volumes produced by members of the Academy of Natural Sciences appeared in mid-1817: William Maclure's *Geology of the United States*, the first small part of Thomas Say's *American Entomology* (ten pages of text and six plates), and, posthumously, Mühlenberg's *Descriptio uberior Graminum et Plantarum Calamariarum Americae septentrionalis*, edited by Solomon White Conrad. Another widely useful but undistinguished botanical contribution of the year was the first of many editions of Amos Eaton's *Manual of Botany for the Northern States*, a text adapted to popular use.[10]

# PUBLICATION

In autumnal numbers of the *Journal* two articles by Nuttall appeared which had each been read to the Academy and approved by a publication committee, a procedure borrowed from the American Philosophical Society. Both were illustrated with plates drawn by Lesueur. The first, read on September 16, describing and naming four aquatic plants which he had found in July on the banks of the Delaware, contained two new species but otherwise proved to be erroneous as the plants were for the most part immature.[11] The other paper, read on November 11, presented the new genus *Collinsia* with the story of the original discovery of *C. verna* in 1810 and its rediscovery six years later.[12] To the second part of the first volume of the *Journal* which came out during 1818 Nuttall made no contribution for he was then completely engrossed in finishing his book and making plans for his southwestern journey. Thomas Say was the most frequent contributor to the early numbers of the periodical. He was a born naturalist who studied intensively in invertebrate taxonomy, working long hours at the Academy as Nuttall did. Associated by their occupations, enthusiasms, and outlook, they became fast friends. Say had an open, sincere, and helpful nature which made him universally liked even though his lack of worldly ambition was difficult for many to fathom.

Nuttall was elected to the American Philosophical Society October 17, at the same time as George Ord, Thomas Say, and Lewis D. von Schweinitz (1780–1834). The latter, a lay official of the Moravian Church, educated in Germany and stationed in North Carolina, was an enthusiastic mycologist. Nuttall seems to have attended the semimonthly meetings of the Society fairly regularly when he was in the city. In November he served on publication committees for papers of Thomas Say and Dr. Daniel Drake. On February 20, 1818, Mühlenberg's fine and large herbarium came into the possession of the Society as a donation from nine of the members, Zaccheus Collins, John Vaughan, William Short, George Pollock, Chief Justice Tilghman, Dr. Caspar Wistar, Dr. James, Dr. Chapman, and Dr. Dorsey. This was a most timely assistance to Nuttall and William P. C. Barton, who were reaching the finishing stages of their taxonomic publications.

At the Philosophical Society, Nuttall became acquainted with two of the most widely known and admired men of the time: John Vaughan (1756–1841) its Treasurer, Secretary, and Librarian, and the learned Abbé Corréa da Serra (1750–1823), Portuguese Minister to the United States from July 22, 1816, to November 9, 1820, a keen botanist. (The latter, though a member of the Academy of Natural Sciences, did not often attend its meetings at this time.) John Vaughan, one of several sons of Samuel who had been a wealthy London merchant and Jamaican planter, established in Philadelphia as a merchant, was widely admired for his debonair and friendly nature and spontaneous generosity.

In December 1817, John Bradbury arrived in Philadelphia, back from a stay of over a year and a half in England where he had published his *Travels in the Interior of North America*. He came to Philadelphia hoping to make arrangements for an American edition. He brought letters of introduction to Zaccheus Collins from John LeConte and Caspar Wistar Eddy of New York in both of which his association with Nuttall was mentioned.[13] We do not know if the two erstwhile Astorians renewed their acquaintance at this time. Bradbury had brought his family to America and settled first near St. Louis and later in Kentucky, where he died in 1823.

Nuttall continued to work long days on his systematic treatment of the North American flora. He did the work at the Academy, for he had no library of his own and presumably no adequate space for spreading out specimens for comparison. He is said to have often worked through the night, resting occasionally under the skeleton of the mastodon, following Thomas Say's example. Finally the writing and printing were finished. At the July 14, 1818, meeting of the Academy the author presented a copy of his classic work on the taxonomy of North American plants.

NUTTALL'S GENERA. The work that Nuttall had first projected as a revised edition of Pursh's *Flora* grew to about six hundred pages of detailed factual writing entailing the incessant consultation and critical comparison of herbarium specimens and botanical publications. In addition to his own plants and those of the Academy, he was able to refer to Mühlenberg's and he often consulted Zaccheus Collins's extensive collection. Professor Barton's herbarium, left to the Philosophical Society, seems to have remained unused, for years later it was found undisturbed in "John Vaughan's garret" by Charles Pickering.[14]

Before starting on the text, Nuttall had to make the difficult decision of whether to use the old-fashioned Linnaean system of classification still employed in the United States or follow the enlightened natural system of Jussieu adopted on the continent of Europe and by Robert Brown and a few others in England. Fearing that an unfamiliar system would prove too great an obstacle to most Americans and wishing to give his book the greatest immediate usefulness he reluctantly decided to arrange the species in the Linnaean manner, but by discussing the natural relationships of each genus he provided an introduction to the newer method. In the Preface he explained his decision in stilted phrases such as often marred his early writing.

As he worked and his objectives shifted from his first concept, the title became *Genera of North American Plants with a Catalogue of the Species through 1817.* The 834 genera included were fully characterized, as were the new species which Nuttall introduced; other species were merely listed except where new information was supplied concerning structure, habitat, or range. All technical descriptions were in English in contrast to those in the floras of Pursh and Michaux, which were in Latin.

As an American production, Nuttall's *Genera* was unique in its scope and in the great quantity of original material that it presented. It was entirely distinct from the local and regional floras of his time, which rarely rose above the level of compilations. Moreover, through the greatly extended knowledge of American species, it surpassed Michaux's *Flora* and in quality far outranked Pursh's. An amazing publication for a young, self-taught botanist who had spent less than seven years in North America, it proved a landmark in American botany initiating the shift of the study of North American plants from the eastern hemisphere to the western.[15]

An analysis of the *Genera* shows that Nuttall faced two general difficulties. One, which confronted all contemporary botanical workers in America, was the brevity of the descriptions in the works of Linnaeus, Michaux, and others, which, without figures or accessible type specimens, often proved insufficient for discrimination, especially when closely related species were uncovered. This handicap prevailed until Gray went to Europe in 1838–1839 to study the types. A second source of impairment of Nuttall's work was due to deficiencies in his taxonomic training; Benjamin Smith Barton was not as enlightened as he should have been in regard to principles of priority adopted by the leading taxonomists of the time, as his own work bears witness.

Nuttall remained oblivious to simple conventions such as the retention of the original specific name when transfer is made to a different genus. It is regrettable that ignorance of so simple a rule marred his work.

A large fraction of the pages had already been printed by midsummer of 1817, and Nuttall expected it would be finished in the autumn, but the work progressed much more slowly than he anticipated. There was no publisher; Nuttall financed the printing. The title page states that the text was "Printed for the Author by D. Heartt," and tradition reports that Nuttall set much of the type. He did not apply for the copyright until April 3, 1818; the Preface was dated May 27, and the book, priced at two dollars, was issued by mid-July. The publication was

Dedicated To his excellency Joseph Correa de Serra, Fellow of the Royal Society, of the National Institute of France, &,&., and Minister of H. M. F. M. of Portugal, Brazil and Algarves to the United States.

SIR

The active interest which you have ever taken in promotion of Natural Science, both in Europe and America, and your desire to elevate it to the rank of Philosophy, demands the gratitude of all its votaries, and inspires the feeble acknowledgments of your humble servant, the

AUTHOR

Abbé José Francisco Corréa da Serra (1750–1823), "one of the most remarkable men of the time, for various learning, acuteness and wit, and for elegant suave manners,"[16] a Portuguese educated in Italy whither his father removed to escape reprisals of the Inquisition, was later himself obliged to flee from an erstwhile influential position in Portugal when the sudden death of the Prince, his pupil, exposed him to the revenge of the clergy. For many years he lived an exile in Paris and London associated with savants.[17] Augustin Pyramus de Candolle in his *Mémoires* dwells on the profundity of Corréa's knowledge and the cleverness with which he got the advantage of Cuvier and von Humboldt in discussions. Nuttall probably received continual encouragement from him in the writing of the *Genera*.

Of the numerous new genera proposed by Nuttall, the twelve named for persons rouse special interest: eight of these were named for scientists or patrons of science — Baldwin, Barton, Collins, Crantz, Maclure, Windsor, Wistar, and Lord Stanley; and four for horticulturists — Enslen, Lyon, M'Mahon, and John Shepherd.[18] John Windsor was Nuttall's "earliest botanical friend," M'Mahon, Shepherd, and Wistar befriended him; Barton, Collins, and Maclure furnished him special support and encouragement, and Baldwin he regarded as the best botanist he had met in America. Crantz (1722–1799), an Austrian, wrote monographs on two of Nuttall's favorite families, *Cruciferae* and *Umbelliferae*. Half of the number honored had been born in Britain, two in Austria, and four in the United States. A special problem hangs over the generic name *Wisteria* which the *Genera* states honors Dr. Caspar Wistar. Tradition says that this name was given at the request of Corréa da Serra although this was said to have been denied by Nuttall.[19] Queried about the spelling, Nuttall stated that it was chosen for euphony.[20] However, in the Wister branch of the family Nuttall had a very good friend, Charles Jones Wister, Sr. (1782–1865), often his host and his companion on mineralogical and botanizing excursions.

Trustworthy estimates of the value of the *Genera* could not be looked for immediately. Its distribution to botanists of America and Europe was a slow process, and, moreover, its nature was that of a workbook which could be best appraised through use. Nuttall could hardly expect to hear any tested opinions concerning it until some time had elapsed. However, he heard with disagreeable promptitude from one offended botanist, Dr. William Baldwin.

Since Nuttall saw him in Savannah in the autumn of 1815, Baldwin's health had deteriorated but his activity in botany was as determined as ever. In consequence of Nuttall's esteem for his work, Lambert offered to propose Baldwin for membership in the Linnaean Society of London, sent him a copy of Pursh's *Flora*, and kept up a correspondence and exchange of specimens with him.[21] In the winter of 1817–1818, in the interest of his health, Baldwin sailed as Surgeon on the U. S. Frigate *Congress* bound on a government mission to South America. The ship put in at Rio de Janeiro, Montevideo, Buenos Aires, Maldonado, and the islands of Margarita and San Salvador, staying long enough in the ports for Baldwin to get many specimens. Henry Brackenridge, who had gone up the Missouri in 1811 with Manuel Lisa, happened to be attached to the diplomatic party as secretary, and he enthusiastically joined Baldwin on collecting trips, which must have stirred memories of Bradbury and Nuttall.

Baldwin returned to Wilmington, Delaware, about mid-July 1818, and quickly received the current botanical news directly from William Darlington and later through correspondence with him and Collins. After cursorily examining the *Genera* he precipitously wrote a long letter to Nuttall complaining of plagiarism and other sins. It is a pity that we do not have the original letter because Baldwin, very jealous of his publishing rights, possessed a devastating facility in the use of invective. What has come down to us are choppy reports of its contents which Baldwin quoted with satisfaction to friends in frequent letters in the course of the summer. On August 8, Baldwin wrote to Zaccheus Collins:

> I have had a peep at . . . the work of Nuttall. The latter unquestionably, contains a vast deal of new and useful information, evincing the great zeal and industry of its author. But I have the charge of *plagiarism* to prefer against him. . . . Nuttall has, it is true, paid me off in compliments. . . . I should have felt infinitely more obliged to him, had he simply given me credit for the little I had done in the work of Mr. Elliott, and omitted *Baldwina, Baldwini, Baldwynii,* and everything else relating to me.[22]

The compliments that Baldwin resented were the naming in his honor of a new genus of the *Compositae,* \**Balduina,* and two new species, *Polygala* \**balduini* and *Silene* \**baldwynii.* Nuttall stated he had seen the two species and one of the Balduinas only in the herbarium of "Dr. Baldwyn," but a second species of *Balduina, B.* \**uniflora,* had been discovered by Nuttall. Baldwin's displeasure in this matter may have been only a temporary reflection of general annoyance: even the great Linnaeus gloried in *Linnaea borealis.*

When Baldwin was in Philadelphia in mid-August, he found that Collins was away for two weeks and that Nuttall was in Germantown. "I shall not see him." Both Baldwin and Darlington were careless in some of the indictments of plagiarisms by Nuttall that they exchanged, for they overlooked credits clearly made to them in the text and failed to take into consideration the possibility of typographical errors in the introduction of the asterisk used to designate a new species of Nuttall, although some are obvious, such as its use before a Linnaean name.

Early in September Baldwin reported to Darlington concerning an answer he had received from Nuttall.

> It is dated the 14 ult. but did not reach me until the 31st. He is most enormously wroth, and says he could have described all the new plants taken from my *Herbarium,* from the now public Herbarium of Dr. Mühl-

enberg, no thanks to me; and further, and *queerer* than all, *he had seen them before in Europe* in Herbariums!! Poor I ought to think it a great favor that my name is mentioned at all: it was merely out of *personal* respect to me. I must see you before I enter into any detail of this curious business, & show you the whole correspondence, which does not readily admit of analysis. . . .[23]

Lacking the correspondence between the principals, we are now in an even less favorable position to appraise the alleged rights and wrongs of the dispute. Nuttall credited Baldwin as being the discoverer of about twenty-four new species and occasionally for information concerning the distribution of a species. Pragmatically the publication of some of Baldwin's species in the *Genera* was useful since Baldwin's rapidly failing health made any major publication impossible for him. About mid-September Baldwin received an invitation to join the scientific staff of the Yellowstone Expedition as Surgeon and Botanist; thereafter his mind was increasingly diverted from preoccupation with the *Genera*.

Only two full reviews of the *Genera of North American Plants* ever appeared. The first was Rafinesque's in the January 1819 issue of the *American Monthly Magazine and Critical Review*. In contrast to the generally disparaging tone of his frequent reviews, this was strikingly laudatory.

We perceive with much satisfaction that it is superior in many respects to any other yet published on either side of the Atlantic. . . .

On perusal of this interesting work, we were in the first instance peculiarly pleased by the neatness of its execution, its appropriate plan, convenient shape, and cheap price: qualities seldom united in modern scientific labors, which are too often swelled by pride into thick quartos. . . . Mr. Nuttall is a zealous admirer of natural affinities; he has in some instances added much to our knowledge of the peculiar affinities of some genera, and he evinces a partiality for the beautiful results of an inquiry into the philosophy of botany. He might therefore have greatly increased the value of his work, by displaying in it the series of natural orders, and families already detected in the United States, and bringing a knowledge of them to a level with the understanding of students and amateurs; but he has preferred the convenience of the sexual system, because it is generally taught, as yet, among us, and its false bases are more easily recorded in the memory of the common readers. . . . if every writer should follow this example, no improvement would ever be adopted in science, and knowledge would remain stationary.

We perceive that this work is very far from deserving the title of a mere compilation like so many of its kind; but is the result of the practical observations of the author since 1809. . . .

Reassuming our perusal of his work, we find that it is not a mere description of our genera; but an enlarged survey of them. After the botanical English names of each genus follows a correct definition of it, in the style of Jussieu, with observations on the habit and peculiarities of it. Next a catalogue of the species . . . including many new ones, of which full descriptions are given; and lastly an account of the number and geography of the foreign species belonging to the same genus. Therefore the whole includes a more correct account of our genera than has ever been published.

The additions to botanical knowledge conveyed by this work are various, and include the discovery and establishment of many new genera and species, new observations on old genera, the introduction of some genera as American, and some remarks on the properties of plants scattered throughout the work. . . .[24]

At this point Rafinesque began the characteristic detailed study of the genera and species by which he reaped the rewards of his reviews. For names that he judged "bad," "erroneous," "wrong," "absurd," and "inadmissible" he supplied substitutes. Wherever there was doubt expressed as to the position of a species, he supplied a new generic name by which it might be called. His own neglected contributions to botanical literature were patiently reinstated in place of the names of other authors. George Engelmann in thanking Short in the 1850s for the gift of some of Rafinesque's papers remarked on "the barefaced impudence with which he urges his decisions and assails better men. The criticism of Nuttall's *Genera* is particularly rich!"[25]

The other careful review of the *Genera*, by Caleb Cushing, appeared in 1821 in a paper on "Botany of the United States" in *The North American Review*. The comments on the botany of the *Genera* are commendatory except for one phase.

He has proposed above sixty new genera . . . chiefly by the subdivision of old genera. And we think here lies the greatest defect of the work; namely, in a disposition to innovate upon the established genera, not always on the safest grounds. Thus to make a new genus Comandra of Thasium umbellatum and a genus Epifagus of Orobanche Virginiana, in separating the genus Juglans into Juglans and Carya, in adopting Desfontaines' dismemberment of the genus Convallaria into Convallaria, Smilacina and Polygonatum, in confirming Michaux's and Pursh's division of the genus Pyrola into Pyrola and Chimaphila, in these and in other instances, that could be pointed out Nuttall appears to us to have ventured upon or assented to changes, which the generic differences he has indicated do not warrant, and which materially injure the science of botany by embarrassing its nomenclature and impairing the symmetry of its arrangements.[26]

That objection should ever have been made to such improvements as these exemplifies the pronouncement that "scientists . . . create not what is acceptable but what will become acceptable."[27]

Cushing found fault also with the literary execution of the work, a vulnerable aspect, and certain typographical mistakes, "the numbers of the genera from 412 to 734 are wholly erroneous, each number requiring an increase of 100 to make it correct."

Few books were yet being published in America and there were few periodicals to print reviews of them. It is in letters of botanists of the time that Nuttall's work was most widely appraised as it was tested by use. The fastidious Francis Boott of Boston sent a copy of the *Genera* to William Jackson Hooker, the outstanding English botanist working on the North American flora, without the apologies which he usually found it necessary to make for American publications.[28] Hooker's verdict was that the *Genera* marked "an era in the history of American botany."[29] J. Duby, Director of the Botanic Garden of Geneva, wrote to Zaccheus Collins of "the excellent work of Mr. Nuttall."[30] William Cooper of New York City, visiting European botanical centers in 1822, found that this opinion of Nuttall's work was general there and that the author was regarded as the first botanist in the United States.[31] Lewis D. von Schweinitz wrote to Torrey: "I think Mr. Nuttall's observations uncommonly excellent. His Genera have given me more light than any other book — it is so evident from all his remarks in that work, that they are the fruits of real personal acquaintance with the plants in nature."[32]

In an article on *Viola* Schweinitz wrote, "The generic description of the genus given by Mr. Nuttall (p. 147, vol. I) is so satisfactory that it is needless to repeat it. . . . that gentleman's talents for correct discrimination being above praise. Botany, I conceive, owes fully as much to him for his excellent distinctions, as on account of the unsparing zeal with which he traverses our most inhospitable wilds, to augment our knowledge."[33] In the narrative of Long's First Expedition, Dr. Edwin James referred to "Mr. Nuttall's valuable work on the Genera of North American plants."[34] Stephen Elliott praised it as "abounding in accurate information respecting the plants of this country." [35] John Torrey in the Preface of a regional flora he published in 1824, which he dedicated to Nuttall, stated that "his Genera contributed more than any other work to advance the accurate knowledge of plants of this country." [36] In 1834 Moses Ashley Curtis wrote from North Carolina to Torrey commenting on the impossibility of differentiating between some of Nuttall's species and those described by Michaux and others, concluding that "he is not *always* accurate in his observations. I have no intention of detracting from the merits of Mr. Nuttall, since I owe more to his work for the little knowledge I have of Botany than to any other. But Homer sometimes napped." [37] In 1890 E. L. Greene looked back on it as "the most influential and serviceable work which had yet been issued in North American botany." [38] Even in the twentieth century John Barnhardt, long-time bibliographer at the New York Botanic Garden, termed it "a little gem," and Merritt Lyndon Fernald stated that "the remarkable Genera" was "a work such as had never before been produced in America in the botanical field." [39]

Nuttall set off in the autumn for the Southwest to commune with himself for a year and a half with his friends' casual words of commendation and Baldwin's hot accusations to mull over as rewards for his long sustained labors.

PATRONAGE WANTED. During the summer Nuttall doubtless relaxed occasionally at the Bartrams' cheerful house. In mid-August he was in Germantown,[40] perhaps visiting Reuben Haines at "Wyck" or Charles J. Wister at his carefully tended estate, "Grumblethorpe," where he enjoyed watching the development of the gardens over more than a score of years while he and his host found inexhaustible conversation in botany, horticulture, and mineralogy. Nuttall is said to have delivered a course of botanical lectures at Germantown Academy about this time, which Wister's son William Wynne Wister (1807–1898) attended and therefrom "received an inspiration for the science which lasted a lifetime." [41] In September Nuttall was in lower Delaware (Lewes), perhaps to get the fruits of plants that he had obtained in flower in June 1809. He wrote of "Anthopogon filiforme" (a *Gymnopogon*), "I first detected this very distinct species on the bushy margins of swamps in Sussex County, Delaware, a few miles from Lewistown, in September 1818." [42]

Nuttall was chiefly concerned with implementing his long-anticipated journey to the Southwest. He had promise of financial support from Collins and others but assiduously sought for an opportunity to join an organized group, evidently hoping that he might get an appointment as naturalist on a government exploring expedition such as the ones that had been sent out after the Louisiana Purchase: while Lewis and Clark were ascending the Missouri, President Jefferson sent William Dunbar and Dr. George Hunter to explore parts of the Red River system of the South (1804–1805), and General James Atkinson as Governor of Upper Louisiana Territory entrusted Zebulon Pike with the missions of locating the source of the Mississippi (1805–1806) and the headwaters and course of the Arkansas and Red Rivers (1806–1807). The hostility on the frontiers which preceded and accompanied the War of 1812 had suspended all such activities, but emigration into the West was again active and there were rumors of new expeditions.

As early as June 30, 1817, Dr. William P. C. Barton in a letter to Brigadier General Daniel Parker recommended Nuttall as a field naturalist. As Parker was married to Zaccheus Collins's daughter Ann, he doubtless already knew of Barton's candidate.

Your hint respecting the employment of a botanist & mineralogist, in the expedition to the frontier I would most cheerfully have profitted [sic] by. . . . there is now in this city an English botanist and mineralogist who has already added much to our stock of information on these subjects. He is poor and destitute of the means of making travels with advantage, to those parts of the U. S. whither novelty and interesting facts, would direct him. He is now engaged in publishing a work on our *Genera of plants*. His name is Nuttall; you will find him spoken of in my Biogr. sketch of Profess. Barton, p. 23. He desires much to visit the Missouri, Red River &. Do you think it likely any governmental patronage could be extended to him, so as to afford him facilities in travelling and pecuniary assistance even of moderate amount. When you recollect that the French Government have paid Frenchmen (Michaux &c) for visiting our country & describing our vegetable productions, and that the English have done the same thing – I am sure you will agree with me in the opinion that we should do something to advance the knowledge of our natural history.[43]

A second letter from Barton to General Parker written on August 17, shows that Nuttall's nationality was considered a bar to a government appointment, but Barton still pressed the point.

I need not tell you how much pleasure your letter of the 10th ult. gave me. Mr. Nuttall is so truly deserving of notice and patronage, that the appointment you mention, if attainable, would be well bestowed. Besides the immediate object, of affording assistance and support in exploring the natural history of our country, he in three months study, could render himself every way qualified to discharge the duties of As. Top. Eng. [Assistant Topographical Engineer] with advantage to the government. This I well know: all his feelings are for America, all his pursuits centered here, and his highest ambition is, to be the means of promoting the knowledge of our natural history; but particularly our botany. . . .

I enclose for your inspection 120 pages of Mr. Nuttalls work which will be completed this fall. He has lent these sheets to me, and without his knowledge I have taken the liberty of letting you see them, that you may have proof of his merit. It will be an admirable, and original work. . . .[44]

Thomas Say also wished to obtain a berth with an exploring expedition to the West. At the meeting of the American Philosophical Society on August 21, 1818, a committee was appointed to try "to associate Say and Nuttall with the U. S. Exploring Expedition to the Northwest." The committee consisted of Du Ponceau, Jones, Cooper, and the two Doctors Patterson.

That very day Dr. Thomas Cooper wrote to Thomas Jefferson, concluding his letter as follows:

I write at present to request your influence with Mr. Monroe to send out in some capacity or other, our Mr. Thomas Say, and Mr. Thos. Nuttal [sic]; really, as Zoologist and as Botanist, in the Macedonian. They have done more than any two other men of late, to extend our scientific reputation abroad, and are noticed with great respect in the Journal de Physique for last January. M. Correa is at Albany or he would heartily join in this recommendation. They want nothing more than a salary that would decently suffice for necessaries of life, during the cruise, and facilities to pursue their objects.[45]

Cooper (1759–1839) came to the United States from England with Joseph Priestley's family and settled in Northumberland, Pennsylvania, as a neighbor of the Priestleys. An extreme and very vocal liberal, he possessed "singular versatility of talent" being versed in law, physic, divinity, chemistry, and general science "although some of his screws were uncommonly loose." At this time he was teaching chemistry at the University of Pennsylvania but he soon went to the University of South Carolina where he eventually raised the tempests which usually followed in his wake. There must have been some misunderstanding by Cooper about the government's plans because the *Macedonian* from 1818 into 1821, was cruising in the Pacific without entering the coastal waters of the Northwest and carried no naturalist.

Within a few weeks after the appointment of the committee of the American Philosophical Society, an opportunity opened for Thomas Say to go the following spring with the scientific arm of the "Yellowstone Expedition" under Stephen Harriman Long. U.S.A., Brevet Major in the Topographical Engineers. The original purpose of the expedition was to establish forts on the upper Missouri to hold the Indians in check and protect the American fur trade; a detail of troops was to prepare the way by starting up the river in the fall of 1818. William Baldwin was asked to go with the scientific group as Physician and Botanist, Thomas Say as Zoologist, Titian R. Peale as Assistant Naturalist, Augustus E. Jessup as Geologist, Samuel Seymour as Artist, and John Biddle as Journalist.

To Nuttall the Southwest was a garden of unknown species which called to him irresistibly and he still was intent on reaching the Rocky Mountains. He evidently read with great interest Dunbar's manuscript journal of his expedition up the Red and Ouachita Rivers to the Hot Springs with Dr. Hunter in 1804–1805, which was sent in 1817 to John Vaughan as Librarian of the American Philosophical Society.[46] However Nuttall finally decided to approach from the north, entering the region by the Arkansas River. Four men sympathetic with his aims, fellow members of the American Philosophical Society — Zaccheus Collins, William Maclure (or Reuben Haines?),[47] Corréa da Serra, and John Vaughan — supplied funds for the journey. Each donated fifty dollars so that Nuttall was assured of two hundred dollars to defray the expenses of a trip of some thousands of miles and a year and a half in duration. He left his small affairs in Collins's hands and set out from Philadelphia on October 2, 1818, with high hopes of gathering "a rich harvest of Botanical treasure" in the Arkansas country.

CHAPTER 9

# EXPLORATION IN THE SOUTHWEST

. . . strong in will
To strive, to seek, to find, and not to yield.
— Tennyson, "Ulysses."

THE ARKANSAS JOURNEY, 1818–1820.

On the morning of the second of October, 1818, I took my departure from Philadelphia in the mail stage, which arrived safely in Lancaster, sixty-three miles distant, a little after sun-set. Though always pleasingly amused by the incidents of travelling, and the delightful aspect of rude or rural nature, I could not at this time divert from my mind the most serious reflections on the magnitude and danger of the journey which now lay before me, and which was, indeed, of very uncertain issue.[1]

The lively eagerness which bursts from Nuttall's first entry in the diary of his 1810 expedition, when spring was in his heart as well as round about him, had completely disappeared in the more experienced man of thirty-two starting on a comparable excursion into the wilderness eight and a half years later.

This was Nuttall's third trip to Pittsburgh; now a better acquaintance with the topography, mineralogy, and fossils made the journey even more interesting than before. At Lancaster he abandoned the stage to have more leisure for observations. He also made collections for his nurserymen customers, spending almost a day gathering seeds of *Magnolia acuminata* west of the Alleghany ridge. On the fifteenth of October he wended his way into Pittsburgh, which was repulsive to him by its dirty smoke and bustle although he admired its fine situation and enterprising population. As the Ohio was too low for loaded boats, no opportunities for descending the river presented themselves, and Nuttall renewed his acquaintance with the city. Of a visit to a glass factory which he had seen also in 1810 he wrote,

132

"Mr. Bakewell was now beginning to employ the beautiful white friable sandstone which had been observed near to a branch of the Merrimec by Mr. Bradbury and myself as well as others in the winter of 1809." [2] The date given was a year ahead of the event, as commonly happens in Nuttall's recordings.

On October 21, Nuttall embarked in a skiff which he purchased for six dollars, accompanied by a young man who, for passage and provision, undertook the job of pilot. At Little Grave Creek, one hundred miles below Pittsburgh, where a stop was made to see a famous Indian mound, Nuttall took in another working passenger as far as the Big Sandy. This arrangement allowed him to walk along the shore when he got tired of the boat. He noted the flora with interest, seeing *Tilia heterophylla* Vent. for the first time near LeTart's rapids, enjoyed the bright colors of the autumn foliage, and found a new species of aster in full bloom, *Aster amethystinus* Nutt., now regarded as a recurrent hybrid. He often saw Indian mounds, coal seams, and fossiliferous strata, for he constantly studied the structure of the shores. The travelers sometimes slept on the ground but, because of the cold, preferred the shelter of even the most miserable log cabin. Nuttall continually lamented the improvidence of those settlers who would rather spend their time hunting than become independent by moderate industry. On November 12 "the insolence of my companion rendered our separation absolutely necessary. . . . My impression now was, that this young man was a refugee from justice or deserved infamy, and in all probability I narrowly escaped being robbed." [3]

The next day he "arrived at Cincinnati, and was again gratified by the company of my friend Doctor I. [*sic*] Drake, one of the most scientific men west of the Alleghany mountains," who was then working toward the establishment of a local medical school. Daniel Drake introduced him to Hugh Glenn, erstwhile sutler to the garrison of Arkansas who gave Nuttall valuable information for the journey and letters of introduction. After a few days' stay in Cincinnati, Nuttall continued down river in his boat. He soon passed North Bend and the estate of William Henry Harrison, which he had visited with Charles Wilkins Short in 1816.

At Louisville he was detained for two weeks seeking a means of continuing his journey below the Falls, where something larger than his skiff was necessary. "Wearied by delay, I at length concluded to

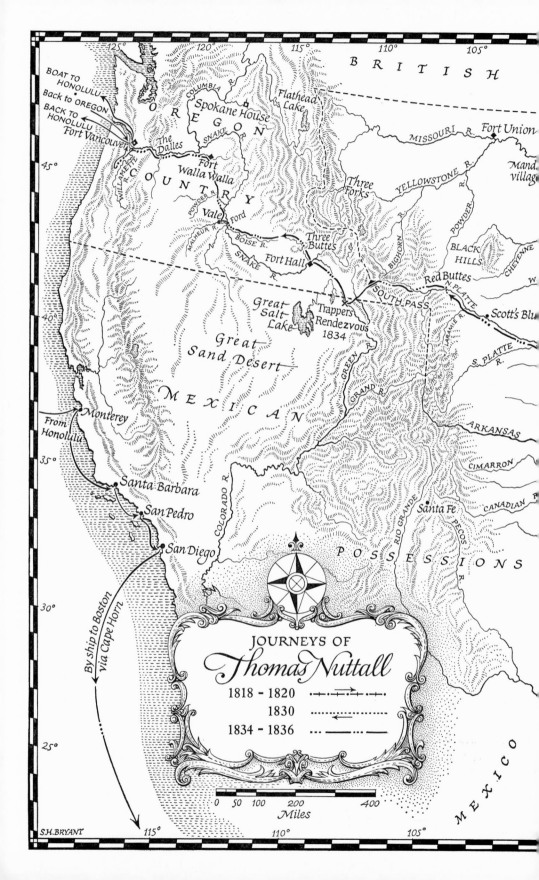

purchase a flat-boat, and freighted it nearly at my own cost, which, for an inexperienced traveller, was certainly an act of imprudence, as the destruction of the boat, which frequently happens would probably have plunged me into penury and distress." [4] After making these arrangements, he wrote to Zaccheus Collins about the main events of his trip and the financial venture he was undertaking.

Louisville, Dec^{br.} 4th 1818

Dear Sir

Circumstances as unexpected as disappointing find me only here instead of the banks of the Arkansaw . . . detained by the extraordinary lowness of the Ohio. — but as I now write the river rises and promises an accelleration [*sic*] to my progress. — . . . My resolution and ardour are the same, and nothing but the most imminent prospect of danger, shall, I hope, deter me from penetrating to the Northern Andes.

. . . I have purchased a boat and freighted her to Natchez. . . . it is this undertaking w^h I know will be very laborious that has induced me on this occasion to draw upon you for the sum of *fifty* dollars through the favour of Doctor G. W. Smith of this place. — Perhaps it was too bold a step, but I hope you will excuse it, as I do not intend to exceed the limits w^h I have prescribed to my expences, but it will equally favour me at this time if you place the above sum to my private account of property in your trust. I have been driven to this speculation, I hope for mutual benefit, almost by force. — [5] . . . I hope you will next hear of me from the banks of the Arkansaw, — in the mean time believe me, your much obliged and devoted humble Servant

Tho^s Nuttall

My remembrance of respect particularly to Tho^s Say, tell him I hear of the steamboat building at St. Louis w^h he is to a [tear in paper] they are hiring hands for the occasion already. I almost envy him, but exertion shall neither be wanting on my part as an individual patronized by philosophers more generous than many princes. — My respects to M^r Vaughan, M. Corea, M^r Haines,[6] and my utmost well wishes detail to D^r Stueve, one of the most disinterested of all my friends, tell him how much I regret that this miserable late season and irksome aquatic conveyance has deprived me of collecting any seeds since I left Pittsburgh. Near Le Tort's Rapids, I saw the *Populus heterophylla* for the first time but could not obtain a single seed.[7] Roots of *Dracocephalum cordatum* mihi [*Meehania cordata* (Nutt.) Britt.], I have planted in D^r Drake's garden. Farewell — [8]

His *Journal* states that on December 7 he left Shippingsport (below the Falls of the Ohio) accompanied by Mr. Godfrey and his son, who were bound for New Orleans.

We floated all night, keeping an alternate watch, and before the expiration of 24 hours, on the 8th, the current alone had carried us without labour near 80 miles! We accompanied another vessel of the same kind, and, for mutual convenience, our boats, according to custom, were lashed together side by side, thus also facilitating our progress by obtaining a greater scope of the current.[9]

During the night of December 12, the flatboat floated by Henderson on the Kentucky shore where Audubon's mercantile undertakings were carrying him to bankruptcy; in the summer just past, Rafinesque had visited him there. After the boat passed the mouth of the Wabash, the boundary between Indiana and Illinois, the cane [*Arundinaria gigantea* (Walt.) Chapm.], which Nuttall had first noticed as he came opposite the Kentucky shore, began to be tall and abundant; the river widened and the forests became gloomy in dense, undisturbed luxuriance.

On the seventeenth they arrived at the mouth of the Ohio and found the Mississippi full of floating ice, which delayed them for a day and a half before they cautiously ventured into it. Nuttall had acquired a copy of the *Pittsburgh Navigator* to assist him in choosing the safest channels of the capricious river. Unfortunately at the end of the first day they were carried onto a miry bar, and it cost Nuttall thirteen dollars, paid to two successive pairs of rascally sharpers ("Yankees"), before the flatboat was free in the morning. Snags and sawyers (submerged trees, the former stationary, the latter bobbing up and down with the current) now became a constant threat, for they occurred in great numbers and in places seemed to range across the full width of the river. Quick and correct choices between channels were often necessary. Suddenly one day, after many narrow escapes, the boat caught on a snag and the sixteen-year-old boy, Edwin Godfrey, was precipitated headlong into the river, together with the steering oar; the boy could swim and was hauled safely on board. The shores of the river were mostly low and clothed with enswamped forests or dense thickets of shrubs or canebrakes, monotonous and dreary, and uninhabited due to annual inundations. The eastern shoreline was briefly relieved of its dull uniformity at the Iron Banks in Kentucky and the four colorful Chickasaw Bluffs in Tennessee. On New Year's Day 1819, they reached the Third Chickasaw Bluff where DeSoto was believed to have crossed the Mississippi and, the third day after, the Fourth Bluff where Memphis was in embryo. Here they ascended the bank to visit Fort Pickering and a neighboring encampment of Chickasaw Indians. On rare grassy banks on the western shore there was an occasional cabin or two. When they got below the mouth of the St. Francis River, Nuttall was "greatly disappointed to meet with such a similarity in the vegetation to that of the middle and northern states."[10] At noon on January 12, the party landed at Mr. M'Lane's Inn near the White River cutoff to the Arkansas River. Here Nuttall was advised to proceed with his

small cargo and flat-boat . . . by the bayou, which communicates between the White and Arkansa rivers. . . . Concluding upon this measure, I hired a man at five dollars to assist me, and parted here with Mr. G——— and son, who soon, to my satisfaction, got a further passage on board a flat-boat. The idea of so soon arriving on the ground which I most immediately intended to explore, did not fail to inspire me with hope and satisfaction.[11]

Nuttall, however, had two almost fruitless days of frustration with the ineffectual drunkard (again denominated a "Yankee") whom he had hired to help him get upstream. The unwieldy boat had to be towed by cordelle against the current around successive sandbars, so, even with a more active assistant, it was several days before it was finally dragged to the Arkansas Post and sold with its cargo to a merchant.

Nuttall had letters of introduction from Mr. Glenn to two of the principal merchants: Mr. Drope and M. Bogy. The latter, a native of Kaskaskia, had long been a resident of the Post. Frederick Notrebe and Eli Lewis, the postmaster, also handled merchandise. Cotton from the neighborhood and peltries from the upper Arkansas were taken in trade and shipped to New Orleans. The little settlement consisted of about a score or so of scattered houses and several stores on two principal streets, Front and Main. The Post, though small, was old for, when Tonti failed to locate LaSalle on the lower Mississippi in 1686, he had left some of his men there among the Quapaw Indians, and the French center had persisted.

The traveler took up his residence with Dr. Robert McKay and felt "once more introduced into the circle of civilization." He was distressed to find that the inhabitants cultivated neither orchards nor kitchen gardens. Already, in January, spring had arrived: it was 67° at midday; cardinals and bluebirds were singing; the ground was white with blossoms of "Alyssum bidentatum"[12] (*Draba brachy-*

*carpa* Nutt.) and innocence; pansies were in bloom about the houses; and the fields of the French settlers were a vivid green. In accompanying the doctor on a trip to shoot wild geese, Nuttall had a view of the Grand Prairie, a vast grassland, extending northwestward for ninety miles, and perceived "vestiges of things that are new and rare."

He wrote to Zaccheus Collins from the Arkansas Post on February 2, 1819:

Dear Sir,

The unexpected delays and disappointments w^h I have met with on this journey still find me but at the outset of my enterprise; in two or three days, however, I shall continue my voyage as far as the Cadron 330 mls. by water from hence, and about 360 from the emboshire of the river. From the Cadron I intend to cross over to the Washita to see the warm springs after w^h I hope without delay to proceed 350 mls. further up to the Fort situated near the mouth of the Pottoe. . . . my intention is to proceed up the Canadian river to the mountains either by land or by water as may be most convenient, and afterwards to descend Red river, when I shall be able to receive any letters with w^h you may honor me at Natchez addressed to some individual who may secure them till my return. The post to this place is extremely uncertain, letters have to go to St. Louis by land thro' an uninhabited wilderness and from thence to Vincennes, etc. and it only leaves this once a month. Nearly all the inhabitants of this place are French, above they are chiefly renegade Americans who have fled from honest society. . . .

Philosophy to mercenary agents and to unlettered men is an incomprehensible bauble. . . . Mr. Glenn a merchant of Cincinnati has, however, at the instance of D^r Drake without my request furnished me with a letter of credit upon the agent. I have already received 250 dollars from you, 200 in Philad^ia and 50 by a note upon Dr. Smith of Louisville, my expenses I limited at 100 more, w^h I perhaps may be obliged to take up at the garrison where I shall probably have to purchase two or three horses and hire a guide for 3 or 4 months, an expense of at least 160 dollars. The time necessary to accomplish this journey as I could wish is still uncertain; while I am in the coming summer engaged in examining the unexplored deserts and mountains of this portion of Louisiana, the lower regions, such as this even, w^h has excited curiosity, must remain a blank for some future naturalist to examine. The wish to explore some portion of the coast of the sea of Mexico, and w^h I could do at an inconsiderable expence, induces me to beg of you, if possible, to make some arrangements for a more extended enquiry. I crave from those my generous patrons of the Philos Soc^ty nothing more than that w^h I have already stipulated, it is to your kindness that I now appeal for more extensive resources. — ? Could you by the approach of the next winter afford me a draft on some person at Natchez for the interest of the money in your trust? upon this, I think,

I can probably manage to subsist another season while leisurely examining the interesting Flora of the contiguous Gulf. I am well satisfied that this season would prove no less interesting in Botany than my most extended researches over the deserts of the Arkansa. I regret that an interchange of communication on this subject and every advice, prior to my arrival at Natchez is rendered impossible. In case of my decease, or otherwise, I leave my inconsiderable collections up to this place in the care of Doctor Makay to be forwarded to Natchez by the first convenient opportunity to Samuel Postlethwaite, Esq<sup>r</sup>

Remember me to D<sup>r</sup> Stüeve, to my intimate friend Thos Say, Mr. Le Seuer, Mr. Ord, Mr. J. Vaughan, Mr. Haines, his excellency J. Correa, Mrs. McMahon. Will you be so kind as to take up all letters remaining for me in the office and instruct Mr. Dobson to collect as soon as convenient my outstanding accounts with the booksellers so that the proceeds may be placed out at interest. In a private drawer in my writing-desk — left at the university? or with you? are some bills w<sup>h</sup> Mr. Say or Mr. Hollingsworth of Race Street will collect for me.[13] — You will say, and that with justice, that all my communications are of a sinister nature, yet it is truly my ambition to be distinguished as the servant of the public. I have laboured hard without sincerely repining, and have exercised what would be to me a mortifying economy with no other view than to ensure pecuniary success to my honourable mission. I therefore look forward to every consequence with calmness satisfied that what I have done has been executed with a sincere desire to promote the honourable expedition so generously confided to me.

Believe me your most sincere and humble servant.[14]

Nuttall wanted to get transportation for his baggage to the Cadron so that he might be free to walk thither across the Great Prairie but, not being able to make such an arrangement, he set out on February 26 with a party in a large skiff. Settlements of one or a few families were not many miles apart on the north bank of the river, and on the south bank were scattered villages of the Quapaws. March 4 was memorable to Nuttall because of the milk and butter served at Mr. Kirkendale's and the meeting there with Ha-kat-ton, the principal chief of the Quapaws. He showed Nuttall a treaty under which his people had sold land to the United States the previous autumn; William Clark and Auguste Chouteau had signed for the United States. A week or so later, after Nuttall had joined Mr. Drope on his large trading boat to continue up the river, they met Nathaniel Pryor, Sergeant of the Lewis and Clark Expedition, descending with a cargo of peltries collected among the Osages. Pryor had resigned from the United States Army in 1815, with the rank of Captain, to engage in the Indian trade. A few miles east of Little Rock, where a few families were living on each bank, the boat passed an ancient war and hunting path which connected St. Louis with the Hot Springs and Natchitoches. Nuttall identified this as the route DeSoto and La Salle followed under Indian guidance. He walked southward on the track as far as Mount Prairie: "on the road to the springs, also, I have obtained specimens of a dark grey amphibolic rock. . . ."[15] Here the river passed through hills clothed with red cedars and ferns, a great pleasure to Nuttall after his months of travel through vast tracts of alluvial lands. He mentions also hereabouts various organic impressions, carnelian pebbles and chert, and continually remarks on ecology and the composition of the soil. About fifty miles further up the Arkansas, at the Cadron, an "imaginary plot" with five or six resident families, Nuttall found a new species of *Eriogonum* (*E. *longifolium*), an American genus whose large size he had predicted, *Petalostemum *multiflorum* and *Phacelia *hirsuta*; thereafter the harvest of undescribed species and genera became abundant.

Mr. Drope decided to go no further up the river than the Dardanelle settlement in the Cherokee lands, 120 miles below the garrison at Belle Point (later Fort Smith), which was Nuttall's first objective. From April 9 to 20, Nuttall remained at the house of Walter Webber, a metis, a chief of the Cherokees acting as an Indian trader, "possessing a decently furnished and well provided house, several negro slaves, well cleared, and well fenced farm; and both himself and his nephew read, write and speak English." While there Nuttall made a drawing of Magazine Mountain to the south which reminded him of Pendle Hill, visible from his native village in Yorkshire.

Nuttall was pleased to see there Reuben Lewis, who had been his host at Fort Mandan and was now United States Agent for the Cherokees. Nuttall gathered from him a full account of the tribe, who were too proud to disclose to a stranger their humiliating experiences. He constantly took pains to ascertain as much as possible of Indian traditions and ancient customs and pondered on the impact of the European cultures to which they had been subjected.

Nuttall finally arrived at Fort Smith on April 24 in the boat of two Frenchmen whom he had engaged to transport him. He wrote to Collins that "mountains as considerable as those of the Allighanys [sic] and of the very same structure traverse the country of the Arkansa from the Little Rock to this place. . . ." [16] The site of the Fort, on a point of elevated land on the south bank of the Arkansas immediately below the mouth of the Poteau, was commanding and picturesque. Major Stephen Long had selected the location in the fall of 1817. Major William Bradford (1771–1826), the Commandant of the garrison, was at first perplexed by Nuttall's equivocal status, a civilian without credentials from the State Department. Nuttall had already been warned by his friends at the Arkansas Post that government accrediting was more or less indispensable for his penetration into the Indian country which lay beyond the Fort, but he was fortunate in winning over the officer and received from him every assistance in carrying on his work.

The surgeon at the Fort, Dr. Thomas Russell (1793–1819), proved a delightful companion on collecting trips over the spring meadows where in a few weeks Nuttall collected about a hundred new herbs [17] including *Nemastylis geminiflora, *Callirhoë digitata, *Nemophila phacelioides, Collinsia *violacea, and Verbena *bipinnatifida. Finding one unknown species is the source of a rare sense of exaltation; surrounded by such quantities, Nuttall must have been in transports of ecstasy. Russell, a young Bay Stater from Salem, the only son of a widow, Nuttall described as "a gentleman, and accomplished scholar, and a sincere admirer of the simple beauties of the field of nature." [18] After he had graduated from Brown University, Russell attended the Medical School of the University of Pennsylvania (M.D., 1814) where he presumably took courses with Benjamin Smith Barton, John Redman Coxe, and Caspar Wistar, who were well known to Nuttall, as was one of Russell's classmates Franklin Bache (a great-grandson of Benjamin Franklin), Recording Secretary of the Academy of Natural Sciences.[19] Unfortunately Russell died of a prevailing fever four months from the day Nuttall met him. He "sleeps obscurely in unhallowed earth," but his name is remembered in Nuttall's Monarda russeliana.

In mid-May Major Bradford, accompanied by six soldiers and two Cherokees, set out for the Red River to order white settlers off land granted to the Osage Indians. Nuttall was invited to accompany the party and thus had a splendid opportunity to view a large tract of country in the present State of Oklahoma during the flowering season. The route started up the Poteau and crossed rough and hilly terrain (Winding Stair or Mazern Mountains) to the waters of the

Kiamichi River, a branch of the Red. Deer, bear, and bison were abundant along their way, and ticks were troublesome. On the sixth day the party reached the Red River 1100 miles above its confluence with the Mississippi.

The people appeared but ill prepared for the unpleasant official intelligence of their ejectment. Some who had cleared considerable farms were thus unexpectedly thrust out into the inhospitable wilderness. I could not but sympathise with their complaints, notwithstanding the justice and propriety of the requisition. Would it had always been the liberal policy of the Europeans to act with becoming justice, and to reciprocate the law of nations with the unfortunate natives! [20]

The company remained three full days on the Red River till the morning of May 26, when preparations were begun for the return which was to start early the next morning from Mr. Styles's. Nuttall lingered behind on the last full day to continue collecting the new plants growing on the "enchanting prairies" and never again rejoined the party. Following the wrong trail he went miles out of the way and was overtaken by darkness while still four miles from the rendezvous; in the morning several hours were lost in locating his horse, which had wandered away. He arrived at a deserted camp too late to overtake the group and "dared not to venture alone and unprepared through such a difficult and mountainous wilderness." Surrounded by extensive stands of handsome new species he was not too much disconcerted by his situation although it was nineteen days before he was able to leave. He wrote appreciatively of the milk and butter served in the Styles's household and rapturously about the flora.

The singular appearance of these vast meadows, now so profusely decorated with flowers, as seen from a distance, can scarcely be described. Several large circumscribed tracts were perfectly gilded with millions of the flowers of *Rudbeckia amplexicaulis*, bordered by other irregular snow-white fields of a new species of *Coriandrum*. . . .
[June] 6th. To-day I went five or six miles to collect specimens of the *Centaurea* [*C. americana* Nutt.], which as being the only species of this numerous genus indigenous to America, had excited my curiosity. . . .
In my solitary, but amusing rambles over these delightful prairies, I now, for the first time in my life, notwithstanding my long residence and peregrinations in North America, hearkened to the inimitable notes of the mockingbird (*Turdus polyglottus*). After amusing itself in ludicrous imitations of other birds, perched on the topmost bough of a spreading elm, it at length broke forth into a strain of melody the most wild, varied,

and pathetic, that ever I had heard from any thing less than human. In the midst of these enchanting strains, which gradually increased to loudness, it oftentimes flew upwards from the topmost twig, continuing its note as if overpowered by the sublimest ecstasy.[21]

"Near the banks of the Red River, about the confluence of the Kiamesha" he commonly saw the "conspicuously beautiful" scissortailed flycatcher which he had already observed nesting in an elm near Fort Smith.[22]

On the 8th I went down to the Red River settlement, to inquire concerning some company, which I had heard of, on my returning route to the Arkansa; and, on conferring together, we concluded to take our departure on Sunday next, a day generally chosen by these hunters and voyagers on which to commence their journeys. . . .

14th. According to our appointment, my traveling companions called upon me, and, although about the middle of a Sunday afternoon, it was not possible to persuade them to wait for Monday morning. So, without almost any supply of provision, I was obliged to take a hasty departure from my kind host and family, who, knowing from the first my destitute situation, separated from pecuniary resources, could scarcely be prevailed upon to accept the trifling pittance which I accidentally possessed. I shall always remember, with feelings of gratitude, the sincere kindness and unfeigned hospitality, which I so seasonably experienced from these poor and honest people, when left in the midst of the wilderness.[23]

The return took seven days of arduous travel for, in the early part of the journey, a roundabout route was chosen by Nuttall's three companions to avoid the roughest of the ridges.

The trip was gratifyingly productive of new species, including some of the loveliest flora of Texas, south of the Red River (then a part of Mexico). On the Red River prairies he first saw *Maclura in abundance and he found a new elm, Ulmus *crassifolia.[24] Some of the new herbaceous species collected were: Habenaria leucophaea (Nutt.) Gray, Eriogonum *annum, Streptanthus *maculatus, Vicia *ludoviciana, Andrachne phyllanthoides (Nutt.) Muell. Arg., Oenothera *linifolia, O. *rhombipetala, the lovely pink O. *speciosa, O. *triloba, Ptilimnium nuttallii (DC.) Britt., Spermolepis echinata (Nutt.) Heller, S. inermis (Nutt.) Math. & Const., Forestiera *pubescens, Sabatia *campestris, Physostegia intermedia (Nutt.) Engelm. & Gray, Scutellaria ovata Hill var. versicolor (Nutt.) Fern., Castilleja purpurea (Nutt.) G. Don, Penstemon *Cobaea, P. *tubaeflorus, Achillea *lanulosa, Centaurea *americana, Coreopsis *tinctoria, Filago

*prolifera* (Nutt.) Britt., *Marshallia* *caespitosa, Rudbeckia* *bicolor,
and *R.* *maxima.*

Nuttall stayed with the garrison at Belle Point (Fort Smith) until
July 6 when he was able to proceed 130 miles further up the Arkansas
in the boat of M. Bogy who, as agent for Mr. Drope, was going to
the trading houses near the mouth of the Verdigris which he and
Nathaniel Pryor were manning. The Verdigris enters the Arkansas
only a few hundred yards west of the Grand (Neosho) River; the
lower courses of these northern tributaries form an acute angle. Nuttall wandered over the plains between them in the company of Pryor
or one of the hunters or on solitary botanizing trips. With two young
companions in a canoe he got about fifty miles up the Grand River
to visit a salt works. There he learned of an incident which filled him
doubly with horror: the salt works were idle, for the owner had been
murdered and scalped by his covetous partner and two employees
who had made off. One of the latter proved to be a man Nuttall had
attempted to hire as a guide at the Cadron! Such barbarity so near
at hand was a shock that gave rise to melancholy reflections mixed
with relief that he had escaped, perhaps, a similar fate. Since his
companions were continuing up the Grand River, Nuttall returned
alone across country through grass three feet deep, keeping a southwest course by compass for about thirty miles and sleeping one night
in the open without fire, food, or water.[25] Shortly after this excursion
an "irregular remittent fever" attacked the post, and he was laid low
by fever, chills, and an excruciating headache.

An Osage trace extended through more or less open country to
St. Louis about three hundred miles away. At the end of the eighteenth century the tribe was living near the confluence of the Osage
and Missouri Rivers, and the Chouteaus profited from trade with
them under an exclusive grant from the Spanish governor. But when
the Chouteaus lost the monopoly of the Missouri trade for a period
of years to Manuel Lisa, Pierre Chouteau persuaded a large part of
the tribe to move south to the Grand River. From the southernmost
Osage village, about sixty miles from the mouth of the Verdigris,
the Indians not uncommonly walked to the trading post in a day.
During Nuttall's stay there from July 14 to August 11, he saw a
great deal of the Osages, who were the first nation of plains Indians
he had encountered on his trip up the Missouri in 1811. He continuously made observations on their character and customs, which

he recorded in his *Journal* along with appalling tales of acts of cruel barbarism inflicted on white men. More than once he was the victim of their dexterous thievery, being robbed of his only penknife and a pocket microscope, and almost losing a mare he had just purchased. Some of his comments of this period show a more practical vein of thought than his earlier reflections on the Indian tribes. He wrote:

Surrounded by a fertile country, the Indian . . . finds it difficult to obtain subsistence, trespasses upon his neighbours, lives in insecurity, and in implacable enmity with those of his own race. A stranger to our ideas of honour, he destroys his enemies by the meanest stratagems, and levels, in his revenge, all distinctions of age and sex. . . . the Indians should . . . be made sensible of the impropriety and illegality of executing summary and unlimited punishment upon the citizens of the United States, who are found travelling or hunting in their country. . . . If the frontier garrisons are not capable of effecting this beneficial purpose, for what were they established? but could not even this be better executed by the governor and the militia of the territory, than by the arbitrary commander and the soldiers of a garrison? [26]

TRY FOR THE ROCKIES. The chief objective of Nuttall's Arkansas journey was to reach the Rocky Mountains. Pike's Expedition had revealed that the Rockies extend farthest east on the Arkansas drainage. To avoid the circuitous course of the main stream, Nuttall determined on going up the Cimarron, which flows into the Arkansas from the west about ninety miles above the Verdigris. He joined forces with an experienced trapper named Lee, and on August 11 they set out on horseback to cut across country south of the Arkansas. The third day they followed a tributary of the North Fork of the Canadian River and in that general area they remained for some time because Nuttall suffered a relapse of the remittent fever and became desperately ill, being often delirious, burned by fever and by the hot sun which penetrated the thin forest, chilled to the bone when the fever abruptly left him, rarely able to eat such food as was available, and fainting in the saddle when it was necessary to move camp. Due to drought, the water in the stream beds was often stagnant or saline. Green blowflies and their maggots, occurring in incredible numbers, annoyed them, ruined their meat, and menaced their horses. Lee believed that they should go back to the Verdigris before his companion's increasing weakness made return impossible, but Nuttall could not bear such a disappointment and argued for delay while death hovered over him. Finally Lee's horse became so incapacitated that even return became a problem, and the argument was dropped. Every few days the camp was shifted a few miles for the sake of Lee's beaver trapping. After Nuttall's condition had sunk to "a kind of lethargy, almost the prelude of death" which afforded "an ominous relief from anxiety and pain," the weather became cooler, and he recovered sufficiently to move by small stages towards the Cimarron. When he and Lee reached it, however, they were disquieted by finding the traces of numerous Osages. Before long they were forced to give up the expedition by the loss of Lee's horse in quicksands. As soon as Lee had constructed a one-man canoe from a cottonwood, which in that region scarcely grew large enough for the purpose, the enforced retreat began, Lee on the river, Nuttall riding along the hot beaches formed by the lowness of the water. The river was a tepid brine, and there was little food although Nuttall began to have a slight appetite. However the sufferer's spirits were temporarily buoyed by the acquisition of several new botanical species, among them "a very curious *Gaura,* and undescribed species of *Donia,* of *Eriogonum,* of *Achyranthes, Arundo* and *Gentian.*" What a short advance they had made up the Cimarron became apparent when they reached the Arkansas at noon on the second day of the descent. Soon smoke from Osage fires was visible in all directions, and inevitably, despite all precautions, an encounter occurred.

[Sept.] 11th. To-day . . . it became impossible to avoid the discovery of the Indians, as two or three families were encamped along the borders of the river. They ran up to us with a confidence which was by no means reciprocal. One of the men was a blind chief, not unknown to Mr. Lee, who gave him some tobacco, with which he appeared to be satisfied. About the encampment there were a host of squaws, who were extremely impertinent. An old woman . . . told me, with an air of insolence, that I must give her my horse for her daughter to ride on; I could walk; — that the Osages were numerous, and could soon take it from me. . . . When we were about to depart, they all ran to the boat, to the number of 10 or 12, showing symptoms of mischief, and could not be driven away. They held on to the canoe, and endeavoured to drag it aground. Mr. Lee tried in vain to get rid of them, although armed with a rifle. At length, they got to pilfering our baggage; even the blind chief, who had showed us a commendatory certificate which he had obtained at St. Louis, also turned thief on the occasion. We had not got out of the sight of these depredators, before another fellow came after us on the run, in order to claim my horse, insisting that it was his, and I could no way satisfy his unfounded demand, but by giving him one of my blankets.[27]

Two Indians on the shore covertly followed them until dark so they kept on their way during the night "amidst the horrors of a thunder storm, the most gloomy and disagreeable situation I ever experienced." Frequent crossings of the Arkansas were necessary from which Nuttall emerged drenched and shivering with cold in his leather garments. The next day the travelers parted, for they were nearing the post, and Lee made better progress in his boat than Nuttall's horse could make on the sandy beaches. On the two nights that Nuttall camped alone he was "mortified" to be unable to start a fire although he had the means of obtaining it. On September 15, he

arrived at the trading establishment of Mr. Bougie [Bogy], an asylum, which probably, at this time rescued me from death. My feet and legs were so swelled, in consequence of weakness and exposure to extreme heat and cold, that it was necessary to cut off my pantaloons, and at night both my hands and feet were affected by the most violent cramp.

I remained about a week with Mr. Bougie, in a very feeble state, again visited by fever, and a kind of horrific delirium, which perpetually dwelt upon the scene of past sufferings. I now took the opportunity of descending to the garrison with an engagée, but continued in a state of great debility, my hands and feet still violently and frequently affected with spasms.

In about five days slow descending, from the feebleness of my invalid companion, we arrived at the garrison.[28]

The unfortunate expedition — a living nightmare — had endured for five weeks. At Fort Smith, Nuttall found that Dr. Russell had died of "a nervous fever," as did also one of two missionaries to the Osages who had recently arrived. "From July to October, the ague and bilious fever spread throughout the territory in a very unusual manner"; a hundred of the Cherokees died of it. Nuttall remained at the garrison in extreme debility until October 16. In the spring Major Bradford had invited him to spend the winter at the Fort.[29] This had then seemed an engaging prospect but now sickness had racked his spirits as well as his body, and he seemed bent on getting himself and his precious collections and notes away from the region as promptly as could be managed; still weak, shaken by horrid memories by day and dreams by night, he felt no temptation to linger. He moved on down river by stages as opportunity offered. His happiest move was away from the Cadron where his aversion to the popular diversions isolated him conspicuously from the only society available. He wrote:

The only tavern, very ill provided, was . . . crowded with all sorts of company. It contained only two tenantable rooms built of logs, with hundreds of crevices still left open, notwithstanding the severity of the season.

Every reasonable and rational amusement appeared here to be swallowed up in dram-drinking, jockeying, and gambling: even our landlord, in defiance of the law, was often the ring-leader of what it was his duty to suppress. Although I have been through life perfectly steeled against games of hazard, neither wishing to rob nor be robbed, I felt somewhat mortified to be thus left alone, because of my unconquerable aversion to this vortex of swindling and idleness. . . .

On the 4th of January, 1820, after waiting about a month for an opportunity of descending, I now embraced the favourable advantage of proceeding in the boat of Mr. Barber, a merchant of New Orleans, to whose friendship and civility I am indebted for many favours.[30]

In December 1820, Audubon came up to the Arkansas Post and there saw Mr. Barbour, an old acquaintance at Pittsburgh. He told Audubon that "he had for Several years past gone up to the Osage Nation about 900 miles and that his Last Voyage he fell in with Nuttall the Botanist and had him on board for 4 Months."[31]

At the Arkansas Post, Nuttall again had to change boats, which gave him three or four days to collect roots of desirable garden plants on the prolific prairie. While he had been up the river, Congress had created Arkansas Territory, cutting it off of Missouri Territory, and the Post had become the capital. Government officials were already in action. Nuttall saw Governor James Miller, leaving the keel boat decorated with his "I'll try, Sir" emblem in which he had recently arrived from Pittsburgh. The botanist reached the Mississippi in the barge of M. Notrebe and transferred to a flatboat going down river.

At Natchez he stayed over for four or five days. In 1811 after his memorable sojourn in the Mandan country on the upper Missouri, Nuttall had stopped briefly at this important river town. Now he called on Samuel Postlethwaite and his wife, the daughter of that William Dunbar who at President Jefferson's behest had made an exploratory ascent of the Red and Ouachita Rivers late in 1804 with Dr. George Hunter. Dunbar, who died in 1810, had contributed scientific papers to the *Transactions* of the American Philosophical Society of which he was a Fellow. At the suggestion of John Vaughan, Nuttall had forwarded his first Arkansas collections to Philadelphia by way of New Orleans in care of Postlethwaite who, like his late father-in-law, had scientific interests. He gave Nuttall much information concerning local agriculture, horticulture, and ethnology. Nuttall was pleased by the friendly hospitality he met with and impressed by the ease and affluence of the community.

Possibly he also visited Major Nathaniel A. Ware, a Corresponding Member of the Academy of Natural Sciences of Philadelphia, who lived in Washington, Mississippi, about five miles from Natchez. Major Ware had been active for many years in Territorial affairs, and Nuttall learned from him much about the history of the Natchez Indians and the abundance of aboriginal remains in the vicinity. However their conversations could have taken place later in Philadelphia.

South of Natchez the prosperous community of Bayou Sara and great sugar plantations were conspicuous.[32] The thought of the hundreds of slaves owned by large planters, a system that reduced each Negro to nothing more than a money-making machine, was revolting to Nuttall. Moreover the resulting fortunes seemed to him to be frivolously expended.

How little wealth has contributed towards human improvement, appears sufficiently obvious throughout this adventitiously opulent section of the Union. Time appears here only made to be lavished in amusement. Is the uncertainty of human life so great in this climate, as to leave no leisure for any thing beyond dissipation? The only serious pursuit, appears to be the amassing and spending of that wealth which is wrung from the luckless toil of so many unfortunate Africans, doomed to an endless task, which is even entailed upon their posterity. "O slavery, though thousands in all ages have drank of thee, still thou art a bitter draught!" [33]

New Orleans, where he arrived on February 18, 1820, was to him only a concentration of the evils he had discerned along the river:

Science and rational amusement is as yet but little cultivated in New Orleans. There are only three or four booksellers to supply this large city and populous neighborhood. The French inhabitants, intermingled with the African castes in every shade of colour, scarcely exceed them, generally speaking, in mental acquirements. Every thing like intellectual improvement appears to be vitiated in its source, nothing exists to inspire emulation, and learning, as in the West Indies, has no existence beyond the mechanism of reading and writing. Something like a museum was begun in the city a few years ago, but by a protean evolution it has been transformed into a coffee-house for gambling. In another part of the city, an assemblage of specimens of the fine arts, busts, medallions, mosaics and paintings, is also associated with the dice and bottle.[34]

In the closing pages of his published *Journal* Nuttall makes comparisons between life in Louisiana and the West Indies which strongly hint that his present return to the eastern seaboard or his passage to England late in 1811, involved stopovers in the islands long enough to permit excursions on shore. However years later he clearly stated that, although he had glimpsed Cuba from a distance, he had never been ashore in the West Indies.[35]

When Nuttall reached civilized areas he should have congratulated himself that he not only had survived his illness and was spared murder at the hands of renegade whites and avaricious Indians but also that he had found a few hundred new species in the Southwest. However, it is probable that his mind dwelt more on disappointments and disillusions than on blessings. His hopes of reaching the Rockies had been dashed and, more devastating, he had learned beyond question that by himself he was unable to cope with the immensities of the West. He could not shoot well enough to secure food; he could not swim; he had even been unable to start fires to warm himself or cook food. The expense of a guide was beyond his financial ability, and in any case a party of two, hampered by ineptitude, was inadequate to deal with the endless threats and dangers of a half continent of wilderness infested by rapacious, bloodthirsty Indians and wild beasts not yet intimidated by rifles. He had thus far been unsuccessful in efforts to ally himself with government expeditions. It now seemed that his ambition to collect in the Rockies might well prove vain. From this period the eager enthusiasm of his early years disappears from his letters, and disillusionment, tinged with bitterness, sometimes creeps in.

> Erloschen sind die heitern Sonnen,
> Die meiner Jugend Pfad erhellt;
> Die Ideale sind zerronnen,
> Die einst das trunkne Herz geschwellt;
> Er ist dahin, der süsse Glaube
> An Wesen, die mein Traum gebar
> Der rauhen Wirklichkeit zum Raube,
> Was einst so schön, so göttlich war.[36]

CHAPTER 10

# PHILADELPHIA

## 1820–1822

Where there is to be found one discoverer we have one thousand compilers. — Linnaeus

ACADEMIC LABORS. Nuttall was back in Philadelphia about the end of April 1820. In returning he probably disembarked at a southern port because personal observations of the Richmond coal mines appear in a paper that he delivered to the Academy shortly after his arrival.[1] He attended a meeting of the Academy of Natural Sciences on May 2 and of the American Philosophical Society on May 5 and promptly became immersed in their activities. For about two years the meetings of these two societies were clearing posts for Nuttall's interests, and their minutes are a guide to many of his occupations. His absences from meetings probably indicate periods when he was away on short trips which he indubitably was making to collect minerals and plants. By the end of May, on motion of Reuben Haines, he had received permission for the use of the Hall of the Academy for a course of botanical lectures, had been appointed to a small committee to confer concerning the future printing of the *Journal* of the Academy, and had presented a geological paper to the Academy which occupied two meetings.[2]

David Landreth, Jr., in 1858 recalled that Nuttall "delivered a hugely successful course of lectures on botany at the old hall of the Academy of Natural Sciences in Arch Street, at which I recollect seeing that able botanist, the Abbe Corréa De Serra, the Portuguese Ambassador and Perpetual Secretary of the Academy of Sciences of Lisbon."[3] The next spring, Nuttall again gave a course of public lectures in botany; in 1821 the lectures started on May 1 and were held at 4:00 on Tuesdays and Saturdays. Tradition reports that he lectured also in Germantown.

Publication by the Academy was stagnant: no issue of the *Journal* had appeared since that of December 1818, the last number of the first volume; the lapse was doubtless due to the absence of the two Thomases, Say and Nuttall. Nuttall served on the Publication Committee of the Academy from November 1820 through 1822, the span of time in which the second volume of the *Journal* appeared, and was also on the Botanical Committee for 1822. He was frequently appointed to the committees of three who passed on the suitability for publication of papers read to the Academy, judging papers dealing with minerals, *Mollusca,* spiders, fish, and mammals.

Nuttall was eager to learn the details of the collapse of the Yellowstone Expedition, rumors of which had reached him. The military section of the expedition was so mismanaged in 1818 that Congress refused to vote the funds necessary for its continuance. The scientists, however, in the summer of 1819, proceeded up the Missouri in the stern-wheel steamboat *Western Engineer,* although some chose an overland trek for the latter part of the journey, and wintered at "Engineers' Cantonment," five miles below Council Bluffs and a mile north of Fort Lisa, the trading post that Manual Lisa established among the Omahas after the War of 1812. William Baldwin, unable to continue on the trip, was left at Franklin, Missouri, where he died of pulmonary tuberculosis on August 31. Baldwin's field experience and critical mind would have substantially enriched American botany had he been able to write his projected miscellaneous sketches of Georgia and east Florida. He published only two brief papers in addition to the few new species he described in the first volume of Elliott's *Sketch.*[4]

Major Long returned to the East to spend the winter and presided at the February 15th meeting of the Academy. At Washington he received new instructions for his party: they were to carry out a limited exploratory trip in the Southwest. Long engaged Dr. Edwin James to replace Baldwin as botanist and to take over the work of Jessup, who had resigned as geologist. James, a young Vermonter, a graduate of Middlebury, was recommended for the position by Major John LeConte of the Topographical Engineers, a naturalist by avocation, and by Dr. John Torrey, a young botanist of New York City. In the late spring, Long's party of scientists and artists with

Captain John R. Bell, U.S.A., and a few enlisted men proceeded to the South Platte and followed it to the eastern edge of the Rockies; there they turned south to explore the courses of the Arkansas and Red Rivers. Their route crossed the present States of Nebraska, Colorado, Oklahoma, and Arkansas. James and two soldiers made the first ascent of Pike's Peak, but no attempt was made to follow the Arkansas to its source beyond the "Royal Gorge." The party split for the return: Long's section, which was to have followed the Red River, went down the Canadian Fork of the Arkansas by mistake; the other group under Captain Bell went down the main river, and the two sections rejoined at Fort Smith on September 13, 1820. Of the naturalists, Say accompanied Bell, and Edwin James and Titian Peale were with Long. So, unexpectedly, "the Yellowstone Expedition" included Nuttall's southwestern course within theirs and garnered abundant specimens more widely than he.

In justice to Nuttall it is important to emphasize that the visit of Long's Expedition to the Arkansas was unexpected and coincidental. Some contemporaries hastily concluded that Nuttall hurried ahead to anticipate the expedition on its chosen grounds: Darlington and Baldwin exchanged such suspicions in February 1819.[5] The case was far otherwise. Nuttall had been eager to visit the Southwest from the time of his ascent of the Missouri, and he was returning from the Arkansas before the objective of Long's party was deflected from the upper Missouri to the Southwest.

Nuttall brought back miscellaneous zoological material. Say named one of his fossil shells from the Red River "in a very perfect state of preservation," *Gryphaea corrugata*,[6] and assigned two species to *Ostrea*. All of Nuttall's Arkansas insects went to Say, who described the new species in their appropriate orders; as early as 1822, Say read a paper on the *Diptera*, which included *Pangonia incisuralis*; other Arkansas species collected by Nuttall were still appearing in posthumous papers of Say — *Mutilla contracta* of the *Hymenoptera* and *Ips vittata* of the *Coleoptera*.[7] Fish collected from the Arkansas River, ponds, and the Gulf of Mexico were discussed by Le Sueur in two papers read at the Academy meeting on December 19, 1820; one species from ponds near New Orleans, brilliantly colored in reddish-golden tints (*Mollienisia latipinna*, which established a new genus), has become a highly valued aquarium fish; one of two new species of flying fish from the Gulf was named *Exocetus nuttallii*.[8]

Nuttall's patrons urged him to write an account of his Arkansas trip from the full daily record which he had kept. It was doubtless pointed out to him that, since Long's Expedition was returning through the region that he had scientifically explored, it was important that his description of his travels should precede rather than follow the narrative of the far longer and more ambitious undertaking. Although he was not eager to publish such a volume (for he had been disappointed and chagrined by the limited sale of the *Genera*) he set about the task forthwith and worked painstakingly through a year and a half getting it into final form. His footnotes and comments and the long Appendix giving accounts of aboriginal tribes on the Mississippi show extensive reading in a great variety of sources ranging from Herodotus, through the histories by Garcilaso de la Vega (1537–1616), Tonti (ca. 1650–1704), and DuPratz (d. 1775), the travels of Charlevoix (1682–1761) and von Humboldt (1769–1859), and accounts of the Indians by Adair (1735–1775), Colden (1688–1776), and Heckewelder (1743–1823) down to the report of Hunter and Dunbar's ascent of the Red River in 1804–1805, and oral information obtained from members of the Long Expedition. The text is rich in continual observations of the flora, fauna, geology, economy, and residents of the entire route. The Preface was written in November 1821, and the copyright is dated November 6. The volume, entitled *A Journal of Travels into the Arkansa Territory during the year 1819, with occasional Observations on the Manners of the Aborigines,* contained five engravings of scenes along the river drawn by the author and a map of the Arkansas River especially prepared by H. I. Tanner.

"The humble narrative of a journey, chiefly undertaken for the investigation of the natural history of a region hitherto unexplored" is dedicated to the four men who financed it — Corréa, Collins, Maclure, and Vaughan — with apologies for

the imperfect performance of the gratifying task which your liberality had imposed, but which was rendered almost abortive by the visitations of affliction.

If, in so tiresome a volume of desultory remarks, you should meet with some momentary gratification, some transient amusement or ray of information, the author will receive the satisfaction of not having laboured entirely in vain.

The tone of the Preface suffers an unfortunate change from the tactfulness of the dedication. It states that the text is not addressed to those

. . . who vaguely peruse the narratives of travellers for pastime or transitory amusement . . . a taste which has no criterion but passing fashion, which spurns everything without charm of novelty and luxury of embellishment. . . .

Had I solely consulted my own gratification, the present volume would probably never have been offered to the public. . . . I may safely say, that hitherto, so far from writing for emolument, I have sacrificed both time and fortune to it. For nearly *ten* years I have travelled throughout America,[9] principally with a view of becoming acquainted with some favourite branches of its natural history. I have had no other end in view than personal gratification, and in this I have not been deceived, for innocent amusement can never leave room for regret. To converse, as it were, with nature, to admire the wisdom and beauty of creation, has ever been, and I hope ever will be, to me a favourite pursuit. To communicate to others a portion of the same amusement and gratification has been the only object of my botanical publications; the most remote idea of personal emolument arising from them, from every circumstance connected with them, could not have been admitted into calculation. I had a right, however, reasonably to expect from Americans a degree of candour, at least equal to that which my labours had met with in Europe. But I have found, what, indeed, I might have reason to expect from human nature, often, instead of gratitude, detraction and envy. With such, I stoop not to altercate; my endeavours, however imperfect, having been directed to the public good; and I regret not the period I have spent in roaming over the delightful fields of Flora, in studying all her mysteries and enigmas, if I have, in any instance, been useful to her cause, or opened to the idle wanderer one fruitful field for useful reflection.

Although the *Journal of Travels* was not a success financially (copies sold at $2.00), it was well received. It was favorably reviewed at considerable length in the *North American Review* by Jacob Bigelow, who praised Nuttall's diverse and unique contributions to American science and stressed his international reputation.[10] A review in the *Literary Gazette* of London recognized Nuttall's relationship to the Caxton Press of Liverpool; it closed with the observation that the merits of Nuttall's volume, "industry, love of science and intelligence, are peculiarly and most commendably his own."[11] George Bancroft in his *History of the United States* (volume I, 1834) referred several times to Nuttall's account of de Soto's route, considering that the author's "opinions are justly entitled to much deference." A present-day geologist[12] finds "very prescient geological observations" in this book. For its personal comments and graphic descriptions it is a valuable record of frontier settlements on the Arkansas in 1819 and a source text for Arkansas and Oklahoma history. Being regarded as "one of the classics of the early frontier," it was reprinted in Thwaites's series of *Early Western Travels*.

A second volume on aboriginal antiquities and Indian languages which was promised in the Preface never appeared. What is more difficult to understand, however, is the long lapse of time before Nuttall published his new Arkansas plants. In 1821–1822 Nuttall read a series of brief papers to the Academy (later published in the *Journal*) describing "some Arkansa plants recently introduced into local gardens": *Coreopsis *tinctoria, Helianthus *petiolaris, Aster oblongifolius* (1818), *Centaurea *americana, Haplopappus ciliatus* (Nutt.) DC. (Donia *ciliata), Palafoxia callosa* (Nutt.) T. & G. (Stevia *callosa), *Nemophila phacelioides, Astragalus nuttallianus* DC. (A. *micranthus), Verbena *bipinnatifida, *Callirhoë digitata*, and four species of *Oenothera* — *linifolia, serrulata* (1818), *speciosa*, and *triloba.*[13] These are plants with striking flowers, the seed of which he had distributed promptly after his return, in some cases at least, gratuitously to nurserymen in Philadelphia, to the Princes of the Linnaean Gardens in Flushing, Long Island, and to customers in England. William Dick, the gardener at the University of Pennsylvania, raised plants for Nuttall, and published *Callirhoë* as Nuttallia in W. P. C. Barton's *Flora of North America.*[14] Dick's "Nuttallia" followed Rafinesque's "Nuttalla" into oblivion. Except for the protective publication of the species distributed to seedsmen, two beautiful species of the *Scrophulariaceae* described in his textbook, a brief paper on two new genera of the *Cruciferae,* and some described and named species sent to Europe for publication, Nuttall presented no taxonomic treatment of his Arkansas collections until 1834. Correspondence reveals his expectations of a far earlier report and in May 1821, the American Philosophical Society voted $30 for the expense of illustrations for the paper which Nuttall was hoping to have soon ready for their *Transactions.*[15] Meanwhile Edwin James's "Catalogue of Plants" collected by the Long Expedition, a list of the species already known, was presented to the American Philosophical Society on August 17, 1821,[16] and John Torrey published three papers on the new species of James's collection from 1823 to 1826, in the *Annals* of the New York Lyceum.

The paper which Nuttall read to the Academy on the geology of the Mississippi Valley so promptly after his return from the Southwest was not published in the *Journal* until January 1821, where it was erroneously stated that it was read in December 1820; the Minutes of the Academy show that it was read seven months earlier at the meetings of May 16 and 23.[17] It presented numerous original observations made from his first arrival in America through his latest journey as well as analyses of the reports of early travelers.

Data submitted as evidence of the extent of the vast central "secondary formation" (essentially what are now called "Paleozoic" rocks) were gathered from the distribution of salt springs extending from Onondaga, the Ohio River system, and the northern Mississippi to the head waters of the Red River; far-flung deposits of gypsum, fluorspar, and coal; the locations of veins of lead that he traced from the Wisconsin River south-southwest through Dubuque and Meramec mines to those on the St. Francis and White Rivers; the occurrence of enormous granitic blocks that he saw strewn for over a hundred miles along the shores of Lake Huron and "the wide extent of granitic gravel-boulders throughout the western states and territories"; the deviation of strata from the horizontal as at the Falls of St. Anthony and the numerous portages on the Ottawa River; and the outcrop of rocks of different composition as at the falls of the Genesee and Niagara.

Of special importance is his correlation of rock strata of North America and Europe. The similarity of the mineral composition and fossiliferous components of certain sedimentary deposits of North America and England was made obvious to him by comparison of his Mississippi River samples with those of the compact mountain limestone of Derbyshire which revealed

not a single dissimilar feature either in regard to composition or organic reliquiae; and I am fully satisfied, that almost every fossil and shell figured and described in the "Petrificata Derbiensia" of Martyn [William Martin, 1809] are to be met with throughout the great calcareous platform of the Mississippi valley. We everywhere perceive the same host of Terebratulites, Alcyonites, and Encrinal vertebrae; the same zoophitic and vegetable impressions, likewise attend the coal formations, and it is only the difference in their elevation above the horizon which in any manner distinguishes the same strata in one country from those of the other.[18]

. . . that immense portion of the Mississippi valley . . . exhibits . . . unequivocal marks of a pelagian origin, its rocks are filled with marine productions of which by far the greater part are now extinct, having disappeared with the ocean that gave them birth. . . . The antiquity of this order of things, apparently anterior to the creation of any other organized beings, is beyond our comprehension. . . .[19]

"Both as the first successful application of modern geological principles in the new world and as the maiden effort, as it proved to be, at world-wide stratigraphical correlation, the event [Nuttall's paper] must ever remain one of the outstanding features in the history of geological science."[20]

Nuttall was presumably familiar with William (Strata) Smith's innovation of dating strata by means of their fossilized contents: he probably visited Smith's exhibit of fossils off the Strand in London (1805–1815) and a copy of Smith's 1817 *Stratigraphical System of Organized Fossils* was in the library of the Academy from 1821. The donor may have loaned it to Nuttall earlier. However, Nuttall had come independently to similar ideas from his own observations. He not only carefully described deposits on the Mississippi belonging to geological periods of the Paleozoic, but he also speculated about younger sedimentary deposits. He collected fossils (*Baculites compressa*) of the Cretaceous on the upper Missouri and noted that among southeastern shells in "floetz limestone" some species occurred "not very dissimilar to the existing species of the coast."

Unhappily his paper was as far ahead of the thoughts of American workers in geology as was his knowledge of the distant West, so his amazing report received no suitable recognition although his observations

antedated by fifteen years Samuel Morton's similar effort on the Tertiaries of our Atlantic coast commonly regarded as the maiden attempt in America along these lines. By two decades they were in advance of the first work of that pioneer paleontologist, Lardner Vanuxem. They anticipated by a full generation the famous investigations of Thomas Conrad and James Hall in New York. Indeed, they were the means of actually and correctly interpreting the true position and biotic relations of the Carbonic rocks of the continental interior a half century before their geologic age was otherwise generally admitted.[21]

The paper reveals unusual powers of observation and a mind highly reflective, synthetic, and philosophic.[22]

At a meeting early in 1822, announcement was made of the gift to the Academy of a copy of *A Description of the Island of St. Michael, Comprising an Account of its Geological Structure, with Remarks on the Other Azores or Western Isles*. The author, Dr. John White Webster (1793–1850), a Boston physician and mineralogical enthusiast, had spent several months in the Azores making detailed observations and included a brief account of the flora in his report.[23] As sailing vessels coming to America usually passed within view of these islands, Nuttall's interest in them was probably already sufficiently awakened to ensure his reading the book.

Nuttall's personal life was enriched at this period by two new friendships. George W. Carpenter (1802–1860), a young assistant to a Philadelphia druggist, and John Torrey (1796–1873) of New York City, with a degree in medicine obtained in 1818 at the College of Physicians and Surgeons, were as different in their personalities as in their formal education but they were both devoted to natural sciences; the former to mineralogy, perhaps largely through Nuttall's influence,[24] the latter primarily to botany, although he spent most of his life teaching chemistry.[25] Like most of the friends Nuttall made in America, these men were appreciably younger than himself, Carpenter by sixteen and a half years and Torrey by ten and a half years. The association between them and Nuttall became close and in the case of Carpenter grew into a warm friendship which lasted to the end. Botanical enthusiasm drew Nuttall and Torrey together until Asa Gray's advent in the field in the 1830s created a disrupting triangular situation.

Torrey had been a strong supporter of the formation of the New York Lyceum of Natural History early in 1817. He worked on a committee appointed to make a list of the plants growing near the city; in 1819 the Lyceum published his resultant "Catalogue of Plants Growing Spontaneously Within Thirty Miles of the City of New York." In the spring of 1818 he went with his friend William Cooper (1798–1864) to botanize in the New Jersey pine barrens famous for residual species of the old Atlantic coastal plain. En route they stopped in Philadelphia armed with a letter of introduction to Zaccheus Collins from John LeConte. After his visit, Torrey started a correspondence with Collins and asked to be put in touch with a young botanical member of the Academy of Natural Sciences with whom he could exchange specimens and opinions.[26] It was perhaps as a delayed outcome of this appeal that over two years later, in the early autumn of 1820, Torrey and Nuttall visited the New Jersey pine barrens together. Torrey evidently went to Philadelphia and hunted up Nuttall for the excursion, for a few months later Chester Dewey, Professor of Natural History at Williams College, wrote to Torrey "I was much gratified with your account [of your trip] to Phil[a] and of your adventures. I could have wished to have been with you. . . . I do not wonder at your gratification in finding Nuttall,

and enjoyed not a little your nocturnal, not to say *naked* visit."²⁷
The earliest extant letter of the correspondence between Nuttall and
Torrey was written by Nuttall at Philadelphia on October 19, 1820,
and is without salutation. "The same day wʰ we parted I arrived in
Philadⁱᵃ just as the sun was setting. I missed the way also about two
miles in the barrens. Finding nothing to amuse me I continued at a
steady pace towards the city occasionally reflecting on our excursion."²⁸
There follows a technical discussion of a grass "wʰ we found at the
Bridge."

Toward the end of the following winter when Nuttall visited Torrey in New York, they examined together critically a collection of
plants which von Schweinitz had sent to Torrey. Nuttall told Torrey that he estimated the number of new species of flowering plants
he had collected in the Southwest as about three hundred; he had
found the distinctive water ferns *Pilularia* and *Marsilea* in Arkansas,
the first report of their existence in the United States.²⁹ All his
Arkansas cryptogams he had given to Collins.

Nuttall may have felt faintly envious of Torrey's working space
and his collection of botanical publications, for the latter had already
begun to build a botanical library on American species and a comprehensive herbarium through exchanges which were to keep him
abreast of work in the field. Nuttall lacked these tools essential for
sound publication. His avid pursuit of botanical exploration coupled
with slim funds deprived him of books and a fixed abode for housing
them and a large herbarium. Hence he depended on his own plant
collections and what the herbarium and library of the Academy offered
and made no attempt to acquire either specimens by exchange or
taxonomic publications. The diverse emphases of these two, who
towered above other American botanists then active, are keys to
their different accomplishments: Nuttall, "a pre-eminent field naturalist" as well as a far-ranging one, was handicapped by limitations in
the taxonomic library and specimens available to him; Torrey was
equipped with tools but had a narrow field knowledge of the rich
American flora.

In midsummer Nuttall wrote to Torrey that he was through with
"the lectures that have kept me so busy" but work on the Arkansas
plants and the *Journal* would prevent him from going to New York
as he had planned. He must have been in a pessimistic mood for he
concludes his letter:

Your plants with the queries stand as they did: — I am a negligent and worthless, but not I hope an incorrigible correspondent. I have thro' life wanted method and rule in my conduct; and am withall considerable negligent even of my most intimate concerns; — plodding industry and firmness of character scarcely belonging to my constitution. — I am even too much governed by temporary impulses, can bend from one thing to another with the flexibility of a willow, enjoy nothing substantially but novelties and travelling. Still I can not say that I esteem versatility of talent or superficial views of any thing. After this confession I hope you will grant me absolution proportionate to its sincerity.[30]

In 1822 a paper by Nuttall entitled "Thoughts on the Proximate cause of Fecundation in Vegetables" appeared in the August issue of the *Philadelphia Journal of the Medical and Physical Sciences* (Dr. Nathaniel Chapman, Editor), and it was reprinted the following year in Froriep's *Notizem aus dem Gebiete der Natur und Heilkunde*. The article accents the difficulties that then confronted botanists in comprehending the life cycles of all groups of plants and the perplexed probings and gropings that preceded the availability of good microscopes and the development of suitable microtechnique. It is also an interesting example of the logic of Nuttall's rationale.

The impregnation of the ovum, according to many successful experiments has been attributed to the action of the pollen found in the anthers of flowers. . . . Many of the disciples of Linnaeus were led to believe that it [the pollen] actually furnished the embryon, . . . Spallanzani's observations however, on Basil, in which the embryon, though infertile, was produced in the total absence of anthers . . . proves its existence was independent of the pollen . . . Gleditsch's experiments with date palm showed pollen necessary to seed production.

Nuttall records his own observations of the abundance of fertile pistillate plants of *Vallisneria* in the tidewaters of the Delaware River, although no staminate plants were to be found in the vicinity, and of a similar situation obtaining in Udora (*Elodea*).

But to conclude as Spallanzani and Smellie have done, that the stamina are either partially or wholly useless in impregnation, is sceptical and unphilosophical. . . . Not only is their necessity ascertained, but their employment in producing hybrid varieties constantly practised by horticulturists and florists. . . .

How subtile indeed, must be that fluid or substance of whatever nature, necessary to elicit the life of the vegetable, which before it can possibly be felt in the *pre-existing* ovulae, must traverse the *vascular* system of the style, and penetrate the umbilical funiculus! for from the nature of the integuments which surround these ovulae, as well as their situation on the placenta, no other possible mode of impregnation can take place. . . .

We are not then to conclude with Smellie, that because external impregnation seemed impossible, the use of the pollen became nugatory, or that the pistillum had the power of impregnating itself!

To his contemporaries Nuttall's place of residence in Philadelphia provided a mild mystery, as John Jay Smith (1798–1881) tells us in his *Recollections.*

Nuttall I knew during his many residences in Philadelphia. He passed most of his many waking hours, when among us, at the Academy of Natural Sciences, in study, or in preparing his publications. He was one of those scientific naturalists, like Say, who seem to have no regard for money, and indeed never possessed much. It was a subject of curiosity where he lived, but no one could find this out, till one night he was followed from the Academy to his lodgings in the poor oyster-cellar of a colored man, where he must have sought for cheap entertainment.[31]

One can readily imagine a clique of young members amusing themselves with speculations about the lodging place of the Englishman, exchanging wild suggestions and reports until finally some prankster shadowed him home after a meeting. Whether or not the details of the story are true, and whatever the period from which it dates, there can be no doubt that Nuttall always lived as inexpensively as he could manage; creature comforts he discounted in favor of Flora.

MINERALOGICAL DIVERSIONS. Shortly before Nuttall left for the Southwest a great impetus was given to American science through the launching of a quarterly journal by Benjamin Silliman, professor of chemistry, pharmacy, mineralogy, and geology at Yale College. Colonel George Gibbs suggested this move as there was no regular publication for scientific papers in these fields; Bruce's *American Mineralogical Journal* (1810–1814) had shown the usefulness of such a publication but his ill health forced its early discontinuance. In March 1818, Zaccheus Collins received a prospectus of the proposed publication, on which Silliman had written a brief personal note soliciting articles. The first number appeared in July 1818, but, as the 350 subscriptions to the first volume proved insufficient to yield a profit to the publishers, they withdrew from the venture after the volume was completed. By assuming equal financial responsibility with a different printer, Silliman was able within a year to continue

the *American Journal of Science* and made it one of the major supports of American sciences.[32] The quality and range of subject matter
in its early articles, and their number, show the need for and the
value of the publication so courageously and devotedly established and
maintained.

Nuttall sent two papers for publication in Silliman's *Journal* in
1822: "Observations on the Serpentine Rocks of Hoboken, in New
Jersey, and on the Minerals which They Contain" and "A Catalogue
of a Collection of Plants Made in East-Florida . . . by [N.] A.
Ware, Esq." Both had been read before the Academy of Natural
Sciences but Nuttall, piqued by the events recounted in the next
paragraphs, departed temporarily from his custom of publishing in
their *Journal*.

At this time mineralogists were becoming aware of the occurrence
of a remarkably large number of rare minerals, many unique, in an
extensive deposit of pre-Cambrian crystalline limestone located in
Franklin and Sparta (Sterling Hill), in Sussex County of northern
New Jersey. The first useful light on the deposit came in 1810 when
Dr. Archibald Bruce (1777–1818) of New York, Professor of Materia
Medica and Mineralogy at the College of Physicians and Surgeons,
discovered zinc in one of the abundant minerals, which he accordingly named zincite. Dr. Samuel Fowler (1779–1844) acquired
about 4000 acres of the formation in 1816 and made every effort to
learn how the ores might be used commercially. Attempts to secure
iron failed but he encouraged the visits of mineralogists, geologists,
and chemists and soon Bruce was followed by Maclure, Troost, Benjamin Say, John P. Wetherill, Henry Seybert, Lardner Vanuxem,[33]
and William H. Keating from Philadelphia. These men were well
trained in chemistry and mineralogy: Troost and Vanuxem had
studied at the School of Mines in Paris with the celebrated mineralogist
Abbe Haüy; Henry Seybert had gone abroad under the tutorage of
his father Adam (1773–1825), a pupil of Werner and Blumenbach,
and spent some time studying in Paris.

Nuttall seems to have first visited the area in the late summer of
1820, and he continued to make periodic visits as long as he remained
in America, sometimes staying for several weeks with Dr. Fowler.
Between his enthusiasm over the rare minerals and his slight knowledge of chemistry, he soon got himself into difficulties. On April 3,
1821, he read a paper at the Academy on two minerals of Sparta,

yenite and chondrodite (brucite of Gibbs). According to custom, the paper was referred to a publication committee which in this case consisted of Troost, Keating, and Franklin Bache, who delayed their report. However, following a request for it, they gave an adverse decision, all criticising the chemistry and Troost and Keating the mineralogy; Bache suggested that the paper be revised. Nuttall took the report with ill grace. His article in modified form, entitled "Observations and Geological Remarks on the Minerals of Patterson and the Valley of Sparta, New-Jersey," published the following spring in the *New York Medical and Physical Journal,* was reprinted by Silliman in the next number of his *Journal.*[34] It gave a brief account of the geology of the deposits at both Franklin and Sterling Hill and "mentions for the first time many of the commoner minerals of both localities."[35]

At about this time Henry Seybert published chondrodite as a new mineral which he called maclurite, pointing out the presence in it of fluoric acid. Soon afterward, learning that it was already known from the United States and still earlier from Finland, and that both Berzelius and Haüy had described it, he published again on chondrodite attempting to minimize his error by attacking Nuttall's "claims" (in 1822) to the discovery of fluoric acid in the mineral even though Nuttall had viewed its presence as accidental. Seybert alleged that Nuttall's published article differed from the paper read at the Academy in this regard, namely in its recognition of the presence of fluoric acid. Nuttall replied that as Dr. William Langstaff (a chemist of New York City) had found that constituent in chondrodite in 1811, he had not laid claim to the honor of discovering it.[36] He had added a footnote to comment on the astonishing similarity of the chondrodite of Sparta to a piece from Vesuvius in the Cabinet of William Wagner, Jr., a fellow member of the Academy. The differences between Seybert and Nuttall were argued in issues of Silliman's *Journal* from mid-1822 into 1823.[37] The reactions of one interested reader, Chester Dewey at Williams College, were expressed in a letter to John Torrey: "How do you like the quarrel between Mr. Nuttall and Mr. Seybert? Both have the advantage, and both appear well and ill."[38] Nuttall's own feelings are revealed in a letter written to Torrey in the summer of 1823.

As to being guarded against such a black-guard as Seybert it is all in vain because he would cavil at anything. If you answer Seybert, say from me in your answer "that if the discussion could have been carried on temperately and scientifically and so rendered of any importance to the public, I might have been willing to answer Mr. Seybert, but as I cannot prevail upon myself to descend to such injurious language as that w<sup>h</sup> he employs in place of argument, I shall not beg any excuse for treating him with silence." . . .

If I am to be abused in the Academys Journal I shall send nothing more to it and throw up my subscription. We have all heard of the moon being made of *Green Cheese,* but never yet of crystallized Serpentine, — in fact, a rock, and no mineral at all.[39] Bad employment and poor pay, when our endeavours at promoting knowledge and exciting an interest, for neg-lected natural History serve only as the but[t] of ridicule and unjust criticism! — I am almost ready to anathematize natural science and banish it from my recollection! Three of the *Keating* faction are now united to write me down and damn everything I do. They are a set of dastards, and I shall treat them as I did Raffy [Rafinesque] with silent contempt.[40]

This disagreeable and fruitless controversy, in which Seybert was clearly the aggressor and in which Torrey, Silliman, and Meade were partial to Nuttall, marked the end of Nuttall's papers on mineralogy and geology although he continued to pursue both subjects as avidly as ever and made reports indirectly.

In his paper on the serpentine rocks of Hoboken, read to the Academy on May 8, 1821, Nuttall gave the name marmolite to a thin, foliated variety of serpentine of green color and pearly lustre and the name nemalite to a fibrous variety of brucite (manganese hydroxide).[41] Both names remain in good usage. He also suggested "manganese marble" as an alternate name for magnesite. These early achievements in mineralogy as well as later ones show the extraordi-nary discernment in detecting deviations that gave such scope to Nuttall's field work, enabling him not only to spot any novel plant or mineral but also to contribute constantly to zoology through the quick recognition of new species of insects, fish, and other animals. He arduously brought back much new material from remote places for the study of specialists. His keenness as a mineralogist becomes more apparent when the number of his acceptable new varieties is compared with those detected by American contemporaries who were exclusively mineralogists and chemists. The only worker of his active period in this field who exceeded him in the quantity of new forms published was his protégé Charles U. Shepard.

Local prospecting jaunts still yielded unusual minerals although not in the exciting quantity of Franklin Furnace. "Near the New

Water Works" on the Schuylkill, Nuttall found phosphate of manganese, a very rare mineral for which no definite American site was given in the literature. Because he had foresworn the mineralogical limelight, Torrey obligingly included the record of its discovery in a paper published in the *Annals* of the Lyceum in 1824. Nuttall found it again in 1823, in Sterling, Massachusetts.[42]

Early in February 1822, Nuttall read a paper at the Academy on a collection of Floridian plants made by Nathaniel A. Ware during October and November 1821 while he served as Commissioner for adjudication of land claims in Florida.[43] He stressed the slight knowledge available of the apparently rich flora of the area and mentioned that William Bartram's collections there had been lost in America "though still, I believe, existing in the Banksian herbarium." The known species in Ware's collection he simply listed, but described twenty-two species and one variety that he considered new. Although this was the only botanical paper Nuttall ever published in Silliman's *Journal*, Baldwin, Bigelow, Dewey, Ives, Torrey, Rafinesque, and other botanists sent articles to Silliman. The spring number of 1822 contained a notable paper on the genus *Viola* by Lewis D. von Schweinitz who had recently been transferred to Bethlehem, Pennsylvania, after ten years' service in Salem, North Carolina. A very productive student of plants, he made his greatest contribution in mycology, a field virtually unexplored in the United States. Before moving north, he wrote to Nuttall "to propose some questions concerning the Cryptogams of the Western country."

After April 9, 1822, Nuttall was absent from the weekly meetings of the Academy until December 17. He went northward to offer courses in botany, first trying to organize one in New York City. Torrey wrote to von Schweinitz on May 3:

> I am very fortunate in having Mr. Nuttall to stay with me, probably for two months. He is to give a course of lectures here on Botany. We are both bachelors & he is to stay altogether at my office, so that I promise myself a great treat from the company of this celebrated naturalist. He is much devoted to mineralogy which is a favorite pursuit of mine also. So that we shall have our hands full while he remains.[44]

Von Schweinitz answered Torrey's letter promptly and sympathetically:

> The enjoyment you are going to have in living together this summer with Mr. Nuttall I can appreciate since I had the exquisite pleasure of

becoming acquainted with that excellent man at Philadephia. Be so kind as to present my compliments to him and to request him to mention once more all the specimens we spoke of which he would be glad to get from me.[45]

In July von Schweinitz was regretting the loss to botany through mineralogy's drawing away "its most able & active cultivators like yourself & Mr. Nuttall." [46]

Nuttall took to New York copies of his *Journal of Travels into Arkansa Territory* which were put on sale at T. & J. Swords. An advertisement of it began to appear in the New York *Evening Post* on May 14.

Probably at Torrey's solicitation, Dr. Hosack obtained permission on May 7, for Nuttall to use the hall of the College of Physicians and Surgeons on May 13, at five o'clock, for the introductory lecture of his proposed course in botany.[47] However a class failed to materialize so, after some prospecting for minerals around the city and at Dr. Fowler's, Nuttall went on to New England where there was great eagerness for all kinds of lectures. Torrey's friend William Cooper wrote to him from Paris:

Dear Torrey,
Yours of April & May 30th have at last reached me. . . . I am more grieved than surprised at the ill success of Nuttall's attempt to get a Botanical Class in N. Y. It must be admitted that our fellow citizens are not distinguished for their knowledge of the exact Sciences as they are called here, they think they know all that is useful when the Multiplication Table has been cudgelled into them. You may tell Nuttall however for his consolation that his Book [the *Genera*] is much esteemed here and he appears to be considered the first North American Botanist of the day.[48]

Earlier Cooper had written to Torrey that Brongniart's son "seemed to know most of our authors on botany & admired Nuttall's Book particularly." [49]

On July 2, Nuttall wrote to Torrey from New Haven concerning his better success there.

Dear Sir,
I have commenced lecturing to a class of about 35 chiefly students in the college. . . . A young man here, Mr. Bowen deserves your acquaintance, as a chemist and mineralogist, he is about to send you some crystals to measure, somewhat curious. They are like Zoisite, but rhomboidal prisms, grey; glassy lustre, somewhat pearly. I have seen them before, with Doctor Mead, and I then thought them allied to Anthophyllite.

Silliman says he will reprint my paper on Sparta, etc. minerals in his journal. Forward a couple of copies as soon as convenient. I have now been informed that the green rubys of Franklin were probably found by Say and Wetherill, at any rate they have lost by acting the Fox, for if I could I would certainly have quoted them.[50]

Tell my good friend, Dr. Langstaff if he can to lay me aside a ruby or two as I have not yet found the Diamonds in their matrix, and have above all a great liking for precious stones, but I will give him something else as good.

Dr. & Mrs. Meads' respects, and when you can get the schorl [?] from Kingsbridge. I expect to get some fine things in the mineral way before I return.

I suppose the box is not yet come from Dr. Fowler, whose agents (merchants) I have forgotten the names of.

Ives and Silliman are very friendly to me and we have had a transient visit from Hare (Prometheus the II^d).[51] . . . This is one of the most delightfull looking villages I have ever seen, a town of gardens, Elysium; they have left off to be inquisitive, are unobtrusive, and have the organ of veneration well developed in their respectfull sober habits, if not in their sculls. Old Jonny Bull is yet honoured as an uncle, at the same time Jonathan loses none of his dignity by the friendly relationship.

I have seen in Gibbs' cabinet, from Vesuvius! a second specimen containing Condrodite. We have tried it and found it infusible, and are going on further with the comparison. It appears that Master Seybert, without consulting his superiors (*i.e.* ourselves) had wickedly and maliciously christened the Brucite, Maclurite, but we are ahead of him.

Farewell for a little.

Thos? Nuttall

My respects to Doctor Hooker, Dr. McKay, Prof. Renwick, and other friends who enquire for me.[52]

It would be gratifying to know whether Nuttall's students from the college included James Watson Robbins (1801–1879), a senior at Yale, who became a botanist by avocation and a specialist in *Potamogeton*. His fieldwork and botanical acumen were ranked at the top by William Oakes, the meticulous student of the New England flora.

Dr. Eli Ives (1779–1861), professor of materia medica at Yale Medical School, which he helped to establish, a sincere and efficient scientist with a large practice in his native New Haven, was too busy with it to fulfill his promise in botany. He espoused the establishment of a botanic garden and the appointment of Frederick Pursh as its curator, compiled lists of plants growing about New Haven, and from time to time published new species, of which *Limosella subulata* has stood the test of time and Gnaphalium decurrens was accepted for a hundred years.

Dr. William Meade was an enthusiastic mineralogist who had come from Ireland to America about the same time as Nuttall. He had contributed a paper or a note to each of the four numbers of Bruce's *Journal* and supported Silliman's *Journal* in a similar way. He was a Corresponding Member of the Academy of Natural Sciences of Philadelphia and occasionally attended its meetings. He and Nuttall became very good friends and probably made some prospecting trips together near New Haven during the early summer. Later in the season Meade got as far as Worcester, Sterling, and Bolton in central Massachusetts [53] but Nuttall did not accompany him thither; however his discoveries thereabouts so aroused Nuttall's interest that he covered the area in the following summer.

"Gibbs' cabinet," a collection of about 10,000 specimens, constituted Yale's museum. It was made up of three great purchases that Colonel George Gibbs of Newport, Rhode Island, had made in Lausanne, Paris, and London before he returned from Europe in 1805. Through Silliman's enterprise it was put on display at Yale in 1812 and later purchased. This immense collection of minerals from various places in Europe, Siberia, Egypt, and the East Indies, carefully arranged and cataloged, furnished a valuable laboratory for Nuttall in his self-education in mineralogy.

In mid-July Silliman wrote to Torrey: "I am much gratified by my acquaintance with Mr. Nuttall of whom I have formed a very favorable opinion both respecting his talents & acquirements & his modest unassuming worth; he is much respected here." [54] And Silliman wrote to Professor Parker Cleaveland at Bowdoin:

> Mr. Nuttall the celebrated Botanist is passing the Summer here, giving a course of Lectures on Botany. — You are aware that he is also a good Mineralogist and Geologist. — If you see no objection, I should like to nominate him [a member of the Geological Society].

Dr. William Meade was also in New Haven and he and Nuttall were settled in the same lodgings. [55]

Silliman may have described to Nuttall his meeting with Frederick Pursh on October 13, 1819, nine months before Pursh died in Montreal. At Sorel, the botanist boarded the ship which Silliman had taken at Quebec for Montreal. Pursh told of marching with a sixty-pound pack through forests and swamps from Anticosti to upper Canada collecting herbarium specimens and living plants. He was sufficiently "high" to tell "Sober Ben" that he was a Tartar, born and educated in Siberia near Tobolsk although he was actually

*Friedrich Traugott Pursch* of Saxony. This whimsical bit of mis-information still appears in sketches of Pursh although his brother supplied accurate information in Reichenbach's *Botanische Zeitung* when it came to his attention.[56] Lambert received at least some of Pursh's Canadian collections.

In September Torrey heard from Chester Dewey in Williamstown that "Nuttall has been to Middlefield [Massachusetts] and seen Emmons & misnamed some minerals for him."[57] Middlefield was only one of numerous collecting spots in western New England which Nuttall was painstakingly searching. After his course in botany was finished, he evidently had set out from New Haven to collect minerals for his swelling collection. Haddam, Connecticut, yielded among other items chrysoberyl and precious garnet. Most of the hunt centered on well-known quarries and sites in Hampshire County, Massachusetts, where he circled through Northampton, Goshen, Plainfield, Cummington, Chesterfield, Middlefield, and Southampton, for the most part on the drainage of the Westfield River. Some of the notable specimens from his collection which were purchased by the Natural History Department of the British Museum in 1860 came from this region: a specimen of cyanite from Chesterfield (no. 31456) which was judged at the time of purchase to be "a magnificent mass . . . the finest specimen known from U. S. A. and also probably from other American localities"; red and green tourmaline in cleavelandite (no. 31457) and dark blue tourmaline with beryl (no. 31475), both from Goshen, were doubtless equally dear to the owner who literally left no stone unturned in meticulous search for specimens of fine quality.[58]

On November 3, Edward Hitchcock, then minister in Conway, Franklin County, Massachusetts, wrote to Torrey "Mr. Nuttall is lecturing in botany in this vicinity but I have scarcely seen him — He is much engaged in mineralogy."[59] A week or so later Nuttall was in New Haven and before the end of November was again visiting Torrey in New York.

Whether his season of lecturing among the Yankees had been financially successful or not would not now greatly concern Nuttall for about midautumn he received an appointment as Curator of the Botanic Garden in Cambridge and Instructor in Natural History and Botany at Harvard College, available through the death of Professor Peck early in October. While he was winding up his affairs in Philadelphia, he attended meetings of the Academy on December 17 and 24, January 24, and February 18.

# CHAPTER II

# HARVARD

This is one of the neatest and best compacted towns of New England, having many fine structures, with many handsome contrived streets.
— Wood, *New England Prospect*, 1633

THE BOTANIC GARDEN. Although throughout Europe a botanic garden was regarded as essential to the serious study of plants, no college of colonial America could boast of such an adjunct. In 1784 the King of France offered Harvard College seeds and plants from the royal preserves, but the General Court of Massachusetts would not provide the financial assistance necessary for establishing and maintaining a garden.[1] However the incident planted an idea which eventually brought forth results. John Lowell (1744–1802), "the Old Judge," a member of the Harvard Corporation and President of the Massachusetts Society for Promoting Agriculture, "formed the design of raising a fund" for creating a professorship of natural history at Harvard and, in conjunction with it, a garden. Soon after his death his two eldest sons, John the Rebel (1769–1840), and Francis Cabot Lowell (1775–1817), took the lead in carrying out his idea. The latter, in charge of the subscription list, had accumulated pledges for $31,333 from about 150 donors early in 1805.[2] Instead of handing the funds over to Harvard, the Board of Visitors of the "Massachusetts Professorship of Natural History" held them as a separate account.

William Dandridge Peck (1763–1822), Harvard College 1782, chosen to fill the professorship, had superior qualifications: besides his outstanding original contributions to American zoology, especially entomology, beautifully illustrated by his artistic hand, his character and family connections were of the best. In fact the professorship had been established with Peck in mind as its first incumbent, but it was not without regret that he left the seclusion of his pleasant farm on the Artichoke River in Newbury.[3] He was formally inducted into office on May 14, 1805. On June 3, he sailed from Boston and spent almost three years visiting savants and long-established gardens in Europe, securing seeds, plants, books, and ideas and engaging a well-trained gardener. His quiet worth made valuable friends not only for himself but also for Harvard and the struggling natural sciences in America. Subsequently the great naturalists of Europe wrote to him in the warmest terms, among them Olaf Swartz, Carl Peter Thunberg, and Adam Afzelius of Sweden, Jens Wilken Hornemann of Denmark, Franz Carl Mertens of Germany, Pierre André Latreille of France, and Sir Joseph Banks, William Kirby, and James Edward Smith of England.[4] As a person Peck is vague to us now, but the scientist is held in remembrance by the names of a rare species of parasitic insect, *Xenos peckii* Kirby, and a handsome alpine plant of the White Mountains, *Geum peckii* Pursh, both discovered by himself, and by the curious Peck's pipefish (*Syngnathus peckianus* Storer), which he described in the first scholarly American paper on systematic zoology.[5]

Ground for the Garden was procured about a mile from the college on the Highway to the Great Swamp and Fresh Pond (later Garden Street), just to the north of the original Cow Common. Andrew Craigie donated an adjoining piece from his great estate, making the Garden a fraction over seven acres.[6] The title to the land was placed in the name of the President and Fellows of Harvard College, but the Garden was under the direction of the Board of Visitors of the Massachusetts Professorship. It was primarily for instruction but was open to visitors at an admission charge of twenty-five cents (or at a yearly rate), and it also sold cut flowers and plants. The gardener whom Peck engaged in England was William Carter, a Yorkshireman. He worked at the Garden for forty years, his pronunciation a joy to generations of students.

Peck did not start his teaching activities until many months after his return from Europe because Dr. Benjamin Waterhouse of the Harvard Medical School, who had been giving a course in natural history annually at the college since 1788, was very loath to hand over the work and the fees to anyone else.[7]

In 1810 Professor Peck electrified the community by marrying. His bride was Harriet Hilliard, the daughter of a pastor of the First Church who had died twenty years before when Harriet was about two years old. Since she was well known to everyone, the village buzzed with that sort of lively gossip which was later to be a trial and an irritation to Nuttall. Dr. Abiel Holmes, the successor of Harriet's father, performed the wedding ceremony.[8] A house, long known as "the Garden House," was built for Peck on the high land in the northwest part of the Garden, under the supervision of John Lowell, who reported that he had "employed an artist well recommended" to draw the plans. Ithiel Town (1784–1844) in July 1811 receipted a bill for $3108 for all work and materials excluding the masonry; it is very likely that this was the first important commission of Town's highly successful career as an architect.[9] The handsome frame building, beautifully proportioned and artfully individualized, although now on a different site, still delights the eyes of Cantabrigians.[10]

Students of Peck's time who reached distinction in some field of natural history included Dr. Francis Boott, 1810; Dr. Benjamin D. Greene, 1812; Dr. James Freeman Dana, 1813; Dr. Thaddeus William Harris, 1815; Charles Brooks, 1816; George Barrell Emerson, 1817; William Oakes, 1820; and Dr. Charles Pickering, ex-1823. Boott and Greene, members of wealthy Boston families, became botanists and patrons of botany in a period when encouragement was much needed in America, and Boott produced a beautifully illustrated monograph on *Carex*, one of the most difficult of genera. Dana, a very successful teacher of chemistry, mineralogy, and geology at Harvard, Dartmouth, and the College of Physicians and Surgeons successively, died at the threshold of a promising career. Harris, one of the early entomologists of the United States, was the only one of Peck's students to work in his special field. Harris once wrote to Thomas Say: "Prof. Peck taught me to define the species in Latin & I have generally adhered to his advice though it savours somewhat of pedantry."[11] Brooks, after some years in the ministry, was appointed as professor of natural history in the University of the City of New York. George Barrell Emerson wrote the *Report on Trees and Shrubs of Massachusetts* (1846) for the State Survey. For Emerson, when a freshman, Peck had the most valuable knowledge in Cambridge: "The first visit I made, after being established in college was to the Botanic Garden, to learn from Prof. Peck the name of the plants I had examined in Wells [Maine] for which I had found no name. He recognized them instantly from my description."[12] William Oakes became the authority of his period on the New England flora.

Charles Pickering, considered the best all-round American naturalist of his time, served as Chief Naturalist of the Wilkes Expedition.

There must have been many students to whom Peck's course introduced a new outlook on the world. Caleb Cushing, 1817, who became a brilliant statesman and diplomat, started his career as a tutor at Harvard; he wrote a masterly summary of the accomplishments in American botany for the *North American Review* in 1821. The early journals and poems of Ralph Waldo Emerson, 1821, reveal a knowledge of phases of nature such as are picked up in a classroom: he used the Latin names of plants, was acquainted with the geographical distribution of some species, and dwelt on the dicotyledonous number five and "the star form" that nature repeats.

A catalog of the American and foreign plants in the Botanic Garden that Peck published in 1818 enables us to estimate the results he accomplished in the Garden in ten growing seasons and pictures its contents much as they were at the time of his death on October 3, 1822.[13]

The college community speculated animatedly as to his successor. Ralph Waldo Emerson in writing to a classmate discussed "the disputed succession of King Peck's dominion . . . it is probable Dr. Bigelow will have a speedy offer of the crown." [14] The general opinion, however, was that, since Jacob Bigelow held the Rumford Professorship at the College and was also Professor of materia medica at the Medical School and carried on a private practice, he would refuse the honor of the Massachusetts Professorship. We have little information about the hurried consideration of possible successors of Peck which must have taken place among the Visitors of the Massachusetts Professorship and the officers of the Corporation although the qualifications of various naturalists were argued without restraint in the local newspapers. A pertinent passage in a letter of October 19, from John Lowell to the Corporation, is so obscure that it reveals only that some differences of opinion must have been ironed out: "And as to the last event, the premature question about filling the professorship of Natural History in which I feel a deep, and intense interest, I have been made without my consent, to stand in the invidious light of opposing a man for whom I feel a most sincere regard and respect." [15]

At Lowell's suggestion the Secretary of the Board of Visitors called a special meeting for October thirtieth at the Boston Athenaeum. It was found that the Funds of the Professorship are not at present competent to the support of a professor, and the repair of the edifices and the establishment of the Garden on such a scale as may render it competent to the necessary wants of such professorship; and it further appearing that the funds originally set apart for the support of a Professor have been impaired.

Therefore, Noted — That it is expedient that the income of the funds should be applied for the present

First — to make good the Capital stock . . . retaining such a portion of the income of said Funds, as may be requisite to put in complete repair the present edifices and fences, and to furnish the Garden with plants, so as to render the instructions of any future professor as useful as they were designed to be. . . .

Voted That Mr. Thomas Nuttall be appointed a Committee, with the title of Curator of the Botanic Garden to hold his office during the pleasure of this board and that his duties so far as respects the supervision of the Garden only shall be the same as are allotted by the Statutes to the Professor on this subject; two members of this board shall be joined with him in the commission, with full power to cooperate and advise him on this subject and to make and require a report of the state of the Garden at each meeting of the board. . . .

That Mr. Lowell and Mr. Brooks be a Committee of this board to contract with the Curator for the performance of his duties, and to advise and co-operate with him as above provided. . . .

That, if the Curator shall in the opinion of the Reverend and Honorable Corporation be competent to deliver Lectures on Botany, or any other branch of Natural History, this board would be gratified at his receiving their Authority and permission so to do during the vacancy of the Professorship, and his being allowed such fees as they may think reasonable.[16]

A week later, on November 6, the Corporation of Harvard College fully concurred in the measures adopted by the Board of Visitors.[17] Nuttall's salary as Curator, paid from the funds of the Massachusetts Professorship was $500 a year; from Harvard College he received $100 for each course he gave in natural history, and he seems to have received the student fees for his course in botany.

Despite faithful and resourceful efforts by the Board of Visitors to improve the finances of the foundation and special grants by the Commonwealth from 1816 on for the maintenance of the garden and assistance by the college, the funds remained so impaired that it was never again possible to fill the Massachusetts Professorship of Natural History.

CAMBRIDGE AND HARVARD IN 1823.[18] The Cambridge to which Nuttall went in 1823 had grown so little that a discerning eye could readily trace the pattern of the first settlement. The center of "The Village" was still the elm-framed area where the meetinghouse stood and where the original streets and the College Yard met. At the Common, a short distance from the Yard, divergent roads, sparsely settled, led quickly into the countryside where some of the most shy species of the rich northeast flora still grew in swamps and woodlands: *Clintonia borealis, Smilacina trifolia, Cypripedium acaule, Orchis spectabilis, Corallorhiza trifida* var. *verna* (Nutt.) Fern., *Rhododendron canadense* and *R. viscosum, Trientalis borealis, Menyanthes trifoliata,* and *Linnaea borealis.* At the Botanic Garden, about a mile from the College Yard, Nuttall had his abode and his work as Curator of the Garden; his lectures were given in Harvard Hall in the Yard.

Although Harvard was referred to as a university in the State Constitution drawn up at Cambridge in 1779, its popular name, the College in Cambridge, better suited its achievements and size. The undergraduates averaged about two hundred and fifty in number and in age generally ranged through the teens. The official college buildings, massed at the western side of the present Yard, numbered eight in 1823. Four were used as dormitories; students also lived in numbered "College Houses," supervised rooming houses, and in approved Cambridge homes. Harvard Hall provided classrooms and sheltered the Library. Holden Chapel, long outgrown for its original purpose, was used by the Medical School, which offered some work in Cambridge to seniors. University, the newest building, designed with Bulfinch's elegant simplicity, its white granite in pleasing contrast with the old red brick of the other college halls, contained separate commons for the four classes, a chapel, an office for the President, and some classrooms. Wadsworth, a gracious clapboard house at the south served as the President's home for well over a century. The water supply for the Yard was provided by three pumps placed near the dormitories.

John Thornton Kirkland, President of Harvard at the time Nuttall was appointed, was the first in the office (and the last) who was held in affection by the students as a whole. He was the unanimous choice of the Corporation for the presidency of the college in 1810. The "scholars" admired his wit, learning, and courtesy and appreciated his interest in them, his humanity, goodwill, common sense, and cheerful presence: a handsome, rosy-cheeked man of the world with a twinkle in his eye and a musical voice.

We are indebted to Tutor George Barrell Emerson for a glimpse of the social life of President Kirkland's day.

There was always a meeting, every Sunday evening at the president's at which Dr. Popkin, Mr. Brazer . . . and some others were sometimes present; and always Mr. Everett, Mr. Cushing and myself. Mr. Farrar and his wife . . . kept the president's house, and were always present when she was well; usually a niece of the president, and almost always, Mrs. Farrar's three sisters. These were far the most pleasant and really the most brilliant parties I have ever attended. Mr. Everett was always full of fun, and pleasant stories and anecdotes.[19]

During Kirkland's administration, since called "the Augustan Age of Harvard," two of the three graduate schools were established, the endowment appreciably swelled, new professorships added, salaries raised, and the number of students increased. To his reputation and to the liberal religious stand of the college is ascribed the large number of students who came from the middle and southern states in the second and third decades of the nineteenth century — in 1820, twenty-seven per cent of the freshman class came from outside New England. The Southerners were especially engaging to the sober-minded Puritan stock, and the experience of all the students was enhanced by the widened contacts.

During Nuttall's years in Cambridge the faculty engaged only in undergraduate instruction usually numbered seven professors, one instructor beside himself, and a few tutors and assistants. Nuttall's associations were among the younger members, who had received their bachelor's degrees after 1800: John Farrar, Hollis Professor of Mathematicks and Natural Philosophy; Jacob Bigelow, Rumford Professor and Instructor on the Application of Science to the Useful Arts; Edward Tyrrell Channing, Boylston Professor of Rhetorick and Oratory; George Ticknor, Smith Professor of the French and Spanish Languages and Literature and Professor of Belles Lettres; and Joseph Green Cogswell, Professor of Mineralogy and Geology and College Librarian. Edward Everett, Eliot Professor of Greek Literature, the youngest of those of professorial rank, "an intellectual prodigy," had graduated in 1811. The tutor in Greek, George Bancroft, had a distinguished career ahead of him although he was unpopular with the students, who gave him a rough time. All these men had attended Harvard College except Ticknor, who had followed his father at Dartmouth. The four youngest, the first Americans to receive Ph.D.s (from Göttingen), were fired by great enthusiasm for the German methods of education. Instructor Francis Sales, for thirty-eight years teacher of French and Spanish, like Instructor Nuttall, held no earned degree, but there was not a happier man in Cambridge.

During Nuttall's first term at Harvard a "rebellion" among the seniors resulting in the expulsion of forty-three from a class of seventy,[20] occasioned serious investigations by committees of the Faculty, the Corporation, the Overseers, and of combinations of these bodies, to determine causes and suggest corrections for periodic uprisings of the students. These searching inquiries resulted in the adoption of new regulations in 1825, which affected the timing of Nuttall's activities. A radical change was made in the academic calendar: the longest vacation had theretofore been in the winter to furnish opportunity for students to teach at country schools and earn the wherewithal to continue their own studies, but the authorities felt that the hot weather of the summer induced uneasiness leading to riotous activities, so the long vacation was transferred to the six weeks before Commencement, which always fell on the last Wednesday in August. The courses so far as practicable were to be divided into sections on the basis of ability, more latitude in electing courses was allowed the upperclassmen, and other minor changes were introduced.

FIRST MONTHS IN CAMBRIDGE. A letter that Nuttall wrote to John Lowell furnished the only light we have about the circumstances of his appointment at Harvard.

Philadelphia Jan.ʸ 21ˢᵗ 1823

John Lowel [sic], Esq.ʳ
Dear Sir,

Absence from town will I hope plead my excuse with you for not immediately answering your very kind and obliging letter.

Through my friend Doctor Bigelow, I believe, I fully understood every thing mentioned in your letter, and I very willingly devote myself to the duties of the office with which I have been so unexpectedly honoured. When I had the pleasure of being in your company the month of February was spoken of as the time when I should come to Cambridge. I doubt, however now whether I can arrive earlier than the close of that month.

I have sent on to the care of Dr. Bigelow two boxes of plants and one matted bundle for the garden, they are rare and I hope the gardener will attend to them. . . . I have obtained . . . a considerable number of seeds and have the prospect of many more. . . . I know of nothing that is wanting to establish a general collection of plants, at Cambridge, but industry and economy. A good botanic garden, in any part of the vast dominions of the United States is yet a desideratum. . . .

I remain, with the highest esteem
Your obdt. humble servant
Tho: Nuttall [21]

Nuttall arrived in Boston on or about the first of March 1823. No record has come down to us of his impressions of the area and its inhabitants. Most British visitors of this period found Boston more English than other American cities. They were pleased by the general cleanliness, the undulating ground and crooked streets, the extensive green Common, the many superior shops, and the handsome but unostentatious homes of the wealthy. Visitors from England were further charmed by the beautiful villages on its outskirts where friendly clapboard houses were surrounded by green lawns and gardens. Foreigners were prone to compare it with Philadelphia: some noticed in Boston a deeper interest in literature and moral pursuits and great intellectual vigor united with a speculative spirit whereas in Philadelphia more emphasis was given to science, accurate knowledge, and experimentation; other travelers wrote of the open and lavish hospitability of the Puritans and the coldness and reserve of the Quakers. Timothy Dwight thought the population of Boston notably homogeneous in stock and character, of pure English speech with knowledge "probably more universally diffused there than in any other considerable town in the world" due to the long-established public school system. The newer houses he considered superior to those elsewhere in America and the food unexcelled. Those who were liberally educated he found to be distinguished by a Greek spirit of bold adventurous ardor and enthusiasm which carried them as pioneer traders to Nootka Sound, China, and other far countries.[22] The urbane Corréa found Bostonians peculiarly to his liking.

Nuttall found trends in the New England character sympathetic with his own, an independence of mind and spirit, reserve, a "self-consciousness akin to modesty," and Harvard fostered virtues that had guided Nuttall's career: disinterested dedication to the increase of knowledge; disdain of the cheap and spurious; courage in following principles. His new duties brought him into contact with bearers of the most distinguished surnames of the Bay Colony from the Winthrops on. In all his associations he was completely successful: all contemporary Cambridge-Boston references to him, as scholar and man, are highly complimentary, completely unshadowed by any suggestion of criticism.

Nuttall was still in Boston on March 5, when he wrote to von Schweinitz in Bethlehem to inform him of the price of some available Cuban herbarium specimens, which he had ascertained before leaving Philadelphia. The letter then ran on to other matters:

I thank you very much for the book you have sent me and the interesting specimens wʰ were blanks in my collection. If the *Sison bulbosum*, the plant I called *Erigenia* should be found in your alluvial lands, I should be much gratified in obtaining a specimen with the seed well developed, so as to remove all doubt concerning its generic character. It is however, most certainly, not an *Hydrocotyle!* nor indeed any way related to it.

Dʳ Torrey showed me during my short stay in N. York, a collection of grasses collected by Dʳ James in Long's expedition. Many were familiar but 2 or 3 were apparently new genera

I shall take an early opportunity after arriving at Cambridge to send you a collection of the cryptogamous plants wʰ I collected in my Arkansa tour, of wʰ on your authority I wish to add a list to my collections toward a Flora of that region. Whether a mere nominal catalogue, or notes and descriptions I shall be very thankfull and publish it accordingly as you may think proper. I do not believe that Mʳ Collins my friend, has attended to the subject tho' i must previously enquire.

I remain, with the highest respect,
Your sincere friend and humble servant
Thoˢ Nuttall

Direct to me at
Cambridge Botanic Garden
Boston [23]

The question arises why Nuttall was delaying in Boston instead of taking over his new duties across the Charles. Doubtless these days were spent in conferences with John Lowell and Peter Chardon Brooks, who had been appointed by the Board of Visitors to act with the Curator as a Committee to administer the Botanic Garden. Lowell, who signed his numerous political pamphlets and public letters with such phrases as 'A Yankee Farmer' and 'The Roxbury Farmer,' doted on the Garden, his father's project, which had materialized through the efforts of his brother and himself. In 1823 he had time to devote to it, for he had retired from several positions of public service.[24] He resigned as of November 1, 1822, from the Corporation of Harvard College, the self-perpetuating governing board made up of the President, Treasurer, and five Fellows. A portion of a long personal letter to President Kirkland at the time of his resignation reveals his tenacious conservatism: "I am, I avow it frankly, decidedly opposed to the *new schemes generally*. . . . I am opposed to pulling down the old edifice, and to rebuilding it from the foundation. Let those who prefer such revolutions make them." [25] Lowell was Senior Fellow although Treasurer John Davis had served for a longer span as a member of the Corporation. From the beginning of Kirkland's presidency, Lowell had given him almost daily assistance in carrying on the various affairs of the college. His conscientious attention to every detail was a reflection of a nature so excessively sensitive as to generate constant ill health. He had given up the practice of law in his early thirties (1803) when nervous exhaustion followed his failure to convince the jury of the innocence of his client, young Jason Fairbanks of Dedham, indicted for murder.

Brooks had retired from a marine insurance business which brought him a fortune reputed to be even greater than those of any of the plutocratic merchants whose ships he had insured. Both men had houses in Boston but the hearths of home were for Brooks at the large Medford estate owned by his family since 1660 and for Lowell at 'Bromley Vale' in Roxbury, which his father had acquired after he moved his family from Newburyport to Boston in 1777. Nuttall was probably staying at John Lowell's town house in Colonnade Row on Tremont Street opposite the Common. Lowell continued in close association with the Garden and Nuttall.

After the business of the committee was finished, Lowell presumably drove Nuttall out to Cambridge in his chaise, taking him to call on Kirkland and then to the Garden House where quarters had been assigned to him. The Minutes of the Board of Visitors state that the Curator is to have the 'North Easterly' room of the Garden House, evidently to serve as an office and study. Someone blundered in this (perhaps the Recording Secretary) for the designated room was the kitchen. The southeast rooms on the first and second floors overlooking the Garden were given to him. Mrs. Peck and her eleven-year-old son occupied the rest of the house until the next academic year. [26] The charming frame mansion, which in general floor plan resembled his Uncle Jonas's red brick house in Lancashire, built in the same year, was somewhat more generous in size, in the country style of New England. Its elegantly pilastered facade rose a full two stories, and the flattened hip roof was concealed and ornamented by a low balustrade. Nuttall's stuffy "garret room," which imaginative writers have created, never existed, for the space beneath the roof was unusable. The writer suspects that Nuttall's reputed eccentricities were as nonexistent as the attic room. The students, quick to note oddities, made no such innuendos.

There was a rush of work awaiting Nuttall: the spring season in the Garden was just ahead, and plans for its future development required consideration on the spot; the Garden accounts had slid along without settlement for months; besides the accumulated bills for supplies, William Carter's salary was in arrears; thought had to be given to a course in botany, which would start at the end of May; and his paper on the Arkansas flora had to be finished for the American Philosophical Society. Nuttall's first season at the Garden must have been discouraging, for the spring was phenomenally late, the coldest that old John Adams had ever experienced.

At a meeting of the Board of Visitors on April 12, a sum of $300 was voted to Mr. Thos. Nuttall for the payment of Garden bills and the gardener's wages.[27] Two days later Nuttall went to Boston to the office of the Treasurer of the College, John Davis (1761–1847), to pick up the voted amount and to deliver $250 which had accumulated from entrance fees to the Garden and from the sale of plants and seeds since Peck's last illness. His own salary of $500 as Curator of the Garden was paid in quarterly installments, but, since he had arrived for the last month of the first quarter, he received from Davis $41.66 as his first payment of salary. Thereafter his salary was paid by Stephen Higginson, Jr., Steward of the College, at his office in Cambridge.[28] Davis, who served with distinction as Judge of the United States Court for the District of Massachusetts for forty years after his appointment by President Adams, had great interest in, and appreciable knowledge of, botany, mineralogy, conchology, and philology. In fact he had served as the first President of the Linnaean Society of New England and had been a Corresponding Member of the Academy of Natural Sciences of Philadelphia since the year it was founded. He corresponded regularly on the subject of Indian languages with the learned Peter Du Ponceau of Philadelphia, with whom Nuttall was acquainted. Moreover, twenty-eight years before, when serving in Philadelphia as Comptroller of the Treasury of the United States, Davis frequently visited young Benjamin Smith Barton "at his Bachelor's Hall."

The college calendar that was in effect through Nuttall's first two and a half years at Harvard scheduled a spring vacation for the last of May. A subsidized holiday of this kind was something new for him, and its occurrence early in the growing season was a double boon, a perfect occasion for a botanizing tour through unfamiliar territory. Accompanied by Paul Trapier, a sophomore from Charleston, South Carolina, and presumably by his "chum" (roommate), Stephen Elliott, Jr., a son of the botanist, and Augustus A. Gould, a sophomore from New Ipswich, and possibly by other students, he went northwestward through New Ipswich in southern New Hampshire making a beeline for Mt. Monadnock (3166 ft.). Apparently the main attraction of the trip was climbing Monadnock to "gaze o'er New England underspread." After conquering Monadnock, the party crossed into Vermont at Bellows Falls and doubtless continued about twenty-five miles up the Connecticut valley to climb Ascutney (3144 ft.).[29] Despite the cold spring, a gratifying array of herbs and shrubs would have been in blossom, especially the species of the woodlands which bloom before direct light is cut off by the expanded foliage of the trees. Nuttall would have taken pleasure in the brooks, clear running like those of Craven, and in the northern plants on the summits: the rich evergreen foliage of the mountain cranberry, which in protected nooks might show pink buds, the characteristic leaves of *Potentilla tridentata*, the swelling flower buds of rhodora, and dwarfed spruce, balsam-fir, and paper birch. Near Monadnock he found *Smilacina trifolia* (L.) Desf., thus adding a new site for it for the second edition of Bigelow's *Florula* (1824). The party had the thrill of finding two species which Nuttall thought were undescribed, an orchid and a grass. The excursion may have extended to Lake Champlain, for at some time before 1825 Nuttall collected "Magnesium Carbonate of Lime, crystallized, transparent and beautiful," at Shoreham, Vermont, on the eastern shore almost opposite Ticonderoga.[30]

Immediately after this interlude, his first class at the College started and continued through the term. About forty students took the course, although botany was an elective for seniors and juniors only and more than half of the seniors were expelled. Henry Coit Perkins of the Junior Class, who doubtless was enrolled, attributed to Nuttall's influence his choice of career as a physician:

To a slight incident (namely, the meeting of a person in the road which led to the Botanic Garden), the writer looks back with pleasure as the turning point of his future employment through life. The individual referred to was Prof. Thomas Nuttall, the distinguished English botanist and naturalist, who had been recently appointed Lecturer on Botany and Curator of the Botanic Garden. A strong attachment sprang up between this teacher and many of the students; this friendship the writer enjoyed, and by it was often enticed away from the drier studies of the course, to a pleasant ramble through the woods and fields in search of their fruits and flowers.

Among the number to whom the volume of nature was first opened by Mr. Nuttall about the same time, was . . . Dr. Augustus A. Gould of Boston [Harvard College, 1825]. He leaves behind him a character untarnished, and a name long to be held in remembrance by every physician and student of natural history.

. . . While an undergraduate, I had attended the lectures of Dr. John C. Warren upon comparative anatomy, and was forcibly struck with the analogies of the skeletons of the lower animals with that of man. I had studied chemistry under Dr. John Gorham, and had often returned from the Botanic Garden with my pockets well filled with minerals from my friend Mr. Nuttall, and my botany box well stored with plants for analysis.[31]

It is interesting to learn that at this early date undergraduates were receiving instruction in *comparative* anatomy, with its implications of biological evolution. There are many indications that the scope of at least some of the Harvard courses was broader than is suggested by the meagre statements in the printed catalogs, which present a rather cheerless and rigid calendar of required work usually based on named textbooks. The two lower classes took a traditional classical curriculum taught by routine recitations, but the program of the upperclassmen was brightened by natural philosophy and the Rumford lectures in technology and by elective half-courses in chemistry, "mechanicks," electricity and magnetism, optics, astronomy, natural history, botany, anatomy and surgery, mineralogy and geology, political economy, law, or modern languages. Throughout the four years, work in rhetoric and oratory developed the verbal and oral facility expected in a Bachelor of Arts.

On June 22, 1823, Nuttall wrote to Zaccheus Collins enclosing a paper on a new species of grass, collected near Bellows Falls, Vermont, during the spring vacation.

Dear Sir,

I have taken the liberty of addressing to you a short communication to the Academy on the genus Oryzopsis of Mich. hoping you will favor me so far as to correct it before publication  when opportunity offers I will send you a specimen of the new species here mentioned of this genus. Will you be so good as to tell Mʳ J. Vaughan our mutual friend, that I greatly regret the still unfinished state of my *Arkansa* collection, but that it may perhaps come in as an Appendix. . . .

Our garden wants plants much, but the funds are not such as to venture on expences [*sic*].

If the Academy should judge this communication worthy of receiving publication, they will favor me by giving it an early insertion otherwise I should be glad to receive the paper again. I have been expecting to hear from you and shall *ever* be glad of any intelligence from so true and faithfull [*sic*] a friend.

Believe me, with the deepest sincerity, your well-wisher, honourᵈ friend, and humble servant.

T. Nuttall.[32]

The paper describing Oryzopsis *parviflora was promptly read at the Academy, approved by a committee, and published in the *Journal*.[33] On July 24, Nuttall received a letter from Torrey who was greatly disturbed because Nuttall's new species of *Oryzopsis* appeared to be identical with his Milium pungens, based on herbarium specimens received from correspondents, and published in Kurt Sprengel's *Neue Entdeckungen* in 1821.[34] Nuttall immediately answered Torrey's letter but failed to convince him that the grass belonged in *Oryzopsis*; time, however, as in many other such differences of opinion in which Nuttall was a party, has proved Nuttall correct although he made no pretensions of being an agrostologist, as Torrey did. Torrey's error was caused by his dependence on dried specimens of a grass which he had never seen growing; he missed evanescent features of the inflorescence which in this case were of critical importance.

Nuttall sent to Zaccheus Collins a second short paper entitled "Remarks on the Species of Corallorhiza Indigenous to the United States." It was read to the Academy on August 5, approved for publication on August 21, and duly appeared in the *Journal* with illustrations of the orchids discussed done by Nicholas M. Hentz.[35] The paper introduced a new orchid that one of his student companions, Paul Trapier, had detected in May "growing in clusters at the roots of the paper birch" in a sphagnous swamp near New Ipswich, New Hampshire. Nuttall published it as C. *verna; but about 100 years later M. L. Fernald reduced it to a variety of a Eurasian species [C. *trifida* Chatelain, var. *verna* (Nutt.) Fern.] The article gave Nuttall the opportunity to recognize as a new species another *Corallorhiza* which in *Genera* he had erroneously equated with a Eurasian species; however, in naming this species he had been anticipated by Rafinesque, who published it as *C. maculata* in 1817. The latter's creed that no plant found in America could possibly be of the same species as a European plant protected him from ever making that sort of mistake.

A letter to John Vaughan, the Corresponding Secretary of the American Philosophical Society, expresses doubt about the quick completion of the report on his Arkansas plant collections.

Cambridge, Aug. 2 1823

Dear Sir,

I beg your pardon for not immediately answering your first letter, and I am now sorry to have to say that, the Communication I intended is still unfinished and not in a state for immediate publication. I will finish it now as fast, but as well as possible, and to do that in the present complicated state of the science is no inconsiderable labor. It will I think be time enough because I always intended it as an appendix for the end of the volume. Call on Mr. Thos. Palmer, Printer, Locust Street, and tell him to give you a copy [of the Arkansa Journal] in my name. As an author, in a pecuniary point of view, I have always been unfortunate. I shall have by it about 100 $ and all my labor. I mean to have nothing more to do with book-making. I shall be in Phil[ia] shortly and then we can arrange matters.

Yours truly<br>Tho[s] Nuttall [36]

Torrey's not infrequent complaints that Nuttall did not keep abreast of the botanical literature were just. He had no library and in Cambridge had no ready access to current taxonomic works or to any herbarium except his own. The prolonged delay in finishing his paper on the Arkansas flora seems to have been due partly to the lack of technical aids and partly to problems inherent in the material. There were peculiar difficulties in working with species from a new region. An axiom that Willdenow annunciated, "Specific characters to be perfect, must be common to no other species of the genus," requires a relative knowledge that could be unavailable for a new flora. It would seem that for many specimens Nuttall lacked bases for satisfactory taxonomic decisions.

Although highly specialized botanical literature was not available in the Harvard Library, there were a number of active naturalists nearby happy to discuss scientific matters with "an ardent and accomplished" confrere. Nuttall was cordially welcomed by his neighbor Dr. Waterhouse,[37] the botanist Dr. Jacob Bigelow (1787–1879), the entomologist Dr. Thaddeus W. Harris of Milton, the arachnologist Nicholas M. Hentz, and the mineralogists Dr. John White Webster and Dr. Joseph G. Cogswell. Cogswell, the only one of the four doctors of philosophy on the faculty, who had given much time to natural science at Göttingen, had plunged into it, studying botany with Schrader "who teaches me very little," mineralogy and geology with Hausmann "who is prime," and natural history with Blumenbach (now regarded as the founder of anthropology). "Saturdays I make excursions with Schrader, and Sundays with Hausmann who makes nothing of 15 or 20 miles."[38] Cogswell probably enjoyed reminiscing about these experiences to such an interested auditor as Nuttall. Dr. Harris, who had received a gold medal from the Massachusetts Society for Promoting Agriculture for a recent "Essay on the Natural History of the Salt-Marsh Caterpillar," at Nuttall's suggestion started a correspondence with Thomas Say, writing to him on July 7.[39]

Nonscientists were equally cordial to the newcomer. Whether or not Nuttall attended President Kirkland's weekly parties, he quickly became acquainted with his colleagues and evidently respected their varied gifts and abilities as they did his. George Bancroft, now ranked as the earliest comprehensive and scholarly worker in United States history, was eager to hear Nuttall's observations on old Indian sites in the Mississippi valley. At Mrs. Peck's pleasant and hospitable home, Nuttall met her French brother-in-law, his "jovial but infinitely courteous" fellow instructor, Francis Sales, who clung to his old-fashioned pigtail and hair powder, and also Mrs. Peck's brother, William Hilliard, of the College Bookstore. The wives of Nuttall's colleagues took great interest in the traveled and distinguished bachelor who was added to their circle; throughout his years in Cambridge he found himself prized as a dinner guest. During his first months in Cambridge he plunged not only into unaccustomed duties but also into a life of relative sociability.

LAST MONTHS OF 1823. Nuttall was eager to introduce his young students to the pleasures of natural history *in situ*. From his first weeks at Harvard he was joined by students on walks about Cambridge or on more extended excursions.[40] Such a walking companion,

George Putnam, a friendly freshman, invited Nuttall to his family's farm in Sterling for the weekend before Commencement (Wednesday, August 27). Putnam prepared his mother for the impending visit with youthful guile:

I recollect your charging me never to bring home any of my classmates, but you never told me not to bring home a Proffessor [*sic*]. I shall introduce you to one when I go home. The case is this. I have become acquainted with Mr. Nuttall, lecturer upon Natural History (particularly botany) and who will probably succeed the present professor of mineralogy who is soon to resign. He has travelled in almost all parts of the U. States, and now wants to scour the County of Worcester for new plants & minerals and as he has made me very fond of the latter interesting science, & given me more than 100 different specimens, I am to accompany him. . . . I shall travel with him in quest of plants, & shall learn their names, natures and uses, as he is acquainted with every known plant in America & is the greatest botanist in the country. . . . You certainly would not have me neglect this very valuable opportunity of travelling with so good a natural Historian who can describe to me every natural object we meet with. For what shall we study in preference to nature? . . . He is a plain, honest & social Englishman. . . .[41]

The mineralogical excursion proved very successful. The two visited quarries and rocky outcrops in Sterling, Bolton, and Worcester. One of their prizes, secured on the Putnam farm, proved on testing to be spodumene, the first reported discovery of it in the western hemisphere. As soon as Nuttall learned that George T. Bowen's analysis confirmed his own identification, he wrote a letter announcing the find to Dr. Isaac Hays, Editor of the *Journal* of the Academy of Natural Sciences, who promptly published it.[42] This report caused a widespread reexamination of specimens that led to the recognition that a mineral which had been called "White Augite" was in reality spodumene.

After leaving Putnam, Nuttall walked through the township of Harvard, prospecting as he went, and at evening he arrived at the steepleless "meetnoss" (his rendering of the Yankee pronunciation of meetinghouse) in Boxboro.

I naturally enough expected to find a tavern or house of entertainment but here I was disappointed, and had serious thoughts of lying down for the night under a tree, for I never had any dislike to view the canopy of heaven as my curtain. Still the singularity of the thing and the well known hospitality of New England induced me, rather reluctantly, (from the boring I expected to receive) to make application to a neighbouring farmer, whom I soon found willing and friendly enough to open his doors and spread his fare to the benighted stranger. Here about ½ past 5 A.M. was I again shown *another* pretended silver-mine, but as fortunately as formerly, for the welfare of this poor but happy country, nothing was to be seen but a pile of weathered rocks of Gneiss. . . .

About a mile north from the meeting-house I came to one of the limestone quarries, the object of my search. . . . The lilac scapolite was here fine and abundant with some few crystals of bright pale blue phosphate of Lime. I here, however, discovered something new, viz. the same Garnet with that accompanying the *Idocrase* at Worcester. . . . There are several other lime-quarries in Boxbury but I had not time to visit them. . . . I met with the coach at 12 o'clock and arrived in good time at Cambridge. Here I found a deserted house and locked doors, instead of my usual friendly reception.[43]

Nuttall presumably attended Commencement on Wednesday. On the day after Commencement, only slightly less important as the Anniversary Day of Phi Beta Kappa, George Bancroft had the honor of delivering the Poem. An English visitor, John Finch, a grandson of Joseph Priestley, after attending the exercises walked out to see the Botanic Garden. His account of the afternoon shows an informed interest in plants.

I had the pleasure of being acquainted with Professor Nuttall, the curator of the garden, and lecturer on Botany to the College. He is well known in the scientific world by his travels in the Arkansas Territory, and by various botanical publications, among which his Genera of North American plants has, I believe, the first place. . . .

After gratifying my curiosity by viewing the most rare plants, I proposed a walk in the neighboring fields, and we made a tour of a mile to a pond in the vicinity.

In our walk we observed several species of Aster, of which nearly seventy varieties are found in the North East States. The sagittaria, the berberis, and the vaccinium, reminded us of the gay fields of England, but the brilliant flowers of the spiraea coccinea recalled the idea that we were in a far distant land. On the borders of the pond we found the scented flowers of the nymphaea odorata, or odorous lily, and returned to Cambridge much pleased with our excursion.[44]

Nuttall had received news from home that troubled him. His Uncle Jonas required his presence in England to confer concerning the ultimate disposition of his considerable estate. The problem had been precipitated by the sudden death the previous autumn of Richard Dixon, a nephew of Jonas and the husband of Thomas's sister Elizabeth, who was left with three children — Frances, Francis, and Maria Louisa — all under six years of age. Jonas, who presumably had planned on leaving his property to Richard Dixon, doubly bound to him through marrying a favorite niece, now considered making Thomas his heir. Thomas felt a moral obligation to acquiesce in the plan in the interest of his sister's children but was very apprehensive concerning possible exactions that might be made of him if he agreed to accept the inheritance because Jonas had never become reconciled to his wanderings in dangerous regions of an untamed continent. Torn by misgivings Thomas obtained permission from the Board of Visitors of the Botanic Garden to go to England.[45]

Added to his apprehensions that his days in America might be nearing their end, a disturbing situation arose at Harvard to plague him. He sought relief from his distress by writing about it to George Putnam on September 16.

I thought it almost certain that I should have been the lecturer or professor of Mineralogy and Geology as you may remember from the seemingly qualified [unqualified?] assurance of the President. . . , but I find that there may be to me a "slip betwixt the Cup and the Lip." Who would have thought that my *seeming* friend D.ʳ Webster should have moved so far out of the honourable track as to endeavour to snatch from me this little additional employment and emolument, yet nothing is more certain than the fact of his endeavours to serve me, after all my confidence in him — this unexpected *"ill-turn".* . . . I have, however, put in my claim, with what success time must show. If I am, however, debarred from this privilege, with the offer of w.ʰ I have, as you know, been tantalised, I intend never again to appear in any part of the college on any occasion. . . . I think it probable that the President is unacquainted with all this brewing, but I am prepared for the consequences, and if unfavourable I shall probably *never return* from England.

The opening for an instructor in mineralogy was occasioned by the departure of Joseph G. Cogswell to start, with George Bancroft, a Gymnasium-type school for boys, based on ideas Cogswell and Bancroft had picked up in Germany — the Round Hill School in Northampton. Cogswell had served as Librarian for three years, and also as Professor of Geology and Mineralogy through the generosity of five patrons who believed that his European training would be valuable to the students. Their donations ceased with his departure, but mineralogy had become generally accepted as a part of a college curriculum (largely through the activities of Cleaveland at Bowdoin and Silliman at Yale) so the Corporation planned to continue the course, financing it from the general funds.

Nuttall, reporting the situation as he saw it to John Lowell, learned that another member of the Faculty had expressed opposition to Webster's appointment. Lowell assured Nuttall that Webster would not be approved for the position.[46] At their meeting on September 8, the Fellows voted that the election of a Professor of Mineralogy be postponed.

Whatever John White Webster may have said to encourage Nuttall in his hopes of securing the lectureship, he was certainly actively working for his own appointment. On October 1, 1823, he wrote to ask Benjamin Silliman to assure the Corporation as to his ability in chemistry, their only uncertainty.[47] The doubts in the minds of the Corporation concerning Webster seem to have been of a different sort than he believed. In January 1824, a circular letter was sent out on a confidential basis by President Kirkland soliciting names of qualified candidates "of talents . . . of well regulated temper and feelings and of fair character."[48] George T. Bowen (1802–1828), Yale 1822, who was doing graduate work with Dr. Robert Hare of the University of Pennsylvania, was unsuccessfully recommended for the position by Hare, Benjamin Silliman, and Nuttall.[49] In the summer of 1824 Cleaveland was offered the position, but he preferred to remain at Bowdoin. On November 15, 1824, in an emergency created by the illness of Dr. John Gorham, the Erving Professor of Chemistry, Webster was appointed Lecturer in Chemistry, Mineralogy, and Geology for two years at a salary of $800, with the usual proviso that he must live in Cambridge. The combining of these sciences was contemporary practice — Silliman at Yale, Cleaveland at Bowdoin, and James Freeman Dana while at Dartmouth taught all three — an economical arrangement well suited to the conditions and knowledge of the times. Since Nuttall made no pretensions of being a chemist, he probably eventually accepted the events more cheerfully than the tone of his letter to Putnam would promise. Webster continued on the Faculty until 1850 when he was hanged for the murder of Dr. George Parkman.

Young Putnam, for whom Nuttall felt a tender affection, and who seems to have been his sole confidant in Cambridge regarding the desired academic appointment, must have possessed a unique degree of human sympathy and understanding for his tender years — he had just turned sixteen. Like Nuttall he was the only son of a mother early widowed. Later he served for almost fifty years at the First

Church of Roxbury (1830–1876) and was one of the most valued leaders of the area: a member of the State Legislature, active in public education, and for twenty-four years a Fellow of Harvard.

In mid-September Nuttall welcomed for a week's visit a young mineralogist, Charles Upham Shepard, a senior at Amherst. Beginning to collect and study minerals in his early teens, Shepard became a prominent mineralogist of the nineteenth century. At Amherst lectures in chemistry and mineralogy were delivered by Amos Eaton, who gave concentrated courses in sciences annually at a number of small colleges and medical schools. Young Shepard furnished minerals for some of Eaton's lectures and with his help started exchanges of specimens with other collectors. Eaton wrote of him in 1824 to Torrey: "He is a great favorite of Nuttall. . . . The corporation of this college already have an eye upon Chas. U. Shepard as Professor of Chemistry and Natural History when the Professorship is established."[50] We have no information about the start of Shepard's acquaintance with Nuttall, but by 1823 a friendship was established which gave Shepard timely encouragement in following his bent toward science. His mother, Deborah (Haskins) Shepard, and two of her many sisters had married eminent clergymen in the tradition of their maternal forbears. Charles was expected to enter the ministry like his cousin, Ralph Waldo Emerson, or, if not that, the law would be acceptable as it proved to be for William Emerson and the most brilliant cousin, Edward Bliss Emerson, first scholar of his Harvard Class of 1824. There was no precedent in the Upham-Greenough-Emerson clan for a career in science; its contemplation by Charles was regarded with misgivings because possibilities of making a livelihood in it were then severely limited except in medicine, which was repulsive to Charles.

Shepard preserved the draft of a letter which he wrote to Nuttall on October 8, 1823, following his visit in Cambridge, which mentioned the collections of minerals and plants he had made during the happiest week of his life. He presented his best respects to Mrs. Peck.[51]

Soon after Commencement, Nuttall was giving a course of "lectures to a large class who appear to be pleased with the subject — w$^h$ is always my highest reward, as next to enjoyment is its participation." This was evidently the elective course in Natural History for upperclassmen. After the course was over and Nuttall had collected his second quarterly check of $125 as Curator of the Garden on October 23, he set out for Philadelphia, leaving the Garden to the care of William Carter, the gardener.

In Philadelphia Nuttall felt at home. To be sure there was some sadness in his return: on July 22, his venerated friend William Bartram had breathed his last, but the beneficent house and garden on the west bank of the Schuylkill still distilled their warm hospitality at the hands of the Carrs, and 'Nuttall's room' was there to welcome him. He would be happy to converse again with Zaccheus Collins and George Carpenter, to hear about Thomas Say's experiences on St. Peter's River, and to linger in the familiar quarters of the Academy. He attended regular meetings there on November 4 and 11. At the next meeting Say delivered four specimens of *Gorgonia,* a coral from the West Indies, presented by Nuttall.

A young Scot happened to be in Philadelphia, sent to America by the Horticultural Society of London to investigate the latest developments in fruit growing and to obtain specimens of new trees and native flora. David Douglas's *Journal* records his meeting with Nuttall:

Sat. Nov. 1  I waited on Mr. William Dick janitor of the University of Pennsylvania. . . . I had the pleasure of meeting here Mr. Nuttall, whom I found very communicative. We looked round Mr. Dick's garden. . . . Mon. Nov. 3rd  In company with Mr. Nuttall I set out this morning to the residence of the late Mr. Bartram; his niece is a considerable botanist and draws well. Mr. Carr, to whom she is married, has but a modest share of knowledge; this deficiency, however, is made up by his pleasing manner. In front of the house stands a very large cypress, 90 feet high and 23 round, planted by the first John Bartram; his son William (the late) held the tree while his father put the earth round. . . . Mr. Nuttall showed me *Asplenium rhizophyllum* [*Camptosorus rhizophyllus* (L.) Link] on a rock on our way home, four miles from Philadelphia.[52]

David Douglas (1799–1834) was a protégé of William Jackson Hooker, Regius Professor of Botany at the University of Glasgow, who was working on North American plants. By Douglas, who had left the position of head gardener at the Botanic Garden of the University of Glasgow in the spring, Hooker sent over a small parcel of plants for Torrey with whom he had started a correspondence that developed fruitfully for American botany. Torrey's next letter to Hooker makes it apparent that there was no rapprochement between him and the emissary of the Horticultural Society. "Is it true," he asked, "as that fellow Douglass [sic] says (he is such a liar I know not whether to believe him or not) that it [*Pterospora* Nutt.] is allied to Pyrola?"[53]

Douglas proved a most intrepid and successful collector, but his erratic disposition, which deteriorated with his accomplishments, did not endear him to his employers. He sailed twice to northwest America, on the first occasion returning eastward across Canada to join Sir John Franklin's second overland expedition as it came back from the Arctic in 1827. William Drummond, who had been collecting plants in the Canadian Rockies, also returned with the expedition, which sailed from York Factory on Hudson's Bay. Douglas was to precede Nuttall as a botanical collector on the California coast and the Sandwich Islands as well as along the Columbia River.

On October 26 the members of Long's Second Expedition reached Philadelphia from the Northwest. They had made a rapid journey of barely six months up St. Peter's River (Minnesota River), down the Red River to the International Boundary, east to Lake Superior, and back through the Lakes. It had been planned that Dr. Edwin James should act as botanist, but the expedition was arranged so precipitously that he failed to receive the final instructions for making connections with the party and waited for them at Pittsburgh while they were bypassing him on the Cumberland Road. Accordingly Thomas Say, who was a member of the expedition, added botanical collecting to his zoological duties. William H. Keating, the geologist of the expedition, was charged with the responsibility of writing the narrative.

Nuttall applied successfully to Stephen Long for the opportunity of preparing the botanical report from the herbarium specimens. However, when it was time for him to sail for Liverpool, he had finished the discussion of only five species. He returned the materials, saying that he would be back in the spring. When nothing had been heard from him by July 1, Keating arranged for von Schweinitz to do the work and the complete report of the expedition was published before the end of 1824. The Appendix contained a section on zoology by Thomas Say as well as von Schweinitz's botanical paper.[54] Say included two rare insects that Nuttall had brought to him from the Arkansas: *Chauliodes semicornis* of the *Neuroptera* and *Xyela ferruginea* of the *Hymenoptera*.

At the end of the year Charles Upham Shepard, writing a long gossipy letter to his favorite sister, Fanny, who was visiting her numerous Haskins relatives in the Boston area, quoted a passage from a letter he received from his friend Mr. Nuttall, on the eve of his sailing for Liverpool: "If I perish, . . . when I am hurried beneath the silent wave, my soul shall again, once more be present to you, in my last act of affectionate remembrance, as I have willed to you, in that event, the half part of my mineral cabinets, of which you will hear in due time from my executor." [55]

Almost nine years had elapsed since Nuttall had last been in England. These years had been filled with repeated changes of scene, occupation, and associates and with many varied experiences ranging emotionally from peaceful dallying in woodlands and prairies and the not infrequent exquisite pleasure of discovering a plant new to science, to the bitter realization that he might never be able to attain his ambition of collecting in the rich vegetation of the Rocky Mountains. His new position in Cambridge provided him, in his thirty-eighth year, with a regular income, a security he had experienced before only during the months he worked as a printer when he first came to America. The appointment at Harvard was gratifying also as an indication of competence and accomplishment in his chosen field. However, as the first stimulating impact of new duties and environment began to fade, disappointing aspects of the situation were appearing. Far the most serious was a dearth of the reference materials that he needed, neither adequate taxonomic publications nor herbaria being available to him. An attempt to shift his major efforts in research to mineralogy seemed headed toward disappointment. Moreover the exactions of his position limited his freedom in ways he had not foreseen. Jonas's intentions introduced another frustrating uncertainty to his botanical career. Nuttall's mind and spirit were in a maze of unease. His months in England furnished a saving interval during which he got a more detached and pragmatic view of his situation, and he was to return to Harvard the following June apparently reconciled to the duties he had undertaken.

# CHAPTER 12

# ENGLAND
## 1824

Beguiled by its charms, I have found no road rough or difficult, no journey tedious, no country desolate or barren. — Stephen Elliott, writing of Natural History, 1814

Regular packet ships sailing between Philadelphia or New York and Liverpool made good running time. Nuttall probably left Philadelphia about mid-November. Jonas had long been expecting Thomas, who, during his second absence in America, had become a success in his uncle's eyes for he had published two books and held an appointment at the oldest college in the United States. The issues between them were evidently concluded amicably: no requirements were made of Thomas beyond his agreement to ultimately accept the estate. Jonas's final will of eleven folio parchment pages was not signed until the end of 1829; in it he left all his property in trust, first for his wife, next for his nephew Thomas and his lineal heirs, and thirdly, if Thomas left no issue, for his great-nephew Francis Dixon and his heirs.

Thomas's younger sister, Elizabeth, after her marriage to Richard Dixon had lived in Burnley where her husband and a younger brother, Jonas Dixon, were established as ironmongers, but after Richard's sudden death in Dublin on September 21, 1822, at the age of thirty-one, the widow and her three small children seem to have taken up residence at Nutgrove. A sampler uniquely depicting Nutgrove Hall and recording the names and birthdates of the three young Dixons, done by Frances, the eldest child, is still cherished by the family.

# THOMAS NUTTALL, NATURALIST

On January 12, Thomas sent a letter from Liverpool to Augustin Pyramus de Candolle (1778–1841) in Geneva.

Professor Decandolle
Dear Sir,

In a package of specimens sent to Monsieur Gay of Paris, I have ventured to offer you a few specimens of some of the rarer American plants wʰ came to my hand at the time of selecting those for Monsʳ Gay. If they are acceptable or if any thing I have should in future be so, pray favour me with a catalogue and from time to time I may attempt to complete it. In consequence of the honor you have done me in your *immortal work,* I am anxious you should possess all the rare specimens of wʰ I have any duplicates. My address is Cambridge Botanic Garden, near Boston, Massachusetts. I hear your *Great work* is not progressing, if so, believe me I regret it as much as yourself. I wish to be considered one of your subscribers and will make arrangements in Paris for obtaining it. In Roemer and Schultes I have but little confidence, in regard to the plants of the U. States of America it abounds in errors, some of them are *twice* or *three* times described!

Forgive the liberty I have taken but believe me your devoted and ardent disciple.

Thoˢ Nuttall [1]

De Candolle had recognized Nuttall in several ways: he adopted new genera of Nuttall that came within the scope of a monograph on the *Cruciferae* and of his *Regni Vegetabilis Systema Naturale* (1818–1821) such as *Stanleya* and *Mahonia* and new species such as *Dentaria heterophylla* and *D. maxima*; he named a beautiful American genus of the *Aquifoliaceae* "Nuttallia," but it had already been named *Nemopanthus* by Rafinesque, another failure of a generic name honoring Nuttall (see Chapter 7); [2] and he renamed Nuttall's Anemone ludoviciana (Pursh's Clematis hirsutissimus), of which he saw a specimen in Lambert's herbarium in 1816, as A. nuttalliana, but unfortunately the plant finally proved to be a variety of Linnaeus's *A. patens.* "The liberty" Nuttall took in addressing De Candolle would not be taken amiss: Jacob Bigelow wrote, "De Candolle is hungry as a shark [for botanical exchanges] & writes letters by the quire." [3] He needed specimens of all the flowering plants of the world for he was already at work on his great *Prodromus Systematis Naturalis,* a systematic treatment of all known plants. [4]

The traveler soon went to Long Preston to visit his mother and other relatives. Susannah, the elder of his sisters, and her husband, Thomas Booth, had three daughters and a son, the eldest barely ten years old. Nuttall looked at his native village and the surrounding uplands and Pennine summits with a fresh and objective interest, for the second time measuring the familiar countryside by new standards. He was eager to see the mountains of the celebrated Lake Country which were so comparatively near, and accordingly in the latter part of January he set out on foot up the valley of the Ribble. The habit of keeping a journal had become so fixed that he took with him for that purpose a child's copybook; its chance preservation furnishes our only knowledge of Nuttall's trip to the Lakes.[5] Some of its pages show the impressions of a few plants which were dried between them, probably the alpine "cistus and Veronica," which he found the first morning on Giggleswick's "romantic craig" about five miles north of Long Preston. The crag is part of the limestone face of the middle Craven fault rising as a lofty rampart along the road just west of Settle. At its foot Nuttall paused to observe the erratic Ebbing and Flowing Well, the waters of which disappeared to rise again in a few minutes or perhaps an hour. A wet afternoon so mired the road that it was with relief that he arrived in the evening at Kirby-Lonsdale in the Lune Valley of Westmorland. In refreshing contrast to the severe criticisms of America made by many early British visitors, we find Nuttall here denouncing scathingly some of the ways of life in England, contrasting them by implication with superior customs in America.

Cap in hand, with a degrading obsequiousness . . . every servant is a slave and a mendicant. In England this system pervades every thing, in consequence of w$^h$ every man is in the power of his servants who . . . are often apt to be insolent. . . . Every-thing thus appears interlinked with the governing system of a country. A just government can only exist amongst a just people. England is not prepared for this. Ancient barbarism and gross ignorance still too much becloud the intel[l]ects of 9-tenths of the country!

The following day he walked in the rain to Kendal, "an antiquated disagreeable" carpet-weaving town, where he spent a few hours at the museum of a Mr. Todhunter from whom he purchased a considerable number of choice mineralogical specimens which he considered very cheap at a shilling or a shilling, sixpence. On Saturday morning at five o'clock with "the sky clean as in America" he took the coach to Ambleside. The distant snow-capped mountains of Cumberland, first visible in the brilliant light of the stars and the moon, then in full daylight, impressed Nuttall as of majestic grandeur surpassing anything he had ever seen — evidence, if it be needed, that he had not attained a view of the Rockies. At Ambleside "at the head of Winandermere [the original name of Windermere] we breakfasted at an elegant hotel called Salutation."[6] Now Nuttall's point of view becomes conservative: "Our breakfast in the usual simple neat style of England without any of those perplexing and ill-as[s]orted medleys of food w$^h$ commonly loaden our American tables at all hours of the day. The charge is & 9d sufficiently reasonable for such superior accomodation." It was the custom at this time at the inns on the American frontier to put every eatable in the house on the table at each meal.

After his gratifying breakfast, Nuttall proceeded on foot in order to have leisure to enjoy the picturesque scenery along the road through Rydal and Grasmere. His descriptions of the scenery *en route* are extravagant and flowery:

I . . . stood still in wonder to view the sublime picture w$^h$ presented itself before me. The beautifull little hamlet of Rigal [Rydal], a new and neat gothic church almost completed a lovely gothic cottage with a view on Winandermere shaded with yews and luxur$^{ant}$ clasping ivy$^s$, parterres, smooth and elegantly artificial amidst native rocks trees and bushes then the splendid Hall of Rigal the seat of lady Fleming with a beautifull garden and extensive lawn bordered by clumps and rows of tall firs and larches.[7] But O! Nature, who can paint like thee, or convey those wonderous and fantastic, ever varied forms, w$^h$ she presents so liberally to every eye.

An aerie of herons in lofty fir trees on an island in Rydal Water caught his attention; he saw *Erica* and numerous mosses and lichens but at this time of year the composition of the rocks and their conformation were the most constant sources of interest. North of Grasmere he noted that the prevailing slate "becomes striped like the rocks of Barren-Hill near Phil$^{ia}$ and like that and the rocks of the neighborhood of Northampton on the road to Hatfield [Massachusetts] it becomes a prismatic Sienite, but still more or less porphyritic, spotted and str[i]ped red & green."

He continued to Keswick on Derwent Water, where he remained over Sunday, starting his return journey Monday afternoon. There he was even more impressed: "I will not attempt to describe the scenery. It is impossible words cannot convey images of objects so sublime . . . what can give ideas of the grandeur of enormous bulk, of the varying moving tints, and surrounding elements of such scenes

All is in vain, O Nature, all sinks into utter insignificance before the majesty of thy incomprehensible power." After discussing the mines of excellent graphite near Keswick he wrote "The scotch graphite like that of Worcester (Mass) appears to be found near anthracite and is little better."

The diary was suddenly abandoned as diaries so commonly are. It reveals a man ardently attached to America and identifying himself wholeheartedly with it.

The partnership of Nuttall, Fisher, and Dixon had been dissolved in October 1818, due to the fatal illness of Francis Dixon. By 1820, Henry Fisher was established in a prosperous printing business in Newgate in London where he is said to have reprinted both of Thomas's books, *Genera of North American Plants* and *Journal of a Journey into Arkansa Territory*. Presumably it was for one of these publications that a portrait of Thomas was drawn by Derby and engraved by Thomson. This shows a serious young man with dark, wavy hair receding from a high forehead, a gentle mouth, and firm chin. Fisher's reprints were not listed in book catalogs of the time, and no copies of the volumes have been located, but a few engraved copies of the portrait have been found in London print shops. These are dated March 1, 1825.[8]

Nuttall took to England some unidentified specimens of minerals on which he wanted expert opinion. At the Mineralogical Department of the British Museum he consulted Mr. Koenig to whom he later introduced Charles Shepard as a correspondent for the exchange of specimens. It was perhaps through Mr. Koenig that he made the acquaintance of Henry Heuland, the largest mineral dealer in London. Heuland, failing to recognize a specimen which Nuttall had collected at Bolton on his August expedition with George Putnam, submitted it to Henry James Brooke (1771–1857), F.R.S., F.L.S., the inventor of a blowpipe widely used in the analysis of minerals and the author of *A Familiar Introduction to Crystallography*, printed in 1823, and many papers on mineralogy.[9] Brooke published the mineral as "nuttallite" under date of April 20, 1824.[10] This white or smoky-brown mineral is now regarded as a variety of scapolite.

From January 1, 1823, through November 1, 1827, the *Botanical Magazine* carried plates of eight of the Arkansas species that Nuttall had published and distributed to nurserymen. The drawing of *Nemophila phacelioides* (t. 2373) was made from plants raised by John

Walker, Esq., at Southgate. The drawing of *Coreopsis* *tinctoria* (t. 2512) was made from plants flowering in September 1823 for William Anderson at the Chelsea Garden. Nathaniel S. Hodson, the Superintendent of the Bury St. Edmunds Botanic Garden, also submitted a specimen. Drawings of *Monarda* *russeliana* (t. 2513), *Oenothera* *triloba* (t. 2566), *Penstemon* *Digitalis* (t. 2587), *Froelichia floridana* (Nutt.) Moq. (Oplotheca florida) (t. 2603), *Callirhoë digitata* (Nuttallia digitata Dick ex W.P.C. Barton) (t. 2612), and *Helianthus* *petiolaris* (H. pubescens) (t. 2778) were done from specimens raised by Robert Barclay at Buryhill, Surrey, from seed that Nuttall gave him in March 1824 when on a visit to his gardens and conservatories, famous for the exotic plants which Barclay received from collectors scattered in remote spots of the world. The editor of the *Botanical Magazine* especially admired the *Penstemon*, "by far the finest species of this genus that we have seen, growing upright to more than three feet in height, and bearing a very large panicle of delicate white flowers, of which the size of our work would not admit half to be inserted [although the plate was folded twice]."

Robert Barclay (1751–1830), of a famous Quaker family, had been born in Philadelphia but at an early age he went to England and entered his Uncle James Barclay's bank. Some years later he purchased Thrale's brewery and made a great fortune that supported a leisure devoted to the cultivation of plants. His gardens, developed from 1805, were famous in a land of beautiful gardens, as famous as his Barclay's Gin. To his passion for rare and elegant plants, the *Botanical Magazine* owed its existence: Barclay, an original member of the Linnean Society, persuaded William Curtis to launch the periodical in order to figure and describe the new species with horticultural appeal that were flowing into England in abundance from all parts of the world toward the end of the eighteenth century.

In distributing seeds Nuttall did not forget the Liverpool Botanic Garden where John Shepherd still presided. Among the herbarium sheets of the Garden which have survived in the Botanical Department of the Liverpool Public Museums are undated specimens of at least three of his Arkansas plants and three from "Boston," presumably grown at the Liverpool gardens from seed presented by Nuttall.[11]

The second volume of Lambert's *Pinus* was published in 1824. Lambert had as keeper of his herbarium and library from about 1820,

David Don (1800–1841), who gave Nuttall a copy of his monograph on the Polemoniaceae.[12] He was a nursery-trained Scot who worked under William Anderson at the Apothecaries' Garden on his first arrival in London. In 1822 he succeeded Robert Brown as Librarian of the Linnean Society; from 1836 he also served as professor of botany at King's College, London. During his too brief life he published fifty-two botanical papers; in 1838 he referred Nuttall's Rudbeckia columnifera (1813) to *Ratibida* Raf. His brother George Don (1798–1856) altered the generic names of a few of Nuttall's species.

Nuttall is not recorded as attending any of the meetings of the Linnean Society at this time, which is hardly surprising. He was in debt to the Society for his initiation assessment and eleven years' membership fees, a total of sixteen guineas. Moreover in June 1823, the Council of the Society, making a special effort to collect outstanding dues, had sent stern letters to members in arrears.

During this visit to England, Nuttall evidently met Francis Boott (1792–1863) of Boston, who, having spent most of his time in England after graduating from Harvard in 1810, settled there permanently in 1820. After receiving his medical degree at the University of Edinburgh in 1824, he resided in London where he was an active supporter of the Linnean Society and of the establishment of London University. He was a friend of all botanists, especially American visitors. Nuttall doubtless had received a letter to him from Jacob Bigelow. Boott esteemed Nuttall's *Genera* highly and maintained a keen interest in the author and his activities.

Nuttall had heard appreciative reports of the English botanist, William Jackson Hooker (1785–1865), not only from his protégé, David Douglas, but also from several Americans. John Torrey, Stephen Elliott, Zaccheus Collins, von Schweinitz, and Jacob Bigelow were among his correspondents; Francis Boott, a devoted admirer, had given his American herbarium to Hooker.[13] Hooker had been elected a Corresponding Member of the Academy of Natural Sciences of Philadelphia in 1821, and Nuttall had sent him several rare specimens in the summer of 1823.[14] Of a gifted family and independent fortune, Hooker had been active in natural history from childhood. He collected in the wilds of Scotland, the Hebrides and Orkneys, and on the continent, and, in 1809, made an expedition to Iceland. In 1806 he was elected to the Linnean Society; thus by the age of twenty-one he had "already penetrated into the innermost circle of

Science of the country." He soon distinguished himself further by several monographs on the mosses illustrated by fine plates made from his own drawings. He carried on a tremendous correspondence and distributed specimens and publications freely. By great industry and dedication abetted by natural generosity and charm, he built up through exchanges the finest private herbarium in Britain. Although only half a year older than Nuttall, he already ranked with Robert Brown as preeminent among British botanists. From 1820 he held the Regius Professorship of Botany at the University of Glasgow.[15]

Nuttall journeyed to Glasgow to meet him. "The University stands . . . in a dense . . . very old and shabby part of town . . . [its] buildings all of dark gray granite, cold, hard and venerable . . . [of] a pervading sternness and grimness." Hooker's lecture room was a "small, dingy building" in the center of the Botanic Gardens, "most unfavorably situated." Nuttall found Hooker to be as friendly, engaging, and devoted to botany as he had been led to believe. He was then in the process of publishing *Flora Exotica* (1822–1827). He gave Nuttall some herbarium specimens collected by Dr. John Richardson, naturalist of Sir John Franklin's overland expeditions to the Arctic. Hooker's prospects of receiving more new species from America were excellent, for in the summer David Douglas was to sail for the mouth of the Columbia River in a ship of the Hudson's Bay Company to collect for the Royal Horticultural Society; and Dr. John Scouler (1804–1871) of Glasgow, the ship's surgeon who was to stay in the Northwest, was an excellent and devoted naturalist.

Nuttall was a guest in Hooker's hospitable home on Bath Street during his Glasgow stay. Mrs. Hooker, daughter of the naturalist Dawson Turner, assisted her husband with his writings, and the boys, William Dawson (1816–1840) and Joseph Dalton (1817–1911), were showing interest in natural history. Nuttall responded wholeheartedly to Hooker's kindly charm and broad botanical knowledge and henceforth valued his good opinion beyond that of any other botanist. Hooker reciprocated by constant interest in Nuttall's activities and publications. However his information about Nuttall was usually indirect, for Nuttall was to prove a poor correspondent so long as he lived in America. He did, however, continue to send herbarium specimens to Hooker.

Nuttall evidently met Professor Thomas Thomson, Regius Professor of Chemistry and an active mineralogist, while he was in Glasgow. After returning to America, Nuttall and also Torrey, sent Thomson minerals for analysis; his results, sent to Nuttall, were reported to the Lyceum of Natural History of New York on November 5, 1827, by Torrey, and published in the next volume of the *Annals*.[16]

On May 16, when Nuttall embarked at Liverpool for Boston on the *Lucilla,* a young companion, Joseph Whitfield (aged sixteen, laborer), was with him. He was probably a son of Jonas's farmer, Thomas Whitfield, and it is likely that Joseph came to America as an assistant to Nuttall.[17] He accompanied Nuttall on some excursions and drew illustrations for papers of Nuttall in 1825 and 1830 and for his botanical textbook published in 1827.

When Nuttall reached Cambridge on June 9, he found that unpleasant changes had taken place at the Garden House: it had been leased to a Mr. Joley, who maintained a rooming and boarding house. Some of the occupants Nuttall found aggressively objectionable; especially difficult was a Mr. White, who wanted free access to the garden for himself and his family. To keep social intercourse with the other residents at a minimum, Nuttall obtained permission from the Board of Visitors to have an east window of his study changed to a door opening to the garden. Other minor changes isolated him further. An enclosed passageway, flanking the chimney, lay between his study and the kitchen; through an aperture cut in the kitchen door he received his meals. A trapdoor cut in the ceiling of the passage opened into the closet of his bedroom so that a ladder gave ready connection between the rooms. By these simple and inexpensive changes Nuttall established a separate apartment for himself with a private entrance.[18]

He was enthusiastically welcomed back by a letter of July 10 from young Shepard, who had just heard of his return. Shepard had been to Cambridge in May and left in Mr. Carter's care living plants of the climbing fern *Lygodium palmatum* from Granby, which Nuttall wanted for the Garden. He was especially disappointed that Nuttall had not yet returned for he wanted his advice as to his future career; he refused to become a physician, a minister, or a lawyer. He urged Nuttall to make him a visit in Amherst.[19]

In his answer of July 25, Nuttall gave advice freely concerning Shepard's future.

On this subject, my dear friend, you well know I shall prove only a partial adviser, for it is not in me to dare to lift up my voice against the interests of Natural Science. Besides your objections to the overcharged professions, urged upon you by kind friends, there is the voice of this great and *growing* nation in w$^h$ we have the happiness to live in favour of scientific devotion. I have ever despised those paltry, tame and trifling conveniences so superlatively valued by the ordinary world, and have always lived ready to part with all that might hinder me from becoming nature's disciple. I recommend not this to you. It will not be your lot, as it has been mine, also to struggle with apalling [sic] poverty, to have to labour for your bread at a mechanical employment, and only to enjoy leisure moments stollen [sic] from ordinary rest, in w$^h$ to acquire the sweets of science! Besides, if you have a love for Chemistry, I make no doubt that you will obtain a professorship, as I well know your industry and talent, if improved, will raise you, at least to rank with your contemporaries. Conceal this advice of mine from your interested friends, for I too well know, how little it would please them, and yet I am bold to defend the interests of science, not merely for the love I bear it, but also for the interest I take in the improvement of the nation of w$^h$ we form a part. I can have no selfish or sinister motives in this advice, I recommend it only from predilection, and feel confident, at the same time, that the enlightened age & nation we live in will not neglect to reward and support all those who may devote themselves to usefull knowledge.

Nuttall was planning a journey to northern New England. In his letter to Shepard he said that he would probably call on him in Amherst in three weeks' time and would like to make a short collecting excursion with him. However he had not appeared by August 20, and it is doubtful that he got to western Massachusetts that year.[20]

## CHAPTER 13

# "VEGETATING AT HARVARD"

He never, however, felt at home in his professorship: his active
mind yearned for sterner occupations in the field of nature, and he
used to describe himself as merely "vegetating" and "doing nothing
for science!" — Thomas Meehan.

THE WHITE MOUNTAINS. "Lofty mountains" in the interior of
New England, seen from the ocean by Verrazano as early as 1524,
were, in two ascents of the highest peak in 1642, found "daunting
terrible" and of no economic interest. Thereafter they remained in
remote isolation until after the Revolution. The first attempt to make
scientific observations of the White Mountains was made in July
1784 by a small party organized by the Reverend Jeremy Belknap
(1744–1798), Harvard College 1762, of Dover, New Hampshire,
with the assistance of the Reverend Manasseh Cutler (1742–1823),
Yale 1765, of Ipswich, Massachusetts, New England's first botanist.[1]
Another distinguished member of the party was Dr. Joshua Fisher
(1748/9–1833), Harvard College 1766, of Beverly, Massachusetts,
president of the Massachusetts Medical Society, who was to endow
Harvard's first permanent professorship of natural history. Three and
a half days on horseback from Dover brought them to the eastern foot
of the highest mountain, which they named Mount Washington.
Here they camped with local guides at 2000 feet near a beaver-
built meadow and made the ascent the next day. Much of the flora
of the upper half of the climb, Dr. Cutler had not seen before; he
described mountain cranberry, Labrador tea, and other plants as
strange to him. Clouds and damage to their barometer caused them
to greatly overestimate the height as about 10,000 feet (correctly
6288). Unfortunately Cutler's plant collection was ruined, but his

observations on the zonation of the plants were published by Belknap in his three-volume *History of New Hampshire*.[2]

Cutler wanted to collect again on the mountain but his many activities in the public interest interfered. It was not until late in July 1804 that he again reached the mountains in the company of William Dandridge Peck.[3] They were joined by a few friends, including Nathaniel Bowditch, and several guides. Peck lost half of his plant collection in descending a gully, but "many new vegetables" (new, that is, to Americans, but many, being circumpolar, were known in Europe) were preserved including *Geum peckii* Pursh, *Empetrum nigrum* L., *Rhododendron lapponicum* (L.) Wahlenb., *Vaccinium Oxycoccus* L., *Diapensia lapponica* L., *Castilleja septentrionalis* Lindl., and some new diminutive willows.

The botanical observations of Cutler and Peck in 1804, and study of the specimens which they had brought back, made it apparent that Mount Washington possessed a rare flora on its open ridges and peaks — so barren to the eyes of the uninitiated — and in the "hanging gardens" of the headwalls of the precipitous ravines. As this knowledge slowly spread, a pilgrimage to the Washington Range became a compulsion for plant enthusiasts of New England for here, they heard, could be seen in narrow compass a succession of growth such as would be met with on a journey to Hudson Straits: dense Canadian-type forests clothing the lower slopes, dwarfed birch and spruce above, and low subarctic plants flourishing on the exposed upper reaches.

In 1807, George C. Shattuck, M.D., with five Dartmouth friends, reached the summit from the western side with a guide; he calculated the altitude as 6268 feet. His account of the ascent and the vegetation was published by Professor Barton in his *Philadelphia Medical and Physical Journal*, where Nuttall would have read it.[4]

In 1816, Dr. Jacob Bigelow, Francis Boott, Francis Calley Gray, Lemuel Shaw, and Nathaniel Tucker from Boston climbed Wachusett, Monadnock, Ascutney, and Mount Washington. Bigelow and Boott were then planning to publish a flora of New England, and Gray and Shaw were interested in zoology. The party, approaching the White Mountains from the Connecticut River, took the road down through the western notch and skirted the southern ridges to reach the eastern notch where Cutler had started his two ascents. On July 2, accompanied by a guide, they followed the Cutler River upwards through the forest, passed the belt of dense spruce thicket with comparative ease "by a path cut by the direction of Col. Gibbs, who ascended the mountain some years since," [5] and after crossing a gentle slope climbed steeply up Boott Spur to the "plain" (Bigelow's Lawn) from which the peak rose. The winter wren was glimpsed, and Shaw noted the cliff swallow, its earliest known occurrence in New England. [6] "In the interstices" of the rocks above tree line "were occasional patches of dwarfish fir and spruce, and beautiful tufts of small alpine shrubs, then in full flower." All along the way plants were collected, some within a few feet of the top. Years later Boott wrote to William Jackson Hooker of the "rapture" he experienced in gathering *Geum peckii* and its alpine associates. [7]

Boott returned to Mount Washington in August with his brother, John Wright Boott (1788–1845), and got fruiting specimens of species collected in flower earlier. In a small collection of Francis Boott in the Liverpool Museum there is one choice specimen from each of the two trips: "Menziesia [*Phyllodoce*] caerulea (Pursh), Mt. Washington, N. H., July 2, 1816" and "Andromeda [*Cassiope*] hypnoides L., Mt. Washington, Aug. 25, 1816." The July excursion, described by Bigelow in the October number of the *New England Journal of Medicine and Surgery,* and the August follow-up yielded about seventy species; six, considered new, were described briefly in Latin. [8]

By 1820 Abel Crawford and his son Ethan Allen Crawford (1792–1846), who lived twelve miles apart in the wild pass on the west of Mount Washington (Crawford Notch), had cut two trails through the woods to open ridges. This attracted climbers to their inns; for years thereafter the eastern route was rarely used by visitors. Early western ascents were made by Amos Binney, Jr., Caleb Cushing, and George B. Emerson, and by James Pierce, a mineralogist whose report of his excursion was published in Silliman's *Journal* to which he was a faithful contributor. [9]

On July 2, 1823, two Lowell cousins recorded in Ethan Allen's guest book that they had made the ascent from his inn unguided. They reached the beginning of the steep climb by the seven-mile trail through the woods and came down off the summit by the great southwest ridge to visit the alpine "Blue Pond" (Lakes of the Clouds) whence they took "Escape Glen by the course of the Amenoosuck to the camp, a passage romantic and precipitous. . . . Here one of our party came near to losing his life, the root of a tree by which he supported himself, having given away over a perpendicular precipice of 50 feet." This is the first known trip through Ammonoosuc Ravine. From the foot of the ravine they took the same foot trail back to the inn.[10] One of the cousins, John Amory Lowell (1789–1881), the son of John Lowell of the Botanic Garden Committee, accumulated a large and scientifically valuable herbarium (now at the Gray Herbarium, Harvard University) to which Nuttall made important contributions. His companion, known as "John Jr." (1799–1836) founded the Lowell Institute.

Two botanists from Boston stayed at E. A. Crawford's in August of the same summer, Benjamin D. Greene and Henry Little (d. 1826), a student working under Dr. Jacob Bigelow's direction at Harvard Medical School. The great wealth of Greene's father enabled him to pursue botany with continuous enthusiasm. Little, an orphaned second cousin of Charles Pickering, like Charles had grown up under the aegis of the gifted Pickering clan in Salem. This pair went up the Crawford Path on the southwest ridge and stayed three days on the "Alps." Their botanizing was very successful: Greene found an extremely rare alpine moss, *Splachnum mnioides* L., and a far-northern honeysuckle.[11]

The several botanical excursions to the White Mountains came to Nuttall's attention, the earlier ones through publications and the later ones by direct or indirect reports of Shattuck, Bigelow, Boott, Cushing, George B. Emerson, Greene, Little, and the Lowells — any or all of whom may have strongly recommended the area to him and informed him of the best collecting spots. Nuttall signed his own name and that of Josh Whitfield in E. A. Crawford's Register on August 12, 1824.[12] Dr. Joseph Barratt (1796–1882), a student of the willows, "was near meeting him" there for he stayed at Crawford's not long afterwards; his disappointment over the missed opportunity of seeing the illustrious botanist, a compatriot, was keen. "Mrs. Crawford told me she was quite surprised to see him pack up such a quantity of plants in new paper. He was a whole day she said in doing this. . . . I told them who Mr. Nuttall was and the extent of his travels. . . . This made Wonders."[13] Nuttall had been perhaps two, three, or more days on Mount Washington before he arrived at the inn, for his collection was very complete. It is most probable that he and Whitfield ascended the mountain on the east side using the route which Cutler, Peck, Bigelow, and Boott had followed up Cutler River

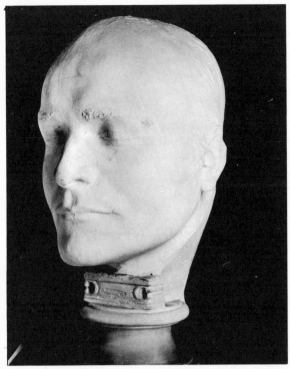

Life mask of Nuttall made by his neighbor Susan Austin, probably in the early 1830s. Courtesy of the Gray Herbarium, Harvard University.

Thomas Nuttall, F.L.S., in 1824; from an engraving published in London in 1825, presumably as a frontispiece for his two books reprinted by Henry Fisher, previously Jonas Nuttall's partner. Courtesy of Dr. Frans Verdoorn.

A Nuttallian specimen. The small label bearing a complete description in Latin of the plant and the site of collection ("R. Mt. woods in the Columbia plains") shows the economy of Nuttall's records. The printed label was added by the Museum. Although the species is labeled "Aster * Sayii," Nuttall published it as "Aster Sayianus," but Lindley's name of *A. modestus* had priority. Courtesy of the Trustees of the British Museum (Natural History), London.

Nuttall's western dogwood, in J. J. Audubon's Plate 367. For Audubon's painting of the band-tailed pigeon (*Columbia fasciata* Say) and the western dogwood (*Cornus nuttalli* Audubon) Nuttall supplied all the specimens from the valley of the Columbia River. The avian species had already been collected on Long's Expedition (1819–1820) by Thomas Say. Therefore this plate associates three of America's most productive early naturalists. Courtesy of the New-York Historical Society, New York City.

The Garden House, Harvard Botanic Garden. Nuttall's study was immediately to the right of the front entrance and his bedroom was above it; obviously there was no habitable garret. This view from the southwest minimizes the ell added on the east for Asa Gray's study. Courtesy of the Gray Herbarium, Harvard University.

Penyghent from the west northwest; a small beck in the foreground drops into the Alum Pot. This photograph strikingly shows Craven's typical karst topography. Nuttall first climbed Penyghent in 1805, and ascended it again in 1845. Photograph by W. A. Poucher, F.R.P.S.

from the eastern notch. That approach to the mountain was being improved by Daniel Pinkham, commissioned by the State to build a carriage road through the eastern pass (Pinkham Notch). Crawford had built some stone huts on the summit the previous summer but they were damp and cold; sleeping in the scrub on a leeward slope would be more endurable, whereas camping in the eastern ravine could be comfortable. In addition to all the known alpines of the range, Nuttall got *Arctostaphylos alpina* L. not found before on the mountain, and his "practised eye" detected two more species of such rarity that they were not found again for a number of years although sought assiduously — *Carex atratiformis* Britt., a sedge, and *Gnaphalium supinum* L., mountain cudweed, "the smallest and most inconspicuous composite" above timberline on Mount Washington. Nuttall also got a new species of butterfly; occurring only on Mount Washington between 5600 and 6200 feet, it "probably occupies a more restricted geographical area than any butterfly in the world." [14] He gave a specimen to Thomas Say, who published it as Hipparchia semidea.[15] Now *Oeneis semidea,* known popularly as the White Mountain butterfly, it is "the most famous single insect on the range." Nuttall left no direct reference to this visit to the White Mountains or to any later one which he may have made. Toward the end of 1831 when immersed in ornithology, he made an excursion to the extreme north of New Hampshire, which may have taken him through, if not up, the White Mountains.

In the summer of 1825 William Oakes of Ipswich and Charles Pickering of Salem,[16] graduate students in law and medicine respectively, went together for their first visits to the area, Oakes prolonging his stay. He became so increasingly engrossed in botany that he soon devoted all his time to working toward a flora of New England which, being a perfectionist, he did not live to write. His ardor was extreme: John Carey said gunpowder was tame in comparison to Oakes.[17]

A record of unusual interest in Ethan Allen's Register appears to have been written by Dr. Ezekiel Holmes, codiscoverer with Elijah Hamlin of the gem-quality tourmalines at Mount Mica in Paris, Maine.

July 27 [1825] Ezekiel Holmes, Gardiner, James Swan Sullivan [Harvard College 1830], Boston, Eugene Abadie, Philadelphia left Mr. Crawfords house at 7 o'clock in the morning and reached the summit at one o'clock. In the afternoon we were joined by Mr. Oakes & his guide. We concluded to camp on the summit & accordingly *stowed* ourselves away upon the lea side of a rock without *fire* or *candles* shivering & shaking in the mountain breeze like aspen leaves and *freezing* with cold — the thermometer standing at sunrise at 38°. In the morning Sullivan and Abadie descended to the Camp & Holmes in company with the others [Oakes and his guide] *coasted* along by *blue* pond & Mt. Monroe and descended the mountain by the most *villanous break* neck rout [*sic*] of the Amonoosuck.[18]

Later Holmes sent Nuttall some of his alpine rarities including Arnica montana (*A. mollis* Hook.) and Potentilla minima (*P. robbinsiana* Oakes), which Nuttall showed to Oakes. In 1841 Oakes wrote to John Torrey somewhat misleadingly that Holmes was "posterior to Pickering and myself."[19] One wonders whether he knew the identity of his temporary companion of sixteen years before.

Oakes became enamored of the region and during most subsequent summers spent a month or more there, Pickering joining him again in 1827. Oakes was the first botanist to enter the inner solitudes of the mountains and linger there studying the many little "hanging gardens" on the walls of the ravines; the name Oakes Gulf is most fitting for the secluded, extensive, and forbidding recesses of the Mount Washington (Dry) River, the true headwaters of the Saco. It irked him that he was not able to find *Carex atratiformis* and the mountain cudweed; he called them "Nuttall's doubtful species"[20] until "a raw pupil" of Dr. Barratt got the *Carex* on Mount Washington in 1841, and he himself finally found the cudweed. He was generally caustic in criticism of his colleagues but he respected Nuttall's work and, in a letter to Torrey in 1828, conceded to Nuttall a preeminent rank among American botanists.[21]

J. Wright Boott who in 1829 found the alpine *Prenanthes boottii*, named in his honor by De Candolle, must have often visited the range for he reported to Nuttall that the cliff swallows, newcomers from the West, began to build at Ethan Allen's in 1818 and that in 1831 he stumbled onto a nest of snow buntings containing young, in the shelter of low woody growth high up the mountain. He probably was one of the observers of golden eagles soaring over the range.

In 1830, Ethan Allen wrote: "I went up the mountain by an express desire from a botanist to collect plants and save them alive. . . . I carefully took them up with a quantity of earth and . . . placed them in a vase with some moist moss . . . and sent it immediately to Boston. It was safely conveyed, and the plants were placed in a botanical garden."[22] This was the Botanic Garden in Cambridge because Pickering told Oakes in the autumn that Nuttall had alpines from Crawford growing there, mentioning particularly *Arctostaphylos alpina.*[23]

Edward Tuckerman (1817–1886) of Boston, who first visited the region in 1837 after finishing his undergraduate work at Union College, equaled Oakes in his enthusiasm, or perhaps exceeded him, for Oakes called him "a botanical fanatic." The following summer he included Mount Mansfield, the highest summit of the Green Mountains of Vermont, in his mountain tour. He was delighted to see on "The Nose" abundant specimens of the Carex atrata [*C. atratiformis*] of Nuttall, which he and William Oakes had considered doubtful despite their admiration for Nuttall.[24] Summer after summer he explored the extensive ridges and ravines of the main range of the White Mountains and the outliers; even more consistently than for Oakes, their "gulfs," streams, waterfalls, and rocky heights became his summer haunts. He became a lichenologist; the alpine region of the range is, as Oakes succinctly put it, "a perfect garden of lichens." During the dormant seasons he lingered in Cambridge, taking degrees at Harvard in Law in 1839, as a Bachelor of Arts in 1847, and finally in Divinity in 1852, in compensation for his youthful exile at Union College.

How predominant botanists were in the early exploration of Mount Washington is attested by the designations firmly attached to some of its most prominent features. The names of Cutler River, Boott Spur, Bigelow Lawn, Oakes Gulf, and Tuckerman Ravine bear no special connotation to most climbers today but, for the informed, they keep in remembrance early New England botanists. Association of other scientists with the White Mountains is found in the names of Huntington Ravine, Edmands Col, and Mounts Agassiz, Bond, Guyot, Hitchcock, Huntington, Jackson, and Pickering.

ROUTINE, 1824–1826. In the summer of 1824, Nuttall formulated an itinerary to cover special interests in the north: mineralogical sites in Maine, the flora of Mount Washington, and the iron furnaces at Franconia. The most spectacular mineral attraction in northern New England was the recent discovery at Paris, Maine, of tourmalines of gem quality, of "astounding size and transparency." Just before heavy snow buried the area for the winter of 1820–1821, two young amateur mineralogists, Elijah L. Hamlin (1800–1872), Brown 1819, and Ezekiel Holmes (1801–1865), Brown 1821, happened on a few extraordinary crystals. The next spring they found many. After Hamlin sent specimens and information about the discovery to Silliman late in 1822, a thin but persistent stream of enthusiasts made their way to the hilly little town. Dr. Webster was so transported by his harvest that he skipped and danced in ecstasy on the rocky slope of Mount Mica, a vivid memory to his guide. A friend of Hamlin, L. Willis, wrote to him on July 15, 1824, that "Prof. Nuttal [sic] of Cambridge" would visit Paris in the course of a few weeks to see Mount Mica, and he heard the same news from one Pedrick of Salem.[25]

Probably Nuttall started his northern tour by taking a ship of the Kennebec Steamship Company from Boston to Bath with his young English assistant, Joseph Whitfield. They followed a more or less direct route on their way to Paris, walking through Brunswick, where Nuttall collected fibrolite (cummingtonite) at Basin Falls, and Lisbon whence he had a specimen of staurotide (staurolite).[26] At Paris, in addition to the known local minerals, he found crystals of ferruginous columbite associated with spodumene, not before reported from the area.[27] He fortunately met Ezekiel Holmes (M.D., Bowdoin 1824) who showed him his own collection, notable among them a crystal of ferruginous tungsten.[28] The two became correspondents, and Holmes sent Say some Maine insects, doubtless at Nuttall's suggestion.[29] Nuttall was delighted to find a very small and very local northern crucifer, *Subularia aquatica* L., not before known from North America.[30] An excursion into new territory furnished happy surprises at any moment to this ardent student.

To reach Mount Washington from Paris, forty miles away as the crow flies, Nuttall had to cover about twice that distance due to the intervening mountain ranges. At Conway, New Hampshire,[31] he presumably turned northward to the eastern notch (Pinkham), twenty-five miles away. As already recorded, when he registered at Ethan Allen Crawford's inn on August 12, he had completed his alpine harvest. His only notable mineral find on the mountain was cyanite accompanied by small single crystals of staurotide.[32] From Crawford's he took the road down the Ammonoosuc River, detouring to Franconia in order to visit the ironworks there and the magnetite mines three miles away. Here he got almandite, a rich red garnet. Nuttall's route from this point is unknown. Whether he continued on his expedition or returned to Cambridge for Commencement is in doubt.[33]

Before classes started in the autumn, Nuttall had visited Franklin Furnace. In Warwick in nearby Orange County, New York, Dr. Fowler had recently obtained enormously large and handsome crystals of spinel of gem quality in pale blue, various shades of rose, and black. Nuttall found them so superb that he wanted to obtain the finest of them for Mr. Heuland. The specimens he himself got at the site were less magnificent.[34] Other locations where he collected in Orange County before 1825 suggest that he may have crossed it to visit John Torrey at West Point and perhaps also William Meade in Newburgh.[35]

Torrey had married in the spring and in August assumed the position of Acting Professor of Chemistry, Mineralogy, and Geology at the United States Military Academy, where he taught for three years. His industrious pursuit of botany displayed its first major results in 1824; in the spring he finished the text for the first (and, as it proved, the only) volume of *Flora of the Northern and Middle Sections of the United States,* on which he had been toiling for more than two years. He dedicated this to Nuttall "as a tribute of respect for his scientific attainments and as a token of esteem for his personal character." Although now removed from the main routes of travel, Torrey received visits from fellow scientists from time to time. In 1827, Schweinitz visited him, and Dr. William Darlington of West Chester, Pennsylvania, botanized with him on Crow's Nest during a visit of several days.[36] Dr. William Meade was relatively close.

Back in Cambridge in September, Nuttall continued to prospect, making at least one foray to Boxboro with Charles Upham Shepard; there they discovered the first ruby spinel found in New England and the very rare mineral gadolinite in a lime quarry that Nuttall had not had time to visit in 1823.[37] Shepard spent the early autumn in Cambridge.[38] From there he sent to Silliman for publication in the *American Journal of Science* his third list of new localities of minerals; some came from near his home in western Massachusetts; other sites, in Worcester and Middlesex Counties, suggest that he may have collected specimens *en route* to Cambridge.[39] On October 29, he was back in Amherst and a few days later sent some minerals to George Putnam enclosing a few to be delivered to Mr. Nuttall and also packages for his cousin, George Foxcroft Haskins, and Samuel Hurd Walley, classmates of Putnam.[40]

While Shepard was in Cambridge he wrote to Professor Gorham of the faculty of the Medical School applying for an assistantship in chemistry. Nuttall sent an accompanying note recommending him. When the course began in November, Gorham was not well enough to handle it, and John W. Webster was appointed to give it. To him in turn Shepard offered his services on December 12, without success.[41]

During the autumn term Nuttall gave the course in natural history. In the academic year 1824–1825 the long vacation of seven weeks occurred during the winter for the last time. Nuttall took this opportunity to visit Philadelphia. At the Academy, he would see old friends and acquaintances whom he valued. He presumably took to Say at this time the fragile White Mountain butterfly and donated to the Library of the American Philosophical Society copies of his *Genera of North American Plants* and *Journal of Travels in the Arkansa Territory*. He was at a regular meeting of the Academy on January 4, 1825, which Major Stephen Long also happened to attend. On January 27, he signed a salary receipt in Cambridge.

The few visits that Nuttall made to Philadelphia during the rest of his years at Harvard were usually incidental to travel elsewhere, for after 1825 the Academy lost much of its attraction for him. Late in that year crippling changes in the active membership occurred through the departure of Troost, Say, and Lesueur to join the New Harmony colony on the Wabash River in Indiana, under the persuasion of William Maclure. The three scientific recruits were sadly missed at the Academy for they were among the most active members. Nuttall felt a warm attachment to Say, his earliest American friend of his own age and interests. His departure from Philadelphia and the Academy's move to new quarters in the spring of 1826 created an unfamiliar and perhaps nostalgic atmosphere for Nuttall to whom the old Academy rooms had been in lieu of a home for several years.

Dr. Samuel Robinson of Providence, one of the mineralogical fraternity who formed the American Geological Society (1819–1826), published with Cummings, Hilliard and Company of Boston a *Catalogue of Minerals with their Localities*; application for the copyright was made on March 19, 1825. The main text was brought up to date by a large Appendix, a substantial amount of which consisted of Nuttall's accounts of lately discovered locations, seemingly written for this catalog. Therein much light is thrown on his prospecting in New England as well as in other areas. The lists for Massachusetts mention ten localities for Nuttallian collections: two adjoined Cambridge (Brighton and Charlestown); four in Worcester County recorded results of excursions with George Putnam in late August 1823 and with Shepard in September 1824; the other four, in Hampden and Hampshire Counties — Chester, Cummington, Goshen, and Middlefield — dated from the summer of 1822. For Chester, Nuttall listed the only known occurrence of heulandite (named by Brooke) in the United States (doubtless recognized by Heuland himself among specimens that Nuttall took to England). Nuttall's description of the staurolite that he got on Mount Washington as "resembling that of St. Gothard" and other similar comparisons reveal that he had closely studied labeled collections of minerals; opportunity for this was afforded him at Yale, at Harvard, and at the British Museum and Heuland's in England.

About this time Nuttall made some carefully selected donations to Harvard's cabinet of minerals, including red and black spinel from Warwick, New York, and also spinel from Sparta, New Jersey, green feldspar, *Belemnites* filled with phosphate of iron and a few other rarities.[42] These were evidently given in response to published requests by Dr. Webster for gifts to improve the Harvard collection.

During 1824 and 1825 Nuttall contributed to the *Boston Journal of Philosophy and the Arts* (1823–1826), edited by Dr. John Ware (1823–1824 only), Dr. J. W. Webster, and Daniel Treadwell. Nuttall's contribution was a series of five lists of plants as they flowered at the Botanic Garden through a twelve-month period; the first list was of the autumnal flowers of 1824.[43] The plants in the greenhouse were generally listed separately from those growing in the open. The whole number of species is impressive. Obviously the Garden was well supplied with a great number of species of native herbs and shrubs and of exotics from remote regions. Shipments of plants to the Garden usually followed any journey of Nuttall. By visiting noted English gardens and seedsmen and through correspondence, Nuttall continued to add exotics from remote areas, and he furnished some fine ornamentals of his own collecting. In July 1824, the Board of Visitors sent a letter of acknowledgment to Robert Barclay of

Buryhill, Surrey, for forty plants given through Nuttall and in 1827 they requested Nuttall to thank donors in Palermo and Paris who had sent seeds and to offer seeds in return.[44]

In the spring of 1825, when little American effort was being made to increase knowledge of the plants of North America, the activity of the British along these lines was emphasized by the arrival in New York of Dr. John Richardson and the botanical collector Thomas Drummond, on their way to join Sir John Franklin's second overland Arctic Expedition, although Drummond would leave it to collect in the Canadian Rockies. Both would collect plants for William Jackson Hooker. They stopped a day at West Point to see John Torrey. Hooker heard of the visit from both host and visitors. Torrey wrote ". . . Dr. R. gave me . . . some specimens of his plants—as you may well suppose most precious to me."[45] Richardson reported that Torrey shied off showing any part of his herbarium except the western plants of Edwin James, which had already been published; the Britishers concluded that he was apprehensive that Hooker would anticipate him in publication.[46]

During the summer Nuttall got together herbarium specimens to send to Hooker and to De Candolle and wrote letters to accompany the packages. To Hooker he wrote:

Cambridge (Mass) Aug. 13th 1825

Dear Sir,

I am ashamed that so much time should have elapsed since I had the honor and pleasure of seeing you in Glasgow, and to have received from you so many favours without acknowledgment until this protracted period. But, believe me, I never did nor ever can forget your distinguished kindness, and hospitality to the almost unknown stranger. I hurried to prepare a packet for you by a friend of yours purposing soon to revisit Glasgow but I could not accomplish the pleasing task in time. I now send you a box of dried specimens both common and rare. . . . Your opinion on any I desire very much especially such as I am about to publish as new. What other plants you may wish, I hope you will inform me of as it will do me great pleasure to collect or send them to you.

Yours truly
Tho.$^{s}$ Nuttall [47]

Among the rare plants Nuttall sent was *Geum peckii* then known only from Mount Washington. Hooker had already received a specimen of this beautiful plant from Francis Boott.

In writing to De Candolle in Geneva, Nuttall gave his views on the state of American botany at length:

# "VEGETATING AT HARVARD"

Cambridge Aug 14th 1825

Professor DeCandolle,
Sir,

By an unaccountable oversight your letter of the 27th of February 1824, was till lately overlooked in the leaves of the monograph in w.ʰ you had placed it. I should have hastened on the instant to have acknowledged and thanked you for this great proof of regard and esteem bestowed upon one so unworthy as myself, but there were propositions in it w.ʰ set me to work with ardour, and I sought thro' my confused collections to offer you something interesting from the little explored wilds of North America. I have therefore sent to you a bundle of rarities in a box directed to Mr. Mercier of Geneva but as it is directed to Paris (to Mrs. P.ʰ Mercier, Rue Taitbout No. 18) and not consigned to any person in Havre, I fear it will be delayed. . . .[48]

Most of the plants I now send you are either rare or undescribed and wishing to publish them now after so much delay I request your candid opinion upon them according to their ticket and tho' new to me they may be known to you.

I am happy to see that your immense work goes on and I hope that its usefulness will be no less than the labour of its author.

In Botany but little is doing at present in the United States of America. Mr. Elliott of Charleston South Carolina has finished his southern Flora, and tho' generally correct, it is by no means free from errors. I conceive, indeed that the author had neither sufficient leisure nor opportunity in that remote province to complete and correct his work, his best friends and assistants also Macbride and Dr. Baldwyn are *dead,* and indeed all science sleeps in a land of slavery.

Dr. Torrey has published the first volume of his Flora of the northern and middle states in w.ʰ are some new things, but the work though usefull betrays marks of haste and inadvertance. The author also has travelled but little and copies everything convenient for his purpose if I did not know that the author made nothing pecuniary by his work, I should have called it an interested compilation.

Hitherto, I have seen no Flora of the United States with all its deficiencies, w.ʰ pleased me like the simple characteristic labours of André Michaux. Michaux observed for himself, and described with a simplicity and acuteness scarcely exceeded by Linnaeus.

I have now begun to collect materials for a general Flora of the United States, but there are in the South and South-west, yet extensive tracts unexamined nay unseen, by any naturalist. Nothing but my present engagement, and the unhealthiness of the climate hinders me from again exploring the desert. The Americans have not sufficient enthusiasm to be naturalists, and the government sanctions nothing like partial patronage however important to the better knowledge of the country. To *possess* a fertile waste and then leave it such, till visited by accident is the peculiar and cold policy of this republic. Hence, indeed, so many partial efforts to study Natural History in this country, but rarely any progress beyond its rudiments, because there is no incentive to its pursuit, neither profit, honour nor support awaits the disciple of Nature.

In this view, I hope you will not be surprised that so little is effectually done in exploring the untrodden wilds of the country in the S & South-West, countries wʰ will one day add important and curious links to the concatenation of the Natural Families of plants and wʰ for your gratification and for those wʰ view the vegetable kingdom with philosophic wisdom, I could wish were already known.

Sir, with consideration of the most profound esteem and unceasing regard, I remain,

Your very humble and Ob. Servant,
Thoˢ Nuttall

Your remarks on any of Michaux's rarer plants, will be peculiarly acceptable.[49]

The plants sent, selected from Nuttall's Arkansas collection, were "ticketed" with names and descriptions for insertion in De Candolle's publications. The first species appeared in the third volume of the *Prodromus* (1828): *Gaura sinuata* Nutt. and *Peplis diandra* Nutt. Nine of his new *Umbelliferae* were included in De Candolle's *Cinquième Mémoire: sur la famille Ombellifères* (1829), and five of his new *Compositae* were published in volumes of the *Prodromus* dealing with that immense family (V, 1836; VII, 1838). Species which required changes in the generic assignation, De Candolle named in honor of Nuttall, such as Discopleura nuttallii DC [*Ptilimnium nuttallii* (DC.) Britt.], *Polytaenia nuttallii* DC., and *Astragalus nuttallianus* DC. At least two of his Arkansas species — *Phyllanthus polygonoides* Nutt. and *Euphorbia hexagona* Nutt. — sent to Kurt Sprengel (1766–1833), professor at Halle, appeared in the third volume (1826) of the sixteenth edition of Linnaeus's *Systema Vegetabilium*.[50] Nuttall's Plantago *purpurascens (*P. virginica* L.) was published by Rapin in *Mémoires de la Société Linnéenne de Paris*, VI (1827), 454.

How much more indulgently and appreciatively than Nuttall did Hooker look on the achievements of botanists in America! In a comprehensive article that he wrote for the Edinburgh *Journal of Science*, reviewing publications on the flora of British North America beginning with Cornuti's treatment of plants of Canada (Paris, 1635) and Catesby's *Natural History of Carolina* and carrying through to Torrey's 1824 *Flora* and articles in late numbers of the American scientific journals, he commended heartily the work that had been accomplished in describing the vegetation. The contributions of Michaux, Pursh, and Nuttall received full discussion. Concerning the latter Hooker wrote:

We come now to the agreeable employment of mentioning a very important work, both on account of the extended nature of the publication, and of the manner in which it has been executed; we allude to the "Genera of North American Plants, and a Catalogue of the Species to the year 1817, by Thomas Nuttall," . . . Mr. Nuttall is an Englishman by birth. . . . His love of botany and mineralogy is exceedingly great, and a personal acquaintance, which his late visit to this country has enabled us to have the pleasure of forming, has only served to increase the esteem and respect which his writings had already taught us to entertain towards him. . . .
The characters of the genera (which he here extends to 807, exclusive of any cryptogamia,) have, as may be inferred from the title, occupied a greater share of the attention from Mr. Nuttall. He has added to the essential characters, those taken from the habit of the plant, and he has noticed their geographical distribution. In the enumeration of species, he has included all that have been described . . . and added a very considerable number of new individuals . . . and we rejoice that the execution of it has fallen into such able hands.[51]

In 1824 Chester Dewey (1784-1867) began in Silliman's *Journal* a series of short papers on *Carex,* called "Caricography." Torrey promptly wrote to Dewey accusing him of having hurried out his paper to anticipate some of Schweinitz's discoveries in that genus and questioned the propriety of Dewey's working on *Carex.* Dewey was not rebuffed. He answered, "I am not going to have a quarrel with you about Carices or anything else. I had rather burn up the whole Caricography and my plants and yours too. Yet I cannot think as you do — and wonder that a man of sense can maintain the points you do."[52] He continued his series until 1866 and his friendship for Torrey also. At his suggestion, Torrey was given an honorary A.M. degree by Williams College in 1825.

It is a bit startling to find Torrey taking upon himself thus early the post of arbiter in American botany, a role which he assumed more patently a decade or so later. He had the botanical confidence necessary for it. That Amos Eaton encouraged this attitude appears in a letter of January 12, 1822:

You are made for the higher walks of science — nice accurate investigation — new discoveries and improvements — to correct the blunders of others and to keep the ship of science in trim. You ought to remain in

N. York or near that place as a kind of scientific center around which such satellites as I may safely revolve . . . what has raised you above every individual of your years in North America? It is your discriminating powers, your indefatigable research, set off to the best advantage by that modest confidence for which you are distinguished.[53]

Torrey's increasing assumption of mentorship was to cause great unhappiness for Eaton and exasperation for Nuttall.

On April 29, 1825, Torrey wrote to Hooker: "You once gave Nuttall some duplicates collected by Dr. Richardson. What could I offer you for such as you may have left? Indeed there is no person to whom they could be so valuable as to me, for you know it is my intention to write a Flora of North America." [54] Torrey asked Nuttall to collaborate with him on such a comprehensive publication but Nuttall refused.[55] Aside from other reasons he may have had, his extensive field experience taught him that the undertaking was premature: having seen the great number of new species across the Missouri Territory and the Arkansas Territory and studied collections in London from the west coast, he was aware that knowledge of the flora of the continent was in its infancy. His efforts continued to be exerted in searching for and making known what he could of the thousands of species still unknown.

At the end of 1826 Torrey presented to the Lyceum his general report on the plants collected by William Baldwin and Edwin P. James on the first Long Expedition (about 700 species), having previously reported on alpine plants of the collection in 1823 and some new grasses in 1824. In the final paper Torrey used the natural system of classification then still shunned by most American botanists.[56] The author credited his "learned friend Thomas Nuttall, Esq. who has devoted more attention to the botany of this country than any other individual" with valuable assistance in the examination of the specimens.

In the early autumn of 1825, Nuttall sent two short taxonomic papers to the Academy through Zaccheus Collins; they were read at meetings in the first half of October and both soon appeared in the *Journal*. "Description of Two New Genera of the Natural Order of Cruciferae" presented two species he had collected in the Arkansas Territory, *Selenia aurea* and *Streptanthus maculatus* (Arkansas cabbage). Illustrations of the two plants were drawn by J. Whitfield.[57] The second article, "Observations on a Species of Anemone of the Section Pulsatilla, Indigenous to the United States," discussed the relationships of De Candolle's A. nuttalliana, a plant which Nuttall had collected in 1811 near the confluence of the Missouri and Platte Rivers and northward; the plant ultimately proved to be a variety of Linnaeus's A. *patens, viz.* var. *wolfgangiana* (Bess.) Koch.[58]

At Commencement in 1826, Harvard University conferred on Nuttall the honorary degree of Master of Arts.[59] Nuttall may have weighed this honor, together with the four brief taxonomic papers he had published during his three and a half years in Cambridge, against what he had accomplished previously for science and for his own knowledge and prestige, during any equal span of his career, and felt little satisfaction in the comparison. He was very conscious that he was contributing little to the enlargement of knowledge. As he aptly said, he was vegetating in Cambridge — the botanical fruits were meager indeed.

TEACHING. In the hundred odd years since his death Nuttall has been described increasingly by popular writers and even by some biologists as a man who was extremely shy, unsocial, and eccentric — judgments not found in contemporary records. Such characteristics are hardly consonant with his voluntary lecturing, his readily established acquaintanceships, and his numerous lifelong friendships. He has become a victim of writers who, preferring an entertaining story to an accurate account, have for dramatic effect exaggerated his undoubted simplicity, independence of spirit, and unworldly sense of values or who misinterpreted the aloofness he habitually assumed when among those he disliked. In the presence of pretensions (the "feeble bucram of self importance"[60]), conceit, affectations, or coarseness, he froze into a reserved Britisher.

The seed from which the current extravagant stories of Nuttall's shyness have grown was probably sown by Asa Gray. When he took over the Garden House as his residence in 1844, he wrote to John Torrey:

Mr. Nuttall . . . left some curious traces behind him. He was very shy of intercourse with his fellows, . . . put in a trap-door . . . and so by a ladder could pass between his rooms without the chance of being met . . . and with a small gate in the board fence surrounding the garden, of which he alone had the key, he could pass in and out safe from encountering any human being.[61]

As already noted, the simple structural changes in the house had been made twenty years before, not for the reason Gray put forward with characteristic confidence, but because the erstwhile pleasant domicile, rented as a source of income for the Garden, was occupied by objectionable boarders. That the Garden gate existed for sociable reasons will appear later. Gray's hasty suppositions have had unfortunate echoes.[62] Nuttall himself believed that he was "very unhappy without society" but he was a discriminating observer of human nature, "capricious" in the "choice of this society." [63]

The student body at Harvard at this time was small, the number receiving the Bachelor of Arts degree each August averaging less than sixty in number. Nuttall's course in botany was generally scheduled for the spring term when nature's seasonal miracles should have aroused whatever latent interest the students might have in the subject. Nuttall was not a brilliant teacher but his dedication to the vegetable world, shining through the technicalities, at least might elicit a reflected interest. To John L. Russell, 1828, we owe one of the few student estimates of Nuttall that have come down to us; in an 1842 talk to the Harvard Natural History Society he said, "the enterprising and modest Nuttall . . . delighted and instructed the world with the rich variety of his scientific research." [64]

The teaching of natural history (largely zoology) in the United States during the first half of the nineteenth century was based on a textbook, *Philosophy of Natural History,* written by William Smellie, a Scot. The students called the course simply "Smellie." As in most courses at the time, the text was more or less learned by rote and recited in class. While Nuttall was in England in 1824, the University Bookstore published an edition prepared by Dr. John Ware "with various alterations and additions intended to adapt it to the present state of knowledge." Nuttall's classes fell heir to this edition. The boredom of recitation must have often been dissipated by the first-hand knowledge of the instructor and accounts of some of his unusual field experiences. What other teacher of Smellie had seen villages of prairie dogs, herds of elk, bounding antelopes, and thousands of buffalo in a strange new country teeming with distinctive animal life? Many of the scholars found the courses in botany and natural history a relief from the traditional work. In their junior year, thirty-six members of the class of 1829 presented a petition respectfully requesting "that they be permitted to study Good's 'Book of Nature' or Smellie's 'Philosophy of Natural History' as a substitute for Gries-bach's Greek Testament." [65] The list of signers looks as though taken from a *Who's Who* of the 1860s.

Andrew Preston Peabody, D.D., Plummer Professor of Christian Morals, 1860–1893, a member of George Putnam's class of 1826, wrote reminiscently concerning Nuttall: "His name was mythical to the members of the college. We used to hear of him as the greatest of naturalists; but I never knew of his being seen. He lived . . . in a then remote quarter of the town. . . . I think that the catalogue promised instruction by him to those who wanted it; but I never heard of his having a pupil." [66] Peabody must truly have lived a life apart because the records show that in 1825–1826, fifty-three seniors and fifty-six juniors took work with Nuttall. Both courses were handled in two sections.[67]

Among the numerous students who elected Nuttall's courses, some had an innate interest in animals or plants and a few in time became notable as professionals or amateurs in some branch of natural science. The most distinguished biologists who were undergraduates while Nuttall was at Harvard were Dr. Charles Pickering, ex-1823, who, beginning as a boy with an interest in insects, developed into an all-round naturalist of first rank; Dr. Augustus A. Gould, 1825, a productive student of the *Mollusca* and also credited with "a familiar knowledge of botany"; and Dr. Jefferies Wyman, 1833, Hersey Professor of Anatomy at Harvard, 1847–1874, an authority on ichthyology, herpetology, and comparative anatomy. Wyman in his undergraduate days was celebrated for his preparation of the skeleton of a mammoth bullfrog from Fresh Pond.

The enthusiasm for natural history stirred by Nuttall in Henry Coit Perkins, 1824, and George Putnam, 1826, has already been mentioned. Stephen Elliott, Jr., later Bishop of Georgia, collected shells of *Mollusca* for such active students as Isaac Lea and enlisted the assistance of others. Sears Cook Walker, 1825, first interested in geology, became an astronomer of note. Addison Brown, 1826, and John Lewis Russell, who entered the ministry, devoted leisure time throughout their active lives to botanical pursuits. John Singleton Copley Greene, 1828, shared the interest in plants displayed by his half-brother Benjamin D. Greene. Charles Thomas Jackson, M.D., 1829, a consulting chemist who carried out early geological surveys for the States of Maine and New Hampshire, very likely did some undergraduate work at the college; the copy of Nuttall's botanical textbook which he purchased in October 1827, is in Widener Library, Harvard University. John McLean Bethune, 1832, who became a lawyer, wrote that in college he "Learned in field, sports and quiet excitement of Natural History, to occupy that time which I ought to have employed far otherwise." It was he who found the olive-sided flycatcher, *Nuttallornis*, in the woods of "Sweet Auburn."[68] William Dandridge Peck, Jr., 1833, found a new species of spider in Northampton, where he was attending the Round Hill School; the find was communicated by N. M. Hentz to the Boston Society of Natural History.[69] Dr. John Witt Randall, 1834, published new species of *Coleoptera* of Massachusetts collected during his college years and a companion paper on new species from Maine;[70] he also published the new species of *Crustacea* that Nuttall brought back from the Pacific in 1836.

Other students of Nuttall's time were active in natural history in later life. Dr. Henry Wheatland and Dr. T. Grafton Page, both of 1832, became Fellows of the American Academy of Arts and Sciences. Wheatland, John C. Lee, 1823, Dr. William P. Richardson, 1834, as well as John Lewis Russell and William Oakes, were leaders in the formation and support of the Natural History Society of Essex County which in 1848, after fifteen years of activity, merged with the historical society of the county to form the Essex Institute, a most productive institution, which Wheatland long served as president.

In memory of Dr. Charles Eliot Ware, 1834, Harvard University was presented with one of its unique treasures — the celebrated and extraordinary products of the Blaschkas's hands — natural-size, glass models of American plants of hundreds of families, astoundingly lifelike and beautiful, accompanied by enlarged dissections in glass of great accuracy and scientific usefulness. It would be hard indeed to believe that Charles Eliot Ware was indifferent to plants, for this memorial was selected with loving care. Indubitably he was interested in birds for he gave to Thomas Mayo Brewer, 1835, four cowbirds he had shot in the marshes of Fresh Pond and an oversized nest of a house wren built "in the clothesline box of Professor Ware."[71] One of the cowbirds attained the distinction of being immortalized in plate 424 of Audubon's *Birds of America*.[72]

In spite of the fact that Andrew Preston Peabody never saw Nuttall, his personality made an impact on the minds of many students not especially interested in natural sciences and there have been long-held memories of him in Cambridge. He was known to Thomas Wentworth Higginson (1823–1911), son of the Steward, who was ten years old when the naturalist left Harvard. Higginson, in his turn, haunted the "deep swamps called the Fresh Pond marshes" to observe rails, ospreys, and the heronry. In 1885 he wrote that England "contributed to the American Cambridge the most delightful of botanists and ornithologists — his books being still classics — Thomas Nuttall." Even later than this, John Holmes, 1832, the inimitable humorous brother of the Autocrat, was still giving impersonations of Nuttall that were remembered through the first half of the twentieth century.

In Nuttall's classes were many able young men who reached great distinction in the whole range of professions. The classes from 1823 through 1834 supplied professors in all fields of knowledge some of whom became deans and presidents of colleges and universities;[73] ministers by the score, including two bishops; outstanding physicians; distinguished lawyers, many appointed to judgeships of local courts, State Supreme Courts, and Federal Courts. Poets,[74] historians, ambassadors, senators, a Speaker of the House, and an Admiral emerged. Perhaps businessmen were as numerous as any group of alumni of these years, men who carried on in successful enterprises established by their grandfathers, fathers, uncles, or brothers. Although Nuttall made no general references to his students, it will be seen that associations which he formed through teaching at Harvard occasionally proved helpful to him in achieving his scientific goals.

Before Nuttall gained much experience in college teaching, he acquired a graduate student on an informal basis. Charles Shepard was determined on becoming a scientist without medical training, the customary preliminary, but he found it difficult to launch himself in a field that offered few openings. He depended on Nuttall for encouragement and suggestions. The winter after his graduation from college, having failed to get an assistantship in chemistry at Harvard, he remained in Amherst giving special courses at a local school "for young ladies," prospecting for minerals, and improving his Cabinet through exchanges.[75] Through the Austrian Consul-General Baron von Lederer, he enriched his "little museum in foreign minerals." The following academic year (1825–1826) he spent in Cambridge and Boston studying botany and mineralogy with Nuttall, giving private lessons, and hoping for a class at William B. Fowle's school for girls in Boston or at other schools. In September he had "made a very successful tour into Maine, where at Paris, I was the fortunate discoverer of the most remarkable green and red Tourmalines then known. With some of these I made profitable exchanges with the British Museum and other large collections." [76] He clung to his decision "to make natural history his life work . . . although strongly advised by President Kirkland not to depend on so uncertain a means of support." [77] Fortunately, through sending short notices of mineralogical locations to the *American Journal of Science,* he became known to Silliman, and in 1826 he was invited to Yale as Silliman's assistant and held that position until 1831 when he became lecturer in botany. Later he went to Amherst as Professor of Chemistry and Natural History and also taught chemistry at South Carolina Medical College in Charleston from 1834 to 1861. His mineralogical collection, sold to Amherst College for $40,000 (destroyed by fire in 1882), was considered to be surpassed only by that of the British Museum. Of Nuttall's several scientifically inclined protégés, Shepard was the most productive; from 1826 to 1885 he published 121 papers in addition to textbooks. [78]

The textbooks used at Harvard were generally written or edited by the professors who gave the respective courses and published by the University Bookstore. For his course in botany, Nuttall first used Bigelow's American edition of Sir James Edward Smith's textbook, *An Introduction to Physiological and Systematic Botany,* but in the autumn of 1826, after arranging with William Hilliard of the Bookstore for the publication of a new text, he set to work on his own textbook, *Introduction to Systematic and Physiological Botany.* He completed a large part of the writing during November and December while visiting Dr. William Meade and his wife at Newburgh, New York.

Meade wrote to Silliman on January 3, 1827: "The Season is particularly gloomy and severe here at present and we should have felt it more but we have had the company of Mr. Nuttall who has been with us these two months and is now detained by the Weather. Since he has been here he has nearly finished a very useful Work which will be published in the Spring." [79]

The textbook was on sale at $1.33 in the spring of 1827, and a second enlarged edition came out in 1830. Whitfield's name appears as the delineator of the last eight of the twelve plates; reproduced on stone by William Pendleton, they are among early examples of American commercial lithography. The book bore the dedication:

To the Hon. John Lowell, LL.D., President of the Massachusetts Society for Promoting Agriculture, &, &.
Sir,
Permit me to lay before you this humble attempt, to render familiar to all, a science to which I have been so long devoted, and for which your attachment has been conspicuous. If I have failed in my endeavours to answer this important end, I hope it may be attributed rather to inability, than to any want of zeal to promote the cause of this interesting branch of Natural History. That my imperfect labors may in some degree prove useful, is the sincere wish of

Your humble servant,
The Author

A tooled calf-bound copy with hand-colored plates presented by Nuttall to Lowell, now in Houghton Library at Harvard, contains the bookplate of Amy Lowell, great-granddaughter of the recipient. We know that at least one other similar copy was made up for his Uncle Jonas and suspect that Peter Chardon Brooks of the Garden Committee may have received such a copy and also President Kirkland, an *ex-officio* member of the committee.

The text first discusses the characteristics of eight of the widespread natural families of flowering plants of the eastern United States: *Liliaceae, Cruciferae, Leguminosae, Labiatae, Scrophulariaceae, Umbelliferae, Compositae, Rosaceae.* Most of the systematic section, however, dwells on the Linnaean system because of its usefulness as an artificial key for beginning students. Moreover the only available flora of the area, Bigelow's *Florula Bostoniensis,* was in the Linnaean arrangement. Nuttall's taxonomic discussion reveals a masterly knowledge of American and world flora with aesthetic appreciation which pauses to note that mountain laurel "is one of the greatest ornaments which the American forest can boast." Unexpected in an elementary textbook is Nuttall's reference to negative results obtained in testing experimentally the effect of climate on form: he planted in the Garden a dwarf goldenrod (Solidago Virgaurea L. var. alpina Bigel., now *S. cutleri* Fern.), brought from the heights of the White Mountains, to observe whether dwarfness would persist under milder conditions of wind and temperature. Also unusual is the publication therein of two new species: *Collinsia *violacea* and *Euchroma* *sanguinea [*Castilleja purpurea* (Nutt.) G. Don] from Arkansas.

The section entitled "Physiology" is more concerned with anatomy and histology than function. In the second edition this part of the text, the study of which was in its infancy, was brought up to date "by some important alterations." Smallwood commented that by emphasizing the cellular composition of plants Nuttall "appears to have anticipated, in part, by eleven years the cell theory of Schleiden"; he also considered it noteworthy that Nuttall did not confuse photosynthesis with respiration.[80] Other precocious observations are scattered passages affirming the network of relationships which he found in plants and the near merging of some genera, suggesting continuous modification (organic evolution); "nature knows no rigid bounds, but plays through an infinite variety of forms, and ever avoids monotony."

A contemporary reviewer praised the method of gradual introduction of technical phrases, forbidding but indispensable, and also the addition of a glossary. Of the reputation of the author he said: "His fame is too widely spread and too well founded to require to be proclaimed by us. . . . Mr. Nuttall is deservedly considered one of the first naturalists of the age . . . he possesses a more intimate knowledge of the whole range of North American plants than any other botanist."[81] Another reviewer (in Silliman's *Journal*) pointed out that it is unusual for "the best qualified to pause for the humble task of writing 'vade-mecums,' especially one whose rank . . . is so conspicuous." After several pages of appreciative quotations from the text he wrote: "In conclusion, we would only remark, that it constitutes by far the most valuable treatise that can be put in the hands of a person just commencing this delightful study. . . . His style is simple, condensed and highly perspicuous."[82]

As Dr. Gorham's health continued to deteriorate, he resigned from the Erving Professorship in 1827; whereupon Webster, who was then serving as Adjunct Erving Professor, quickly applied for the full professorship as originally set up for chemistry only. His officious letter to the Corporation shows that amicable relations had been reestablished between him and Nuttall.

Dr. Gorham having resigned his office the subscriber respectfully requests, that he may be permitted to perform all the duties of Erving Professor, & if so, to resign the professorship of Mineralogy & Geology; in doing which he should feel it incumbent on him to relinquish that part of his salary which (from the proportion of time occupied in the performance of those duties) may be considered as derived from the lectures on Mineralogy & Geology, viz. $400. . . .

The subscriber feels the more readiness to propose this arrangement, as there is a gentleman on the spot abundantly qualified to instruct in Mineralogy & Geology & he is authorized to say that M⸱ Nuttal would feel perfectly satisfied with this addition to his duties & to his salary. With his present salary that gentleman might easily be induced to leave us, & an effort is in fact making to connect him with the College at Princeton. M⸱ Nuttal's papers in the American Journal of Science, & in the Memoirs of the Philadelphia Academy, afford ample evidence of his acquirements in Mineralogy, & Dr. Hooker, Professor of Natural History in the University of Glasgow, has, in D⸱ Brewsters Journal, recorded his estimation of him as a mineralogist. My own knowledge of his acquirements in this science enables me to say, that he is second to no one in the country in this department of science. . . .

Respectfully submitted
J. W. Webster

Harvard College
Feb⸱ 15th 1827 [83]

Webster's reference to Dr. Hooker's estimation of Nuttall as a mineralogist is surprising, as Hooker, whose attention did not wander far from botany, would not lightly pass judgment on a man's standing in another field. Actually he committed himself thus far: Nuttall's "love of botany and mineralogy is exceedingly great." Whether an *official* effort was in fact being made to connect Nuttall with Princeton seems very questionable; no evidence of it appears in the Princeton Archives.[84] In 1827 Princeton's student body had dropped to such a low point with only eighty students that it was considering closing its doors. Dr. Luther Halsey was Professor of Natural Philosophy, Chemistry, and Natural History from 1824 to 1829. No additions were made to the faculty until 1830 when, among other appointments, John Torrey became Professor of Chemistry and Natural History, continuing to hold a similar position at Physicians and Surgeons in New York; in 1832 Joseph Henry took on the professorship of Natural Philosophy. The Corporation in June 1827 appointed Webster as Erving Professor of Chemistry *and Mineralogy*.

In midsummer of 1827 Webster and Nuttall, at the request of the Corporation, looked over an accumulation of miscellanea in the "Museum" to make suggestions for the preservation of such objects "as appear in any tolerable condition." One of several recommendations was "that the vegetables and dried plants be placed on one of the shelves in the room now containing them, the room being previously thoroughly cleaned,"[85] implying the lack of a formal college herbarium. Peck's collections had been personal property as were Nuttall's; this was the practice of the time.

Nuttall was a valued member of the college community and of the Boston area; he had been elected a Fellow of the American Academy of Arts and Sciences on November 12, 1823. On an inadequate budget he worked conscientiously to improve the garden. His teaching was well received and his public lectures greatly appreciated. Discriminating elite — Caleb Cushing, Edward Everett, George Bancroft, Ralph Waldo Emerson, President Kirkland, Josiah Quincy, the Bootts, the Lowells, the Lymans, the Winships, the Winthrops, and many more — looked him over at close range and approved him as a scientist and an individual.

# CHAPTER 14

# RECREATION

Durable satisfactions. — Charles William Eliot

VISITORS AND FRIENDS. The Botanic Garden was among the local points of interest recommended to strangers. Most Americans, little used to formal gardens, were generally pleased by the wide paths, the grass-bordered planted plots, the specimen trees and flowering shrubs, and the water-lily pond well stocked with flashing goldfish and were enthusiastic about the exotic plants in the conservatory; but traveling Europeans were too accustomed to long-established landscaping and skillful horticulture to find anything noteworthy in a recent effort on such a modest scale. However, one of the first distinguished foreign visitors whom Nuttall guided about the Garden, John Finch, being a genuine plant lover, enjoyed his ramble through the Garden. Toward the end of July 1825, Duke Bernard Karl of Saxe-Weimar visited Harvard. He wrote that "Professor Nutall," an Englishman who had made natural history journeys in the West, showed his party around the Garden.[1] He found the Garden and the greenhouse not very large and saw few unusual bushes and flowers but noticed some brilliantly colored beetles new to him and beautiful butterflies about the shrubbery. He was impressed that *Strelitzia* plants had been raised from seed produced in the greenhouse.[2]

Zaccheus Collins must have visited Nuttall and the Botanic Garden before the autumn of 1825 when Say described some shells that Collins had collected in Boston Harbor and on the nearby coast. William Cooper, a member of the New York Lyceum and a long-time friend of John Torrey, wrote to him of a visit to Nuttall in the summer of 1829. He thought the Garden "very good and handsome." Cooper's early botanical flair took him on collecting trips with Torrey, but his interest shifted and he became an enthusiastic amateur ornithologist and paleontologist. However he was assisting his botanical friends in the solicitation of subscriptions for shares in the collections of plants, animals, and minerals to be made by Dr. Hezekiah Gates between the Arkansas and Missouri Rivers. "Nuttall took some circulars, and seemed much interested in the success of the collections, as he wants I believe roots and seeds for his garden."[3] Dr. Daniel Drake of Cincinnati got to the Garden in 1830,[4] and Pickering stopped to call on Nuttall that year.[5] Reuben Haines of Germantown, Pennsylvania, faithful attendant at the weekly meetings of the Academy of Natural Sciences who had befriended Nuttall in many little ways, called on him when he attended the annual Brighton Cattle Show in October 1830. Nuttall took the opportunity of sending by him an ornithological paper to be presented to the Academy in Philadelphia.[6] On July 4, 1832, Maximilian, Prince of Wied, bound on a scientific expedition up the Missouri, disembarked in Boston. The next day he went to see "Cambridge College." "My visit might have been very interesting if I had known that Mr. Nuttal, one of the most active naturalists and travellers in North America, held an office in this college."[7]

The most important guests each year were the Visitors of the Massachusetts Professorship of Natural History, who arrived in a body on a Saturday in midsummer for their annual appraisal of the Garden. No pains would be spared to have the plants in the best possible condition for inspection, for the gentlemen of the Board of Visitors had had long experience with horticulture on their country estates. Among the members at Nuttall's time were Peter Chardon Brooks, Elias H. Derby, Dr. Aaron Dexter, John Chipman Gray, Benjamin Guild, John Heard Jr., Dr. James Jackson, John Lowell, Samuel G. Perkins, Samuel W. Pomeroy, William Prescott, Israel Thorndike, and Thomas L. Winthrop.

Harriet Martineau, visiting Cambridge soon after Nuttall's departure, was pleased with what she saw although she disapproved of the "management" of Harvard and found symptoms of decay in the college.

The aspect of Cambridge is charming. The college buildings have no beauty to boast of, it is true; but the professors' houses, dropped around, each in its garden, give an aristocratic air to the place, which I saw in no other place of the size, & which has the grace of novelty. The greensward, the white palings, and the gravel-walks are all well kept, and nowhere is the New-England elm more flourishing. . . .

We set out for the Botanic Garden . . . very prettily situated and well taken care of. . . . From a small cottage on the terrace at the upper end of the garden came forth Mr. Sparks, the Editor of Washington's Correspondence. While engaged in his great work, he lives in this delightful spot. He took me into his study.[8]

The study was the one which Nuttall had used for almost eleven years. The lady was unreasonable or forgetful in calling the roomy Federalist house with two generous staircases "a small cottage."

During Nuttall's frequent absences from Cambridge, William Carter, the gardener, guided visitors about and carried on all routine duties. At such times the members of the Garden Committee might defer any unusual business for the consideration of the Curator of the Garden or take action themselves.

Nuttall found that Dr. Jacob Bigelow, Harvard College 1806, Dr. Walter Channing, Harvard College 1808, of the Faculty of the Harvard Medical School, and Dr. George Hayward, Harvard College 1809, later also on the medical faculty and a Fellow from 1852 to 1863, had taken their medical degrees in 1810, 1809, and 1812, respectively, at the University of Pennsylvania where they had established pleasant relations with Benjamin Smith Barton. Hayward seems to have been an especially congenial acquaintance, as Nuttall often mentioned him. Dr. George C. Shattuck, Dartmouth 1803, M.B. 1806, a leading physician of Boston, had also attended the University of Pennsylvania Medical School in the same class as William Baldwin.

Bigelow, who worked intensively in botany from about 1810 through 1824, was the only active botanist of the Boston area known to Nuttall when he arrived in Cambridge, so he relied on him for botanical conversation and information about rewarding collecting grounds in New England. When Nuttall got what he considered a new species of grass near Bellows Falls in May 1823, he made sure that it was equally unknown to Bigelow before publishing it. As Rumford Professor, Bigelow was regularly in Cambridge to lecture to undergraduates, and Nuttall stopped occasionally at his Boston office.[9] His *American Medical Botany* in three volumes (1817–1820), based on personal experimentation rather than on old wives' tales, was hailed by the *Port Folio* as "by far the most elegant and useful book on the science of Medical Botany which has been published in the United States." The expanded second edition of his *Florula Bostoniensis,* published in 1824, was his last botanical contribution except for the little-modified third edition of 1840. As a botanist, Bigelow now appears as "an amateur rather than . . . an experienced botanical scholar"; he was unwilling to assume the burden of shifting nomenclature that progress demanded. As his medical practice grew, this gifted man — classical scholar, artist, and technologist (to use a term which he introduced) — became increasingly absorbed in his profession. His medical papers were among the most important ever written in America; especially significant was "The Self-limited Character of Disease," which, by placing reliance on the recuperative powers of nature, attacked the use of heroic remedies, previously the favored method of treating disease.

Nuttall was no doubt pleased to encounter Nicholas M. Hentz (1797–1856), a young French emigrant, an arachnologist. Nuttall had been on a committee that considered the publication of a paper of his submitted to the Academy of Natural Sciences in Philadelphia in 1820. Removing from Pennsylvania to Boston, Hentz continued teaching French and painting. On an occasion when he was in the greenhouse with Nuttall, he found an unknown spider on a plant and named it *Attus nuttallii.* Some years later Nuttall reciprocated by naming a *Phlox* collected by Hentz in his honor; unfortunately it had already been published by Conrad Loddiges, the London nurseryman. In September 1823, Hentz went to teach at the new Round Hill School in Northampton.

Some of Professor Peck's old pupils with a love for natural history made periodic visits to see the Garden and to converse with Nuttall on the state of the natural sciences; notably George Barrell Emerson, Dr. Thaddeus William Harris, and William Oakes. Oakes wrote gossipy letters about botany and botanists; in 1828, in reply to a request from Torrey that he recommend a botanist for a proposed expedition, he wrote in favor of James W. Robbins, M.D., of Colebrook, Connecticut, weighing on his own scales the contemporary botanists: "[He is] not . . . such a man as Mr. Pickering of very rare talents. But if you, Pickering, Nuttall, Schweinitz or myself do not go I doubt exceedingly whether you can obtain another person equally qualified with Mr. Robbins. . . . I doubt if either of those I have mentioned, except perhaps Nuttall, are superior." [10]

# RECREATION

Charles Pickering had grown up in the household of his grand-father, Timothy Pickering, a statesman of the Revolution, who had been successively at the head of every executive department of the federal government under Washington and later a Congressman. Charles was extremely modest; one suspects that this might have been a reaction to close association with his grandfather who was, as an articulate young lady noted, "a great egotist and has a most exalted opinion of himself, probably well founded." [11] A friendship arose between Charles Pickering and Nuttall which developed into close companionship later in Philadelphia where the new-fledged doctor began the practice of medicine and became a strong supporter of the Academy of Natural Sciences.

Mrs. Peck was the first Cantabrigian with whom Nuttall became acquainted. When she left the Garden House, she bought a small house near the Washington Elm and kept a motherly eye on some students from 1824 through 1831. Unlike the other ladies, she was not a respecter of weather — the famous Cambridge mud did not keep her from daily trips to the Village — so Nuttall probably encountered her frequently. Her only child, not an exemplary student as an undergraduate, received his M.D. in 1836.

Although Nuttall enjoyed many aspects of the associations with his colleagues, and was frequently invited to dinner and tea by their wives, he formed no close friendship among them. His chosen companionship lay for the most part outside the college circle. His closest friend in Cambridge was young James Brown (1800–1855), a founder of the publishing firm of Little, Brown and Company, whom Nuttall first knew as William Hilliard's clerk in the University Bookstore. Brown's childhood had been spent on a farm in Acton but at thirteen his father's death threw him onto his own resources, and he soon went to Cambridge, attracted by its aura of learning, and got employment as a choreboy in Professor Hedge's household. Brown's genial, serious, and scholarly nature so appealed to Hilliard that, when Brown reached eighteen, Hilliard offered him a clerkship.[12] The youth had abundant scope to prove his worth, for Hilliard was daily at his Boston bookshop. Brown's love of nature and knowledge of the out-of-doors doubtless was the basis of a growing acquaintance with Nuttall that ripened into an enduring friendship through the alchemy of his warm temperament. Brown's special companion in rambles in the country and on fishing and hunting trips was Nathaniel

Jarvis Wyeth (1802–1856) who lived at his father's hotel on Fresh Pond. Nuttall enjoyed the companionship of Wyeth as well as Brown. Both men profoundly influenced the course of Nuttall's activities.

Nuttall had few neighbors since dwellings near the Garden were widely scattered: Job Wyeth's farm lay just to the north on the lonely road to Fresh Pond; the mansion of the great Craigie estate on the west was at a distance; the land to the south, which had been cow common until 1724, was unsettled except near the Village; whereas to the east only one house stood between the Garden and the comparatively well-populated Lexington Road (North Avenue) a half-mile or so away. This house faced on a rural lane, inevitably known as "Love Lane" (Linnaean Street), which connected Garden Street and the Lexington Road. Nuttall must have often strolled along this undisturbed way and admired the pleasing old clapboard house surrounded by fields and apple orchards.[13] Behind the house rose the Gallows Hill and in front stretched the old Common. Here lived Martha Frost Austin, widowed in 1816, and her young daughter Susan (1809–1884). That Nuttall became an intimate of this hospitable home and enjoyed many hours of friendly converse here is certain although we have no direct information concerning the friendship. Evidence that it existed first reappeared in the early twentieth century through the discovery in the old chaise house of a beautifully made life-mask of Nuttall. This was obtained for the Gray Herbarium in 1918 by its loyal Librarian, Mary A. Day, and the identification has been carefully authenticated. We can imagine the gay enjoyment of the artist and the subject in the production of the head. For over a half century it stood on a bookcase in the sitting room of the old house until a tenant removed it to storage in the outbuilding. Associations with this household, comparable in some ways with his own childhood home, must have been one of the durable pleasures of Nuttall's life in Cambridge. Nuttall's private gate in the southeast corner of the Garden fence opened on Love Lane away from the direct route to the Village. The only reasonable explanation for the gate is that it greatly facilitated visits to the Austins, for which it would be a great convenience.[14]

Another feminine friend was Miss Pomeroy who, on a visit to relatives in the Azores in 1830, took seeds of Nuttall's *Coreopsis tinctoria* (calliopsis) hoping to naturalize the colorful and prolific plant on Fayal Island. She was a relative, probably a daughter, of Samuel Wyllys Pomeroy, on the Board of Trustees of the Massachusetts Society for Promoting Agriculture from 1804 to 1823 and therefore on the Board of Visitors of the Garden. She quoted Nuttall in 1830 as saying that he was "enveloped completely in feathers and neglects Botany now." [15]

Most eccentric among the friends Nuttall made in Cambridge was Elizabeth Shaw Craigie (1772–1841), widow of Andrew Craigie (1744–1819), who had donated an adjacent lot of four acres to the land bought for the Botanic Garden. Craigie's two-hundred-acre estate, confiscated during the Revolution from Colonel John Vassall, its original Tory owner, and used as George Washington's Headquarters during the Siege of Boston, extended from the Botanic Garden almost to the Charles River; the house stood on Tory Row (Brattle Street). During the Revolution Craigie, as Apothecary-General of the Army, was quartered at the Vassall House and purchased it in the early 1790s. There he lived sumptuously but finally became so overextended in commercial enterprises that his widow, receiving only one-third of his estate, was left land-poor. The belief still persists that Elizabeth Shaw, a young Nantucket beauty, had been engaged to a sailor away on a long voyage when she married Craigie in 1793 for love of his money. As a widow she turned the fine Georgian house to profit by renting rooms to a few select persons: Edward Everett and Jared Sparks, future presidents of Harvard, and Henry Wadsworth Longfellow were among her paying guests and probably also Joseph Emerson Worcester. [16]

Idiosyncracies of the aloof, turbaned lady were retailed by all the villagers: she read Voltaire and was a freethinker in religion; she saw God in nature and felt no need of a mediator between herself and Deity; she refused to molest the cankerworms that annually defoliated her magnificent elms which reached the ground with their pendant boughs, for, she said, "They have as good right to live as we; they are our fellow worms." Being passionately fond of flowers, she may have frequently visited the Garden and its greenhouse to select cuttings and seeds of some of the new exotics for her own garden and conservatory. Doubtless the friendship between Mrs. Craigie and Nuttall began in this way. At the auction sale of her property following her death in 1841, a sizable oil portrait of Nuttall was purchased by young Edward Tuckerman who years later presented it to the

Gray Herbarium, writing twice to Asa Gray about it in 1865: "I have an original oil painting of M.ʳ Nuttall painted for Mrs. Cragie [*sic*], and secured by me at her sale, which I shall be happy to contribute. . . . The Picture requires cleaning and framing — but it is after all the *portrait* which is valuable. . . . Portraits of such men as Nuttall are likely to be rare." [17] It is of interest that Mrs. Craigie bequeathed a valuable collection of shells to Harvard University and that Nuttall did not collect shells (except fossils) until he lived in Cambridge.

The well-known geographer and lexicographer, Joseph Emerson Worcester (1784–1865) became a friend of Nuttall. He financed himself through Andover Academy and Yale after he had worked on his father's New Hampshire farm until the age of twenty-one. After a stay in Salem, he settled in Cambridge in 1819 in order to use the libraries of the area. He came into lasting conflict with Noah Webster in 1830, by bringing out a new dictionary, preferred to Webster's in the Boston area for its closer adherence to English usage. Modest and reserved, he was remarkable for enormous industry and common sense. He and Nuttall found a bond in their substantial personal qualities. A younger contemporary described Worcester as "another of those eccentric characters of whom the university town was then prolific." During Sunday evening calls he

was wont to sit silent, literally by the hour, a slumbering volcano of facts and statistics, while others talked . . . and might perhaps have been suspected of a gentle slumber, when the casual mention of some city in the West, then dimly known, would rouse him to action. He would then . . . lean forward, and say in his peaceful voice: "Chillocothe? What is the present population of Chillocothe? or Columbus? What is the population of Columbus?" and then . . . would relapse into his rocking-chair once more. [18]

Worcester must have found Nuttall a unique and highly interesting source of information concerning the west and southwest. He had an opportunity to check statistics in the Ohio country himself when he journeyed there bearing a letter of introduction from Nuttall to Charles Wilkins Short in Lexington, Kentucky.

Cambridge, Mass. April 14, 1831

Dear Sir

Permit me to introduce to you my friend M.ʳ Worcester, so well known by his Geographical labors both at home and abroad. M.ʳ W. travells [*sic*] chiefly for the benefit of his health, and also would no doubt be highly gratified by any statistical information respecting the western country. . . .

I confess myself a miserable & negligent correspondent, and this fault has now become a habit. You sent me the commencement of an interesting work on the plants of your state for w$^h$ I am greatly obliged and indebted to you. — I shall not soon forget the pleasant hours I passed in your society, moments precious — but never to return, — for I fear that my days of travelling are drawing to a close in the vale of declining years. You will I hope never visit New England, without letting me see you again. I felt delighted to learn that you still continued to cherish the same ardour for our favorite Botany. If the season would admit, you can perhaps send me by M$^r$ Worcester *roots* and seeding specimens of the Erigenia, if it have not yet wholly disappeared into the bosom of the earth.

Excuse this hurried, careless scrawl & believe me

Your obt. humble Servant & well wisher

Tho$^s$ Nuttall [19]

Probably the most socially active lady in Cambridge during Nuttall's residence was Eliza Ware (Rotch) Farrar (1791–1870), the second wife of the genial John Farrar, eloquent teacher of natural philosophy and astronomy from whose lectures no student was ever willingly absent. Eliza, the daughter of Benjamin Rotch of London, educated in England, had been living with her grandfather William Rotch in New Bedford for about ten years before her marriage to Professor Farrar. Most of the stories she tells in her *Recollections of Seventy Years* are gossipy and romantic tales of the great and near great whom she knew in her youthful years in England. She published several books for children, *Unsettled Points of Etiquette* and, in 1836, the first edition of *The Young Lady's Friend, By a Lady*. A probable reference to Nuttall appears in the latter book in an account of a Mr. N———'s filling a lady's wineglass too full, allowing a drop to trickle down the decanter. This the author condones: "Mr. N———'s parents were not in a situation of life to teach their son such niceties. His talents and industry have made him what he is, and he has so much real merit that I hope you will forgive his being that one drop out of the way." [20] An indefatigable person, she entertained constantly and was especially ardent in receiving foreign visitors. Nuttall, of the scarce *genre* bachelor, was doubtless often on her dinner list.

His special interests in mineralogy and geology were the basis for an acquaintance not only with Dr. John White Webster but also with Dr. Charles T. Jackson (1805–1880), M.D. 1829, and Francis Alger (1807–1863). Jackson and Alger had made two prospecting visits together to Nova Scotia by 1829, Alger having previously been there on the same business with his father, a Boston iron manufacturer. Their final report on the Province was published in the *Memoirs* of the American Academy of Arts and Sciences in 1832, through Nuttall's sponsorship. Jackson attributed to "the celebrated naturalist Thomas Nuttall" the original introduction of the mineral richness of Sussex County, New Jersey, to the scientific public. Alger, who called crystals "the flowers of the mineral kingdom," prospected there with gratifying results. "For years he was in correspondence with Heuland, the great mineral dealer of London, who sent boxes of specimens to Mr. Alger to select what he wanted." [21]

As nurseries were magnets to Nuttall, he became acquainted with the seedsmen and nurserymen of the area and was especially friendly with the Winships who had twenty-five closely planted acres across the Charles River in Brighton (part of Cambridge until 1807). They introduced locally the buffalo-berry (*Shepherdia argentea* Nutt.) that Nuttall had discovered on the Missouri in 1811. [22] Joseph Breck also had a nursery in Brighton. The oldest nursery near Boston was that of the Kendricks of Newton. Charles M. Hovey (1810–1887) of a large Cambridge nursery, who published a *Magazine of Horticulture* (1835–1868) and exhibited his *Camellia* hybrids in London personally, wrote years later: "it was our good fortune to enjoy his [Nuttall's] acquaintance. . . . Quiet and unobtrusive in his manners, simple in his wants, enthusiastic in his devotion to botanical pursuits, he was loved and esteemed by a large circle of acquaintances." [23]

Nuttall had the happy opportunity of meeting the famous John James Audubon in the summer of 1832, when he came to Boston bringing a letter of introduction to the botanist, probably from Dr. Richard Harlan, an active member of the Philadelphia Academy of Natural Sciences. A sympathetic chord was immediately struck between the reticent Englishman and the exuberant Frenchman. Audubon wrote to Harlan on August 14, "Nuttall is a Gem — a most worthy, agreeable man — quite after our heart, and I am very happy to know him *as such*." On the same day he wrote to his friend and patron, Edward Harris of Moorestown, New Jersey, that he had ". . . made drawings of 3 rare species; one is the Marsh Wren, for which I searched in vain when near Salem; the 2nd is a Flycatcher, described by Mr. Nuttall and the last a Thrush." [24] The specimen of the first was furnished by Nuttall, and probably the third also. The drawings appeared as Plates 175, 174 and 164 (short-billed marsh wren, olive-sided flycatcher, veery) of *Birds of America* in 1833.

A curious incident regarding the olive-sided flycatcher was recorded by Audubon. "On the 8th of August 1832, while walking out from Boston towards the country seat of the Honourable Thomas H. Perkins, along with my friend Nuttall, we were suddenly saluted with the note of this bird." Audubon watched while Nuttall went in search of a gun. "He returned with a large musket, a cow's horn filled with powder, and a handful of shot nearly as large as peas; but just as I commenced charging this curious piece, I discovered that it was flintless!" They were nearly a mile from Mr. Perkins's house in Brookline, but they got a satisfactory gun and Audubon brought down the bird shown in his plate. [25] This distinctive flycatcher, a "new" American genus, was named *Nuttallornis* (Nuttall's bird). The song of *Nuttallornis* is rendered "hip-three-beers," an amusing term to be associated with a teetotaler.

Audubon was delighted with his first Boston visit. "Although I have been happy in forming many valuable friendships in various parts of the world, all dearly cherished by me, the outpouring of kindness which I experienced in Boston far exceeded all that I have ever met with." [26] The friendship between him and Nuttall was fostered by mutual help and subsequent meetings.

THE BIRDS. The year that Nuttall arranged to write his botanical textbook, William Hilliard of the University Bookstore took into partnership James Brown, his general assistant for eight years. Brown, probably knowing that Nuttall was irked by the routine of his duties, suggested to him the publication of a treatise on American birds, modestly printed and priced. No such text existed. [27] The bookman, a bird lover as well as a sportsman, offered the assistance of his friend Nathaniel Jarvis Wyeth as well as his own in the collection of facts. We do not know how eager Nuttall was to adopt the suggestion, [28] but, having accepted it, he plunged into intensive ornithological study that occupied a substantial part of his attention for five years.

A fine collection of skins and mounted birds, which included Alexander Wilson's specimens, was available for examination at Peale's Museum.[29] Nuttall studied these, took measurements of them, and drew up concise descriptions; this work was presumably started in the early part of 1829 when a prolonged stay in Philadelphia is attested by his attendance at meetings of the Academy on January 20, February 3, 17, and 24, and March 17. Persistent field observations were supported by intensive reading in the works of Alexander Wilson, Charles Lucien Bonaparte, the first volume of Audubon's *Ornithological Biography* (1831), and ornithologies by various Europeans. Moreover he used observations of travelers in the Americas from an amazing number of sources, covering countries from the Arctic to Chile.[30] The two resultant volumes are thoughtful compilations of the facts then established for each species, augmented by his own observations and those reported by friends and acquaintances, with thorough discussion and symbolic representation of the various calls and songs interpreted by his sensitive ear.

Nuttall first concentrated on the land birds. Early in 1830, he made a 1200-mile pedestrian journey through the southeastern states, including western Georgia, Alabama, and west Florida, which were new to him, studying resident birds and migrants from the north as well as collecting rare plants and seeds for the Botanic Garden. He spent most of the preceding December in Philadelphia (attending meetings of the Academy on December 8, 15, and 22), probably continuing his analyses of the birds at Peale's Museum. He either left Whitfield in Philadelphia to complete the task or took him as a companion on the long journey. In December he observed an enormous colony of crows on Reedy Island in Delaware Bay,[31] probably from the ship which he took to Charleston, where he arrived by January 12. On that date he saw ruby-crowned kinglets and bluebirds, a few warbling "their simple notes."[32]

A brief summary of his route was contained in a report to the Board of Visitors who published it in the *New England Farmer*.

On arriving at Charleston, S. C., I commenced my pedestrian journey, and proceeded to Augusta in Ga, thence to Macon, afterwards to Columbus, at the Falls of Chatahootshee, on the line of the State; I then continued through the Creek reservation to the town of Montgomery, in Alabama, and at length arrived at Tuskaloosa, the capital of that State; I now proceeded to Cahaba and Greenville, and entering Florida not far from Pensacola, continued to Tallahassee, the capital, from whence I returned through the lower part of Georgia, crossing the Apalachicola,

Altamaha, and Ogechee, to Savannah. . . . upwards of 1200 miles, . . . from middle January to close of March.[33]

Although Nuttall recorded seeing a long-billed curlew on the muddy shores of the Santee River[34] and over its broad waters "observed a strife" between a pair of fish crows and a herring gull,[35] it appears likely that he mistook the wide estuary of the Cooper River for the Santee, which lies forty miles north of Charleston.

Passages describing two feathered friends of his tour will serve not only as examples of his text but also give something of his impressions of the country he traversed. Of the tufted titmouse, "our favorite," he wrote

The *Peto,* as I may call this bird from one of his characteristic notes, and the Carolina Wren, were my constant and amusing companions during the winter, as I passed through the dreary solitudes of the Southern States. The sprightliness, caprice, and varied musical talent of this species are quite interesting, and more peculiarly so, when nearly all the other vocal tenants of the forest are either absent or silent. To hear, in the middle of the coldest season, the lively, cheering, varied pipe of this active and hardy bird, is particularly gratifying; and, though his voice, on paper, may appear to present only a list of quaint articulations, mere skeletons of musical compass, yet the delicacy, energy, pathos, and variety of his simple song, like many other things in nature, are far beyond the feeble power of description.[36]

Then follow two pages of careful description of the full repertoire of the bird, which Wilson covered in a single sentence. The next excerpt is from the pages on the Pine Warbler.

In winter they rove through the pine forests and barrens of the Southern States in companies of 20 or 50 or more . . . and . . . are most frequently employed in capturing the small insects which infest the opening buds of the pine, around which they may be seen perpetually hovering . . . with restless activity; . . . The principal body of the species probably remain the year round in the southern forests, . . . great numbers are also bred in the Northern States. . . . I have had a male Pine Warbler, domesticated for a short time; he fed gratefully, from the instant he was caught, upon flies, small earth-worms, and minced flesh, and was so tame and artless, as to sit contented . . . and scarcely shift himself securely from my feet.

The song of the Pine Warbler, though agreeable, amidst the dreary solitude of the boundless forests which he frequents, has but little compass or variety; sometimes it approaches the simplest trill of the Canary, but it is commonly a reverberating, gently rising, or murmuring sound, like er 'r 'r 'r 'r 'r 'r ah; or in spring, 'twe 'twe 'tw 'tw 'tw 'tw 'tw, and sometimes like 'tsh 'tsh 'tsh 'tw 'tw 'tw.[37]

Of its song Wilson says, "Its note is a simple reiterated *chirrup,* continued for four or five seconds."

Back in the North, Nuttall continued bird watching for two breeding seasons before completing the text of the first volume. In those days birds were everywhere abundant: "in the most populous and noisy streets of Boston" the red-eyed vireo "is commonly heard from the tall Elms." [38] The Botanic Garden attracted many nesting pairs, and the countryside extending northwest to Fresh Pond and beyond — open land, marshes, and woods — supported heavy spring populations. Mount Auburn, then an almost undisturbed wooded hill on the Charles River, is still one of the best birding spots of the Boston basin. Nuttall did not limit his observations to Cambridge; he mentions specifically Roxbury, the Blue Hills, Acton (James Brown's old home) and nearby beaches — Chelsea, Nahant, Cohasset, Nantasket.

He increased the general knowledge of the range and concentration of species. "The Honorable T. H. Perkins informs me" that in 1798, roosts of passenger pigeons became wastelands for thousands of acres, the trees killed and the ground strewn with great branches torn down by the weight of the birds.[39] From Lt.-Governor Winthrop he learned of the early abundance of the heath hen, "so common on the ancient bushy site of the city of Boston, that laboring people or servants stipulated with their employers not to have *Heath-Hen* brought to table oftener than a few times in the week!" [40] The eastward movement of the cliff swallow, first found only west of the Mississippi, was pieced together from various observations: Audubon first saw them at Henderson, Kentucky, on the banks of the Ohio in 1815;

in 1818, as I learn from J. W. Boott Esq., they began to build at Crawford's, near the base of the White Mountains of New Hampshire; in the summer of 1830 a few nests were seen by General Dearborn at Winthrop in Maine; he had also heard of one at Gardiner. . . . The hibernal retreat of this species would appear to be in the West Indies, as they were seen in Porto Rico by Vieillot, and one was also observed in St. Domingo by the same author.[41]

The wood thrush, "according to my friend Mr. Ware, breeds as far south as the vicinity of Natchez, in the territory of Mississippi." [42]

# RECREATION

Nuttall sometimes referred to long-past personal experiences, as in writing of the golden eagle: "About 30 miles inland from the Mandan Fort on the Missouri, I once had occasion to observe the eyry of this noble bird, which here consisted of but a slender lining of sticks conveyed into a rocky chasm on the face of a lofty hill rising out of the grassy, open plain. It contained one young bird." [43] The detailed description of an observation made twenty years before must have been based on records in one of his early field journals which he seems to have habitually kept fully and carefully.

Of present interest is his statement concerning the nesting of Ospreys on Gardiner Island.

Unlike other rapacious birds the Ospreys may be almost considered gregarious, breeding so near each other, that, according to Mr. Gardiner, there were on the small island on which he resided, near to the eastern extremity of Long Island (New York), no less than 300 nests with young. Wilson observed 20 of their nests within half a mile. I have seen them nearly as thick about Rehobeth Bay in Delaware. [44]

He was successful in rearing several young birds for limited periods, companions who gave him a good deal of pleasure and amusement as well as knowledge and understanding. The captive pine warbler has already been mentioned. A young screech owl he kept for some months.

A dark closet was his favorite retreat during the day. In the evening he became very lively and restless, gliding across the room in which he was confined, with a side-long, noiseless flight, as if wafted by the air alone; at times he clung to the wainscot, and, unable to turn, he brought his head round to his back, so as to present, by the aid of his brilliant eyes, a most spectral and unearthly appearance. [45]

For many months he had as his "pensioner" a kingbird which was able to endure the severe cold of winter

basking, however, like Diogenes, in the feeble rays of the sun, which he followed round the room of his confinement, well satisfied when no intruder or companion threw him into the shade! Some very cold evenings he had the sagacity to retire under the shelter of a depending bed-quilt; was very much pleased with the warmth and brilliancy of lamp-light, and would eat freely at any hour of the night. . . . His taciturnity, and disinclination to friendship and familiarity in confinement, were striking traits. . . . At length we became so well acquainted that when very hungry, he would express his gratitude on being fed, by a shrill twitter, and a lively look, which was the more remarkable, as at nearly all other times he was entirely silent.[46]

A male Baltimore Oriole he found easy to raise; it proved literally omnivorous; "no bird could become more tame." The most entertaining and affectionate of his pets was a brown thrasher which

courts the attention of his master, follows his steps, complains when neglected . . . and is jealous of every rival. . . . His petulant dislike . . . is . . . displayed by various tones and gestures. . . . His language of fear and surprise could never be mistaken . . . besides a playful turn for mischief and interruption, in which he would sometimes snatch off the paper on which I was writing . . . he had a good deal of curiosity, and was much surprised one day by a large . . . beetle . . . which I had caught and placed in a tumbler . . . his looks of capricious surprise were very amusing. . . . My late friend, the venerable William Bartram, was also much amused by the intelligence displayed by this bird, and relates that one which he kept . . . discovered that the painful prick of the wasps on which he fed, could be obviated by extracting their stings.[47]

The most unusual of Nuttall's captives was a loon. He found that "the young are unable or unwilling to fly" and on land are easily captured.

A young bird of this kind which I obtained in the salt marsh at Chelsea Beach, and transferred to a fish pond, made a good deal of plaint, and would sometimes wander out of his more natural element and hide and bask in the grass. On these occasions, he lay very still until nearly approached, and then slid into the pond and uttered his usual plaint. . . . Though at length inclined to be docile, and showing no alarm when visited, it constantly betrayed its wandering habit, and every night was found to have waddled to some hiding place, where it seemed to prefer hunger to the loss of liberty, and never could be restrained from exercising its instinct to move onwards to some secure or more suitable asylum.[48]

Other feathered companions included an amusing catbird, a lively and trusting young red-eyed vireo, an immature black-poll warbler (Wilson's autumnal warbler), a sociable bay-breasted warbler, a voracious cedar waxwing, and a silent and timid veery. An opportunity to observe and listen to a caged mockingbird furnished him a great amount of information about "this inimitable and wonderful composer."[49] Mr. Winship of Brighton, the nurseryman, told him of a young cedar waxwing which, although at large, became friendly enough to regularly attend "dessert of the dinner table for his portion of fruit, and remained steadfast in his attachment to Mr. W. till killed by an accident."[50]

# RECREATION

On April 6, 1831, Nuttall read to the Boston Society of Natural History a paper called "Remarks and Inquiries concerning the Birds of Massachusetts," which solicited ornithological information both generally and on specific problems.[51] The following remark, like others elsewhere, reveals belief in the modification of species: "It is curious thus to find, among both the plants and the animals of North America, types of form so nearly identic, that they may almost be presumed to be the same species altered by extraneous circumstances." He brought his paper to a close with a gentle defense of his own way of life.

It is only by attentive, careful, and diversified observations, that we can ever expect to arrive at any certain knowledge concerning the animals which live around us. To those severe and heartless economists, who accost every pursuit with inquiring for its utility, we may not have perhaps the most ready answer; but if the close contemplation of nature, sublime, innocently amusing, and often instructive, deserve the attention of the rational mind, we shall not fail to derive profit from the pursuit of Natural History. Nor need we doubt the discovery of connexions with our own wants and advantages in this pursuit, as well as others; for the labyrinthine avenues of knowledge, as they are pursued, often lead to useful results, which could not have been anticipated by their discoverers.

The first volume of *A Manual of the Ornithology of the United States and of Canada,* covering *The Land Birds,* published by Hilliard and Brown, Cambridge, and Hilliard, Gray, Little and Wilkins, Boston, is dated 1832, but it was on sale by December 1831. It differs from all other volumes of Nuttall in lacking a dedication. The Preface gives recognition of help from several persons.

To a number of obliging friends who have assisted him in obtaining specimens or relations concerning the habits of our birds, the author offers his grateful acknowledgments; particularly to Charles Pickering, M.D., to whom he is indebted for much information on their geographical limits; to William Cooper, Esq., well known by his devotion to the study of ornithology; to Mr. Oakes of Ipswich; to T. W. Harris, M.D., Librarian of Harvard University; to S. C. [S. Eliot] Greene Esq. of Boston; and to Mr. Nathaniel J. Wyeth, Mr. James Brown, Mr. John Bethune, and Mr. Russell, of Cambridge.

The last two assistants were students.

The book begins with a valuable general introduction which discusses external and internal structure, sense organs, habits, manners, conjugal fidelity, parental affections, habitats, instincts, and migrations. Each species is then considered in detail, to make up about 700 pages of factual writing. Specific characteristics follow the name and a concise diagnostic description closes each general discussion, the latter a new feature in American texts. To ensure a moderate price, the wood engravings (by Bowen and Hall) are limited, usually to the commonest birds. An important improvement is the arrangement of the species according to systematic relationship instead of the meaningless, chance disorder which obtains in Wilson's and Audubon's treatments.

Nuttall often paraphrases Wilson's pioneer accounts of the habits of the various species in regard to haunts, temper, food, nest building, distribution, and migration. The retelling, generally based on more complete information, is done with zest and usually focuses and improves the rather rambling originals. He not infrequently corrects statements hazarded by Wilson: the tufted titmouse is *not* more abundant north of Pennsylvania; the hermit thrush is *not* mute; the nest which Wilson describes as that of the pine warbler is built by the red-eyed vireo, and so on and on.

*The Land Birds* was received with general appreciation. A few weeks after its publication Ralph Waldo Emerson, recommending a brief reading program to a young relative, wrote, "Then there is a beautiful book on American Birds, the Ornithology of Mr. Nuttall, that everyone who lives in the country ought to read." [52] William Oakes's review emphasized the definite objectives of the publication: "A book . . . containing a sufficiently extensive description of all our birds, arranged in systematic order, . . . of such a size and price as to be generally accessible and convenient. . . . acceptable to the general reader and to the student." He commended the printing and the engravings. [53] W. B. O. Peabody regretted that the illustrations of this "valuable" work were uncolored and limited in number. [54]

More recent commentators praise Nuttall's "fine literary style" in the *Ornithology*. A reviewer of an 1892 edition commented: "Nuttall's writing of the . . . birds he knew had a real fragrance, and in the course of years acquired a particular smack, comparable to that of Bewick." [55] Peattie remarked:

There is nothing over-personal or elaborate in Nuttall's Manual such as there is in Audubon's "Biography" or Rafinesque's writings. The beauty of Nuttall's phrase and diction is not something perceived at once, as it would be in a poet's style; he is economical with his gift, and inserted it almost invisibly into his science.[56]

This quality appears in his comment on the note of the Chipping Sparrow "given from time to time in the night like the reverie of a dream."

Before *The Land Birds* was issued, Nuttall was afield in pursuit of ducks, sea, and shore birds for his second volume, *The Water Birds*; day or night might find him in the marsh or on the beach. "On the 6th of October (1831) having spent the night in a lodge, on the borders of Fresh Pond, employed for decoying and shooting ducks, I heard, about sunrise, the Yellow-Breasted Rails begin to stir among the reeds that thickly skirt this retired border of the lake."[57] During one mid-August he visited Chatham and Martha's Vineyard to observe the great flocks of migrating shore birds (knots, marbled godwits, etc.) for which Cape Cod is a favored stopover. In his account of the American merganser he says:

Early in the month of May (1832) [1830 in 2d ed.] while descending the Susquehannah near to Dunnstown, a few miles below the gorge of the Alleghanys, through which that river meanders near the foot of Bald Eagle Mountain, G. Lyman, Esq. and myself observed near the head of a little bushy island, some Wild Duck, as we thought, with her brood . . . making off round a point which closed the view. On rowing to the spot . . . we . . . perceived . . . a female Gooseander or Dun-Diver, with a small but active little brood of 8 young ones. . . . we succeeded in cutting off the retreat of one of the family, which was at length taken from behind a flat boat under which it had finally retreated to hide. We now examined the little stranger, and found it to be a young Merganser of this species, not bigger than the egg of a goose, and yet already a most elegant epitome of its female parent, generally grey, with the rufous head and neck, and the rudiments of a growing crest.[58]

In the second edition of the *Ornithology* (1840) Nuttall added a new reference to this excursion with George Williams Lyman, dating it also in 1830. "In the woods around Farran[d]ville, on the Susquehannah, within the range of the Alleghany chain, in the month of May (1830), I saw and heard several males [of the chestnut-sided warbler] in full song, in the shady forest trees by a small stream."[59]

One of the most delightful of Nuttall's accounts of water birds concerns solitary sandpipers, visitants to the Garden.

A pair, but oftener a single individual, have usually frequented, very familiarly, the small fish-pond in the Botanic Garden in Cambridge. Attracted by the numerous *Donatias* and their larvae, which feed upon the water lily (*Nymphaea odorata*,) I observed one of them tripping along upon the sinking leaves with great agility, expanding its wings, and gently flitting over the treacherous element in the manner of the Rail.[60]

There is an entertaining passage wherein Shakespeare is found in error in his ornithology in contrast to the general praise of his knowledge of most subjects. Under Nuttall's discussion of the precipitous cliffs on which the razor-billed auks lay their eggs, he quotes the famous passage portraying the cliffs of Dover:

> How fearful
> And dizzy 'tis to cast one's eyes so low!
> The Crows, and Choughs that wing the midway air
> Show scarce as gross as beetles; Half-way
> Hangs one that gathers Samphire, dreadful trade!
> Methinks, he seems no bigger than his head:

Nuttall approved the samphire collecting (the European plant so-called being the rock-loving Umbellifer, *Crithmum maritimum*), but he appended a footnote to crows and choughs to state that birds in that locale would probably be razor-billed auks, murres, and guillemots.[61]

In the summer of 1833 Audubon went to the Labrador coast to observe and collect arctic birds to swell his Elephant Folio. Promptly on his return he sent information to Nuttall for the volume which he was then bringing to completion and received "an extremely kind letter in answer." [62] The facts pertained to such northern birds as kittiwakes, jaegers, petrels, eider and harlequin ducks, gannets, and guillemots; in each instance Nuttall acknowledged the source of his information in a footnote.

Nuttall again drew on his field notebooks of 1810, 1811, and perhaps 1819, for he recorded several observations of ducks seen on the Mississippi and the Missouri.[63] He did a great deal of dissection and meticulous microscopic examination to ascertain the feeding habits of the water birds. In the stomachs of pintails, for instance, he found seeds of *Zostera*; in the wood ducks', seeds of *Zizania aquatica* and *Ruppia* and also *Donatia*, a small member of the *Coleoptera*. For his first volume he had examined the upper digestive tracts of imperfectly known land birds: the stomachs of three specimens of olive-sided flycatchers were filled with torn fragments of wild bees, wasps, and other *Hymenoptera*.

The *Water Birds* (1834) is a volume of 627 pages of which about a tenth forms an Appendix of information about land birds uncovered since the first volume was printed. Here Nuttall stated that Swainson had already published the olive-sided flycatcher, which he had supposed to be new. He recorded the unusual occurrence of the arrival of redpolls in Cambridge in considerable flocks early in November 1833. "They now regularly assemble in the birch trees every morning to feed on their seeds." On the 11th, red- and white-winged crossbills appeared in a grove of evergreens in Mount Auburn that they had visited the previous winter. A northern shrike, harrying them, was heard mimicking the song sparrow and the catbird.

In this volume Nuttall successfully authored a new species — *Sterna forsteri*. This tern, being very similar to the common tern, was not distinguished from it until distinct characters were pointed out by Edward Forster, "eminent naturalist and voyager" and Treasurer of the Linnean Society of London. Nuttall, believing the differences were of specific magnitude and also perceiving a difference in the calls of the two birds, proposed that the newly recognized species should be named in honor of Forster.[64]

The second volume did not attain the popularity of the first, perhaps because the larger birds lack the spontaneous appeal of the songsters. Moreover Nuttall's intimate knowledge and keen appreciation of many of the smaller birds lend to the first volume a warmth and charm which is missing in much of the second. *The Ornithology* so satisfactorily stood the test of late nineteenth century knowledge that Little, Brown and Company put out three editions of it, only slightly revised, near the turn of the century.[65]

Nuttall's avian activities resulted eventually in the conferring of his name on the first ornithological association ever formed in America. A Cantabrigian group of pioneers in modern scientific study of American birds formed the Nuttall Ornithological Club in 1873. "The name [chosen at the first meeting] seems always to have been looked upon with approbation, not only within the Club but far more widely."[66]

CHAPTER 15

# LEAVES OF ABSENCE

Nuttall . . . was easily the first man of science in Augustan Harvard.
He was the first scholar to whom the University gave an appointment
with the permission to devote most of his time to research.[1] — Samuel
Eliot Morison, *Three Centuries of Harvard.*

At the end of the summer of 1827 "Mr. Nuttall the Curator requested
leave of absence for three months, with a view to make additions to the
Garden by Exchange or otherwise." This request was referred by the
Board of Visitors to the committee having supervision of the Garden,
Lowell, Brooks, and Kirkland *ex officio.*[2]

Late in 1827 Nuttall sailed for England, probably on one of the
Philadelphia-to-Liverpool packets for, on November 13 and 20, he
attended meetings in Philadelphia of the Academy of Natural Sciences at its new location on the corner of 12th and George Streets.[3]
On his way south he visited the Princes' Linnaean Gardens in Flushing, which had been supplied for several years with his plants of
horticultural interest. He also saw Torrey who had recently returned
to New York City to assume the professorship at the College of Physicians and Surgeons made vacant by the death of James Freeman Dana.
Torrey, a "closet botanist" with no urge to search the fields and
woods of distant places or even of those nearby once he had passed
his early youth, was always eager to secure new herbarium specimens.
Some obliging West Point graduates ordered to frontier posts sent
him a batch or two of specimens but they soon lost interest, and he
had begun to look toward paid collectors as the best means of securing
plants from a distance. He had in view a system of dividing the expenses and the specimens on a percentage basis with other botanists;
von Schweinitz, Darlington, Short, and the Greenes were among
those glad to cooperate. After Nuttall's visit, Torrey reported to von

Schweinitz: "Mr. Nuttall thinks that we may procure a collector on very reasonable terms in England or Scotland & he promised to bring out with him in the spring such a person, if he could find one of the proper description."[4]

Information is meager concerning Nuttall's activities during this visit to England. While he was in London seeing seedsmen and gardens, he probably stayed in Newgate with Henry Fisher, Jonas's erstwhile partner. Through Francis Boott, settled in practice at 24 Gower Street, we learn that Nuttall visited Robert Barclay's garden at Buryhill, Surrey. The hypersensitive Boott, hurt and indignant that Nuttall neglected his botanical acquaintances during an appreciable stay in London, wrote to Hooker on May 29, 1828, "Did you see Nuttal? He was here some time, but called on no one — Lord Stanley met him at Bury Hill. I do not relish such conduct for he had obligations to discharge to those who had been more than kind to him on his last visit."[5] David Douglas was among those who saw Nuttall in 1828, presumably at Douglas's own headquarters, the garden of the Horticultural Society of London at Chiswick. He evidently heard criticism of Nuttall's aloofness, perhaps from John Lindley (1799–1865), Assistant Secretary of the Horticultural Society, who had superintended the laying out of the garden. Four and a half years later Douglas wrote of the gossip to Hooker from the west coast of North America where time became a burden to him and home memories flowed through his mind.

Nuttall is a poor fellow . . . he did not come from his pinnacle of greatness to visit the Linneans in 1828 though his fees of admission have not yet been paid, much less his annual subscription. . . . I am not surprised that Mr. Nuttall should think the *Arkansas and Missouri his own,* for I have heard from some who had reason to know him that he does not practice the liberality he professes. So far as I know Mr. N. personally he appears the reverse and we must not credit all we hear.[6]

It is noteworthy that, despite criticisms made of him from time to time, Nuttall always retained favor in the eyes of Hooker who had an understanding and sympathetic spirit: he would immediately realize that Nuttall's pride would not permit his attendance at the Linnean Society with his dues unpaid. Douglas had been taken into the Society as an Associate with all fees remitted; Nuttall was a Fellow owing all assessments. Fortunately he was finally taken off the Society's list of defaulters in 1833 through the suggestion of Francis

Boott, then recently appointed Secretary of the Society, doubtless strongly supported by the Vice-President A. B. Lambert. The Council voted on March 17 of that year: "On the representation of the Secretary as to the Arrears due to the Society by Mr Thomas Nuttall, it was specially ordered that the same and all future payments be remitted in consideration of the eminent services he has rendered to Science by his works on Botany and Ornithology and by his travels in North America." [7]

We may assume that Nuttall visited his mother in Long Preston and saw Susan Booth's growing family and other relatives in the neighborhood. While staying with Jonas at Nutgrove Hall, he wrote two letters to Hooker in Glasgow.

Sutton, nr Prescott, March 14th 1828

Professor Hooker
Dr Sir

I am sorry that the shortness of my present visit to England prevents me the pleasure of again enjoying your society. I had been informed mistakenly, it appears, of your appointment in the London Institution,[8] and in consequence delayed sending to you a very fine volume on Ornithology supplemental to Wilson's large work by Charles L. Bonaparte, well known amongst us for his zeal and attachment to that branch of Natural History. You will now I hope safely receive it by the Glasgow packet. It is from a young man, Dr Green[e] of Boston whom I have frequently heard to speak of you with the most pleasing recollections. No letter accompanies it, as I received it in haste. Both Dr Green and myself I believe have grown negligent in our pursuit of Botany. I have added little to my stock of information or materials and I fear, upon the whole, natural history is beginning to fall into neglect among us. Our garden at Cambridge is not adequately supported tho' considerably better than when I found it.

I hope you are in good health and shall be very happy to receive a line from you when you find leisure.

Your most obliged, humble servant
Thos Nuttall [9]

Bonaparte's work was a gift for young William Dawson Hooker from Benjamin D. Greene who later sent him Nuttall's *Ornithology*.[10]

Prescott, May 5th 1828

Professor Hooker
Dr Sir

Some time since I forwarded for you to Glasgow a volume on Ornithology from Dr Green of Boston wh I hope you received in safety. In the same package was inadvertently sent a copy of an Elementary work on

Botany w.ʰ I published last year in America, but w.ʰ had been presented to a friend in this place. It happens to be the only color.ᵈ copy in the country, and as the work is about to be republished in London with colored plates it will be required by the printer to copy, otherwise, the person here for whom it was intended

Excuse the great haste
Yours
Tho.ˢ Nuttall

Please forward it to
Messrs. Fisher, Son & Jackson
No 38 Newgate Street [11]

On the reverse was written "There is a book forwarded to Professor Hooker by the Henry Bell which leaves this Port (Liverpool) tomorrow May 8.ᵗʰ 1828." Evidently Nuttall sent a standard copy of his textbook to replace the copy with the colored plates.

In the late summer or the autumn of 1828, Nuttall probably made a foray into New Hampshire for early the next year Oakes wrote that Nuttall had found a new species of *Chara* there.[12] During the winter of 1828–1829, Nuttall seems to have gone no farther than Philadelphia.

The following winter a return to ornithological work in Philadelphia and his journey through the Southeast beguiled the barren northern months. At Augusta, Georgia, he visited Dr. Thomas Jefferson Wray, his friend and admirer, a persevering botanical enthusiast who some months later was undertaking to raise a fund to enable Nuttall to collect in the Southwest.[13] He stopped also in Milledgeville, the capital of Georgia from 1807 to 1868, to see Dr. Samuel Boykin (1786–1848) who wrote years later, "Shortly before Mr. E's death [Elliott's, March 28, 1830] I had Mr. Nuttall at my house for a few days. I turned over to him my entire lot of dried plants — among which he said there were many requiring investigation. They were all shipwrecked in Boston Harbour and lost." The following autumn Nuttall sent plants and seeds to these friends and to Mr. Oemler in Savannah.[14] In 1834 he named a southern genus of the *Saxifragaceae* in honor of Boykin and a species of *Coreopsis* for Wray.

From Milledgeville, Nuttall continued on the Federal Road to Alabama. That this route crossed the Flint River in an area where William Baldwin had collected when he first went to the Southeast would be peculiarly gratifying to Nuttall, who took great interest in retracing regions visited by earlier botanists. He was delighted to find *Catalpa bignonioides* Walt., for its distribution had long puzzled him; "at Columbus in Georgia, on the banks of the Chattahoochee I for the first time in my life beheld this tree decidedly native, forming small, haggard, crooked trees leaning fantastically over the rocky banks of the river. Around Philadelphia, and other parts of the Middle and warmer States, it appears to be perfectly naturalized and very common." [15] He found it native also in lower Alabama and west Florida. At Columbus he saw in considerable abundance Michaux's Stillingia ligustrina [*Sebastiania fruticosa* (Bartr.) Fernald]. A few years later he described a new aquatic species, *Podostemum \*abrotanoides*, that gave "the appearance of a submerged green field of some kind of *Fucus* to the shallow water of the Chatahoochee" and remarked that it was "much sought after as a pasture by the deer and domestic cattle." [16]

On crossing the river he entered Alabama and proceeded to Montgomery. From that point his exact route through the state becomes obscure (due to discrepancies in his own accounts) although it is clear that he tarried in both Cahaba and Tuscaloosa. [17] His most detailed record was written eleven years later in the *Sylva*:

> I met with abundance of the *M[agnolia] macrophylla*, 70 miles from Tuscaloosa, on the bank of the Coosa [error for Cahaba?] in Bibb County, Alabama . . . to the town of Cahaba I still saw the Magnolia and afterwards in the immediate vicinity of Tuscaloosa on the banks of the Black Warrior, towards Florida I observed this species in the greatest abundance. [18]

In the little town of Cahaba on the west bank of the Alabama River [19] Nuttall had the pleasure of meeting Dr. Gurdon Saltonstall, a graduate of Union College and the College of Physicians and Surgeons (1815) who had been appointed to serve as Professor of Mathematics and Natural Philosophy at the new University of Alabama. He was "an elegant and engaging person, . . . of easy manners." [20] The conversation was, naturally, professional. Saltonstall ordered two copies of Nuttall's botanical textbook. Evidently the suggestion was made that the University might buy Nuttall's large and superb collection of minerals. Perhaps it was in pursuit of this proposition that Nuttall went to Tuscaloosa where he remained for a week or more in February observing especially hawks and a domesticated Carolina parakeet and recording in detail "almost endless" imitations and variations in the song of a Carolina wren.[21] Preparations were being made in the town for the opening of the University in the spring of 1831. Although there is no statement that Nuttall met President Alva Woods, D.D., who was a classmate at Harvard of George Bancroft and George B. Emerson, an extant letter strongly suggests that he did.[22]

After Nuttall returned to Cambridge, he made a formal proffer of his cabinet of over 3000 mineral specimens for $1500. Writing to Saltonstall at the end of the year in an effort to learn the attitude of the Trustees to his proposal, he said: "in case of leaving this dreadfull [sic] climate (the thermo[ter] this moment near zero) I must sacrifice all my labor for whatever it will bring at an auction among tradesmen! . . . and I wished, besides realizing a trifle for my labors, to know that the fruits of my industry in a mineral cabinet, might have a . . . usefull [sic] station to the public."[23]

From Tuscaloosa Nuttall went southward through rich prairies, the black lands of Alabama, where he first heard the mockingbird singing on February 26.[24] In southern Alabama he was surprised to get a maidenhair fern, which he considered to be *Adiantum trapeziforme* of the West Indies; in this area and in west Florida he got *Baptisia *microphylla, Petalostemon *gracilis, Aster *adnatus* and perhaps *Helenium *tenuifolium* and *Helianthus *heterophyllus.*[25] On the Escambia River he was pleased to find *Myrica inodora* Bartr., which "the amiable and excellent" William Bartram first collected in 1778 on the Tensaw bluff.

In the forests of west Florida early in March he heard the northern yellowthroat singing and by the middle of the month saw the oaks in leaf and *Cornus florida* in full bloom. Abundant along the southernmost part of his course was Cliftonia ligustrina Sims [*C. monophylla* (Lam.) Sarg.] the buckwheat tree, "exceedingly ornamental in flower, which takes place in early spring, in the month of March when the whole surface of the tree is covered with the most delicate, elegant, and somewhat fragrant flowers. . . . In the intervals of their shade . . . we frequently saw . . . in flower, the Atamasco Lily, or Amaryllis of the North."[26]

About ten miles from Tallahassee he was excited by meeting with a distinctive species of pitcher-plant which was new to him. Without consulting the floras, he hastily reported it early in May to the American Philosophical Society as a new species, Sarracenia calceolata. It was printed with a plate drawn by J. Whitfield. However it was already known as *S. psitticana* Michx.[27] At Chipola he had found a genuinely new species of *Gratiola*, which he published in 1834 as *G. *floridana*. Near Tallahassee he again found *Castanea alnifolia* Nutt., first discovered in the vicinity of Charleston in 1816.[28]

"On the borders of swampy open thickets" in Florida and Georgia he got *Rudbeckia *nitida*. On his way across Georgia to Savannah he crossed the Altamaha River into Tattnall County (then more extensive than now) where he again saw his "new" pitcher-plant. In sandhills along the river he got "Lupinus *gracilis." A shell that he got in the river although a well-known species, Unio [*Elliptio*] complanatus, was of value to Isaac Lea of the Philadelphia Academy as evidence of the distribution of the species; it was the first shell Lea had seen from the Altamaha. From this general area had come some of Baldwin's new species that Nuttall had published in the *Genera*.

At Savannah where he embarked for the north, Nuttall renewed his acquaintance with Mr. Oemler, the algologist, whom he had met in 1815. The coastal vessel on which Nuttall took passage put in at Chester, Pennsylvania, where "on the 17th of April . . . I again recognized my old and pleasing acquaintance [the Carolina wren], by his usual note."

The next winter Nuttall kept busy in Cambridge writing the first volume of the *Ornithology*. His unbroken winter residence there was evidently a trial to him — like the birds, he throve on annual migrations — for in June 1831, a Committee of President Quincy and Dr. Bowditch was appointed by the Corporation "to make a definite arrangement for the continuance of Mr. Nuttall at the University." [29] Late in 1831, Nuttall went to the northern extremity of New Hampshire and in February 1832 he was granted $260 for three months' stay in the southern or middle states; he was to be back by April 1.[30]

His official report submitted to the Corporation on June 21, recounts his chief activities in some detail.

Gentlemen,

In compliance with your request I take the liberty of briefly stating to you my employment in the three winter months of my absence from the institution to w.h I have the honor to be attached. The principal part of my time was spent in the vicinity of Newbern in North Carolina from whence I forwarded a considerable collection of living plants for the garden. The species sent were somewhat more than a hundred kinds with a sufficient number of duplicates in order if possible to ensure their success. The long list of their names I have now necessarily omitted.

On the banks of the river Neuse, while in the neighbourhood of New-bern, I carefully examined for fossils of w.h an immense stratum is here exposed to view by the washing of the river. Many of the species, tho' 40 miles from the present sea-coast are still identic with those which line the strand of Shakkleford bank and Cape Hatteras. Other species among them are now extinct and a few belong at this time exclusively to tropical climates. These organic reliques are the deposit of the last great change which has modified the Surface of the earth to its present form, — in short, — the palpable remains of the universal deluge: similar beds of interred shells and fossils with the remains of large quadrupeds and reptiles are also observed over every portion of the Old World as well as the new. The study of these objects so as to discover their individual characters and above all the circumstances w.h accompanied their deposition, have now claimed a great portion of my attention, with a view at no distant period to offer some general remarks upon this much neglected geological forma-tion with a precise list, if possible, of all the objects w.h have as yet been discovered in it, within the limits of the United States. in the mean time an arranged collection of these fossils will be placed in the museum of the University. With a view to make an actual comparison between the fossil and recent shells, I also made a journey to the neighbouring coast, and have thus been enabled to verify with certainty the existing and diluvial species.

I have likewise collected for the mineral cabinet a suite of specimens of crystallised Muriate of Copper, w.h formed part of the freight of a ves-sel from the port of Valparaiso in Chili.

> I have the honor to be
> Your Obt Servant
> Tho.s Nuttall [31]

Wherever he went in these years Nuttall found material for the *Ornithology*: in the Neuse River, canvas-back ducks and buffleheads were abundant, and nowhere had he seen such quantities of bald-pates; at Beaufort ("the neighbouring coast") he studied a small flock of laughing gulls. Benjamin Greene met Nuttall in the South and reported to Torrey, "Nuttall has flown away from birds as well as botany & is now driving away at antediluvian bones  fossil shells Conchology  Geology etc etc." [32] But Nuttall did not fail to garner specimens of the vanilla-scented ladies'-tresses of the marshes [*Spiranthes odorata* (Nutt.) Lindl.], which towered among the grasses along the Neuse.[33]

He was fortunate in some of his fossil finds. At a meeting of the Academy on June 19, Dr. Hays exhibited the anterior molar of a mastodon that Nuttall got and more than a year later announced from the same source a tooth of "a Tapir," the first evidence found in North America of this animal. Years later Timothy A. Conrad (1803–

1877) told Dr. Leidy that Nuttall had also found there teeth of *Equus americana*. Two new species of marine shells that he collected at New Bern (*Amphidesma bellastriata* and *Tellina lutea*) and one from deep water at Beaufort (*Scalaria turbinata*) were published by Conrad in 1837.[34] Dr. Harlan named an arboreal mouse which Nuttall found near Norfolk, Virginia, in his honor, the northern golden mouse (*Peromyscus nuttalli*).[35]

At New Bern, Nuttall became acquainted with an active and enthusiastic botanist, Hardy B. Croom (1799–1837), who the next year published with Dr. H. Loomis a "Catalogue of Plants, Observed in the Neighbourhood of New Bern, North Carolina." Croom was also interested in the local fossilized animal remains; from his collection he gave Nuttall a choice specimen, a vertebra eight inches in diameter, very likely with the hope that he would be able to get it identified, for in August 1833, after a visit to England, Nuttall reported to him that he had been unable to get any light on the New Bern fossils. Since Croom's cotton plantations in North Carolina were deteriorating through the impoverishment of the soil, he was renting land on the Apalachicola River in west Florida to test the growing conditions. His botanizing thereabouts yielded in 1833 the thrilling discovery of what ultimately proved to be a new genus of the gymnosperms. He promptly sent a specimen to Nuttall but unfortunately only vegetative material was then available so identification had to remain in abeyance; Nuttall tentatively suggested that it might prove to be "Taxus montana" of Mexico.[36] By the time Croom obtained reproductive structures Nuttall had left civilization behind him and Torrey became Croom's advisor in regard to the plant, which Arnott was to name *Torreya taxifolia*.

On September 19, 1832, Nuttall again wrote to the Honorable Corporation. After reiterating the accomplishments of his spring trip, with the additional information that most of the plants shipped to the Garden lived and were in cultivation and that the fossils, chiefly "Testaceous animals," numbering nearly 100, had been named as far as practicable, he arrived at his interest of the moment.

I have now to beg of you the further indulgence of again pursuing my favorite investigations in the coming winter, and, it is my intention by your permission to visit the Azores or Western Islands, and collect such objects and facts in Natural History as may prove usefull to this institution. After w.<sup>h</sup> it is also my desire to proceed to London to open and renew a correspondence for the benefit of the Botanic Garden by exchanges of our natural productions, and furthermore to cultivate an acquaintance with Societies and Naturalists in aid of my endeavours to be more usefull to our University.

With gratefull acknowledgments for your Indulgence and Patronage,

I remain, your Obt. Servant

Tho.<sup>s</sup> Nuttall [37]

This request was approved on September 20.

He sailed on October 7, probably on a ship of the Dabneys or Cunninghams, Bostonians who carried on trade in and with the Azores, bringing oranges and wine to New England.[38] For three generations, Dabneys held the United States Consulship on Fayal which, at Horta, has the best harbor in the Azores. John Bass Dabney, the first Consul of the family, was a member of the Massachusetts Society for Promoting Agriculture; Frederick Dabney (1809–1857) graduated from Harvard in 1828, and Edward Linzee Cunningham in 1829. The naturalization attempted on Fayal of Nuttall's colorful *Coreopsis tinctoria* from Arkansas through Miss Pomeroy's enthusiastic efforts may have added allure to the Western Isles. The Pomeroys, relatives of the Dabneys, as were the Cunninghams, were frequent visitors at the Dabneys' Fayal estates "Bagatelle" and "Fredonia."

Although we know nothing of the human companionship aboard ship, Nuttall had feathered friends alongside all the way to the Azores, a flock of Wilson's petrels (Mother Carey's chickens) whose habits he studied with faithful attention. "There is something cheerful and amusing in the sight of these little voyaging flocks, steadily following after the vessel, so light and unconcerned, across the dreary ocean. . . . as humble dependents, they follow for their pittance of fare . . . we were followed by the same flock to the soundings of the Azores." [39]

An English description of Fayal written during the reign of Queen Elizabeth I was still applicable.

This Fayal is the principall towne in all that island, & is situate directly over against the high and mighty mountaine Pico, lying towards the West Northwest from that mountaine, being divided therefrom by a narrow Sea, which at that place is by estimation about two or three leagues in bredth betweene the Isles of Fayal and Pico.

The towne conteyned some three hundred housholds, their houses were faire and strongly builded of lime and stone, and double covered with hollow tyles. . . . Every house almost had a cisterne or well in a garden on the backe side.[40]

Fayal had been visited by some famous botanists — George Forster with Captain Cook's Expedition in 1775 and, a couple of years later, Francis Masson, the first collector for Kew Gardens. The native flora of the Azorean group is, nevertheless, very limited. A few species of indigenous evergreen trees and shrubs form a dense cover under which relatively few herbs develop, and most of these were introduced in early days. However interesting the ecology of Fayal and the peak of Pico (7613 ft.) may have been to Nuttall, the number of herbaceous species must have been very disappointing.

Several years later in the *Sylva* Nuttall gave two descriptions of the characteristic horticulture of the islands.

In the Azores, the cultivation of the Orange as an article of commerce is of great importance to the inhabitants, and every means are employed for its success. The trees in Fayal are defended from the severe sea-breezes by very high stone walls and plantations of young trees of the Faya (*Myrica Faya*) planted between them. . . .
The Fayal Myrtle . . . is . . . the principal article of fuel; it . . . attains the ordinary height of a peach tree.[41]

In 1832 King Pedro IV of Portugal was using the Azores as the base for a successful campaign to wrest back his inheritance, seized by Napoleon. The young king and his court were royally entertained by the Dabneys who were, as it were, Princes of Fayal. Even if Nuttall were a guest of Frederick Dabney, gay festivities would not affect his observations and collecting of plants, minerals, and marine shells. Five new species of *Mollusca* which he secured on the rocky coast were described by T. A. Conrad early in 1837; two named in his honor permanently associate his name with Fayal.[42]

The Dabney gardens presented the "novel beauty" of masses of tropical growth from diverse remote spots of the earth: palms, camphor tree, dragon tree, bamboos, bananas, cork oaks, *Pittosporum*, many species of passion flowers, and two magnificent Norfolk Island "pines" (*Araucaria excelsa*). The great crater in the interior of the island, five miles around and 1800 feet deep, could be reached on foot or by donkey.[43] The richer soil of Pico with its soaring blue cone emitting thin mists of hot volcanic air encouraged Nuttall to examine that islet across the narrow strait.

After a six-weeks' sojourn on Fayal, Nuttall sailed for the port of

London. He spent the winter and spring negotiating for plants and collecting ores and mineral specimens for Harvard. In London, besides visiting various nurserymen and gardens, including Loddiges, William Young at Epsom, and the garden of the Horticultural Society, he took time at the British Museum to study specimens of North American birds donated by the Hudson's Bay Company.[44] He spent eight weeks at the famous tin and copper mines at Redruth, Cornwall (visited in 1805 by Benjamin Silliman), and examining mines in Devon, studying the deposits and selecting specimens of the ores. It was probably at this time that he became acquainted with a budding botanist, I. W. N. Keys (1818–1890), a boy from Plymouth being trained as a printer, who was to write a flora of Devon and Cornwall; Nuttall named one of his far eastern rhododendrons for him in 1853.

As always Nuttall visited the various members of his family in the North. Elizabeth and her two older children, Frances and Francis, then in their early teens, were living at Nutgrove Hall; the youngest, Maria Louise, Jonas's favorite, had died in 1831. In the North also, Thomas gave close attention to the aviary of Lord Stanley and also to his museum where he noted with particular interest the skin of an American avocet taken by John Bradbury at the Great Bend of the Missouri in 1811.[45] Jonas probably insisted that Thomas ride on the new railroad opened between Liverpool and Manchester in mid-September 1830; there was a station at Rainhill close by Nutgrove. Such an excursion would have given Nuttall an opportunity to call on his old friend, Dr. Windsor, who practiced medicine in Manchester.

In Long Preston, also, he was preoccupied by thoughts of the birds. His mother, who had become an invalid, gave him information about the species of birds that visit the Yorkshire moors. In writing of the snipe he says,

> My aged maternal parent remembered, and could imitate with exactness this low wailing murmur, which she had for so many years heard over the marshes of my native Ribble, in the fine evenings of spring, when all nature seemed ready to do homage for the bounties of the season; and yet at the age of 70, the riddle had not been expounded with satisfaction.
>
> Over the wide marshes of Fresh Pond, about the middle of April, my attention was called to the same invisible voice, which issued from the floating clouds of a dark evening; the author was here called the Alewife Bird, from its arrival with the shoals of that fish in the neighboring lake.

. . . all my sporting acquaintance were familiar with this quivering call, but had never decided upon its author.[46]

The mysterious sounds of the snipe, known as winnowing, are now recognized as arising from vibrations of the spread tail feathers as the bird dive bombs high above the earth.

Nuttall took care to observe the marsh titmouse, which was generally believed to be identical with the American black-capped chickadee, and was therefore able to point out a difference of an inch in length, some variation in coloration, and also dissimilar behavior. He concluded that it is "wholly different from our lively and familiar Chicadee. Unlike our bird it is rather shy, seldom seen but in pairs or solitary, never in domestic premises."[47]

Nuttall sailed from Liverpool early in May on the packet *Helen*, Captain Butnam, which did not reach New York until June 18. His report to the Corporation on July 7, 1833, epitomizing the eight and a half months of his absence from Cambridge, explained his late return: "To add still further to the delay I experienced the longest passage I have ever had out of 8 transits across the Atlantic. I was still further retarded in New York by what appeared to us an unnecessary quarantine regulation and a delay in clearing my collection thro' the Custom-House."[48] The long return passage was not Nuttall's eighth crossing of the Atlantic, but his ninth. Neither was it the longest; but it was the longest of eight of them, which is perhaps what he was carefully saying. (Or he may have omitted the crossing via the Azores as not comparable; his 1815 passage was the longest.)

A further outcome of the deliberations of the committee appointed in June 1831, "for the continuance of Mr. Nuttall at the University" was the increase of his salary for the calendar year 1833 to a thousand dollars. This made a neat round sum for Nuttall to remember as the last salary he received from Harvard.

# CHAPTER 16

# GROWING WANDERLUST

Every man truly lives, so long as he acts his nature, or some way makes good the faculties of himself. — Sir Thomas Browne

LAST YEARS AT HARVARD, 1826–1833. The germ of an administrative revolution at Harvard was introduced in June 1826, with the election to the Corporation of Nathaniel Bowditch, mathematician, author of *The New Practical Navigator*, and a very successful self-made man — a sharp deviation from the custom of electing the five Fellows from clergymen, lawyers, and, in later years, merchants educated at the college. Bowditch had become an honorary *Magister in Artibus* at the Harvard Commencement of 1802, in recognition of his important contribution to navigation. As a Fellow he very soon started a campaign to put the institution on a sounder financial basis and aggressively carried through fundamental changes and economies, including salary cuts, which were distasteful to the community.[1] The resignations of the Treasurer and Steward were demanded on the charge that their books were in confusion. Goaded by Bowditch's incivility, Kirkland, the students' beloved president, resigned on March 28, 1828, and was succeeded by Josiah Quincy, whose inauguration took place on June 2, 1829. A forceful, practical man with a fine record of public service in Congress, Quincy had just completed five successful years as Boston's second mayor. As an administrator he served Harvard well but, having little understanding of the sensibilities of his young charges, he dealt with them impatiently and won their hearty dislike. His brusqueness was reflected in one of their favorite witticisms: "Oh, good morning, Smith [or whatever]. What is your name, Sir?" He seems to have sympathized with Nuttall's ambitions to carry on field investigations and was generous in endorsing leaves of absence for him.

267

# THOMAS NUTTALL, NATURALIST

On June 24, 1829, Benjamin Silliman, writing to Professor John Griscom of New York, suggested Nuttall as a regional collaborator at Cambridge for the *American Journal of Science and the Arts,* commenting, "I am told he is a good Zoologist." [2] This was the sort of routine responsibility that became intolerably irksome to Nuttall. In any case he was already devoting every free moment to the birds.

The Massachusetts Horticultural Society, a natural outgrowth from the Massachusetts Society for Promoting Agriculture, was founded in 1829, General Henry A. S. Dearborn being elected President. [3] On September 12, the Visitors of the Botanic Garden voted that Mr. Nuttall be permitted to furnish flowers from the Garden for the tables at the first dinner of the Society. [4] Very soon the new group under the leadership of Jacob Bigelow established Mount Auburn Cemetery and an experimental garden on a beautiful tract of Cambridge woodland, a favorite ramble of generations of Harvard students. To diversify its sylva several hundred ornamental trees were transplanted from the estate of General Dearborn in Roxbury.

The Board of Visitors having asked Nuttall to submit papers suitable for publication in *The New England Farmer,* mentioning especially experiments with medicinal plants, [5] he sent them two short papers in September and October 1829. For information for the first he was indebted to his neighbor Job Wyeth, who

called my attention to a very remarkable fact in vegetable physiology, and very much at variance with the general opinions and facts on the subject. On a productive and vigorous Russet apple tree well filled with fruit of the ordinary character, appears a *single ungrafted* branch bearing thirty Harvey Apples with smooth skins, not distinguished in any way from fruit of this variety growing contiguous to the russet. . . . No Russets appeared on the Harvey tree. That the latter by its influence has given rise to this phenomena on the russet, need not be questioned. . . . By cross impregnations, particularly among ornamental flowers, a sort of fairy creation has arisen around us, superior in beauty to simple nature, and producing a new era in the existence of the flower garden. [6]

This full-grown apple tree had never before presented this phenomenon.

The second communication, entitled "Observations on the Drug Sarsaparilla," discussed the substitution of spurious plants for the genuine tropical one, the roots of which were imported from Mexico and South America although the identity of the plant remained unknown to science. It was stated that the late Professor Barton attributed some medical efficacy to our northern wild sarsaparilla (*Aralia nudi-caulis* L.) but Mr. Carpenter, the well-known druggist of Philadelphia, denied that it has any value.[7] The identity of tropical plants, the roots, stems, or leaves of which were imported for use in medicine, seems to have been a baffling problem to the doctors and druggists of the time. Dr. John Redman Coxe of the University of Pennsylvania in a paper on the plant which yields the official jalap, which he had secured from Xalapa, Mexico, and raised in Philadelphia, quoted a technical description that Nuttall had made for him from a dried specimen and his determination of it as *Ipomoea jalapa.*[8]

Elias Durand recorded an episode that he says occurred during the first six or seven years of Nuttall's residence in Cambridge: "Mr. Nuttall paid a visit to Philadelphia in company with several gentlemen of Boston, on their way to the coal and iron districts of Pennsylvania. Joined by Dr. Pickering, they proceeded to Pottsville; hence over the mountains to the Susquehanna, and up its west branch as far as the crossing of the Alleghany ridge."[9] The Bostonians were launching an extragavant venture in remote bituminous coal country, establishing in the wilderness the Lycoming Coal Company, sawmills, a plant for manufacturing nails, other industries, and a large farm, all under the management of William P. Farrand, whose name was given to the isolated community. Doubtless Nuttall accompanied the group as one versed in mineralogy and geology.

George Williams Lyman (1786–1880), Harvard College 1806, who joined Nuttall on birding trips about Farrandville,[10] was the eldest son of Theodore Lyman, an eminent merchant in the Northwest-and-China fur trade who had developed a handsome country estate in Waltham, a few miles from Cambridge, with a level park a mile in length, planted with groups of English limes, elms, and oaks and masses of native trees and shrubs, watered by a fine stream and stocked with deer. The well-supplied greenhouses were and still are famous for their camellias. The senior Lyman subscribed $1200 toward the establishment of the Massachusetts Professorship of Natural History and the Botanic Garden; but, being a canny New Englander, when the funds suffered impairment, he refused to pay the last $200 of the pledge. George, who inherited "Lyman Place," had a natural enthusiasm for plants: in his last years he described in detail the notable Boston gardens of his early teens for Winsor's *History of Boston.* Like his father, he supported the projects of the Massachusetts Society for Promoting Agriculture, serving as a Trustee for twenty-three years and as President for thirteen.

The "most conspicuous, extensive, and elegant Garden" in Boston was that of Gardiner Greene, father of Benjamin D. and John Singleton Copley Greene, reputed to be the wealthiest citizen of his time. Located on the crest and eastern slope of Pemberton Hill, it commanded an extensive view of the harbor and its headlands; the terraced grounds displayed a great diversity of handsome plants both ornamental and fruitful. Soon after Greene's death in 1832, a building development completely obliterated the estate but through the efforts of Jacob Bigelow a ginkgo tree from it was successfully transplanted to the nearby Common.

The Boston Society of Natural History, organized during the first half of 1830 by a remnant of the New England Linnaean Society, elected Nuttall as its first president. However he declined the honor on the plea that he was only a transient resident in the Boston area.[11] His view of himself as a temporary Cantabrigian suggests that the routine of academic life with its recurrent mechanical duties had become a burden which he did not intend to bear indefinitely. In August, perhaps with characteristic Bostonian thought of future benefactions, the membership chose Benjamin Greene in his stead. A large majority of the charter members had been students of Peck; in a few years Nuttall's students became leaders in the Society.

Late in 1830 Nuttall participated in a series of eighteen lectures presented by several scientists — eight with the degree of Doctor of Medicine and himself — in the hall of the Boston Athenaeum under the auspices of the Boston Society of Natural History by giving four botanical talks on Tuesday evenings during November (9, 16, 23, 30).[12] The only lectures of the series reviewed in *The Boston Evening Transcript* were three by Nuttall; the reporter was deterred by the elements from attending the lecture on November 23.

A distinguished naturalist of Cambridge, delivered a lecture on Tuesday evening. The subject was a general survey of the vegetable kingdom — or, in other words, an introduction to the science of botany. His language was beautiful; the matter exceedingly interesting and appropriate; but the lecturer's voice was so soft — so much wanting in power, that it was almost impossible to understand a sentence at the extremity of the hall. Perhaps when he becomes more accustomed to the room this defect, in some measure, may be overcome. . . .

A second lecture was delivered on Botany. Much curious information was given in relation to the roots of vegetables, as it respects their physiology, and the uses to which many of them are subservient, in domestic economy. On the whole this is distinctly a fashionable assembly of ladies and of gentlemen. Surely knowledge hath charms to bring together such a concourse of intellectual auditors, from all sections of the city on one of the most cheerless of November evenings. At each succeeding lecture the hall becomes more closely filled: the necessity for repeating the lectures is very obvious.

Mr. Nuttall's fourth lecture . . . gave a learned discourse on the anatomy and physiology of vegetables. If his course has been faulty in any respect, it was in being . . . too scientifically detailed, and therefore, sometimes almost incomprehensible, to such as never before heard of petals, anthers and the like paraphernalia of a flower. . . . As an eminent and practical botanist, no one in our estimation ranks higher, in this country, than the gentleman of whom we have been speaking.[13]

At a charge of $3.00 for the course, with compensation of $20 for each of the eighteen lectures, the series yielded $174.58 to the Society. Following the series Nuttall gave a full course of botanical lectures under the same auspices, receiving $100 and $5.50 for expenses; the gross receipts were $170.[14]

During 1830 arrangements were made for the Academy of Natural Sciences of Philadelphia to purchase Nuttall's principal herbarium of North American plants.[15] Zaccheus Collins was a leader in securing subscribers and agreed to make up any insufficiency if the subscription list should not be filled. Nuttall shipped part of the specimens from Cambridge in the late summer and the rest in the following spring. He did not, of course, part with any unpublished species, but he retained few, if any, of his Missouri specimens. Francis Boott, who heard through Boston friends that the herbarium was being sold, was greatly disappointed that he was too late to secure it; he wrote to Hooker in mid-October, "I sent to my Brother to make enquiries about Nuttal's Herb^m & was mortified to find that he had just sold it for £100 to a person in Philadelphia." [16] Boott wanted it as a gift for Hooker to whom he had given his own American herbarium excepting the *Cyperaceae.* Nuttall also sold a large duplicate collection to John D. Prescott of St. Petersburg, Russia.

The Trustees of the University of Alabama having finally authorized the purchase of his mineral cabinet, Nuttall wrote to President Woods on November 3, 1831, that on the previous day he had shipped twenty-seven boxes of minerals (3070 [?] specimens) to the University. However the Trustees repudiated the contract, which had been signed by a committee of the Faculty and Nuttall, and transferred to the library fund the sum "which had previously been given to Professor Wallis for the purchase of a collection of minerals from Mr. Nuttall." [17]

It is startling to find Nuttall selling his herbarium, the tangible achievement of his years in America, which had cost so much in time, care, and jeopardy, as well as his mineral collection, as cherished by him as jewels. We cannot but speculate concerning his motives. During these years he was securing successive leaves of absence in the winter for varying projects which involved visiting areas new to him but still unsatisfyingly short of botanically untouched frontiers. Although he wrote to Saltonstall that he had "advanced too far in the dark eve of life to make any more distinguished exertions" and in similar vein to Short, events suggest that these remarks arose from fears that he would not have an opportunity to reach the Rockies but that, despite misgivings, he was clearing the way by turning assets into cash and minimizing possessions that would have to be stored during an absence. With his herbarium in the hands of the Academy at Philadelphia — where Charles Pickering would keep a protective eye on it — it would still be available to him.

When Nuttall sent off the second portion of his herbarium to Philadelphia on April 15, 1831, in care of Dr. Morton, he asked to have the payment of $250 made to his agent, G. W. Carpenter, druggist, Philadelphia, who could give a receipt therefor.[18] This obligation, it happened, could not be fully met immediately, for the funds on hand lacked $50 of the required amount, and Collins was completely incapacitated by a paralysis that he had suffered the previous autumn. When he died intestate on June 12, the situation became more entangled for the Academy, because his heirs were not disposed to view his botanical commitments generously. More was involved than the balance due on Nuttall's herbarium, for Collins had bought William Baldwin's collection, rich in southeastern plants, from his widow with the expressed intention of ultimately giving it to the Academy, which he had long served as Vice-President and supported through many years by regular weekly attendance. On June 3, 1833, both Baldwin's and Collins's herbaria were auctioned in Philadelphia. Von Schweinitz purchased Baldwin's with his papers for $105 and, on his own death in the following year, left them to the Academy. Collins's herbarium contained his own harvests and exchanges made through many years, including a few of Nuttall's Missouri species and a complete set of his Arkansas plants, numerous contributions of the LeContes from coastal Georgia, and plants from Labrador. John Vaughan acting for Charles Wilkins Short bid $150 for it, but the collection was bid in at this sum by General Daniel Parker, the Executor, and deposited with the American Philosophical Society. However, Rafinesque, who had often received good advice and occasionally financial help from Collins, made claims against the estate for payment for herbarium specimens he had furnished to Collins, almost certainly unsolicited; this virtual extortion resulted in Collins's herbarium being turned over to Rafinesque in 1837 to satisfy the doubtful debt. Since Collins had never published, Rafinesque probably expected to find quantities of new genera and new species among the specimens.

In a letter to John Torrey of October 24, 1837, Rafinesque appears to be justifying his action, seemingly against some criticism of Torrey: "I neither envy you nor Nuttal your fine studies & researches, but pray do not envy my own, nor immense discoveries, for such they are; they have cost me dearly in time, money, and vexations. I took Collins Herbal in payment for $130. I publish all at my Expense, & I meet no reward as you do!" [19]

Characteristically Nuttall abstained from correspondence with Rafinesque but promptly after his death in 1840 named a western genus of the *Compositae* in his honor. Torrey, on the other hand, for over twenty years exchanged letters with him that, on Rafinesque's part, were increasingly given to complaints and upbraidings that Torrey and others did not recognize his genera and species and, on Torrey's side, to various criticisms and to frequent excuses and explanations for repeated failures to call on Rafinesque when in Philadelphia. On March 30, 1836, Rafinesque wrote Torrey that his own publications were based on what he had seen or collected from 1802 . . . "Who can boast of so much except perhaps Nuttal?" [20]

In April 1831, Thomas Drummond, who had already spent two collecting seasons in the Canadian Rockies, arrived in New York headed for the southwestern United States. He would supply specimens at £2 per hundred, to be paid on delivery; Hooker fixed the conditions. Drummond found Torrey, as previously, not too communicative botanically.[21] Two weeks later he wrote from Philadelphia, "I find there is some little jealousy among them [the American bota-nists]." [22] John Vaughan, the patron of all worthy travelers to the Quaker city, showed Drummond about and introduced him to local botanists and seedsmen and to Benjamin D. Greene, who was passing through bound on a botanical excursion to Harper's Ferry. The two happened to meet again at "Fredrickstown." Two letters of introduc-tion were secured for Drummond: one from John Jacob Astor to employees of his American Fur Company, the other to General Ash-ley of St. Louis, cofounder of the Rocky Mountain Fur Company.[23] Both the Greenes subscribed for shares in Drummond's collections. He herborized very successfully in Texas and was planning on a thorough exploration of Florida when he died suddenly in 1835 in Havana.[24]

Stay-at-home botanists in America were beginning to encourage their own plant collectors by making advance subscriptions for shares of their garnerings. Torrey had secured cooperation in commissioning Dr. Hezekiah Gates to collect in the southern and southwestern states and belatedly received from him "a considerable collection of Alabama plants." Edward F. Leitner, a German who for a time was in Boston and later lectured in natural history and botany at the College of South Carolina, went to Florida to collect early in 1833, subsidized chiefly by Benjamin D. Greene, who heard in the summer that he was back in South Carolina suffering from intermittent fever after narrowly escaping death from the bite of a water moccasin. When he had recovered his health, he returned to Florida.[25] Two years later the news arrived that he had been killed by Seminole Indians who were waging rash war under Osceola. His latest specimens were lost, but earlier collections had been sent north.

In May 1831, the Trustees of the Massachusetts Society for Pro-moting Agriculture resigned their management of the Garden and turned over funds, account books, and all responsibility for the Botanic Garden to the Corporation of the University. The Board of Visitors of the Massachusetts Professorship had struggled almost from the beginning to finance the trust for which they were responsible. The grants by Massachusetts of a township in Maine and monetary aid, an annual income of about $500 from admission fees to the Garden and the sale of plants,[26] plus grants from the College for a decade, did not suffice. After Peck's death, when the expense for salary was reduced and a little additional income was expected through renting the Garden House, there was still no improvement in the situation. On the contrary, expenditures became necessary for the repair of the house, the greenhouse, the fencing, and the gardener's house, which was "a very old fabric." The Garden House was often without a tenant, and once acquired one who became bankrupt after having lavish improvements made. A committee appointed to analyze the reasons for the depletion of the funds pointed out the large capital outlay in setting up the project: the expense of Peck's three years in Europe on salary, the cost of the land, the house, and the greenhouse, and grading and fencing the land. These so reduced the original capital of about $30,000 that the income from the remainder, eked out though it was, was insufficient for the annual running expenses — salary, labor, fuel.

The year before the Garden passed into the hands of the University, ill health caused John Lowell to resign from the Board of Visitors, but he was asked to continue as a member of the Garden Committee. He acceded to the request but in 1833 withdrew from all public activities.

In Nuttall's last years in Cambridge, between leaves of absence, preoccupation with the preparation of the *Ornithology*, public lectures, and his regular duties in the Garden and classroom, he so neglected his correspondence that it lapsed except when some urgency like requests for letters of introduction brought former correspondents temporarily to attention. Two such letters were written to De Candolle, both for members of the class of 1828.

Cambridge (Mass^tts) April 4^th 1831

Prof. Decandolle
Dear Sir,

Permit me the liberty of introducing to you, (the bearer), M^r J. Jackson, Jun^r the son of one of the most distinguished medical professors in the U. States.[27] — M^r J. who has attended to the botany of his native country, visits Europe with the desire to acquire information in the professions of medicine and natural history. Any information you may have leisure to afford him from the vast employments w^h so steadily absorb your attention in botany, will be esteemed a particular favor, by your

humble Servant

Tho^s Nuttall

I thank you sincerely for your monograph on the *Umbelliferae*, in w^h you have done me more credit than I well deserve. It was truly fortunate, that with my slender means, I did not attempt to publish the plants of this difficult family w. I had the good fortune to discover. . . . I still continue to collect plants whenever opportunities offer but my time for this subject is very limited, as I do not feel myself, at present, at liberty to make any extensive journies in the summer season. . . . Nothing of a scientific nature, no attempts to explore still farther the ample wilds of our country, have been undertaken in the present presidency, . . . The public good has been left a blank by Jackson.[28]

Sept 8th 1832

Professor Decandolle
Sir,
    Allow me to introduce to you my friend and pupil in Natural History, C. Greene, Esq. [John Singleton Copley Greene] a young gentleman of taste and fortune who visits Europe for instruction and amusement, and who would be highly gratified with the society of the naturalists of Geneva during his transient stay in your interesting country. Your monograph on the Umbelliferous Plants gave me great pleasure, and I therefore hastened to adopt the first important arrangement I have seen introduced into that hitherto chaotic family. . . .
    Hoping you and my friend M. Mercier, etc. are in the enjoyment of health, I remain, your most

obliged & humble Servant
Tho. Nuttall [29]

After Copley Greene's prolonged sojourn in Europe, Francis Boott wrote to Hooker that the Greenes were "too wealthy to be labourers in the vineyard . . . and Copley was inoculated by the pleasures of high life here and in Paris. I found after his return from Italy that he looked with indifference on Botany and I do not expect anything from them." [30] However Benjamin D. Greene gave the support of alert interest and donations to the Boston Society of Natural History which fostered some fine publications through the middle of the nineteenth century, especially in zoology, and finally he left it a substantial bequest. A new species, discovered and described by Greene, *Utricularia resupinata,* was published in Edward Hitchcock's *Catalogue of Animals and Plants of Massachusetts* in 1835.

In 1831, Torrey issued an American edition of John Lindley's *Introduction to the Natural System* with an appendix listing the common eastern American species arranged in the natural order. Thereafter all his work was based on this classification as were most American botanical publications, including Nuttall's. Hooker's *Flora Boreali-*

*Americana* was coming out periodically in separate papers, the first appearing in 1829, and the completed two volumes in 1840; Francis Boott did the *Carices*.

The 1833 Commencement exercises were the last held in the old meetinghouse. At the Phi Beta Kappa exercises Edward Everett was the Orator, and Henry Wadsworth Longfellow gave the poem. Nuttall, working persistently to finish the second volume of the *Ornithology*, was looking forward to the return to Cambridge of Nathaniel Wyeth from an overland journey to the mouth of the Columbia River. Having instructed Wyeth in the preparation of herbarium specimens, Nuttall was expecting that he would bring back to him a collection of plants from the Rocky Mountains.

NATHANIEL JARVIS WYETH. His Cantabrigian friend, Nathaniel Jarvis Wyeth, was to transmute into reality Nuttall's cherished dream of collecting in the Rockies. Endowed with an adventurous spirit suited to bold enterprises, Wyeth was dissatisfied with his life in Cambridge where he assisted with his father's hotel, a summer resort on Fresh Pond, and directing ice cutting for Frederic Tudor, "the Ice King," who supplied cities in the southern United States and tropical ports from South America to India with the winter harvests of New England ponds and rivers, turning the rigorous climate to profit.

> Rough, bleak and hard our little State
> Is scant of soil, of limits strait,
> Her yellow sands are sands alone,
> Her only mines are ice and stone.

Tudor had refused to attend Harvard, "a place for loafers like all colleges," and started working for a Boston shipping office at thirteen. The inspiration to sell ice to the tropics came while he was serving on a voyage to the West Indies; after years of financial loss in launching the project he made a fortune.[31] Wyeth, who also had no interest in college, patented valuable improvements of tools used in cutting ice and introduced new methods of storage, but as a young man he yearned for greater scope for his ability and energies than cutting ice.

In the autumn of 1831 he became interested in the Oregon Colonization Society which Hall Jackson Kelley (1790–1874), a schoolteacher in Boston, was promoting in newspapers and by mass meetings. Although Wyeth joined the Society, study of the situation convinced him that Kelley's plans for colonizing were impracticable but that there were great commercial possibilities in the salmon and fur trade of Oregon. He determined to act independently of Kelley, and promptly ventured all his assets and secured other financial backing for organizing a trading company to operate in the Oregon Territory.[32]

The ownership of Oregon was still an unsettled question between the United States and Great Britain. The American ship *Columbia,* under Captain Robert Gray, had discovered the great river of the West in 1792, Lewis and Clark were the first to explore it, and John Jacob Astor established the first trading post on it. During the War of 1812, Astoria had been taken over by British fur interests, which thereafter monopolized all trade on the river although by treaty (1818) the region was open to joint occupation. Kelley had patriotic hopes of winning Oregon for the United States through settlement. Wyeth, preparing to compete with the powerful Hudson's Bay Company in its entrenched position, was, in George Bancroft's opinion, the inadvertent agent for the accomplishment of Kelley's aim.

On December 19, 1831, under cover of a letter of introduction from Nuttall, Wyeth wrote to Edward Everett, his Representative in Congress, offering his services to the government in obtaining information about conditions in the Oregon country. He enlisted a small group of volunteers as inexperienced as himself for the overland journey. One was a young Cambridge boy about seventeen years of age, John Bound Wyeth, one of the five sons of Nuttall's neighbor, Job, and a second cousin of Nat Wyeth. Cambridge was agog with interest in the hazardous, if not foolhardy, enterprise. At the smithy "under the spreading chestnut tree," hybrid wagons were built which were to function as boats at river crossings — "amphibiums" and "Natwyethiums" the students derisively called them. (At St. Louis, "mountain men" judged them unsuited to western conditions and they were abandoned.) On an island in Boston Harbor, "Captain" Wyeth trained his band of about twenty before they embarked for Baltimore whence they started on the long overland journey.[33] A ship, *Sultana* under Captain Lambert, was sent around the Horn with trading goods.

West of the Missouri, the little party crossed the plains and the continental divide safely because they were able to travel under the protection of the caravan of the Rocky Mountain Fur Company commanded by William Sublette, which was conveying goods to the annual rendezvous of the mountain trappers at Pierre's Hole (Teton

Basin). To this picturesque mountain valley on the west of the Tetons the company trappers and the independents, with their Indian companions and associates, swarmed in hundreds to bring in their peltries and get in exchange fresh supplies of tobacco, fancy clothes, trinkets for the Indian girls, and to enjoy tests of prowess in horse racing, skilled riding, and wrestling, and an unstinted flow of liquor and the uproarious society of their fellows. This solace, extending through a week or more, was savored in retrospect the rest of the year.

During this breathing spell the disillusioned among Wyeth's party who had not already deserted decided to return with William Sublette's party, who were to take the furs of the Rocky Mountain Fur Company to St. Louis. Wyeth gave them such equipment as he could spare. Among them was John Bound Wyeth, who soon after reaching Cambridge published with Dr. Waterhouse's sardonic assistance a malicious account of the expedition entitled *Oregon; or a Short History of a Long Journey*.[34] Nat's oldest brother, Dr. Jacob Wyeth, Harvard College 1820, also elected to return; later Nat wrote to his parents, "Jacob could go no farther than the mountains. His heart looked back to the things of home and he could not see the return convoy depart alone." [35]

Hostile Indians skulked about the area throughout the rendezvous, and the first brigades to leave were suddenly plunged into combat with Gros Ventres through the treachery of a half-breed of Milton Sublette's party, Antoine Godin, who sought revenge for an old incident. A bloody day-long battle ensued. The Indians suffered heavier losses than the trappers, who had immediately sent back to the rendezvous for reinforcements. William Sublette organized and led the attack on the fortification that the enemy hastily constructed. Wyeth's greenhorns, assigned to protect the baggage, shook in terror, but Nat was in the thick of the fighting. During the night the Indians vanished leaving their dead. Jacob Wyeth treated the injured men, including William Sublette, who was badly wounded.[36] Although mountain men made little of any hurt not mortal, it was probably fortunate for William Sublette that Jacob returned with his brigade.

Wyeth continued westward on the south bank of the Snake River with eleven plucky men in the company of Milton Sublette's party, whose protection and guidance they enjoyed for more than a month. On October 29, just two months after parting with Sublette and his men, the little group arrived at Fort Vancouver, the Hudson's Bay

Company post on the lower Columbia, and Wyeth released all his party from further obligations. There he heard that his supply ship had been wrecked in the Society Islands; Captain Lambert and the men were safe. Undaunted he reviewed not his losses but his assets, all intangible — the knowledge he had acquired of the country and its inhabitants and of the wasteful management of the fur companies — and began to plan a second expedition. Unfortunately he did not realize that the fur trade as carried on in the Rockies had started on a decline from which it could never recover, for the destruction of the beaver was approaching extirpation, and no other fur was suffi-ciently valuable to support the costly business. The Hudson's Bay Company forbade Americans' trading for furs on the Columbia.

Wyeth's expedition from the lower Missouri to the lower Columbia was the first to make the through traverse by the general route which became famous as "the Oregon Trail." However, parts of the trail were not yet established; on his second expedition Wyeth chose to find a way through the mountains to the north of the Snake valley rather than again encounter the lava plains along the river.

Into the winter Wyeth was generously entertained at the Fort by Dr. John McLoughlin, Chief Factor west of the Rockies. Some of Wyeth's men tried farming on fertile land in the Willamette Valley, and John Ball, Dartmouth College 1820, forming a school for the half-breed children at the Fort, became the first teacher in the North-west.[37]

David Douglas, the British plant collector, arrived in the autumn for his third visit to the Columbia whence he had supplied the Hor-ticultural Society of London with many strikingly beautiful plants which are still favorites in British gardens. For the previous eighteen months he had been gathering California plants from headquarters in Monterey. While he was there, Thomas Coulter had arrived over-land from Mexico with the first botanical collections from the interior of California. Douglas was not in a happy frame of mind; he had recently sent off his resignation to Lindley in London, after nine years' service as collector.[38] He and Wyeth had a dispute about some features of the grouse — they were probably talking about two different species for they were both good observers.[39]

On February 3, 1833, Wyeth and the two of his Yankees who wished to remain with him started east with Francis Ermatinger of the Hudson's Bay Company. "I parted with feelings of sorrow from the gentlemen of Fort Vancouver. . . . Doct McGlaucland the Gov. of the place is a man distinguished as much for his kindness and humanity as his good sense and information and to whom I am so much indebted as that he will never be forgotten by me"[40] After visiting a couple of days at Fort Walla Walla, reckoned 203 miles from Fort Vancouver, they moved northeastward and north to Spokane House and Fort Coville; in mid-April Wyeth's group stayed at the Flathead Post on Clark's Fork of the Columbia for a fortnight. (Clark's Fork receives the Flathead and Bitterroot Rivers, but Wyeth, and consequently Nuttall, called Clark's Fork and all its branches the "Flat-head" River.) The reunited brigade then moved southeasterly, remaining for a few days in camps favorable for trapping beaver.

On April 30, Wyeth "went out to collect some flowers for friend Nuttall."[41] He may have got Eriogonum *caespitosum on this occasion; he had already prepared dried specimens of Clematis columbiana (Nutt.) T. & G. and Phlox *caespitosa. The Bitterroot Fork seems to have been followed southward. While Wyeth was still on the "Flat-head" drainage, several more new species and a new genus were obtained: Fritillaria *atropurpurea, Zigadenus paniculatus (Nutt.) Wats., Rumex *paucifolius, Chrysopsis *alpina, *Wyethia helianthoides, and W. *amplexicaulis.

On May 27, after crossing two small streams of the Missouri system (branches of Jefferson Fork) they encamped on a third; it was on this stretch presumably that Wyeth got two more new species of Eriogonum — *heracleoides and *ovalifolium. Two days thereafter they came to a small creek that they followed to the Salmon River. They proceeded leisurely southeastward and were on Little Godin River (Little Lost River) for a period; on June 7 they were about ninety miles west of the Trois Tetons. In dry prairies on June 6 and 9 respectively, Wyeth collected two species of Indian paintbrush, Castilleja angustifolia (Nutt.) G. Don, and C. bradburii (Nutt.) G. Don,[42] and, on the borders of the river, Penstemon *pumilus. Thereafter they were on Snake River itself (Wyeth usually called the Snake system the "southern sources of the Columbia") until July 7, when they started for the rendezvous on Green River (the "Colorado of the West").

On July 4 and 5, at Captain Bonneville's Camp on the Plain of the Three Buttes, Wyeth wrote many letters to be dispatched from the rendezvous. One letter was to Nuttall:

Mr. Thomas Nuttall
Dear Sir

I have sent through my brother Leon[d] of N. York a package of plants collected in the interior and on the west coast of America somewhere about Latt. 46 deg. I am afraid they will be of little value to you. The rain has been so constant where I have been gathering them that they have lost their colors in some cases, and they will be liable to further accident on their route home.

I shall remain here one more year. You if in Camb. may expect to see me in about one year from the time you receive this. I shall then ask you if you will follow another expedition to this country in pursuit of your science. The cost would be less than living at home.

I have several times attempted to preserve birds to send you but have failed from the moisture and warmth. Excuse the shortness of this as I have many letters to write and little time to do it in.

Resply Yr. obt. servt.
Nath. J Wyeth

P.S. By the notes on the paper my journal will show the place from which the plant comes if kept in its proper sheet until I come home.[43]

Soon after his two days' drudgery on correspondence Wyeth decided to return east immediately to fit out a new expedition for 1834. Consequently he marked the letters of July 4 and 5, which outlined other plans, "Not sent," but the letter to Nuttall was not so marked, probably through inadvertence.

Wyeth joined Bonneville's brigade for the trip to the rendezvous, following the Snake to Henry's Fork on July 7, moving thence southeast through Pierre's Hole and across the Teton Range, then southward following tracks over the divide to the valley of the Green River. In the mountain valleys he collected *Oenothera *heterantha*, *Mertensia oblongifolia* (Nutt.) G. Don, *Phlox *longifolia*, *Stachys palustris* L. var. *pilosa* (Nutt.) Fern., and on July 11, in descending the eastern slope of the Tetons, Penstemon *micranthus. The party reached Bonneville's Fort at the junction of Horse Creek and the Green on July 15. Here Wyeth received letters from home.

On July 17, he moved ten miles down the Green River and camped with the brigade of the Rocky Mountain Fur Company until the 24th. It was here that he completely changed his plans, determining to organize an expedition for the next season. This was because he signed a contract with Milton Sublette and Thomas Fitzpatrick to supply $3000 in trading goods to be delivered to the Rocky Mountain

Fur Company on or before July 1, 1834, within two hundred miles of the Three Tetons (that is, at the rendezvous). The Rocky Mountain Fur Company at this time was owned by Robert Campbell and William Sublette, and Fitzpatrick and Milton were furnishing transportation.[44]

After the rendezvous Wyeth joined brigades which, after crossing the continental divide at South Pass, turned northward along the eastern slope of the Wind River Range to reach the Bighorn, which they followed downstream. On the upper waters of the Missouri, Wyeth collected many specimens for Nuttall, but the percentage of new plants was far lower than in the collection on the Columbia watershed. New plants from the sources of the Missouri were *Potentilla gracilis* Dougl. var. *rigida* (Nutt.) Wats., *Astragalus *mortoni* and *Solidago *missouriensis*. When the Big Horn became navigable, bull boats were built to descend it and the Yellowstone to the Missouri. Wyeth had his boat ready first and started ahead on August 15, with his friend Milton Sublette, headed for Bill Sublette's crude camp just below the mouth of the Yellowstone and a few miles from Fort Union, a post of John Jacob Astor's American Fur Company. The Rocky Mountain Fur Company was preparing to develop a trading post here to compete with Fort Union.

In his travels through the mountains, visiting the best beaver grounds on both sides of the Rockies, living off the country with traders and fur trappers of the Hudson's Bay Company, Bonneville's outfit, the Rocky Mountain Fur Company, and the American Fur Company, Wyeth became as adept as his competitors in dealing with Indians and other dangers of the western wilderness. "He had got thus far 'by hook and by crook' a mode in which a New England man can make his way all over the world and through all kinds of difficulties," and he depended on the same means for getting down the tricky Missouri. At Fort Union he abandoned his bull boat for a twenty-foot cottonwood canoe in which to descend the Missouri. He had with him two young protégés: a Nez Percé Indian about twenty years old and Baptiste Payette, a half-breed Flathead thirteen years of age, whom he hoped would be useful to him in time as an interpreter.[45] Wyeth and his two Indians arrived in Cambridge early in November, the boys having been shipped from Baltimore with the baggage.

There Wyeth was as busy as three men. He interested Boston capital in organizing the Columbia River Fishing and Trading Company, shopped about for a ship to carry his trading goods to the Columbia and engaged Captain Lambert to take her around the Horn, made arrangements to purchase trading goods to ship to Oregon and to carry to the rendezvous for the Rocky Mountain Fur Company, quietly repudiated his young cousin's book "of little lies told for gain," did work for Mr. Tudor,[46] and even assisted the Methodist Mission to the Flatheads in raising funds in Boston by appearing at a service at the Bromfield Street Church, on November 29, with his two Indians, who subsequently were a drawing card at many such meetings. Wyeth invited the missionaries — Jason Lee and his nephew, Daniel Lee — and their lay assistants to join his brigade and offered them space in the *May Dacre* for their supplies.[47]

Milton Sublette arrived in Cambridge in mid-January to help in the selection of the trading goods for the rendezvous. Elizabeth Jarvis Wyeth must have been far from idle. She became attached to Baptiste and later in letters to Nat she inquired solicitously for him. From St. Louis she received the report that he "continues a pretty good boy"; from the rendezvous she received his "compliments."

The herbarium Wyeth collected for Nuttall proved an exciting enticement. The preservation of the specimens was excellent. Nuttall's analysis yielded one hundred and twelve species of flowering plants, fifty-one of which he judged to be new. A new genus represented by a stout "dwarf sunflower" he named for Wyeth.[48]

Nuttall made ready to seize the opportunity of crossing the Rockies after so many years of disappointment, hurrying to finish the text of the second volume of the *Ornithology*. If he made overtures to President Quincy for a leave of absence, he received no encouragement. Since some years later Nuttall was accused of *pecuniae amor* by Asa Gray, it is important to notice that he left Harvard at a time when there had been an increase in his salary; moreover, the will of Dr. Joshua Fisher, probated May 3, 1833, gave to Harvard $20,000 for the teaching of natural history or any of its branches. But Nuttall was still as indifferent to money and position as he had been at twenty-one when he refused an interest in a profitable business to devote himself to Flora; in that service he was consistent and content to the end.[49]

PREPARATIONS FOR LEAVING. Nuttall, having finished the second volume of the *Ornithology*, stored some personal possessions with

James Brown, including an excellent oil portrait of himself painted some years before,[50] made tentative arrangements for meeting Wyeth, and set off for Philadelphia to consult the herbarium and library of the Academy of Natural Sciences in order to finish the taxonomic papers he had on hand.

On the way he spent "a short time" in New York with Torrey and gave him some seeds from Wyeth's plants.[51] Since they had last met, both had been abroad. Torrey sailed from New York in February 1833 and was back by August. He had stayed over a month at Hooker's home, where he received many specimens and books. At Kinross he spent a week with Dr. Arnott, who was working with Dr. Wight on a flora of India. In London he met outstanding botanists and studied Pursh's plants and type specimens of many eastern North American species; in Paris, he examined Michaux's herbarium.[52] No doubt he enjoyed telling Nuttall of his European experiences and talking about the British botanists whom they both knew.

In the next years Torrey carried on an active correspondence with Hooker, who inquired for news of Nuttall in almost every letter although through his friends in the Hudson's Bay Company he had fuller information than reached the United States. Answering one such query, Torrey wrote in a disparaging vein startlingly unlike his accustomed attitude toward Nuttall:

> You enquire about Nuttall. He was still on the N. W. Coast when I heard of him last. I know not whether his collections amount to much. He never gathers many specimens. When he told me that he was fully equipped for a two years residence in California & N. W. America, I enquired what quantity of paper he had sent round in the ship — he said there was a great deal — he thought as much as a ream! [53]

After Nuttall's visit in New York with Torrey, he went on to Philadelphia and was present at all of the weekly meetings of the Academy from January 21 through March 11, 1834, except that of February 18, when Wyeth was in the city;[54] he also attended the February 7th meeting of the American Philosophical Society, to which he presented a copy of the first volume of his *Ornithology*.

Some of the newer members of the Academy whom Nuttall saw at this period were Dr. William Blanding, Dr. Joseph Carson (elected to the current Botanical Committee), Timothy A. Conrad (1803–1877), Elias Durand, William Hembel, Dr. Edward F. Rivinus, Henry D. Rogers, and Dr. Thomas B. Wilson. On February 10, Durand wrote to Torrey asking his opinion concerning a *Corydalis* which Nuttall told him had not been described. Durand later wrote

I made the acquaintance of the great American botanist. . . . His appearance and manner made a lasting impression upon those who approached him. He was a remarkable-looking man: his head was very large, bald, and bore the marks of a vigorous intellect, his forehead expansive, but his features diminutive, with a small nose, thin lips, and round chin, and with grey eyes under fleshy eyebrows. His complexion was fair, and sometimes very pale from hard labor and want of exercise. His height was above the middle; his person stout with a slight stoop; and his walk peculiar and mincing, resembling that of an Indian.

From information drawn from Nuttall's friends, Durand assessed his social qualities:

Nuttall was naturally shy and reserved in his manners in general society, but not so with those who knew him well. If silent or perhaps morose in the presence of those for whom he felt a sort of antipathy, yet, when with congenial companions, he was affable and courteous, communicative and agreeable.

From long solitary study the cast of his mind was contemplative and abstracted; but when doubts and difficulties were solved, he was apparently light and buoyant — "at the conclusion of a piece of work," says one who has been most intimate with him, "I have seen him rise from his chair, approach the stove, and, in his own peculiar way, put his hands behind his back, and, for an hour or two, pour forth a torrent of narrative and scientific facts on which was the cast of his own philosophical thoughts and conclusions. I have frequently seen him in social circles, when he was the delight of the company, from his cheerful and natural replies to all interrogatories, and his voluntary details upon the subject of his travels and adventures." [55]

On January 23, Nuttall wrote to Dr. Darlington in West Chester asking for the loan of his copies of the first three numbers of Hooker's *Flora Boreali-Americana* to be directed to "the Western Hotel, Mr Taylors or Mr. C. Pickering, 173 South Eleventh Street." On February 1, he again appealed to Darlington for the use of Hooker's *Flora,* saying that he was the "most part of the day at the Academy in Twelfth Street, where I hope to have the pleasure of seeing you previous to my departure for the west." [56] Darlington had published *Florula Cestrica,* a well-received flora of Chester County, in 1826, and being in course of expanding it to *Flora Cestrica* (1837) he would probably be making use of Hooker's North America flora, but he loaned it to Nuttall.

At the first meeting of the Academy in February, Nuttall donated specimens of two new species of plants, eighteen minerals, and fossils and rocks from the Rocky Mountains and westward. "Dr. Pickering made some observations on the fossils . . . the proof evinced by them of the existence of the Cretaceous formation, already traced as far as the Yellowstone, within the rocky Mountains and the obsidian showing volcanic action west of the Mountains at a greater distance from the ocean than has been hitherto observed with certainty." This gave rise to a discussion in which Nuttall and Henry D. Rogers, then Lecturer in Geology at the Franklin Institute, took part. Pickering, Harlan, and Nuttall were named as the committee to consider a paper by John Bachman of Charleston, which was read.[57]

At the following meeting a committee consisting of Dr. Rivinus, Dr. Pickering, and Nuttall was appointed to express the sympathy of the members to the family of von Schweinitz, who had died on February 8, in his early fifties. His "Synopsis Fungorum in America Boreali," describing more than 3000 species of fungi, 1200 of which he had authored, was published by the American Philosophical Society. He had also named about two hundred species of flowering plants. Such productive botanists as he were then rare in the United States. His herbarium of many thousands of cryptogams and phanerogams was left to the Academy of Natural Sciences.

The previous August, Nuttall's mineralogical friend Dr. William Meade had died. Catherine Meade, William's widow, advertised his minerals as for sale in Silliman's *Journal*.[58] She evidently gave a picture of Nuttall to Andrew Jackson Downing, a prominent horticulturist and architect at Newburgh, who kept it "in good preservation" and inquired of Torrey the "name of the nephew who painted it."[59]

In October American zoology was to lose a devoted worker and Nuttall a valued friend by the death of Thomas Say at New Harmony. On May 5, 1829, Say received the high honor of being elected a Foreign Member of the Linnean Society of London, endorsed by Francis Boott, A. B. Lambert, and others. Besides many miscellaneous zoological papers, he described about fifteen hundred new species of North American insects.[60] His entomological library was given to the Academy by his widow, Lucy, who was unanimously elected a member of the Academy in 1841.

Nuttall's steadfast friend George W. Carpenter had become very prosperous. He started a wholesale drug business on Market Street in 1828, securing capital for the venture by selling his collection of minerals for $1200. (He was able to buy this back again later for half his selling price.) He had become a member of the Academy of Natural Sciences and for many years served as Treasurer. After Collins's illness, Carpenter handled Nuttall's local financial affairs whenever he was away from Philadelphia.

Nuttall had probably eagerly studied Wyeth's plants and drafted descriptions of them before he left Cambridge; his report on the collection was read to the Academy by Charles Pickering on February 18, in the author's absence. In this paper Nuttall registered a protest against the neglect of a scientific name he had published in Fraser's 1813 catalog: in listing *Ribes aureum* Pursh as one of the species in the collection, he took the opportunity to present his own name, R. *longiflorum,* "so named *one* year previous to Pursh's publication." Unfortunately Nuttall's name was a *nomen nudum.* After he returned from the Pacific, Nuttall continued the effort to reinstate his 1813 names.

The long-deferred and eroded paper on the Arkansas plants, entitled "Collections towards a Flora of the Territory of Arkansas," was presented to the American Philosophical Society on April 4, after his departure.[61] No *Cruciferae, Umbelliferae,* or *Compositae* appeared in it. Only one person was honored in its nomenclature — a new genus of the grasses was named for Benjamin D. Greene; but as Wight and Arnott had published an Indian shrub of the *Rubiaceae* as *Greenea* the modest American grass could not bear his name; it became *Limnodea arkansana* (Nutt.) L. H. Dewey. Uncertainties in Nuttall's mind still prevented him from publishing all of his southwestern species; more appeared in later papers.

He had time to prepare a third article on some miscellaneous species, under the title "A Description of Some of the Rarer or Little Known Plants Indigenous to the United States, from the Dried Specimens in the Herbarium of the Academy of Natural Sciences in Philadelphia."[62] Of the eighty-three species described in this interesting paper, forty-five had doubtless been collected by Nuttall although he made no statement as to the source of these species except in the case of six of his Arkansas plants which Dr. Zina Pitcher, Surgeon in the United States Army, had also secured at a later time.[63] All species not attributed to a named collector grew along Nuttall's known collecting routes: twenty came from Arkansas; twenty-two were from the southeastern states covered on his 1200-mile pedestrian tour of 1830; two grew in North Carolina (one on the Neuse); and one was from New England. In some cases there is commentary evidence that Nuttall was the collector: *"common"* and *"v.v."* confirm respectively that *Aster *adnatus* of "Alabama and West Florida" and **Warea cuneifolia* of "sandy barren grassy ridges in southern parts of Georgia, Alabama and West Florida" were collected by him; in the *Sylva* a detailed description is given of the appearance of *Podostemum* growing in the waters of the "Chatahoochee." Another confirmation of the writer's opinion that Nuttall was the collector of all the unassigned species is that in his herbarium at the British Museum of Natural History are three specimens of *Gratiola *floridana* (marked as type specimens) and two characteristically small labels bearing the place of collection given in the 1834 paper — "near Chipola, in West Florida." One label gives the date, "Mar.$^h$ 1830," an amazing bit of *data* for a Nuttallian specimen. The other label suggests how he prepared his text for the publication of new species. His labels, less than 2½ inches by 2 inches, bear the name he ascribed to the plant — the generic name may have undergone a change or two and the specific name not infrequently was changed once, twice, three or more times (the *Gratiola* was first named *g.........); next a full Latin description in clear script; and last the site of collection is given, usually in a sweeping manner like "Rocky Mts." Of the twenty Arkansan species that Nuttall included in his paper on the specimens in the herbarium of the Academy of Natural Sciences, fourteen were *Compositae* whereas composites are conspicuous by their absence from the paper on his Arkansas collection, which suggests that the Arkansas paper had received its final form in Cambridge. He had already published several composites through De Candolle and in later years more Arkansan species of that great family were described in his own papers.

In the paper on the Rocky Mountain plants a genus and a species were named for Nat Wyeth; John Bradbury, Dr. Samuel G. Morton of the Academy, and Torrey were recognized by specific names. In contrast the paper on miscellaneous plants contained several genera and species named in honor of persons: genera for Dr. Samuel Boykin of Milledgeville, Georgia, the late Solomon W. Conrad of Philadelphia, Charles Pickering, Dr. Pitcher, and Nathaniel A. Ware; species for Boykin, Collins, Dr. Robert E. Griffith of Philadelphia, Nicholas

M. Hentz of Alabama (1834), Dr. H. Loomis of Newbern, North Carolina, Dr. Pitcher, Dr. Charles Wilkins Short, Thomas Walter (pioneer botanist in the Carolinas), and Dr. Thomas Wray of Augusta, Georgia. The genus named for Boykin was based on a "curious plant" in Mühlenberg's herbarium which had been collected in the Alleghany mountains "by the late arduous and eccentric Prussian collector, Mr. Kinn." It is of interest that after Nuttall's "Bartonia" failed to stand, he made no attempt to name even a species in honor of Barton.

Nuttall's paper on miscellaneous plants was the source of such irritation to Torrey that he complained of it to Hooker.

> Nuttall occupied himself all last winter in Philadelphia . . . in preparing three papers. . . . These have just been printed. . . . I have . . . sent [them] on . . . for you, as I knew you would be glad to receive the latest information. . . . Mr. Nuttall has not treated me well in describing many of the plants collected by Gates in Alabama & Pitcher in Arkansas — as *he knew* I had been engaged in describing them. He had better spent the time in completing his account of the plants collected in his journey of 1819–20 — but he left that work & employed a month or two in gleaning out of the Herb. of the Academy, all the new species he could find! I had taken much pains to describe the Alabama plants, in particular, & had drawings prepared of many of the new species, by my friend Decaisne of the Garden of Plants. The Petalanthera you will recognize as the plant resembling a Mentzelia, which you examined & sketched for me. It was brought home by Dr. James on Long's 1st Exped[n] but I did not publish it in my Rocky Mt. plants, as I had not determined it to my satisfaction.[64]

Analysis of the "many" plants collected only by Dr. Gates and Dr. Pitcher that Nuttall had described resolves them to a few. He described two species collected by Gates only (one presented to the Academy "by the late lamented Reuben Haines") and four species secured by Pitcher only. Why Nuttall published any species in which Torrey had a vested interest it is impossible to know; however, three of the six species he placed in *Liatris,* a genus which had always attracted him — early in 1816 he had written to A. B. Lambert that he was "now acquainted with 14 species of the genus," and in 1818 in the *Genera* he enumerated eighteen species, three of which were his contribution.

A little later another matter in which Nuttall was involved disturbed Torrey, and he sought Hooker's assistance in the restoration of his rights.

Did I give you a specimen of Nuttall's Conradia fuchsioides (Journ. Acad. Phil. 7. p. 88) from Alabama? I have lately described a second sp. from Georgia, where it was discovered by LeConte five or six years ago. Did I never send you this under the name of Macranthera? I have long had it in my herbarium, & bestowed the name Macranthera upon it. . . . In the revision of the genera of Scrophularineae published in the Bot. Reg. by Bentham, you will find the genus Macranthera, with *Nuttall*, as the authority for it. This is *my* genus, & it is synonymous with *Conradia*, but cannot be adopted, as the latter was published first. How did Bentham get hold of this name? It must have been from some of the specimens which I have distributed & Nuttall has been given as authority for it by mistake.[65]

That the error was Bentham's was obvious. Torrey's *Macranthera* was automatically established because Nuttall's name of Conradia was preempted. Nuttall knew nothing about the various grievances that Torrey held against him until his last year in America, when Asa Gray upbraided him on these points in wearisome detail.

After Nuttall had left Philadelphia announcement was made of the gift to the Academy of his herbarium of exotics from the Cape of Good Hope, New Holland, New Zealand, Straits of Magellan, East and West Indies, Siberia, and Europe — about 4000 species acquired as gifts or by exchange. The Cape of Good Hope plants, presumed to be from the herbarium of Masson, and South Sea plants collected by Forster, had been given to him by Lambert; Labilladiere was another famous explorer represented.[66] That part of his own herbarium of North American plants which he had retained he left at the Academy in the care of Pickering, who selected duplicate specimens from Wyeth's collection to make up sets for the Academy, Hooker, and Torrey.[67] He sent also copies of Nuttall's papers to Hooker when they became available.

Nuttall's most disagreeable chore must have been the formal resignation of his position at Harvard. Loath to give up this security, he hinted in his March 3rd letter (in characteristic fashion it was dated 1833 instead of 1834) that a leave of absence would be very acceptable. He wrote:

President Quincy
Honoured Sir,

After some deliberation and reluctance I have come to the conclusion to relinquish my connections with our University in order to undertake an exploratory tour across the Continent. As this project cannot be effected in less than the long period of two years, it appeared to me, of course, incompatible with my duties as an instructor or resident in my appointed station. If the Corporation of the College, however, see fit to appoint a temporary instructor, &c. for the period of my absence, by appropriating the funds of the Natural History institution, for that purpose, they may probably conceive themselves justified in so doing, and for w^h consideration if it can be done without objection, I shall consequently feel justly gratefull. In proposing this arrangement, I have also merely acceded [sic] to the suggestions of my friends made during my absence and I hope that no personal consideration in my favor may be allowed to interfere to the prejudice of the Natural History appointment in your University, and that this motion of mine and theirs may at once be negatived by any important and reasonable objections.

With feelings of profound gratitude and high Esteem for your favours and the liberal indulgence of your official associates toward me,

> I remain your unworthy and humble Servant
> Tho.^s Nuttall

A line addressed to St. Louis to the Post Office will find me probably to the close of this month as we do not leave the town of Independence (Missouri) before the 28^th of April.[68]

Although Nuttall is regarded as "easily the first man of science of Augustan Harvard," the Corporation was satisfied to allow his services to come to an end; his resignation was accepted on March 20.

At the end of January, Nuttall had written to Wyeth that he had invited a second scientist to join the party, John Kirk Townsend (1809–1851) of Philadelphia, an ornithologist twenty-four years old who had been elected to the Academy the preceding September.[69] Townsend received modest financial assistance for the venture from both the Academy and the American Philosophical Society — $100 from each — in consideration of collections which he would make for them (one specimen of each object obtained). The two left Philadelphia together on the morning of Thursday, March 13, taking the stage for Pittsburgh and thence the steamboat *Boston* for St. Louis. This was Nuttall's fourth visit to Pittsburgh and his third descent of the Ohio. Sixteen years before, owing to low water, it had taken him several weeks to get down the Ohio in a skiff; now the naturalists reached St. Louis after only twelve days' travel from Philadelphia.

The waterfront of the city was lined with bustling wharves backed by crowded warehouses; the population, grown to 7000, was as cosmopolitan as ever it had been. Townsend tells of shopping with Wyeth the day after their arrival: "He accompanied us to a store in the town, and selected a number of articles for us, among which were several pairs of leathern pantaloons, enormous overcoats, made of green blankets, and white wool hats, with round crowns, fitting tightly to the head, brims five inches wide, and almost hard enough to resist a rifle ball." [70] The next day at the Jefferson Barracks they saw about a hundred Sauk Indians elaborately painted and dressed in their finest regalia, who were treating for the sale of land. Their decor fascinated Townsend. Nuttall should have called on the Postmaster of St. Louis, Wilson Price Hunt, whose kindness in 1810–1811 had made it possible for him to get from Michilimackinac to the upper waters of the Missouri River, and perhaps he did. But, because of his diffidence, we can be more confident that he went to see how the Osage orange trees (*Maclura pomifera* Raf.) in the garden of Mr. Chouteau fared after almost a quarter of a century. In any case the travelers soon wearied of the diversions of St. Louis and, eager to observe the natural history of the countryside, started westward on foot. Later they joined Wyeth on a steamboat which took them to Independence, the jumping-off place for the Santa Fe and Oregon Trails, where Wyeth's brigade was to organize. [71]

Nuttall has not been forgotten in St. Louis: a marble bust of him, mounted at the entrance of the Conservatory, overlooks the Missouri Botanical Garden of Washington University. [72] A stone monument, a small obelisk, also was erected in the Garden incised

TO THE MEMORY OF

THOMAS NUTTALL

BORN IN ENGLAND, 1786

HONOR TO HIM THE ZEALOUS

AND SUCCESSFUL NATURALIST,

THE FATHER OF WESTERN AMERICAN

BOTANY [73]

# CHAPTER 17

# ACROSS THE ROCKIES,
# AROUND THE HORN

An expedition at once the most extensive, toilsome, perilous and
successful which has ever been made in the interests of North American botany. — E. L. Greene, *Pittonia*, I (1888), 240.

THE OREGON TRAIL. Townsend gives an animated picture of the
departure of Wyeth's brigade from Independence in his *Narrative of
a Journey across the Rocky Mountains.*[1]

On the 28th of April, at 10 o'clock in the morning, our caravan, consisting of seventy men, and two hundred and fifty horses, began its march;
Captain Wyeth and Milton Sublette took the lead, Mr. N. and myself
rode beside them; then the men in double file, each leading, with a line,
two horses heavily laden, and Captain Thing (Captain W.'s assistant)
brought up the rear. The band of missionaries, with their horned cattle,
rode along the flanks. . . .

It was altogether so exciting that I could scarcely contain myself. Every
man in the company seemed to feel . . . the same kind of enthusiasm.[2]

The following day was less exhilarating for it brought rain, hail-
stones which caused panic among the horses, and a wet and muddy
camping ground. In a week the weather became very warm, and,
when the breezes failed, intensely hot. In these conditions the brigade
made about twenty miles a day.[3] The party met successively Kaws,
Ottos, and Pawnee Loups. The Indians were a disappointment to
Townsend: the chiefs did not show the lofty characteristics attributed
to them in the books.

Birds were abundant — yellow-headed blackbirds, pipits, lark sparrows, chestnut-collared longspurs [*Calcarius ornatus* (Towns.)], bobo-
links, and ravens populated the plains. A few miles out of Independence, Nuttall observed a sparrow with a monotonous plaintive call

that accompanied them during their first days in the prairies, which he published in 1840 as Fringilla querula [4] — now *Zonotrichia querula* (Nutt.), the mourning sparrow; it is popularly known as Harris's sparrow, the name Audubon gave it in 1843. Wolves, herds of antelope, marmots, gophers, rattlesnakes, elk, and wild horses furnished excitement. All the men were thrilled on topping a rise to get a glimpse of about eighty square miles of grazing buffalo, which, almost immediately alerted, galloped rapidly away.

The next day the South Fork of the Platte was crossed, and the trail, as it approached and roughly followed the North Fork, took them away from grassy plains into sandy wastes. New harassments cropped up: "We were suddenly assailed by vast swarms of most ferocious little black gnats; . . . their sting caused such excessive pain, that for the rest of the day our men and horses were rendered almost frantic. . . . the faces of all the men were more or less swollen . . . and poor Captain W. was totally blind for two days afterwards." [5] The parched, treeless expanse all about him was an ordeal to Nuttall, who years later commented, "the passing traveller . . . urged by hunger and thirst, hurries over the desert, a region doomed to desolation, and amidst privations the most appalling, lives in the hope of again seeing forests and green fields in lieu of arid plains and bitterweeds, which tantalized our famished animals with the fallacious appearance of food. . . ." [6]

Still for the naturalists there were gratifying compensations.

The birds thus far have been very abundant. There is a considerable variety, and many of them have not before been seen by naturalists. As to the plants, there seems to be no end to them, and Mr. N. is finding dozens of new species daily. In the other branches of science, our success has not been so great, partly on account of the rapidity and steadiness with which we travel, but chiefly from the difficulty, and almost impossibility, of carrying the subjects. Already we have cast away all our useless and superfluous clothing, and have been content to mortify our natural pride, to make room for our specimens. [7]

On May 28, the brigade had their "nooning" at Scott's Bluffs, a striking landmark of a curiously weathered mesa of layered limestone and clay, resembling parts of a dilapidated feudal castle. Hereabouts the naturalists saw the blue grosbeak and the lark bunting. Discussion arose about the distance from the trail to "The Chimney," an isolated pillar towering 500 feet above the plains, which they had passed a day or so before; Jason Lee estimated it as half a mile, but Nuttall, who evidently did not confine his botanizing to the immediate route, had ridden out there and said that it was at least five miles.[8]

The next day the party took a bypass through a deep ravine about three miles long, made briefly glorious by spring blossoms.

The road was very uneven and difficult, winding from amongst innumerable mounds six to eight feet in height, the space between them frequently so narrow as scarcely to admit our horses. . . . These mounds were of hard yellow clay, without a particle of rock of any kind, and along their bases, and in the narrow passages, flowers of every hue were growing. It was a most enchanting sight; even the men noticed it, and more than one of our matter-of-fact people exclaimed, *beautiful, beautiful!* Mr. N. was here in his glory. He rode on ahead of the company and cleared the passages with a trembling and eager hand, looking anxiously back at the approaching party, as though he feared it would come ere he had finished, and tread his lovely prizes under foot.[9]

Species from "hills near Scott's Bluffs on borders of the Platte," published years later, probably coming from this natural garden, included *Gilia* *spicata* and *Aster canescens* Pursh.

A camping spot on the North Platte, verdant with cottonwoods and bushes, was cheering to all after weeks on the barren plains, pungent with the inevitable sagebrush. The spring migration of birds was at its height. The next morning before dawn the birding was exciting, the grove being full of beautiful creatures, among them Bullock's oriole, western tanager, and western kingbird (Say's Arkansas kingbird). However Townsend was prone to be concerned with the ones which he might have missed: "None but a naturalist can appreciate a naturalist's feelings — his delight amounting to ecstacy — when a specimen such as he has never before seen, meets his eye, and the sorrow and grief which he feels when he is compelled to tear himself from a spot abounding with all that he has anxiously and unremittingly sought for." [10]

Years later in describing the narrow-leafed poplar Nuttall wrote:

As we ascended the banks of the river Platte . . . about Larimie's Fork . . . we observed scarcely any other tree along the alluvial plains but the present and the Cotton-wood, and those were chiefly confined to islands, a circumstance accounted for by the annual burning of the prairies, which wholly strips the streams of their margin of forest, so that we behold far and wide nothing but a vast plain, a sea of grass undulating before the breeze, and the allusion appears more sensible by the fact that the only variation to the scene is produced by the scattered islands of lofty Poplar which give life and variety to the wild and boundless landscape.[11]

On June 1, in crossing the Laramie River [12] they first met with the red-shafted flicker (*Colaptes cafer collaris*) "in the narrow belt of forest which borders Lorimie's [sic] Fork of the Platte, and never scarcely lost sight of it in similar situations to the shores of the Pacific. Its manners in all respects are . . . entirely similar to those of the common species," but it frequents the ground less.[13] The following day they rode over a grueling range of high and stony mountains (Laramie Mountains), then called the Black Hills from the distant effect of their cover of "dark Red Cedars [*Juniperus virginiana*] and Pines." Here were Say's phoebe, the mountain bluebird, and the sharp-tailed grouse.

They crossed the North Fork of the Platte on June 7 and reached the Red Buttes, their summits shining with snow patches 2000 feet above the river, a famous landmark where the river takes a sharp change of direction. Here the Oregon Trail left the Platte and struck across to the Sweetwater, a tributary rising in the Rockies near South Pass, an easy route across the Continental Divide. Camp was made at the Red Buttes. Nuttall, foraging for plants, collected "on shelving rocks on the summit of a lofty hill" a small shining-flowered alpine which in over a hundred years was not found again in this region.[14] In publishing *Parthenium alpinum* (Nutt.) T. & G. (he placed it in the genus Bolophyta), he gave June as the time of flowering but unfortunately located it at "Three Butes" (a landmark in southeastern Idaho), "towards the sources of the Platte." This incongruous description, caused by the absent-minded confusion of two place names, an inadvertence not unique in Nuttall's writings, has been a troublesome source of uncertainty for botanists eager to rediscover the site. He gave the same time of flowering and location and also the same habitat, "shelving rocks," for the alpine Actinella *acaulis, but a third species flowering in June, *Tanecetum capitatum* (Nutt.) T. & G., he placed "on a high hill, near the Red Butes of the Platte, towards its northern sources on the Sweet Water." *Polemonium *viscosum seemingly came from the same area. The two species placed incorrectly at Three Buttes appeared in the first part of his paper on the *Compositae* read in October 1840, whereas the plant correctly attributed to Red Buttes was in the second part of the paper prepared later.[15]

On June 9, the brigade paused at Independence Rock, an isolated broad dome of granitic rock on the Sweetwater, inscribed with the names of wayfarers, the "register of the desert." "We saw here great numbers of a beautiful brown and white avocet (the *Recurvirostra americana* of ornithologists). These fine birds were so tame as to allow a very near approach. . . . They frequent the marshy plains in the neighborhood of the river, and breed here." [16] The next day they came in sight of the snow-blanketed peaks of the Wind River Range and met with bighorns and an angry grizzly. Nuttall experienced a private triumph in finding a new whippoorwill, Nuttall's poor-will, *Phalaenoptilus nuttalli* (Audubon); [17] Townsend got his mountain plover, *Eupoda montana* (Towns.), and a specimen of the sage thrasher, *Oreoscoptes montanus* (Towns.). As they followed "the clear stream, diminished to a small purling brook," Nuttall first saw the western birch (*Betula occidentalis* Hook.) which grew on its borders. And he got a more animated specimen in South Pass. Surprised to hear a "distinct bleat, like that of a young kid or goat," he looked about. "At length I may almost literally say, the mountain brought forth nothing much larger than a mole," a tiny mountain mammal, the pika or little chief hare (*Ochotona princeps*).[18] It had already been discovered far to the north in the Canadian Rockies and was named by John Richardson in 1829. On the central tableland they met several birds new to them — violet-green swallow, yellow-crowned sparrow, Lewis's woodpecker, arctic towhee, blackheaded grosbeak — as well as the familiar goldfinch; nests were often located. Soon the party left South Pass, open country at 7526 feet elevation, and were west of the Continental Divide on Pacific Creek and larger streams. Townsend was distressed by losing the second volume of his journal when crossing a swift stream but was comforted by the recollection that Nuttall also kept a daily record, which he later borrowed.[19]

In a few days, after crossing the Siskadee (Green River), which Nuttall called the Colorado of the West, they reached the rendezvous on Ham's Fork of the Siskadee. Townsend described the pretty little valley with rich pasturage that Wyeth selected for his brigade's sojourn of almost a fortnight. Although located a mile from the main encampment, they were surfeited with visitors. "The principal of these are Indians, of the Nez Percé, Banneck [sic] and Shoshone tribes, who come with the furs and peltries to trade for ammunition, trinkets, and 'fire water.'" There were also French Canadians and half-breeds. "These people, with their obstreperous mirth, their whooping, and howling, and quarrelling, added to the mounted Indians, who are constantly dashing into and through our camp, yelling like fiends, the barking and baying of savage wolf-dogs, and the incessant cracking of rifles and carbines, render our camp a perfect bedlam." [20] Two Britishers joined Wyeth's party, a young man named Ashworth and a Scottish sportsman, Captain William Drummond Stewart of Grandtully (later a Baronet), who found life in the wild west greatly to his liking.

Abundant trout, grayling, buffalo, and elk supplied food. Flocks of inedible cocks-of-the-plains, or sage hens (*Centrocercus urophasianus*), entertained the naturalists by their spirited attitudes and the beauty of their plumage; the familiar yellow warbler sang to them. Townsend secured a western form of the red-tailed hawk after locating its nest, and Nuttall studied the habits of the rock wren, a species first described by his friend Thomas Say. "But," wrote Nuttall, "the botanist . . . fails to recognize one solitary acquaintance of his former scenes: he is emphatically in a strange land; a new creation, even of forest trees, is spread around him, and the tall Andes and wide deserts rise as a barrier betwixt him and his distant land." [21]

Wyeth suffered a serious financial loss by the refusal of Fitzpatrick to take the trading goods for which he and Milton Sublette had contracted although the indemnity required for breach of the terms was paid. [22] William Sublette, who had beaten Wyeth to the rendezvous, persuaded Fitzpatrick, his long-time friend and associate, to take the goods that he had brought. Milton Sublette, who would have been Wyeth's advocate, had been forced by a leg infection to return East not far out of Independence. Wyeth was outspoken in his condemnation of the breach of faith, but he did not dwell on it. Promptly after his company had encamped, he wrote letters to his wife, his parents and brothers, James Brown, and other friends without referring to the blow he had just sustained. In three letters to business associates he briefly broke the bad news, writing, "The companys here have not complied with their contracts with me and in consequence I am obliged to make a fort on Lewis River to dispose of the goods I have with me." To his brother Leonard he confided that there had been few beaver caught since the last rendezvous. [23]

To Colonel E. W. Metcalf, in the printing and publishing business with Hilliard in Boston and Cambridge, he wrote that Mr. Nuttall had made an immense collection of new plants. Elizabeth Jarvis Wyeth must have been continually quizzed by Cantabrigians wishing to learn if Nuttall were *really* going to Oregon because Nat, writing to her from St. Louis, had assured her that there was "no doubt of his going" for he had already passed through the city and his goods had gone on the *May Dacre*.[24] In letters to Nat at the rendezvous she had evidently forwarded some of Cambridge's comments on Nuttall's western venture; Nat replied "Mr. Nuttall is well and is cursing the tittle tattle of Cambridge in high style."[25]

Early in July Wyeth's company broke camp and followed up Ham's Fork for some miles. Nuttall heard the western or willow veery (*Hylocichla fuscescens salicicola*) singing, but he did not think of it as a subspecies: "On the 3d of July we were serenaded by this old acquaintance, in the very central chain of the Rocky Mountains, or the borders of Ham's Fork of the Colorado, as well as in the thickets of Lewis River of the Shoshonee."[26] They cut across northwesterly to the Bear River, the stream feeding Great Salt Lake. At the "Beer Springs" in good grassland, a stop was made from July 8 to 10, for the sake of the horses. Nuttall described the springs in telling of a new prostrate willow (*Salix brachycarpa* Nutt.) that he found nearby: "so strongly impregnated with carbonic acid as to sparkle and effervesce like champaigne . . . the waters afforded us a most delicious treat during the warm weather in those arid plains."[27] Here he saw for the first time the picturesque mountain mahogany (*Cercocarpus ledifolius* Nutt.) which looked to him like a stunted olive tree.[28] In crossing westernmost Nebraska, the whole width of Wyoming, and southern Idaho, Nuttall was in territory never before seen by a plant hunter, let alone a botanist; however as he approached the main streams of the Columbia River, he came to territory in which Lewis and Clark and Hudson's Bay Company men and protégés had reaped.

In a thicket of common red cedars at the Beer Springs, Townsend got specimens of Lewis's woodpecker, Clark's nutcracker, the rock wren, and the violet-green swallow and nearby saw the rough-legged hawk, "the whooping crane, and white pelican numerous," and shovellers, canvas-back and black ducks with young broods. One suspects that Townsend's "whooping cranes" were sandhills. Young horned larks flying about recalled nesting larks seen a month before on the Sweetwater.

The march continued northwestward. The rough lava-strewn plains were very trying for the horses, and the country proved to be generally arid and stiflingly dusty, poor in game and infested with tremendous and aggressive grizzlies. The aromatic odor of the sagebrush (*Artemisia tridentata* Nutt.), familiar to Nuttall from 1810, continually pervaded the air. Before many days the Tetons came into distant view, and soon the party reached streams that fed the Snake (Lewis or Shoshonee), the great southern branch of the Columbia.

Wyeth had decided to utilize the goods unexpectedly left on his hands by establishing a trading post on the Snake River. Early on July 15, a rich grassy plain on the south side of the river a few miles above the mouth of the Portneuf was selected as the site for "Fort Hall." The Three Buttes formed a prominent landmark; the nearest and most westerly, "Big Butte," rising 2350 feet above the plain across the Snake, was thirty miles away. While most of the men set about the construction of the post, a select group of hunters were sent to buffalo country to prepare a supply of dried meat as there was no big game nearby. Townsend accompanied the hunting party. They enjoyed abundance of fresh meat and cold water, convivial campfires, and tall yarns with only the average number of alarming encounters with grizzlies and the normal apprehensions of attacks from hostile Indians. The hunters' return to the fort with a large quantity of dried meat was heartily acclaimed, for all hands at Fort Hall were on short food allowance. Townsend found that Nuttall had become so exceedingly thin that he scarcely recognized him.[29]

Fort Hall was located near favorite hunting grounds of the aggressive and treacherous Blackfeet, not an area where it would have been safe for Nuttall to go far afield "in pursuit of his science." One of his few observations made hereabouts concerned the shy western marsh wren which he saw "in a marsh near Fort Hall. It is a remarkably active and quaint little species, skipping and diving about with great activity after its insect food and their larvae among the rank grass and rushes."[30] Here he first saw the American magpie. He recorded finding the dusky willow (*Salix melanopsis* Nutt.) at Fort Hall growing on the alluvial upper banks of the river.[31]

Three weeks after the site for Fort Hall had been located, the construction was finished and "for the first time, the American flag was unfurled to the breeze that sweeps the great naked wastes of the central wilderness." [32] Hence it has been said "Oregon was taken at Fort Hall." A crew of men were assigned to the post, most of whom would trap in the mountains. The missionaries' party had already left with Thomas McKay of the Hudson's Bay Company and Captain Stewart.

At midday on August 6, the company going to the Columbia, reduced to twenty-nine persons, set out in a northwest direction toward the nearest of the Three Buttes, starting on a circuitous route not familiar to Wyeth, to avoid the awful Snake River lava field, a vast jagged volcanic plain cut by unpassable chasms, without water and without grass. Crossing the narrowed eastern portion of it was sufficient ordeal for the horses and men. "The air feels like the breath of a sirocco, the tongue becomes parched and horny, and the mouth, nose and eyes are incessantly assailed by the fine pulverized lava, which rises from the ground with the least breath of air." [33] The next evening, thirst forced the party to climb to a spring high on the southernmost of the Three Buttes. Here Nuttall again observed his new poor-will: "It flew about hawking for insects for two or three hours near our elevated camp." Nuttall first saw it and heard its "low wailing cry" on the Sweetwater on June 10 and heard it again on June 16 near the Sandy River (an eastern branch of the Green).

In this horrible terrain "where nothing meets the eye but desolation and awful waste," they came on great expanses of a low, densely formed plant completely insulated by silvery wool, Silver Plant, *Eriogonum *ovalifolium*. Nuttall had already named it, from specimens that Wyeth had brought him from the headwaters of the Missouri. To see it growing in such dominating luxuriance was doubly gratifying to Nuttall for he had prophesied that *Eriogonum* might prove to be a large genus when the great West was botanically explored. He got at least fourteen species along the Oregon Trail.

On their fourth day out, they began to encounter laborious climbs and descents in "some of the highest mountains we have yet seen." Here they observed "beautiful pebbles of chalcedony and fine agate"; in the passes were an abundance of large yellow currants (*Ribes aureum* Pursh), so welcome to men ordinarily restricted to a meat diet that they were with difficulty persuaded to proceed.

During the four-week trek from Fort Hall to Fort Walla Walla on the Columbia River the men and horses often suffered from thirst, food was scanty and uncertain, high mountain ridges made the journey arduous and sometimes fearful for both man and beast, and small

bands of Indians with whom they traded for salmon were usually unfriendly. Danger, discomforts, and hunger accompanied them. But
at any moment on the most difficult trail Nuttall might get a plant
new to him. Thus on their most grueling day, when, in "Thornberg's
Pass[34] . . . about ten thousand feet above the level of the sea," the
peaks about them deeply buried in snow, it was discovered to the
consternation of the exhausted party that a hopeless route had been
followed and the dangerous way must be retraced, Nuttall's spirits
were sustained by finding two strange species of *Aster* (A. *andinus*
and A. *integrifolius*), *Salix nivalis* Hook., several beautiful alpines
of which *Ledum *glandulosum* proved new, seeing again the mountain mahogany, and observing a "pheasant" (sharp-tailed grouse) in
the evergreen woods of "a tangled alpine dell."[35] Nat Wyeth in reconnoitering in the cul-de-sac on Thornberg's Ridge lost his foothold
on a steep snow bank and had a close miss from going over a precipice; he wrote in his log that they got to a camping spot "during the
night through an infernal rough rocky prickly Bruisy swampy woody
hole."

As the brigade proceeded, the route became increasingly obscure
and much time and energy were lost in following misleading tracks.
The last mazes they encountered were in the Blue Mountains of
Oregon. There Steller's jay, the red-breasted sapsucker, and the
rufous hummingbird were first sighted. Wyeth usually moved ahead
of the party scouting the route, alert for water and browse for the
horses. When they were a short way from the Columbia, he disengaged
himself completely and hurried on with two men. The day before
the rest of the party sighted the Columbia, the cupboard was completely bare. Townsend wrote:

[September] 2d. . . . Having nothing prepared for dinner to-day, I
strolled along the stream above the camp, and made a meal on rose buds,
of which I collected an abundance; and on returning, I was surprised to
find Mr. N. and Captain T. picking the last bones of a bird which they
had cooked. Upon inquiry, I ascertained that the subject was an unfortunate owl which I had killed in the morning, and had intended to preserve,
as a specimen. The temptation was too great to be resisted by the hungry
Captain and naturalist, and the bird of wisdom lost the immortality which
he might otherwise have acquired.[36]

Nuttall found that "the sweet berries of a hawthorn (*Crataegus sanguinea* Pallas) which occurred sporadically from the Rockies westward were welcome food."[37]

The long-anticipated arrival at the Columbia, Townsend described
with enthusiasm. "On rising a sandy hill, the noble Columbia burst
at once upon our view . . . I gazed upon the magnificent river, . . .
and reflected that I had actually crossed the vast American continent. . . . There stood the fort [Walla Walla] on the bank of the
river, . . . and . . . we recognized the white tent of our long lost
missionaries." [38] The missionaries had taken a longer but easier route
from Fort Hall for the sake of their cattle, guided by Thomas McKay
as far as the Boise River. They and Captain Stewart's party had already
made arrangements to go down to Fort Vancouver in a large barge,
but there was no room for them when they arrived later than the
others. They rode along the banks of the Columbia, therefore, eighty
miles to The Dalles where the river, confined in a succession of narrow channels, was a cauldron of seething water. Beyond there Wyeth,
who was keeping ahead of the men, had engaged canoes to take them
to the fort. Unfortunately they met a gale, driving prodigious waves
which half filled the canoes, soaking the baggage and necessitating
return to shore.

12th. — The gale continues with the same violence as yesterday, and we
do not therefore think it expedient to leave our camp. Mr. N.'s large and
beautiful collection of new and rare plants was considerably injured by
the wetting it received; he has been constantly engaged since we landed
yesterday, in opening and drying them. In this task he exhibits a degree
of patience and perseverance which is truly astonishing; sitting on the
ground, and steaming over the enormous fire, for hours together, drying
the papers, and re-arranging the whole collection, specimen by specimen,
while the great drops of perspiration roll unheeded from his brow. Throughout the whole of our long journey, I have had constantly to admire the
ardor and perfect indefatigability with which he has devoted himself to
the grand object of his tour. No difficulty, no danger, no fatigue has ever
daunted him, and he finds his rich reward in the addition of nearly *a
thousand* new species of American plants, which he has been enabled
to make to the already teeming flora of our vast continent. My bale of
birds, which was equally exposed to the action of the water, escaped
without any material injury. [39]

On September 16, a delightful day, the two naturalists stepped on
shore at Fort Vancouver at the end of their 2000-mile trek from Independence. They were met and cordially welcomed by Dr. McLoughlin, who promptly provided a room and a servant for them.

OREGON, THE ISLANDS, AND CALIFORNIA. Fort Vancouver, situated on a large, gently sloping plain on the north bank of the Columbia River about ninety miles from the sea, consisted of a strong stockade twenty feet high enclosing about eight acres. Dr. McLoughlin's residence was in the center with dwellings of the traders and clerks and the offices and warehouses placed about three sides. A large open space was thus left where, during the working hours, activities of a self-supporting community were busily carried on by smiths, wheelwrights, carpenters, coopers, tailors, bakers, and furriers. Between the fort and the river, about forty log cabins of the laborers — French Canadians, half-breeds and Kanakas — were neatly arranged in rows. Dr. McLoughlin conducted the naturalists over the extensive farm. Seven hundred acres of tillage were laid out in apple and peach orchards, grapevines, field plants — wheat, corn, barley, oats, and peas — and a great vegetable garden, all presided over by a Scotch gardener with an experimental turn of mind. Hundreds of cattle, sheep, hogs, and horses were maintained on never-failing pasturage. There were threshing and grist mills and five miles up river a sawmill. The farm supplied food to all the Hudson's Bay posts of the far West and had produce to sell to the Russians in Alaska and chance comers.[40]

The gentlemen of the fort dined in the officers' messroom with all the ceremony suitable to an outpost of the British Empire with fine china and glass and service by half-breeds or Kanakas in livery of sorts, a strange mixture of refinement and barbarism.[41]

The fort's resident physician, Meredith Gairdner (1810–1837), a young graduate of the University of Edinburgh and a student of Ehrenberg, had been suggested for the post by William Jackson Hooker. On November 7, he wrote to Hooker of Nuttall's arrival reporting that he had "made a fine collection of alpine plants from the headwaters of the Snake, Colorado and Platte rivers," but "he arrived too late for the vegetation of the plains this side the mountains, which is exceedingly fugitive not lasting more than three or four months owing to the excessive drought in the summer."[42] However Nuttall almost immediately on arriving at the fort found the tall western dogwood (*Cornus nuttallii* Audubon)[43] and collected seeds which were later raised in England; a planting of it is one of the featured displays each May at Kew Gardens, for its "silvery flowers" as Nuttall observed "equal in splendor" the magnolia of the Gulf states.[44] Although Dr. Gairdner had little time to spare from his duties, he sent herbarium specimens to Hooker, a preserved steel-head salmon (*Salmo gairdneri*) with data to Richardson,[45] and bird skins to Robert Jameson, Regius Professor of Natural History at Edinburgh, for the University Museum of which Jameson was Keeper. Audubon painted some of these specimens for his *Birds of America*.[46]

A second physician who had arrived with Gairdner in the spring of 1833, Dr. William Fraser Tolmie (1812–1866), trained at the University of Glasgow, was another of Hooker's protégés. He was serving in the north when the naturalists arrived but in the winter of 1835–1836, after Nuttall had gone, he was on duty at Fort Vancouver. Townsend, who remained a year longer than Nuttall, named a warbler for him, *Oporornis tolmiei*.[47] Tolmie wrote to Hooker about that time that some of the plants in a package he was sending him had been given to him by Townsend.[48]

Wyeth, two days ahead of the naturalists, had continued down river being anxious about his brig, the *May Dacre*. He was relieved to encounter her coming up under full sail. She had been damaged by lightning and forced to remain three months in Valparaiso for repairs, thereby missing the spring salmon fishing on the Columbia. Wyeth seemed fated to defeat on every venture. A berth was found for her below Fort Vancouver at Warrior Point of Wapato (Sauve) Island near the lower mouth of the Willamette River. Wyeth selected a site for a trading post on the island and promptly had tents up, forges at work, and construction of storehouses and workshops going forward.

The missionaries, as eager as Wyeth to be about their business, went up the Willamette River searching for a favorable area of level fertile land for their Mission. Dr. McLoughlin had confirmed the Lees' opinion that the Flathead country was too savage for their purposes and that they could best help the Indians by developing an all-round farm and an Indian school through which they might hope to gradually win converts to a more reliable and civilized mode of life. The Doctor had observed with pleasure the results obtained at the little school which John Ball had conducted at the fort in the winter of 1832–1833. Jason Lee had already learned of the attractions of the Willamette Valley from Thomas McKay, who had a farm there. The Lees found a suitable spot sixty miles up the valley on the east of the river above French Prairie where a few retired Hudson's Bay Company trappers had settled with their half-breed families and also a couple of men from Wyeth's first expedition. The Lees and their lay assistants immediately started building a house. In March, Cyrus Shepard began teaching the children of French Prairie, and soon the Mission sheltered a few Indian children including Wyeth's protégé, Baptiste.

Wyeth was searching the Willamette Valley for a good location for a farm. On his second excursion he took one of the brig's boats with a crew of eight and invited Nuttall and Townsend to join him. Although it was only the end of September, gloomy showery weather was already initiating the rainy season.[49] In this dreary season the only new bird to be seen was the California jay. Nuttall, who had been surfeited with the treeless plains and "the dark unbroken mass of gigantic Firs and Pines" in the Rockies, was now delighted in being again surrounded by cheerful deciduous forests. "We never lost sight of the Long-leaved Willow [Salix *fluviatilis] . . . fringing the banks of the streams . . . reflected by the water and in constant motion, . . . a silent picture of exquisite beauty. Immediately behind . . . arose the . . . lofty Poplars, . . . majestic Oaks and Maples."[50]

For the next two weeks Wyeth, "fertile in expediency," was occupied with making arrangements with Dr. McLoughlin and Captain Lambert for the brig to take a cargo of lumber to Honolulu and also forming further plans for setting up the trading post on Wapato Island and for all necessary preparations for the winter and spring. Although commonly called Fort William, this second trading post was christened Fort Williams in honor of a partner of the Boston firm which had a large interest in the venture. About the middle of October, Wyeth started up the Columbia to check on the fortunes of Fort Hall and to deliver trading goods brought by the May Dacre. Twelve Sandwich Islanders from the crew were delegated to transport the baggage under Thing's supervision. In this as in other undertakings, Wyeth's affairs suffered disastrously, for the bearers and the goods vanished en route.

Toward the end of October the Hudson's Bay Company's annual overland brigade from California brought in Hall Jackson Kelley, suffering severely from malaria. He had left Boston in the autumn of 1832 for New Orleans and from there had proceeded alone to Vera Cruz in Mexico and to California, whence he came north with Ewing Young and others, driving a herd of horses. A letter received from Governor Figueroa of California warned that the men were a gang of horse thieves, so Dr. McLoughlin would give them no countenance.[51] However, because of Kelley's illness, he arranged quarters for him outside the stockade and provided medical attendance, a nurse, and meals from the fort. Kelley was not grateful for the care which restored him to health during his five months' sojourn. His bitter resentment extended to Wyeth and Nuttall.

> Neither . . . did that man [McLoughlin] care, so much as once, to visit me, or, in a single instance, to permit his American guests . . . to come. . . . I had not the happiness, even for once, of beholding the faces of the two naturalists who were the recipients of the company's civilities. . . . One of them had resided in Cambridge, Massachusetts, for many years, within a mile of my place of abode, and had read my books, seen my works, and learnt, more or less, about the spirit which moved me. He was not ignorant of the fact that the only path leading to the country of *pretty flowers* west of the Rocky Mountains had been opened, wholly, at my expense; and his journey thither, had been made easy and pleasurable through my means.[52] [Kelley blazed only metaphorical trails.]

Jason Lee made a few brief calls on him, and Cyrus Shepard, the Mission teacher from Weston, Massachusetts, was a more frequent visitor. "Wyeth called once, but his attitude was unfriendly and his language abusive." It should be pointed out that Wyeth and the naturalists were away from the area during almost all of Kelley's stay.

In November news arrived that David Douglas had died July 12, on Hawaii, trampled to death by a wild bull in a pit dug to trap the beasts. Suspicion of foul play was entertained by many — his money had disappeared and a servant also; the generally accepted explanation, however, was that he had accidentally slipped into the pit, his eyesight being very poor. No more impressive monument will ever rise than the Douglas fir which, in its popular name, commemorates him.

Early in November, Nuttall and Townsend made the brig their headquarters for some days of successful collecting of plants, mammals, and shells and for observation of the Chinook and Klikatat Indians who constantly came to trade game and salmon for powder and shot, knives, paint, and diluted rum. The Indians called Nuttall "Grass Man," as they had Douglas. He gathered shells of at least twenty-three new species of fresh-water *Mollusca* in Oregon, his most productive collecting ground being the "Wahlamet, near junction with the Columbia River." Isaac Lea, who published most of them, named several species for Nuttall including "Helix Nuttalliana" [*Monadenia fidelis* (Gray)], which he considered the finest representative of the genus found in the United States, and *Anodonta nuttalliana*, which Coues called a "notable species." [53]

The naturalists decided to go to the Sandwich Islands, the name then given to the present State of Hawaii, on the *May Dacre*, exchanging the dormant and cheerless months of the north for the opportunity to observe and collect Pacific flora and fauna. Early in December they boarded the brig, ready for the voyage. About halfway to the sea, Nuttall would have scanned the shore for traces of the settlement his friends the Winships had started twenty-five years before.[54] Navigation of the river was difficult and negotiating the exit channel dangerous except under the calmest conditions, so it was over a week before they got to sea. Meantime at the mouth of the river, the site of Astoria was examined, Indians observed, and the seashore searched for shells. Nuttall secured four new species of *Crustacea* and, in muddy salt marshes near Point Adams on the estuary, new species of marine bivalves; one of these, *Clinocardium nuttallii* (Conrad), is popularly called "Nuttall's Cockle."[55] Here Nuttall completed the first crossing of the present United States by an experienced scientist.

After the brig had passed the bar, pelagic birds surrounded her — ducks, guillemots, cormorants, dusky pelicans, and brown albatross; *Medusae* occurred in great quantities. As the travelers got further out, petrels and puffins appeared and occasionally sperm whales. When the weather grew milder, tropic birds and dolphins entertained them. A month after leaving its moorings, the *May Dacre* came in view of three islands of the Sandwich group and a couple of evenings later she was at anchor off "Diamond Hill, Ouau" (Oahu).

The next morning, January 5, 1835, the pilot boat brought two Americans aboard, Captain William Sturgis Hinckley (1807–1846) and P. A. Brinsmade, American Deputy-Consul, presumably friends of Captain Lambert. The passengers viewed "Waititi Bay" and "the lovely sylvan looking village of Honoruru." The British Consul, Captain Charlton, and the captain of a Hudson's Bay Company brig came aboard, took the naturalists ashore in their boat, and accompanied them to the house of the American Consul, John Coffin Jones, Jr., Harvard College ex-1816, who promptly provided them with comfortable quarters.[56] Dining "at the sumptuous table of W. French Esq., an American gentleman, and one of the most thriving merchants of the town," they met several foreign residents. The foreigners on the islands were largely Americans and for the most part New Englanders, either merchants, who were usually capable sea captains, or missionaries; both groups had been arriving from the early 1820s but they did not usually mingle socially. "The foreign settlement at Honolulu . . . was as Yankee as a suburb of Boston." [57] In the afternoon a few of the dinner guests conducted the newcomers on a tour of the town of about three hundred homes. Everything native was of interest: the construction of the houses — most composed of grass — and their irregular placement with hard clay passages between; the tapa or calico dresses of the fine-looking natives; the distant glimpses of green patches of taro from which *poi*, the national dish, is made.

A few days later while Nuttall was collecting shells on the beach, the Reverend Hiram Bingham, one of the earliest missionaries in the Islands, called. The first Sunday Mr. Jones took them to two services: in the morning to the Seamen's Chapel officiated over by the Rev. John Diell, in the afternoon to the large native church where the Rev. Mr. Bingham conducted the service in the native language before native royalty.

The naturalists were escorted on an elaborate excursion on horseback to the favorite beauty spot near the town — the fertile valley of Nuuanu, enclosed by precipitous hills terminating at the "Pari" (Pali); on its shelving ledges Nuttall collected a *Vaccinium* the fruits of which were used as a preserve by the missionaries. They attended all types of social affairs including a three-day picnic at "Pearl river on the west of the island" for which King Kamehameha III supplied accommodations by turning natives out of their houses. While the King and his bosom friends were guzzling food and drink, Nuttall, abstemious and a teetotaler, was happily discovering in the muddy marshes of the river five new species of shells including *Lioconcha hieroglyphica*, *Atrina nuttalli*, and *Pteria nebulosa*.[58] Townsend wrote: "The natives have very generally become acquainted with the pursuits of my companion and myself, and . . . bring shells, pearls, living birds, cocoanuts, bananas, &c., to sell, . . . others are attracted by curiosity . . . in regard to the use which we intend making of all the strange things they bring us." [59]

Captain Hinckley invited Nuttall and Townsend to go with him in the brig *Avon* to the island of "Atooi" (Kauai), famed for its natural beauty, for a period of collecting. The oldest and most disintegrated island, it is far the most verdant due to the heavy rainfall of from 400 to 600 inches, forming many rivers and waterfalls. The young Captain, a handsome, jovial man, immensely popular with the natives, came from the Boston area. He loaned the visitors his large native house near the beach at Koloa, where he left them. They had scarcely finished the breakfast prepared by their servant when the King called; he promised them provisions which were promptly delivered — "a very large hog, three pigs, three or four turkies, and several pairs of chickens, all living; with . . . taro, sweet potatoes, melons, &c.," with the King's assurance "that in *tree* days he would send them as much more." The recipients were aghast and determined to see the King immediately to have the order countermanded, especially as they knew that the food was a levy made on the natives.

A missionary, the Reverend Peter J. Gulick, Princeton 1825, who lived two miles away, also called promptly and took the naturalists to visit his wife and three pretty children.[60] The next day they were persuaded to move to the Gulick's home, which was nearer the valleys, lush with tree ferns, and the hills, covered by "Tu-Tui" and *Pandanus*, which they wished to explore. The species of birds they saw were identical with those of Oahu except for the short-eared owl of the continent.[61] For Nuttall the highly endemic flora, largely unrelated to the continental flora, although exciting to observe, was probably too unconnected with his work for extensive collecting to be worthwhile; some of the North American families were represented in the Islands by surprising species: the *Violaceae* by shrubs and the *Geraniaceae* and *Lobeliaceae* by trees and shrubs. However he did collect many ferns and adventitious species and published several plants from Oahu and Kauai. Of the seventeen new species of shells Nuttall got at the Sandwich Islands, two he found only on Kauai. The naturalists stayed over a month there enjoying most the agreeable company of the Gulick family. Mrs. Gulick was a relative of Captain Hinckley; hence, doubtless, his house on the shore.[62] Luther Halsey, the oldest of the three children, named for Peter Gulick's professor of natural history at Princeton, was approaching seven; John Thomas, three years old, became a naturalist — a student of the *Gastropoda* — and an evolutionist by avocation.[63]

Nine days after their return to Oahu with Captain Hinckley, on March 26, 1835, the *May Dacre* sailed for the Columbia River with cattle, sheep, and goats for Fort Williams. She crossed the bar of the river on April 16, in fair time for the early spring flowers and migrating birds.

All was busyness at the mooring ground in preparation for the salmon fishing. Through the winter the coopers had been making barrels for the catch, and several log buildings had been constructed for various purposes. About two months before, Wyeth had returned from trapping "in the upper country," where the gathering financial panic was evident to him. While now convinced that his whole project was hopeless and that he would have to cut ice for years to pay his debts, he pushed the salmon venture, pioneer of a great industry of the Northwest.[64] Despite heavy personal losses, Wyeth seemed never to regret his experiences. American settlements in Oregon resulting from his two expeditions were doubtless the determining factor that secured for the United States the 49th parallel as the northwest boundary in the Treaty of 1846 with England.

The rainy season still ruled for about a month after the return of the naturalists. Soon birds were nesting in abundance: band-tailed pigeons, a new swift that Townsend named for William S. Vaux of Philadelphia, rufous hummingbirds, a new variety of the hairy woodpecker that Audubon named for Edward Harris, Traill's flycatchers, Canada jays, chestnut-backed chickadees, bush tits, Bewick's wrens, western bluebirds, solitary vireos, several new warblers (Audubon's, black-throated gray, Townsend's, hermit, Macgillivray's, pileolated), black-headed grosbeaks, Oregon juncos, rusty song sparrows, and several species frequenting the East. During the spring Nuttall collected plants around Forts Williams and Vancouver: *Ceanothus cuneatus* (Hook.) Nutt., *Githopsis specularioides*, *Heterocodon rariflorum*. On July 4 at "the estuary of the Columbia near Point Chinhook" he heard a thrush (dwarf hermit) and collected *Moneses uniflora* (L.) Gray var. *reticulata* (Nutt.) Blake. In mid-summer he spent some weeks at The Dalles, where he got *Physostegia *parviflora*.

In August he was on the Willamette and stayed with the Lees for a few weeks. They had then several buildings, and some Indian families had settled near them. At French Prairie there were a surprising number of old acquaintances of Nuttall — former voyageurs of the Astoria party who, after years of service with the British fur companies, had retired to farm near each other. Daniel Lee wrote, "Seeing him gathering flowers and plants appeared to the Canadians no less idle and foolish, and a subject of merriment, now, than when he accompanied Mr. Hunt up the Missouri River in 1811." [65] Nuttall may not have recalled Joseph Gervais and Louis Labonte, but he would certainly remember Marie Aioe, the widow of Interpreter Dorion, now married to one Toupin.

Toward the end of September Nuttall took his departure from the Columbia River on the Hudson's Bay Company barque *Ganymede* (Captain Eales) bound for Honolulu. Dr. Gairdner, fatally ill with tuberculosis, and Daniel Lee, suffering from a throat disease, were also on board. Nuttall had decided to return to the United States by water, and this was the first move in that direction.[66] He spent about four months in the Islands in the winter of 1835–1836. Years afterwards he appreciatively enumerated the natural sources of their bountiful economy.[67] During the winter he visited the Island of "Owhyee" (Hawaii); he gave a collection of pressed ferns he gathered there to the Liverpool Botanic Garden, and his "cabinet" contained lava from Hawaii.

It is probable that in making arrangements for getting on with his journey Nuttall had the advice and assistance of John Coffin Jones and Captain Hinckley. The *Isabella* of Hinckley's partner, Nathaniel Spear, sailed from the Islands to California in 1836. Spear had long had a store in Monterey and started one in San Francisco in this year. More than half of the carrying trade from the United States to the west coast and China at this time was in the hands of the firm of Bryant and Sturgis of Boston. It is more than likely that William Sturgis Hinckley, a nephew of William Sturgis (?), made arrangements for Nuttall's passage from Honolulu to California, down the California coast, and around the Horn to Boston. The cargoes which Bryant and Sturgis carried from California consisted of hides from the great Spanish ranchos and the missions; these were picked up at the few ports the coast afforded and assembled in a hide house at San Diego where the final loading of a home-bound ship was made. Three company ships were on the coast in the spring of 1836 — *Alert, Pilgrim,* and *California.* In March, Nuttall arrived in Monterey and from there went down to San Diego on the *Pilgrim,* which made a stay at Santa Barbara and a brief stop at San Pedro.[68]

In the vicinity of Monterey, the little Spanish capital of Upper California which Douglas had made his headquarters during his stay of over a year and a half in California, Nuttall made hurried observations. The population of about 700 occupied one-story, whitewashed adobe houses with red tile roofs surrounding a large central square.[69]

The forest trees were new to my view. A magpie [a new species] . . . chattered from the branches of an Oak with leaves like those of the Holly, (*Quercus agrifolia*). A thorny Gooseberry, forming a small tree, appeared clad with pendulous flowers as brilliant as those of a Fuchsia [*Ribes speciosum* Pursh]. A new Plane tree [*Platanus *racemosa*] spread its wide arms over the dried up rivulets. A *Ceanothus* [*thyrsiflorus* Esch.], attaining the magnitude of a small tree, loaded with sky-blue withered flowers, lay on the rude wood-pile, consigned to the menial office of affording fuel. . . . The scenery was mountainous and varied, one vast wilderness neglected and uncultivated; the very cattle appeared as wild as the bison of the prairies, and the prowling wolves (*Coyotes*) well-fed were as tame as dogs, and every night yelled familiarly through the village. In this region the Olive and the Vine throve with luxuriance and teemed with fruit; the Prickly Pears (*Cactus*) became small trees, and the rare blooming Aloe (*Agave americana*) appeared consigned without care to the hedge row of the garden.[70]

He observed *Alnus *rhombifolia* and the California buckeye [*Aesculus californica* (Spach) Nutt.] in flower "sparingly on the border of a small stream in the immediate vicinity of Monterrey," and other new shrubs and herbs including *Rhamnus *crocea*, *Ceanothus *rigidus*, *Arctostaphylos *pumila*, *A. bicolor* (Nutt.) Gray, and a composite belonging to a new genus *Stylocline gnaphaloides*. Here he also saw the ornate crested quail (*Lophortyx californica*).

"Around Santa Barbara the Olive Trees were in full flower in the latter end of March and beginning of April and put on the appearance of a willow grove." The coast live oak (*Quercus agrifolia* Née) was here a conspicuous and dominant feature of the vegetation; Nuttall admired the wax myrtle (*Myrica californica* Cham.), "a very elegant evergreen tree," and the holly-leafed cherry (*Prunus ilicifolia* Walp.). Among the numerous undescribed plants that he found in and about Santa Barbara were the subspecies *californica* of *Paeonia brownii* Dougl. in valleys of the nearby mountains; a shrubby evergreen oak (*Quercus *dumosa*) forming thickets at the base of hills flanking the village; a second species of the mountain mahogany (*Cercocarpus *betuloides*), a genus he had first seen at the Beer Springs in the Rockies; two species of *Rhus*; and four more species of *Ceanothus*, a large and showy genus of shrubs in California. His collections at Santa Barbara contained three new genera: *Pickeringia, *Leptotaenia, and *Psilocarphus.

The birding at Santa Barbara was gratifying. Nuttall's quarters in a house with a tree-bordered garden near the Mission was a happy observation post. A black pewee was nesting thereabouts.[71] In April he saw flocks of tricolor redwings and of white- and yellow-crowned finches, many western bluebirds, and in mountain thickets numbers of the diminutive chestnut-crowned titmice [*Psaltriparus minimus* (Towns.)]. The magpie of the plains was replaced by the yellow-billed pie [*Pica nuttallii* (Aud.)]. He discovered the nest of a yellow-crowned (Anna) hummingbird attached to a small twig of the shrubby *Photinia arbutifolia* Lindl. (Toyon); its rough exterior led him to believe it unfinished, but he soon found that the female was sitting on two eggs. Audubon relates that "having cautiously approached, he secured the bird with his hat. The male in the meantime fluttered angrily around, but as my friend had no gun, he was unable to procure it." [72]

On the voyage from Santa Barbara to San Diego a brief stop at San Pedro enabled Nuttall to collect two April-flowering *Compositae* — *Grindelia* \*robusta and *Hemizonia fasciculata* T. & G.

At San Diego from April 15 to May 8, he awaited the sailing of the *Alert*, Captain Thompson, on which he was to return around the Horn. Here he got a large number of new species, almost as many as at Santa Barbara. He found a seventh species of *Ceanothus* (*C.* \*verrucosus*) and several new genera. \*Streptanthus heterophyllus* established a new genus for the *Cruciferae*; \*Isomeris arborea, for the *Capparidaceae*; \*Apiastrum angustifolium, for the *Umbelliferae*; \*Nemacladus ramossimus, for the *Campanulaceae*; and \*Pentachaeta aurea, \*Rafinesquia californica, and \*Uropappus linearifolius, three new genera for the *Compositae*. Of special interest was \*Pholisma arenarium, a brownish, fleshy-rooted parasite belonging to a very small family (Lennoaceae) then known only from Mexico. Nuttall's species, the first of the family discoverd in the United States, formed a new genus. Although the plant is now known to be widespread in the southwestern deserts, its dull color and low, strict growth protected it from being found again until 1875, when it was collected by a resident of San Diego.[73]

Of the fifty-four new species of shells Nuttall got on the California coast, one was secured only in Monterey, twenty-six only in Santa Barbara, and twenty-one only in San Diego.[74] John Witt Randall, Harvard College 1834, who named the *Crustacea* that Nuttall gathered, considered fifteen to be new; a Californian species is called *Taliepus nuttallii*.[75] Preeminent as a field worker, Nuttall seemed to miss no plant or animal however small, nor any unusual geological formation or unfamiliar mineral that came within his ken. Alert to the full scope of natural phenomena and eager for the enlargement of all scientific knowledge, wherever he went he collected whatever was feasible and put each treasure into competent hands for study and report. He appreciated the breadth of his opportunities in new regions and assumed responsibility beyond his own immediate interests. He showed himself conscientiously dedicated to the enlargement of knowledge without concern for credit, recognition, or commendation.

As Nuttall strolled along the San Diego beach collecting shells, he was recognized by one of the crew of the *Alert*, a Cambridge boy and a Harvard student who had shipped as a seaman to recuperate from eyestrain. Richard Henry Dana's classic account of life on a sailing vessel, *Two Years before the Mast*, spins an amusing yarn of his encounter with Nuttall and the sailors' ideas of the life of a naturalist.

This passenger . . . was no one else than a gentleman whom I had known in my smoother days, and the last person I should have expected to see on the coast of California, — Professor Nuttall, of Cambridge. I had left him quietly seated in the chair of Botany and Ornithology in Harvard University, and the next I saw of him, he was strolling about San Diego beach, in a sailor's pea-jacket, with a wide straw hat, and barefooted, with his trousers rolled up to his knees, picking up stones and shells. The second mate of the Pilgrim told me that they had an old gentleman on board who knew me. . . . He could not recollect his name, but said he was a "sort of an oldish man," with white hair, and spent all his time in the bush, and along the beach, picking up flowers and shells and such truck, and had a dozen boxes and barrels full of them. . . . I knew him at once, though I should hardly have been more surprised to have seen the Old South steeple shoot up from the hide-house. He probably had no more difficulty in recognizing me. . . . Owing to our different situations on board, I saw but little of him on the passage home. Sometimes, when I was at the wheel of a calm night . . . he would come aft and hold a short yarn with me; but this was against the rules of the ship. . . . I was often amused to see the sailors puzzled to know what to make of him, and to hear their conjectures about him and his business. . . . The Pilgrim's crew called Mr. Nuttall "Old Curious," from his zeal for curiosities; and some of them said that he was crazy, and that his friends let him go about and amuse himself in this way. Why else a rich man (sailors call every man rich who does not work with his hands . . .) should leave a Christian country and come to such a place as California to pick up shells and stones, they could not understand. One of them, however, who had seen something more of the world ashore, set all to rights, as he thought; "O, 'vast there! You don't know anything about them craft. I've seen them colleges and know the ropes. They keep all such things for cur'osities, and study 'em, and have men a purpose to go and get 'em. This old chap knows what he's about. He a'n't the child you take him for. He'll carry all these things to the college, and if they are better than any they have had before, he'll be head of the college. Then, by and by, somebody else will go after some more, and if they beat him he'll have to go again, or else give up his berth. That's the way they do it. This old covey knows the ropes. He has worked a traverse over 'em, and come 'way out here where nobody's ever been afore, and where they'll never think of coming." This explanation satisfied Jack; and as it raised Mr. Nuttall's credit, and was near enough to the truth for common purposes, I did not disturb it.[76]

Rounding the Horn in the depth of the southern winter was a dangerous, rigorous, and irksome feat: icefields twice barred the eastward course of the *Alert,* but the third attempt to find a passage through was successful. Soon thereafter the cry of "Land-ho" brought all hands on deck.

Friday, July 22d. . . . There lay the land, fair upon the larboard beam, and slowly edging away upon the quarter. All hands were busy looking at it, — the captain and mates from the quarter-deck the cook from his galley, and the sailors from the forecastle; and even Mr. Nuttall, the passenger, who had kept in his shell for nearly a month, and hardly been seen by anybody, and whom we had almost forgotten was on board, came out like a butterfly, and was hopping round as bright as a bird.

The land was the island of Staten Land, just to the eastward of Cape Horn; and a more desolate-looking spot I never wish to set eyes upon, — bare, broken, and girt with rocks and ice, with here and there, between the rocks and broken hillocks, a little stunted vegetation of shrubs.

In the general joy, Mr Nuttall said he should like to go ashore upon the island and examine a spot which probably no human being had ever set foot upon; but the captain intimated that he would see the island — specimens and all — in another place, before he would get out a boat or delay the ship one moment for him.[77]

Four and a half tedious months of sailing brought the *Alert* into Boston Harbor on September 20, 1836, "in the afterglow of sunset." After the anchor was cast, the church bells rang nine o'clock.

# CHAPTER 18

# BACK IN THE UNITED STATES

If I estimate the importance of the collectors included here on the three counts of scientific qualifications, breadth of knowledge of the living plant derived from actual field experience, and publication of personal discoveries, I find that Nuttall rates high on each count and stands virtually alone as the possessor of all three desiderata. — S. D. McKelvey, *Botanical Exploration of the Trans-Mississippi West, 1790– 1850*, xxi.

NUTTALL'S HARVEST. Early in September 1836, Audubon arrived in New York City after two years in England devoted to supervising the reproduction of the elephant folio plates for his *Birds of America* and to writing the descriptive text for the second and third volumes of the *Ornithological Biography*.[1] The approximately three hundred and fifty plates he had finished included most of the birds which he had collected from 1831 through 1833, in Florida, in Maine and New Brunswick, and on the Labrador coast. To complete his great work he needed species that frequented the western prairies and plains, the mountain ranges, and the far west. His luck was great. Awaiting him in New York was a letter from Dr. Harlan telling him that Nuttall and Townsend had forwarded to the Academy of Natural Sciences about a hundred skins of new western species of birds,[2] and he received from his young friend and patron, Edward Harris, an enumeration of the kinds which so excited him that he decided to temporarily abandon subscription getting and go to Philadelphia to see the collection for himself.[3] Dr. Pickering allowed him to examine the skins thoroughly;[4] their immediate value to Audubon was obvious. However, the birds which Townsend had collected belonged to the Academy, and some of the members might be interested in publishing the new species if the collectors did not wish to do so. Harris was offering $500 for the skins for Audubon. Having this friend at court, Audubon went to Boston to solicit subscriptions in accordance with his original plans. By happy chance he arrived a day or so before the *Alert* anchored in Boston harbor. An entry in Audubon's journal reads:

Called on Dr. Storer & heard that our learned friend Thomas Nuttall had just returned from California. I sent Mr. Brewer [1814–1880] after him, and waited with impatience for a sight of the great traveller, whom we admired so much when we were in this fine city. In he came, Lucy, the same Thomas Nuttall, and in a few minutes we discussed a considerable portion of his travels, adventures, and happy return to this land of happiness. He promised to obtain me duplicates of all the species he had brought for the Academy at Philadelphia . . . and we parted as we have before, friends, bent on the promotion of the science we study.[5]

The day following, Audubon wrote: "This has been a day of days for me. Nuttall breakfasted with us, and related much of his journey on the Pacific, and presented me with 5 new sp. of birds obtained by himself, and which are named after him." [6] A few days later Audubon recorded attending a dinner party given by Benjamin D. Greene, President of the Boston Society of Natural History, and his wife Margaret Morton (Quincy), the fourth of President Quincy's five "articulate" daughters. Quincy and Isaac P. Davis were also present, and Nuttall was a house guest.

While Nuttall was in Boston he stayed first with the Greenes and then with Francis Boott's Scottish mother, long widowed. The first visit is inferred from a number of allusions such as Greene's comments in a letter of January 14, 1837, to Sir William Jackson Hooker congratulating him on his knighthood.[7] "You have anticipated Nuttall in many plants in . . . Flora Boreali-Americana. Your Dendromacon he spoke of as a true poppy . . . the Platystigma also is . . . among his plants — and probably nearly all the plants you have described from Monterey. . . . he nearly got by heart while with me the whole of your botany of Beechey's Voyage." [8] Nuttall must have expected that British botanists would have received many of his Monterey species since Douglas stayed thereabouts over a year and a half and Thomas Coulter was also there; he could be more hopeful that his Santa Barbara and San Diego plants were unknown.

Nuttall's sojourn in Mrs. Kirk Boott's mansion at 10 Bowdoin Square, is clearly set forth in Francis Boott's letter to Hooker of November 21, in which he tells of his mother's arrival from Boston in excellent health. "Nuttall lived with her early in October & was in high health and spirits. He had given 8 new birds to Audubon & had heard of a legacy left to him by his Uncle — Some say it is very large — at all events it makes him comfortable if not rich. He intends to come to England in the spring."[9] Most of the Boott brothers were botanically active. William, the youngest, followed Francis's predilection for the sedges. Nuttall would find the Boott greenhouse especially enjoyable for it contained many specimens furnished by Dr. Boott's English acquaintances and possessed the best collection of amaryllises and orchids in the country.[10]

While with the Bootts, Nuttall doubtless heard of the offer of a Professorship of Natural History made to Francis Boott by the Harvard Corporation, the bequest of Joshua Fisher having again made possible the support of a professor. On December 30, 1834, President Quincy had written to Boott: "I have great pleasure to inform you that at a meeting this day of the Corporation of Harvard University, it was unanimously agreed to nominate you Professor of Natural History in Harvard University on the foundation established by the last will of Joshua Fisher."[11] The duties enumerated included instruction in the three branches of natural history and general superintendence of the Botanic Gardens; the remuneration proferred was $1500 and residence in the Garden House. Boott's reply was a keen disappointment to his wholehearted supporters for he felt "in no degree qualified to teach the various important brances of Science included in the duties . . . & I owe it to the officers & patrons of my Alma Mater at once to exonerate them from the obligation & responsibility they have in a manner so flattering to myself incurred on my behalf."[12] Counterproposals were subsequently made to Boott, but he could not be moved to accept a position in which knowledge of zoology and mineralogy as well as botany was expected. "They find it difficult to fill the place. — Nuttal is the only man for them but I fear he is of too wandering a mood of mind. He is a man of great merit — & one who wants encouragement — & I think was not duly appreciated when at Cambridge."[13]

An obligation claiming Nuttall's early attention in Boston was a call at the offices of Bryant & Sturgis to pay for his passage "round the Horn." Tradition has it that no charge was made because he traveled "not for his own amusement, but for the benefit of mankind."[14]

On visits to Cambridge to see old friends and haunts, he found Harvard looking its best in honor of the recently celebrated two hundredth anniversary of the founding of the college. The Botanic Garden showed no change under the curatorship of William Carter but for a new gardener's house.[15] The course in natural history had been given by Dr. Thaddeus William Harris, the College Librarian, in the spring of 1834[16] and by Dr. Augustus A. Gould in 1835 and 1836. The next year Harris gladly took it over again and continued to teach it until the Fisher Professorship was filled. His enthusiasm for teaching is vividly described by Thomas Wentworth Higginson, Harvard College 1841, a son of the former Steward of the College:

I was fortunate enough to be among his pupils. There were exercises twice a week, which included recitations in Smellie's "Philosophy of Natural History," with occasional elucidations and familiar lectures by Dr. Harris. There were also special lectures on botany. This was the only foothold which natural history had then secured in what we hopefully called the "University." Even these scanty lessons were, if I rightly remember, a voluntary affair; we had no "marks" for attendance and no demerits for absence, and they were thus to a merely ambitious student a waste of time, so far as college rank was concerned.[17]

The news of Nuttall's arrival in Boston spread promptly for, on September 28, John Torrey wrote of it from New York to Dr. Joseph Barratt in Middletown, Connecticut. On October 13, Barratt responded: "I was glad to hear from your letter that Mᵣ Nuttall had returned in safety I never had the high gratification of seeing him. If he is going to make any stay in New York let me know and I will hasten there to see him . . . a traveller and botanist like Nuttall is . . . worth seeing"[18]   On October 8, Torrey wrote to Hooker that he expected Nuttall at his house every hour. Nuttall was completely unaware of Torrey's annoyance with him over some aspects of an 1834 paper.

During his sojourn in New York, Nuttall probably met for the first time Torrey's young protégé, Asa Gray. In the early spring Gray had become Curator of the New York Lyceum, which had recently achieved a building of its own on Broadway; Gray had a comfortable apartment there as well as "a pretty good salary." He established himself as a serious botanist by two taxonomic papers presented to the Lyceum in December, 1834.[19] Torrey, with hopes of soon being able to concentrate his efforts on his cherished ambition of preparing a flora of North America, was bent on securing Gray's assistance. In August, Torrey read a "Monograph of North American Cyperaceae" to the Lyceum;[20] this he now hoped to amplify by an appendix describing the sedges that Nuttall had brought back from the west.

On October 23, Audubon wrote from Philadelphia to young Thomas M. Brewer of Boston: "Where is my learned friend Nuttall? Not a word has any person here received from him as yet, altho he himself has been expected here for the last past 2 weeks."[21] Audubon wanted Nuttall to know that Dr. Morton, the Corresponding Secretary of the Academy, had informed him that he would be allowed to portray the western birds collected by Nuttall and Townsend and that more than ninety duplicate skins had been sold to him. Nuttall must have arrived in Philadelphia about the time Audubon's letter was written, for he attended the October 25th meeting of the Academy.

Pickering, judging from the boxes and barrels of specimens from the Columbia River that had arrived at the Academy in June consigned to his care, imagined that the senior collector would have "employment for the rest of his life."[22] Nuttall found that the physical job of sorting his miscellaneous collections into major categories occupied many weeks. Soon after arriving in Philadelphia, Nuttall gave Audubon some birds' nests, western *Lepidoptera*, and specimens of western plants for use in his backgrounds and arranged that Audubon should figure in his plates two new western trees — *Platanus racemosa* Nuttall and *Cornus nuttallii* Audubon. He also promised to supply him with accounts of the characteristics of the new birds of the collection for the *Ornithological Biography*.[23] Audubon journeyed via Washington to John Bachman's in Charleston to paint his new treasures — "upwards of seventy figures." He was extravagantly grateful; in his *Ornithological Biography* he wrote:

Mr. Nuttall generously gave me of his ornithological treasures all that was new, and inscribed in my journal the observations which he had made respecting the habits and distribution of all the new and rare species which were unknown to me. All this information . . . while it proves his zeal for the furtherance of science, it manifests the generosity of his noble nature.[24]

The much-traveled *Lepidoptera* finally reached the British Museum. Their history is recorded in a letter which Dr. Thaddeus W. Harris wrote to Edward Doubleday of the British Museum in 1840.

As I was accidently turning over the fourth volume of Audubon's Birds of America, . . . I saw on plate 359 a figure of your *Hera chrysocarena*, together with another moth marked exactly like it, but of a rich ochre or Indian yellow color, and w$^h$ I suspect is the other sex. Aud . . . was here at the time, and I asked him about these insects. He told me that he received them from Nuttall; and . . . were taken by Nuttall near or among the Rocky Mountains. And . . . that as soon as he had drawn and colored them he gave the original specimens to Mr. Bachman. From the latter gentleman it seems that you received yours, and thus you get its true locality.[25]

Scientific reports on some of the western collections appeared with gratifying promptness. At the November 15th meeting of the Academy, Dr. Morton read a paper (prepared by a committee) on twelve new avian species collected by John Kirk Townsend, published promptly to ensure their authorship to the collector,[26] and Dr. Harlan made some remarks on specimens of a known species of horned lizard (Agama cornuta, now *Phrynosoma cornutum*) that Nuttall had captured in California and had kept as docile pets for many weeks.[27] A new species of tortoise that Nuttall got in ponds near the Columbia River, Harlan named Emys oregoniensis (now *Chrysemys picta belli*).[28] At the first meeting of 1837, Timothy A. Conrad began reading an article entitled "Descriptions of New Marine Shells from Upper California. Collected by Thomas Nuttall, Esq." [29] The title is inaccurate. Although the greatest number of the fifty-four or so species were from California, there were seventeen from the Sandwich Islands, five from Fayal in the Azores, three from the Columbia estuary, two from the far Pacific, one from the Massachusetts coast, one from Beaufort, North Carolina, and two from New Bern. The Massachusetts specimen was a mussel that Nuttall got near Salem while observing shore and water birds. Conrad included a few of his own specimens, which leaves the source of some southern shells in doubt. Forty genera were represented by Nuttall's shells and Conrad named twelve species in his honor: among them members of the genera *Pterorytis* (Nuttall's Thorn Purpura), *Phacoides* (Nuttall's Lucina), *Saxidomus* (Washington clam), *Sanguinolaria* (Nuttall's mahogany clam), and *Schizothaerus* (Pacific gaper). Nuttall's new freshwater shells, described by Isaac Lea, were scattered through a series of papers read to the American Philosophical Society from July 1837 into 1846.[30] In March the first part of a paper by John Bachman on North American hares was read in which Lepus Nuttalli, Nuttall's

little hare [*Sylvilagus nuttalli* (Bachman)], was described and the collector quoted: "This little hare we met with west of the Rocky Mountains, inhabiting thickets by the banks of several small streams which
flow into the Shoshonee and Columbia rivers. It was frequently seen,
in the evening, about our encampments, and appeared to possess all
the habits of the *Lepus americanus*."[31] Bachman quoted Nuttall's
observations on other western species also and published a new mole,
*Scapanus townsendi*, which Nuttall asked him to name for Townsend.[32] On September 12, 1837, Pickering read to the Academy John
Witt Randall's paper on Nuttall's collection of over thirty new western *Crustacea*.[33] The fourth and last volume of Richardson's *Fauna
Boreali-Americana* consisting of Kirby's work on the *Insecta* of northern North America (1837) contained a beetle from 65°N named
"*Buprestis Nutalli*"; Nuttall had collected new species of this genus
on the Missouri in 1811.

In addition to sorting his western garnerings and turning the specimens over to qualified workers, Nuttall was evidently continuing
his earlier efforts to reduce his possessions. In January he gave nineteen publications to the Academy including Rousseau's *Elements of
Botany* in English translation (used in writing his own textbook) and
three monographs by Augustin Pyramus de Candolle. The following
week he presented a collection of European minerals. In April he
donated a collection of fossils and minerals from the Columbia River
and an *Echinus* from the Massachusetts coast. To the American Philosophical Society he gave "a hat of grass, and bark Cordage, a Mat
resembling those of the Sandwich Islands, a Bag of the Helonias
Tenax, and bark Cordage from the Chinhook Indians, on the Columbia River. — A war Club, from the Fejee Islands. — A common Marine
Idol, for the head or stern of a canoe in the Sandwich Islands." Early
in the following year he gave to the Academy the shells of 143 species
of *Mollusca* collected in Oregon, California, and the Sandwich Islands,
presumably already described.[34]

On December 26, 1836, Nuttall wrote to Torrey:

Professor Torrey
Dear Sir

I hope you will excuse my want of punctuality as a correspondent, and
construe my silence into no want of respect  I am indeed highly gratified
after a long absence still to find that old friends have still kept me in
remembrance. For some time past I have been engaged in filling up a

cabinet with the shells I have collected, now nearly finished, and I shall without much delay turn again to my herbarium, i.e. go on and ticket everything as far as my present knowledge extends, making up as soon as may be a large collection of named duplicates for Dr. Boot of London, etc. As to the Cyperaceae I will give them all up to you as soon as I can conveniently lay hands on them, and adopt your names with great pleasure.

For the books you sent receive my warmest thanks. Is it not curious that Hooker tho' so exact in general, should have mistaken my *Cornus g*\*\*\*\*\*\* [*Cornus nuttallii* Aud.], a stout tree 60 or 70 ft. high with an even bark like a birch . . . for the *C. Florida*, but, in the sequel you will find more examples of the same kind, as 2 *Cimicifugas*, given as old, are new sps. The *Aquilegia canadensis* is *A. formosa* of Siberia etc, etc, etc.

I mean to visit New York and see you as early in the spring as I can. At present we are in the midst of an arctic winter here, which after two winters successively at the Sandwich Islands feels severe enough.

My respects to Mrs. Torrey, and all enquiring friends.

Yours truly and much obliged<br>
Tho⁵ Nuttall [35]

In the spring Torrey wrote to Hooker concerning Nuttall: "He lost several months in studying and arranging the shells which he brought home." [36] Although Torrey was naturally disappointed to have to wait for the promised western sedges, this comment is unexpected in a chemist who pursued botany and mineralogy as avocations and who might be supposed to have an interest in the progress of all aspects of natural history.

Nuttall, working constantly at the Academy during the winter of 1836–1837, is recorded as attending all the weekly meetings into June except those of January 3 and April 11. He was elected a member of both the Botanical and Zoological Committees for 1837. He seems also to have attended the biweekly meetings of the American Philosophical Society. [37]

Years of study would be required for the task of describing his new species of plants on which he was then launched. The quantity of specimens with which he had to deal presented a problem in itself. Estimates of the number of his new species increased in botanical gossip from 1000 through 1200 and 1400 to 2000, and of each kind he had usually gathered duplicates. A large working surface was needed for sorting the dried plants into families, tribes, and genera for their subsequent study. Fortunately Charles Pickering as a Curator arranged for space at the Academy for these tasks.

From October 1836, when Washington Irving's *Astoria* appeared,

Nuttall received some wide-reaching publicity that he may have resented. This fascinatingly romantic account of Hunt's 1811 expedition across the continent was unfortunately sometimes woefully weak in accuracy, for Irving's magic pen flowed with little stay for certified facts, which were, it would appear, often unavailable. His facile imagination produced from Brackenridge's description of Nuttall a vivid caricature:

> Mr. Nuttall seems to have been exclusively devoted to his scientific pursuits. He was a zealous botanist, and all his enthusiasm was awakened at beholding a new world, as it were, opening upon him in the boundless prairies, clad in the vernal and variegated robe of unknown flowers. Whenever the boats landed at meal times, or for any temporary purpose, he would spring on shore, and set out on a hunt for new specimens. Every plant or flower of a rare or unknown species was eagerly seized as a prize. Delighted with the treasures spreading themselves out before him, he went groping and stumbling along among the wilderness of sweets, forgetful of everything but his immediate pursuit, and had often to be sought after when the boats were about to resume their course. At such times he would be found far off in the prairies, or up the course of some petty stream, laden with plants of all kinds.
>
> The Canadian voyageurs, who are a class of people that know nothing out of their immediate line, and with constitutional levity make a jest of anything they cannot understand, were extremely puzzled by this passion for collecting what they considered mere useless weeds. When they saw the worthy botanist coming back heavy laden with his specimens, and treasuring them up as carefully as a miser would his hoard, they used to make merry among themselves at his expense, regarding him as some whimsical kind of madman.[38]

As Thwaites says, "Irving's Astoria has charm of style but lacks the ring of truth." A little exaggeration adds spice to the tale but unfortunately it borrows credulousness through the years, and the distortion grows.

PLANS FOR COLLABORATION. After the June 6, 1837, meeting of the Academy, Nuttall set out for New York and Boston. In New York he found that Torrey and Gray were definitely planning to work together on a flora of North America even though no botanical specimen had yet been culled from tremendous areas. Then and there an agreement was made that Nuttall should describe his hundreds of new species in their publication under his own name. Understandably they wanted to make their flora as complete as possible but the arrangement was somewhat surprising in the light of the comments Torrey had been making about Nuttall to Hooker during the spring. In April he wrote: "Mr. Nuttall . . . will write to you as soon as he can select for you some of his specimens. . . . I fear he has become too *rusty* in botany to work up his materials in the manner demanded by the present condition of our science. They are badly off for modern works in Philadelphia."[39] And at the end of May, after expressing the same views in much the same words, he added: "With the help of your Fl. Bor.-Am. he can study those [plants] of Oregon — but he has not the means of examining those which he found in California,"[40] an ironic revelation that he was less well informed than Nuttall, who the previous September had studied Hooker and Arnott's papers on the plants of the Beechey Expedition to California. These thoughts are new in Torrey's letters; their obvious source was Asa Gray, whose aggressive personality was modifying Torrey's relative passivity. From 1834 to 1842, Torrey's letters to Hooker, and later Gray's, almost invariably contain some criticism of Nuttall. On such points Hooker ordinarily maintained a discreet silence; a warmhearted Christian gentleman at all times, he had a special friendliness for Nuttall which was wholeheartedly reciprocated.

The youthful Gray (1810–1888), educated at a small medical school in upstate New York, was intellectually gifted, ambitious, "extremely sure of himself and impatient with slowness in others." An "intense, almost arrogant, self-confidence" blinded him to the importance of the achievements of the past for which he always showed a want of appreciation — he lacked an understanding heart.[41] At the age of twenty-five he wrote a friend, "If I . . . pursue Botany undividedly for a little time I shall (entre nous) be soon the best botanist in the country."[42] As he gained years and experience, he became less brash and sarcastic but not less aggressive, dictatorial, and argumentative. His friends and peers, appreciating his scientific ability, took him in their stride. In 1859, his friend Joseph Dalton Hooker wrote to him, "I am shocked to think you were shocked at the tone of your returned letter. My dear fellow it never occurred to me to take your dogmatic tone in any thing but a Pickwickian sense."[43] His autocratic disposition and his tremendous capacity for hard work secured for him the leading position in American botany in the mid-nineteenth century but he has not proved as infallible as he deemed himself to be.

Gray's dominance over his patron shows most strongly in his alienation of Torrey from Amos Eaton although their friendship dated from Torrey's early teens. Eaton had given Torrey his first instruction in botany and the two had never lost touch with each other. Eaton, lecturing on sciences at academies, "female seminaries," several medical schools, and colleges, and in public courses in eastern New York State and western New England, a firm pioneer supporter of the education of women and the virtual founder of Rensselaer Polytechnic Institute, had brought out edition after edition of a *Manual of Botany*, based on the Linnaean system, for the use of his students. Gray himself, one of the thousands who were introduced to botany by this unpretentious text, was still making use of his own copy of Eaton's *Manual* as late as the spring of 1834.[44] Yet meeting Eaton, apparently for the first time, in Torrey's home in the autumn of 1835, Gray, not yet quite twenty-five, told a man of fifty-nine that his botanical publications were a handicap to botany in the United States because they were based on the Linnaean system of classification — "as if he [Gray] . . . held the destinies of the science in his hands, and the ground whereon he stood was Holy." Eaton was made deeply unhappy by this encounter, not because of Gray's "vituperative and consumately impudent course" but because his words were countenanced by Eaton's long-admired and most valued friend, John Torrey.[45] Despite Eaton's written remonstrances, Torrey did not relent from complete support of his protégé's verdict.

Gray's view of Eaton's threat to North American botany completely lacked perspective, as Torrey should have appreciated. Eaton's textbook, which purported to be merely introductory, was of inestimable value in spreading botanical interest widely: all plant lovers were not bent on becoming professional botanists. In 1836, Short protested at length to Gray for undervaluing Eaton's services to American botany.[46] Chester Dewey, ever sane in his outlook, rebuked Torrey for supporting aspersions made by Gray; he wrote in reference to a disdainful unsigned article by Gray in Silliman's *Journal* that was obliquely aimed at Eaton: "I trust you have & no friend of yours, has taken up this work, — it is too *small game* for a man. If the object was to attack Eaton, then I would have taken the Manual. If it was to oppose the Linnaean system, I regret it. Once you thought that system wonderful. Is it less so because you have one more wonderful?"[47] Ambition and rivalry clouded Gray's evaluations. Eaton's *Manual* was the most generally known botanical treatise in the country and enjoyed relatively wide sales. When he met Eaton, Gray was occupied in preparing an elementary textbook which he hoped would displace Eaton's taxonomic treatise as well as other texts. He wrote that "nothing but the stimulus of dire necessity could induce me to undertake it" and that he was "pretty familiar with the ground — perhaps rather more so at the moment than any other Botanist in the Country."[48] His *Elements of Botany* was issued in May 1836.

When Nuttall returned in the autumn of 1836, Gray was probably dismayed to find such a percipient intellect at work in American botany; and Torrey's use of the word "rusty" was probably born of wishful thinking. Torrey knew that Nuttall had been away from civilization for long periods more than once without impairing his botanical judgment and that he had handled capably, although deliberately, plants from the little-known Missouri and Arkansas regions. Gray fell into a habit of openly finding fault with Nuttall in personal matters — his unhurried working pace, his frugality, his disinclination to drop his work to do errands for Gray — until censure became a habit of which he was, perhaps, not fully conscious. Even when an appreciative remark was wrung from him by the protests of friends of Nuttall, he ended on a derogatory note, seemingly obsessed by a deep-rooted wish to impair Nuttall's reputation. In any case he achieved this result to an extent that is now difficult to appraise and also gave a warped picture of Nuttall's personality that still crops out.[49] Gray had no understanding of Nuttall's background, motives, and ideals, which differed basically from his own. An inherent incompatability divided them, for Gray was practical and Nuttall idealistic; Gray was quick, assured, and personally ambitious to excel; Nuttall was reflective, diffident, and devoted to the advance of natural history rather than of himself. With no cushion of warm feeling between them, their relationship became increasingly unpleasant.

The occasion for Nuttall's trip to New England was the wedding of Susan Austin, his erstwhile young neighbor. Known in her later life as a most demanding lady, she had perhaps exacted a promise from Nuttall the previous autumn that he would attend this important function. Among the guests was Henry Wadsworth Longfellow, who took the bride a carefully selected rose. The groom, the Reverend Reuben Seiders (1809–1847), a Unitarian minister and sometime schoolteacher, adopted the bride's family home and the name Richard Thomas Austin.

Nuttall found the Boston Society of Natural History in a very flourishing condition at the beginning of its eighth year. Benjamin D. Greene resigned in May from the presidency of the Society and was succeeded by George B. Emerson, who remained in office until 1843. The exhibits and library were becoming notable. Professor Hentz's collection of insects was currently purchased, and in the next years numerous valuable zoological collections were donated or bequeathed as well as works on natural history, including fifty volumes from Francis Boott. In 1837 the Society recommended to the Legislature a resurvey of the State of Massachusetts. On the acceptance of the recommendation, the work was assigned to specialists: the geological survey was allotted to Edward Hitchcock, President of Amherst College, the mammals to Professor Ebenezer Emmons of Williams College, the birds to the Reverend William B. O. Peabody of Springfield, the fishes and reptiles to Dr. D. Humphreys Storer, the insects to Dr. Thaddeus William Harris, the *Mollusca, Crustacea,* and *Radiata* to Dr. Augustus A. Gould, the trees and shrubs to George Barrell Emerson, and the herbaceous plants to Professor Chester Dewey.[50]

Nuttall doubtless visited his good friend James Brown at his farm on a hill overlooking Fresh Pond. It is probable that they discussed the publication of a new edition of the *Ornithology* to include the new western species. Near Cambridge, Nuttall found a strange woodpecker in full adult plumage. By coincidence this form had been found in April in woods near New Orleans by Dr. James Trudeau who read a description of it on June 27, to the Academy of Natural Sciences;[51] Trudeau named it for Audubon. Nuttall's specimen was a wanderer, for it is now classed as a southern variety of the eastern hairy woodpecker (*Dendrocopus villosus auduboni*).

Nuttall was back in Philadelphia in time to attend the regular weekly meeting of the Academy on August 1. He had already begun the study of his new plants but, since he had now agreed to their insertion in the text of Torrey and Gray's *Flora of North America* which was to be published in parts as sections were completed, an urgency prevailed through the next fifteen months in preparing descriptions and making determinations of the species, family by family.

For some time American naturalists had been excited over the expedition to the Pacific authorized by Congress in May 1836. Its purpose was to explore and survey islands, reefs, and harbors in the Pacific and South Seas with special concern for the protection of American commerce, particularly the whaling industry. A start was being made in the selection of a full scientific staff to which Charles Pickering was appointed as Chief Naturalist. The long delay that intervened before the organization of the expedition allowed Nuttall the enjoyment of Pickering's congenial comradeship at the Academy almost daily for a year after Nuttall's return to Philadelphia from the far West.

Pickering (1805–1878) was one of Nuttall's most compatible friends. Remarks in obituary descriptions of Pickering are reminiscent of some accounts of Nuttall: "[He] was singularly retiring and reticent, . . . delicate and keen in perception and judgment; . . . to those who knew him well, communicative, sympathetic and even genial. . . . No one ever had less . . . a gift for display . . . the love of knowledge was the one passion of his life." He possessed all the virtues for which his gifted family were widely known. He was upright, mild, cultivated, learned, scholarly, with simplicity and kindness of manner and "freedom from pride or guile." [52] Born at Starucca Creek, Pennsylvania, on the East Branch of the Susquehannah, [53] he had been taken in his infancy, on his father's death, to grow up on the farm of his celebrated grandfather in Wenham, near Salem, Massachusetts. Natural history interested him from boyhood; insects first attracted him, but he recorded that an excursion with William Oakes in 1823 diverted his attention to plants. He became a well-rounded naturalist with a longing to comprehend the factors controlling the geographic distribution of species, an interest which he attributed to "the wonderful accuracy of Michaux [fils] in defining the limits of our forest trees." [54] Early in 1827 he started medical practice in Philadelphia although he thought that "the city is rather overstocked with Physicians who are a quarrelsome set of people, and scowl at a Yankee mightily." [55] This change of residence made him a regular member of the Academy of Natural Sciences, for he had already been elected a Corresponding Member.

In the eleven consecutive years that Pickering lived in Philadelphia he gave effective support to the natural sciences. He so filled the breach which had been made fifteen months before his advent by the departure of Say, Lesueur, and Troost to New Harmony that it is conceivable that the Academy of Natural Sciences might have suffered dissolution but for his timely arrival. He was rarely absent from a meeting. He served on the Zoology Committee for ten years, on the Botanical Committee for eight years, on the Publication Committee for four years, and for one year on the Library Committee; he was Librarian for five years and a Curator for the next four. He botanized in the New Jersey pine barrens and on the eastern shore of Maryland in 1828, and the next year gave to the Academy two hundred species of plants he had collected as well as the herbarium of his deceased cousin, Dr. Henry Little, a student of Bigelow. To him was entrusted the incorporation of the great Schweinitz Herbarium into the Herbarium of the Academy. At the request of the Academy, he spent three months at New Harmony selecting for the library 2259 volumes which Maclure offered to the Academy after Say's death. He was active also in the American Philosophical Society, presenting a paper in October 1827 on "The Geographical Distribution of Plants." For the new Pennsylvania Horticultural Society he acted as Recording Secretary from February 1830 to September 1837.

From late October 1836 into October 1837, Nuttall and Pickering worked at the Academy side by side. Pickering, who was destined to visit some of the same regions of the northwest that Nuttall had covered, was keenly interested in the thousands of plant and animal specimens which were gradually unpacked, sorted, and arranged.

With the appointment of Lt. Charles Wilkes, U.S.N. (1798–1877) to command the United States Exploring Expedition, the preparations proceeded encouragingly. Although the squadron of six vessels did not sail until August 19, 1838, Pickering left Philadelphia toward the end of the previous October, when the scientific staff was called to New York to assist with preliminary work. Asa Gray, who had been appointed Botanist, became discouraged by the delay and finally resigned and accepted a professorship at the University of Michigan, an institution which was still in embryo. William Rich was then elevated to Botanist and William Dunlop Brackenridge (1810–1893) was appointed Assistant Botanist and Horticulturist. Joseph P. Couthouy and Titian R. Peale (1788–1885) were added to the staff of naturalists, and James Dwight Dana (1813–1895) became the Geologist and Mineralogist of the expedition. A philologist, an interpreter, taxidermists, and artists brought the number of the civilian staff to twelve. Throughout the four-year expedition, Pickering made extensive trips into the interiors when possible and climbed every feasible peak, proving himself a vigorous, devoted explorer. In the Oregon country with a small party he ascended the Columbia

River to the neighborhood of Walla Walla and penetrated the Blue Mountains.

In great contrast to the Lewis and Clark Expedition, the reports of the United States Exploring Expedition were published at government expense, nineteen volumes of the proposed twenty-four appearing in the years from 1844 to 1874. Two volumes on botany came out in 1854, one on the *Phanerogamia* (Part I) by Asa Gray; the last volume published contained Torrey's report on the phanerogams of Pacific North America (edited by Gray), but Gray's concluding volume never appeared. Pickering's observations and conclusions on *The Races of Man and Their Geographical Distribution* were published in the ninth volume (1848) after he had extended his information by exploration in Egypt, Arabia, India, and East Africa in 1843 to 1845. His proposed work on the geographical distribution of animals and plants was not officially published, although sections were issued privately in 1854, 1863, and 1876.[56]

At about the time that Pickering left Philadelphia, Nuttall sent to England a paper concerning some plants which he had collected in the West. Seeds of some new Californian species that promised to be horticultural moneymakers Nuttall had placed in the care of Robert Buist, a Philadelphia nurseryman. The plants had done well, and Nuttall sold them to English nurseries. Prior to their shipment he described them in a taxonomic paper which Buist forwarded for him to Hooker. Buist's letter reads:

Philadelphia, October 19, 1837

Sir W. J. Hooker
Sir

I take the liberty of handing you a m. s. s. of Several new plants found by Tho⁵ Nuttall Esqʳ in California in 1835 & 6. If it is your pleasure it is his desire that you may publish them in an early Nᵒ of your Miscellany. The drawing Sent of *Diplacus punicea* is very correct . . . [It] has been in bloom with me since April last past. — *Anemia* \*\*\*\*\*\*\*\*\*\* has also bloomed . . . Mr. Low of Clapton is to get the whole Stock of *Diplacus punicea* & the Messrs Youngs of Epsom are to have the whole of *Anemia* \*\*\*\*\*\*\*\*\*\*.[57]

Two new genera were represented by the plants: Anemia (renamed *Anemopsis* by Hooker as Nuttall's name was preempted), an aromatic herb of the *Sauraceae,* and *Diplacus,* a group of evergreen shrubs of the *Scrophulariacae* separated from *Mimulus* only by their woody habit. The paper was printed in 1838 in Hooker's *Annals of Natural History;* the drawing of \**Diplacus puniceus,* done by Nuttall, was reproduced as Plate 3655 (1838) in the *Botanical Magazine,* and the *Anemopsis* in Plate 5292 (1862).[58]

Some plants from Buist's nursery were sent to the Harvard Botanic Garden. Charles M. Hovey stated that Buist sent seed of *Collinsia heterophylla* Graham, collected by Nuttall in California, to Scotland where plants were raised about 1838 and figured in the *Botanical Magazine;* they were also grown in Salem, Massachusetts, by J. L. Russell, one of Nuttall's students.[59] A brief paper by Nuttall on the arrowroot of the Hawaiian Islands was printed in the *American Journal of Pharmacology* in 1838.[60]

In October 1837, American botany sustained a blow in the loss of an active and careful worker. Hardy Bryan Croom, returning south with his family after a summer stay in New York City, was lost in the grounding of the *Home* near Hatteras. He had contributed a local flora with Loomis and four botanical papers, had discovered a new gymnosperm in Alabama, which Bentham named *Torreya,* and was planning, at Torrey's suggestion, to write a supplement to Michaux's *Sylva of North America.*[61]

John K. Townsend arrived in Philadelphia in the autumn after leaving the northwest coast in 1836 and proceeding by chance stages to Chili whence he shipped "round the Horn." He attended the November 21, 1837 meeting of the Academy. The members voted him an additional sum of $100 for duplicate specimens that he furnished. Some of the bird skins Townsend collected in the Sandwich Islands are now very rare specimens "owing to the rapid extermination of the native fauna." [62] From his diaries he compiled a spirited account of his adventures, *Narrative of a Journey Across the Rocky Mountains,* that was published in Philadelphia early in 1839; on April 16, he presented a copy to the Academy.

On October 21, 1837, Jonas Nuttall died. A copy or a résumé of his will of eleven legal-sized parchment sheets must have been sent to Thomas, who was left a life interest in the estate on the death of his Aunt Frances, with the proviso that he could not be absent from England for more than three months of any calendar year. Frances, faithful to her lifelong enthusiasm, was soon making plans to enlarge the building which housed Nutgrove Chapel and School and also to increase their endowment. She had the satisfaction of attending the opening service in the reconstructed Chapel about a year before her death on August 17, 1841.

Toward the end of 1837, the news reached Nuttall that Torrey was acting as agent for the University of Michigan, then being organized on paper, in negotiating for the purchase of Baron Lederer's fine mineralogical collection. Nuttall's own collection, purchased by the University of Alabama in 1831, had come back to his hands when the Trustees decided that books for the library should have first claim on their limited funds. He sent a notice to Torrey that his collection of about 2500 minerals was available at one dollar a specimen.[63] The following October Torrey informed him of a would-be-owner and Nuttall responded: "I . . . thank you much for your prospect of a purchaser for my cabinet, and will give an explicit answer as soon as I know what can be offered. At any rate I will sell as cheap as it is possible for me to do." [64] No sale resulted. The prospect Torrey had in mind was probably the United States Military Academy at West Point, for Jacob Whitman Bailey of the staff was asking him for more information concerning the contents of Nuttall's cabinet about this time.[65] In his October letter Nuttall urged Torrey to send him samples from a prospecting trip which Torrey was planning to make. Even though he wished to sell his collection, Nuttall was eager to study all available minerals and familiarize himself with their characteristics.

Nuttall's hope of selling his minerals at this time was headed for disappointment, for the year 1836 had seen the beginning of the first great financial collapse in the United States, "the panic of 1837," which crippled industry and cramped rich and poor alike for several years. Money was "tight" and became tighter; even the most wealthy were not in a mood for unnecessary expenditure. Dr. Benjamin Waterhouse wrote in his journal: "Bankruptcies daily occur, like the children's play with Bricks, one brick knocking down the next one to it until the whole row is prostrate in one dismal scene of obliquity." Benjamin D. Greene told Audubon in the summer of 1842 that he had lost $70,000 in the previous year and a half. The opening of the University of Michigan was delayed indefinitely, and Asa Gray's precocious professorship lapsed. Nuttall watched his savings with concern for he had no expectation of immediate income except for such small sums as he might receive from the sale of herbarium specimens, seeds, or plants. Committed to the tremendous task of publishing his new species, necessarily on a gratuitous basis, the last years he spent in America expounding her flora were anxious ones financially.

# CHAPTER 19

# LAST YEARS IN AMERICA

[Nuttall's] whole career is, to this day, simply without a parallel in
the annals of natural science in the United States of America. — E. L.
Greene, *Pittonia*, I (1888), 244.

DISILLUSIONMENTS. Francis Boott wrote to Hooker on April 13,
1835: "Torrey is compiling a general Flora — which will add little to
our Knowledge. We want local floras worked up with care like Elliott's & Torrey would have consulted his own reputation more had
he completed his original work."[1] The uncompleted work referred
to was the first volume (1824) of Torrey's *Flora of the Northern and
Middle United States* which he had abandoned because it was based
on the outmoded Linnaean system of classification. The authors of
the proposed *Flora of North America* planned a work to be issued
in parts to be later assembled in volumes. It was undertaken at their
own expense, for such a technical text was far too hazardous an investment for a publisher.

Although Nuttall was unhurried in the study of his plants, came
to decisions cautiously, and was noticeably circumspect in selecting
appropriate names, he wasted no time or paper in writing. The very
small labels he prepared for each species carried whatever names he
had under consideration, a technical analysis, and the general locale.
When he was ready to compile a taxonomic paper he presumably
assembled the slips in proper order and took off the names on which
he ultimately decided and the rest of the data. Ecological discussion
might be added, presumably based on observations recorded in his
field journals.

Nuttall found that the collections he had made on the forced
march along the Oregon Trail and in other western areas often pre-

sented problems for taxonomic determination since the specimens usually showed only one stage of development: both flower and fruit were rarely available; indeed many intriguing species chanced to be only in bud or in immature fruit, creating unresolvable uncertainties. Moreover an unusually favorable or unfavorable environment of soil or exposure, producing lusty or meagre growth, could lead to errors. Not infrequently he encountered problems in a group of specimens taken at one site that showed diversities such as might occur within a single species or, contrariwise, could be interpreted as a species and a variety or even as two closely related species or prove to be a variety of a species not yet known. He struggled to come to the right conclusion in each such puzzle, having in mind the large number of species characteristic of many of the genera of the western flora. His great acuteness of observation would have magnified this difficulty. As a result of such dilemmas he left many of his species unpublished. One suspects that the uncertainties in his work harassed him and that he was further distressed to find that some of his decisions gave rise to the imputation that he made new species for his own aggrandizement. It is noteworthy, however, that fuller knowledge of the western flora has often supported Nuttall's views rather than his critics'.

In his contributions to Torrey and Gray's publication Nuttall made a sustained effort to establish his authorship and names for western species which he had published in the Frasers' catalog a year before Pursh's *Flora* came out. At that time he had not been in a position to contest Pursh's authorship since the scientific rights to the plants belonged to Benjamin Smith Barton. When he wrote his *Genera* he generally used his own names, placing Pursh's in synonymy where they differed from his. No further opportunity arose for him to claim any of his Missouri species until he described Nat Wyeth's Rocky Mountain collection, which contained a specimen of Pursh's *Ribes aureum*. Now again he pointed out that he had named the species *R. longiflorum* one year previous to Pursh's publication and maintained that, although the 1813 catalog carried no description of this beautiful, spicy species, the living plants in Fraser's Nursery had been adequate identification.[2] It should be recalled that at this time there was a dearth of clearly formulated and accepted rules controlling formal publication. He took the opportunity to try to reclaim more of his 1813 species, but his efforts had no effect: of the sixty-nine new species presented in the catalog, Nuttall is credited with the sole or primary authorship of fourteen to sixteen, depending on the judge.

The first volume of Torrey and Gray's *Flora,* which covered the *Polypetalae,* was printed in four parts, two of which were issued in July and October 1838 [3] and two in June 1840. Nuttall sent the descriptions of his new species, family by family, to New York for insertion in the text. Specimens were sent with the manuscript, and Torrey and Gray accepted or modified his conclusions as they saw fit, not without remonstrances from Nuttall. He completed his large contribution to the first volume within a year and a half after he agreed to collaborate in the work, describing about 340 new species, more than two-thirds of all the new species, in which the value of the work lay.

During this period Nuttall more than once annoyed Gray by not being alert in assisting him. One such occasion occurred early in 1838 when Gray enclosed in a package of plants he sent to Nuttall a letter for Dr. William Darlington of Westchester that Nuttall failed to find.[4] In April Gray wrote to Elias Durand of Philadelphia asking him to copy a description of a plant for him from a volume of the *Botanical Register* at the Philadelphia Library Company, adding "I should have asked Nuttall to do this for me if I felt certain he was in town, as I heard he was going on a mineralogical excursion and moreover I fear he might neglect it until it was too late." [5] The record of attendance at the Academy meetings shows that Nuttall did take the liberty of being out of town as he was not at any weekly meeting between April 3 and May 29, 1838, although on May 22 his name appears with Townsend's and Pearsall's in endorsing the proposal for the election of John Coffin Jones, U.S. Consul in Honolulu, as a Corresponding Member.[6] Nuttall was not the only irritating botanist in Gray's path: on one occasion the latter wrote that he had to wait for some information from Tuckerman until he returned from a fishing trip in the White Mountains, "What dependence can be placed on such a fellow?" [7]

On August 2, Torrey wrote to Darlington that a parcel for him had been left at the Academy which Nuttall was to forward but it proved that Nuttall was not in Philadelphia. Torrey feared that his absence would delay the printing of the Flora [8] but Nuttall soon returned and immersed himself in the Rosaceae and Polypetalae.[9] The truant, after conferring with Torrey and Gray in New York about mid-June, had been visiting his friend Dr. Fowler at Franklin Furnace and presumably other friends in the area for about six weeks but was back at the grinding job in Philadelphia by the middle of August. At the September 11 meeting of the Academy he presented specimens of *franklinite* and *troostite* from Sterling, New Jersey. On October 16, he wrote to Torrey, "By Mr. McMurtrie I send you back your manuscript of Onagraceae & Rosaceae with my own accompanying. I shall go on to finish the Umbellatae." [10] On October 27, he wrote that Dr. Durand had found a means of forwarding his specimens of *Rosaceae, Onagraceae,* and *Loasaceae,*[11] families not published until June 1840.

Among the many new species of *Rosaceae* that Nuttall had found in the far West was one which formed a new genus, an especially attractive shrub known as Indian plum, with nodding racemes of fragrant white flowers. Torrey and Gray christened this as the fifth Nuttallia. Gray, the more active author, had temporarily eliminated any possible claims of "Nuttallia digitata" Dick ex Barton (Nuttall's *Callirhoë digitata*) by reducing that species to *Malva,* but in 1849, after examining several related species newly collected by Fendler, Gray restored *Callirhoë*. In 1891, Edward Lee Greene, hastily assuming that Gray had arbitrarily retained *Callirhoë* to save his own Nuttallia and that ultimately Dick's Nuttallia would be restored, changed the name of the rosaceous genus honoring Nuttall to *Osmaronia*. The change was adopted seemingly without investigation. As thorough an examination as is now possible of the dates of the two malvaceous generic names strongly suggests that Greene's premise was mistaken and that the first generic name for the Indian plum should stand.[12]

The delay in the appearance of the third and fourth parts of the first volume of the *Flora of North America* was an intentional sacrifice of promptness in favor of greater accuracy. The authors became convinced early in the work that an inspection of the type specimens of American species in European herbaria was essential to their work. Fortunately Gray was able to make advantageous arrangements to go abroad. In July he was appointed Professor of Botany at the university being formed for the new state of Michigan and plans were made for him to act as agent for the university in purchasing books and equipment in Europe at $1500 (as a year's salary) and traveling expenses. Early in August Torrey, sending a copy of Part I of the first volume of the *Flora of North America* to Hooker, told him of Gray's plans to go to Europe in the autumn.[13] Hooker promptly invited Gray to visit him in Glasgow.

Gray's sailing for Europe on November 9, 1838, was a stimulus to Nuttall not only for getting together some of his western novelties for Francis Boott and Hooker, but also for writing a note to Boott and a long overdue letter to "my good friend Sir W. J. Hooker whose kindness I have never forgotten, nor is there a man in Europe I more esteem in all respects." Hooker had not heard directly from his admirer for many years but in almost every letter to Torrey he still asked news of him: "Tell me about Nuttall & his discoveries and his journeys;" — "What is Nuttall doing?" — "What lots of new things you have from Nuttall!" — "He answers none of my letters & refuses all intercourse with me; yet I think we might have been serviceable to each other." [14] Nuttall's note of November 3, reads:

Sir W^m J. Hooker
Dear Sir,
It is with sincere pleasure that I now take this very favorable and safe opportunity of writing to you and of sending you a few of my duplicate specimens of plants, collected in my late journey over the American Continent. I am very sorry they are so few. The difficulty of making collections on horseback over a vast desert must plead my excuse for not collecting more than I have done. I am in hopes, however, that a scientific expedition exclusively will soon be undertaken from this place with better opportunities than I possessed for making collections, when, no doubt, besides many new things a good many of mine, otherwise rare will be brought. As to collecting an herbarium myself it is out of the question, moving about, as I ever am, and without house and home, except for a few weeks or months at a time, I can of course set no value on extensive collections I so seldom see.
With my best wishes for your health and happiness,
I remain,
Your most obliged Servant
Tho^s Nuttall [15]

Torrey received Nuttall's packages and letters for England submitted "to the care of friend Gray" on November 6.[16]

Gray was heartily approved by the European botanists as a most promising young American botanist. He spent about three weeks with the Hookers. William Dawson (1816–1840), the Hookers' elder son, an enthusiastic ornithologist, had gone to the West Indies hoping to arrest tuberculosis.[17] Their son Joseph Dalton (1817–1911), who

340

had been seeking an opportunity to go as botanist on a scientific expedition, was at home but joined the Ross Expedition to the Antarctic early in 1839. In London Gray met the eminent botanists, Dr. John Richardson, the zoologist-explorer of northern Canada, and other distinguished men. He described Lambert as "the queerest old mortal I ever set eyes on." Before the year was over, Gray had met the leading botanists of Edinburgh, Paris, southern France, Italy, Vienna, Germany, and Geneva and became conversant with the newest refinements in taxonomy and the management of herbaria. He arrived back in New York on November 4, 1839, intent on finishing the *Flora of North America* and on making many corrections in the two published parts of the first volume.[18]

At the August 7, 1838, meeting of the Academy when Nuttall was prospecting for minerals in New Jersey, a motion was made and carried that the members be asked to remove personal property from the Hall. This was followed by similar motions at the first two meetings the following January. This action, evidently aimed at Nuttall's piles of plant specimens, suggests a decline in earnestness in the membership of the Academy from the early days when both Say and Nuttall used the rooms for intensive study. Nuttall was furious at the display of indifference to scientific accomplishment; he wrote to Torrey on October 27,

In regard to the Institution as it is managed *at present* I am in the situation of buffeting with the Dog in the Manger. Would you believe it, I hung up one of your proposals in the hall till about two days since and got but *one* subscriber, and he Mr. Haldeman of Columbia on the Susquehannah![19] for any interest taken here in botany one might as well be amongst the Hottentots themselves. I am now very sorry that they ever had a specimen of anything from me — but my hand is now effectually closed to them, nor shall my pen ever indite another line for their Journal. Of all the papers I furnished them I have *never been able* to obtain, in any way, (except by buying their Journal) a single copy for distribution. So much for the gratitude of public bodies! and (would be) Scientific Societies.[20]

After the August 7 motion Nuttall attended only one meeting of the Academy in 1838 — that of September 11 (probably he had not then heard of the motion); during 1839 he was present on five scattered occasions; in 1840 he weakened sufficiently to attend twelve meetings and on December 29, 1840, the Minutes show that "Thomas Nutall was duly elected a Member of the Academy." His occasional attendance suggests that he had not resigned but had, probably, allowed his dues to lapse. In 1841, his last year in America, he was present at twenty-eight meetings. Although of quick temper when affronted, he was normally pacific and did not nurture grudges.

Toward the end of October he wrote to Torrey: "If I get through the *Umbelliferae* . . . it is as much as I can do for I intend going . . . South, the Carolinas and perhaps Georgia — I am so miserably accommodated here . . . *without a fire*, that it is impossible . . . to consult the Herbarium, . . . I cannot take the bundles . . . to any other place." [21] Amos Eaton saw Nuttall at the Academy on November first, and Nuttall was still in Philadelphia on the fifteenth. Two brief notes that he wrote to Samuel Breck of Philadelphia seem to have been preserved because the recipient valued his autograph: the first note is endorsed, "Original letter from a well-known professor of Natural History . . . Mr. Nuttall succeeded to a large fortune in England, which he took possession of about the year 1842 — S. B." On the second note Breck wrote, "Autograph of the celebrated Naturalist written 15 Nov 1838 at Phil." The business between the two was the purchase of some Nova Scotia minerals from Nuttall's collection, obtained from Alger, C. T. Jackson, or Webster.[22]

His western plants were bringing in a little money at the rate of ten cents a specimen. Durand bought duplicates of all the species Nuttall described for the *Flora of North America*.[23] Among Torrey's purchases were a full set of the western *Leguminosae* — the best specimens next to Nuttall's own.[24] William Oakes purchased 500 specimens,[25] John Carey 600, and Gray brought back an order from Philip Barker Webb, F.L.S., for a number of the western compositae for his great herbarium,[26] which already contained some of Nuttall's Arkansas specimens that he had given to Mercier.

There seems to be no record of the area of the South which Nuttall visited during the winter although the few specimens (zoological and mineralogical) which may reasonably be attributed to this period came from North Carolina. With him was a companion-student, William Gambel of Philadelphia.

WILLIAM GAMBEL. Nuttall's warm reaction to juvenile enthusiasm for natural history and his sympathy for orphans brought him a new young friend in 1838, William Gamble, Jr., born in Philadelphia in June 1823.[27] His father had emigrated from northern Ireland to

Lancaster County, served in the War of 1812, and after the death of his first wife removed to Philadelphia. There in August 1822, he married Elizabeth Richardson (1802–1867) of County Tyrone, who came to the United States when eighteen. William Senior died of pneumonia in 1832, leaving his widow with three children under nine years of age, the two youngest being girls. Chiefly by teaching, the mother was able to support the family. William early showed a flair for study and for friendship and gave great promise. He evidently was sensitive about the family name for he consistently spelled it Gambel.

From a letter written to him by a young friend we discover that he left "Jackson's" and was missing from his favorite haunts in Philadelphia from late in 1838 until October 1839.[28] During "nearly eleven months" absence he had accompanied Nuttall on his trip to the South and, after a brief stop in Philadelphia in the spring, during which Nuttall attended the April 30 meeting of the Academy, paid a visit to Dr. Fowler's where both collected minerals. On the way to Franklin Furnace, Nuttall called on Torrey, for in a May 28, 1839, letter Torrey detailed to Darlington an accurate report of his progress; he was uncertain as to Nuttall's intentions of contributing further to the *Flora of North America.*[29]

Nuttall attended the October fifteenth meeting of the Academy. George B. Emerson of Boston, who was in Philadelphia during the autumn, probably visited the Academy and saw Nuttall, who must have been working on his new *Compositae.* Through a Mr. Clay, Gambel presented a specimen of native gold from "Fany's" mine in Rutherford County, North Carolina, to the Academy. Gambel's young friend wrote to him "I want to see your Cabinet of Minerals. I expect it is an extraordinary affair—my lot of Stones is in 'Statu quo;' they are not worth calling minerals." Gambel was alert to financial opportunities for in February 1840 he received thirty-five dollars for minerals that Henry P. McClellan of West Chester purchased from him and an order for a second "Chrystal of Apatite."[30] At that time the young naturalist was on the point of setting out on an excursion to New England with Nuttall.

Early in December 1839, Nuttall had received a letter from John Amory Lowell, the only son of his old patron John Lowell, inviting him to present the third series of lectures under the newly established Lowell Institute. John Amory Lowell was sole trustee of the foundation set up by the will of his cousin, the so-called John Lowell, Jr. (1799–1836), son of Francis Cabot Lowell. John, Jr., frequently traveling for his health in the mode of that day, had died in Bombay in his thirty-seventh year. His thoughtful will established a trust for series of free lectures, among other educational projects, which for well over a hundred years have contributed to the intellectual stimulation and pleasure of the residents of the Boston area. The activities of the Lowell Institute were launched on the last evening of 1839, "at the Odeum before a crowded audience" with an address by the golden-tongued Edward Everett, Governor of Massachusetts and the admiration of New England from his precocious youth. The first series of lectures was given by Benjamin Silliman of Yale on geology; the second series by John Gorham Palfrey, D.D. (1796–1881), first editor of the *Christian Examiner,* owner-editor (1835–1843) of the *North American Review,* and recently Professor of Sacred Literature at the Harvard Theological School, was entitled "On the Evidences of Christianity." Nuttall's lectures on botany were scheduled to start on Tuesday evening, March 17, 1840.[31]

On February 18, 1840, an important event in the history of the Academy of Natural Sciences was celebrated: the weekly meeting on that date was held in a new, four-story fireproof building constructed at the desire and expense of William Maclure, the president of the society for over twenty-three years, a loyal and generous friend despite his long absences from the city. The donor died on March 23, 1840, in Mexico, and William Hembel was elected to succeed him. Nuttall attended the first meeting in the new home of the Academy and thereafter was absent until the meeting of August 11.

Nuttall and young Gambel left Philadelphia the last Friday in February. Gambel outlined their progress in the letter he dutifully wrote to his mother to report their safe arrival.

Cambridge Mass March 3rd 1840

Dear Mother

We arrived in Boston Sunday morning [March 1] by about nine o clock from New York where we staid friday afternoon and Saturday until 4 oclock. then taking the Steam boat Cinderella we got through Long Island Sound safely arriving at Stonington about 3 o clock the nex[t] morning from thence we got to Providence by about 5 and then to Boston by nine. New York is a fine and large city with a great many pretty buildings. Boston is a pretty place also looks a good deal like Philadelphia. Cambridge is about 3½ miles from Boston and is a splended town

Cambridge University is the best College in the United States We expect
to stay here some time I will write again soon

remaining<br>
Your affectionate son<br>
W<sup>m</sup> Gambel [32]

In the valuable herbarium that John Amory Lowell amassed and
finally donated to the Boston Society of Natural History (later given
to the Gray Herbarium, Harvard University) were a large number of
Nuttall's Far Western species, probably presented at this time. That
Nuttall, "the Lowells' academic protégé," [33] called promptly on John
Lowell may be assumed. Always a valetudinarian, Lowell remained
in his accustomed ailing but semiactive condition until the morning
of March 12, when he quietly died while reading the newspaper
before his fire.[34] A few weeks afterward, the life of John Thornton
Kirkland came to an end — the friend whose regime at Harvard
Lowell had so devotedly supported as long as he served as a Fellow
of the Corporation.

The novelty of free lectures in Boston stimulated such a widespread desire to learn about geology, evidences of Christianity, and
the generally unnoted vegetable world that the demand for tickets far
exceeded all reasonable expectations. The crowds that applied at the
Old Corner Bookstore for tickets for the second course of lectures
were so great that they broke the windows and created a near riot;
moreover the requests far exceeded the seating capacity. The method
of dispersal of tickets was necessarily changed to assignment by lots
following preliminary application.[35] For Nuttall's course of nine lectures there were 12,000 applications. Two series were therefore arranged, one being held on Tuesday and Friday evenings and the
other on Wednesday and Saturday afternoons in an old theatre which
accommodated 1500 persons.

We are fortunate in having comments of Dr. A. A. Gould, Harvard College 1825, an outstanding zoologist and a former student of
Nuttall, on the initial lecture.

Mr. Nuttall made his debut on Tuesday evening, with such success
as every one who knew him must have anticipated. . . . He had been
moving his lips about five minutes, before the audience was aware he
had begun. The cry *louder, louder,* soon began, & threatened to become
a regular tumult; but a gentleman of influence arose & promised better
satisfaction, which somewhat quieted them. The 3000 will dwindle to 300
very soon, & I doubt whether he will be permitted to go on. I am sorry,

345

because he was my master & a very learned botanist — but it was a mistake to bring him before such an audience. Every citizen, you perhaps know, has a right to a ticket, if he can get it.

On March 24, after the second lecture Gould added, "Mr. Nuttall continues and gives better satisfaction." In April he went to the country to recover from a cough and wrote nothing further about the lectures.[36]

On May 30, Torrey reported to Hooker: "Nuttall has been lecturing on Botany in Boston before the Lowell Institute — 8 lectures for $1000. This will do pretty well for plain Jane. The science has received such an impulse that a new ed[n] of Bigelow's Flora of Boston has been published. Nuttall will soon resume his examination of the plants collected on his last expedition. We have his notes only as far as the Compositae."[37] The arrangement to give two series of lectures increased Nuttall's honorarium, presumably to $1575. His expenses of residence (in Cambridge) were also provided for.

A letter to the editor (Lynde M. Walter, Harvard College 1817) printed in *The Boston Evening Transcript* on April 25, 1840, which discussed the Botanic Garden, rouses interest in the identity of the author.[38]

Mr. Editor: You used to like — so long ago that I suppose you would willingly forget how long, as you are still a young man — to go to the Botanic Garden, at Cambridge, and witness the fine effect of Carter's cultivation. If you should make him a visit now, you would be well paid for your trouble. He has some flowers well worth going to see. The finest of them, and perhaps the finest flower of the kind that grows — certainly the richest in color — is the Rhododendron Arboreum — a native of Nepal — which was introduced into England in 1817 — a memorable epoch. It is of a magnificent scarlet, and the morning light must give it great splendor. I saw it by the afternoon light. I shall certainly take an opportunity to visit it before noon, some sunny day. Besides this, Mr. Carter has the always curious Strelitzia, in perfect order, and the Red Multiflora Rose, just coming into fine flower. For some years this has been the admiration of visitors to the Garden. . . .

Mr. Carter's collection is not great, but it is very choice, and he is now, as he has always been, distinguished for the skill with which he cultivates and propagates exotics. The season is not yet come to see his collection of native plants, but if you go now, to see the Green House, you will be very likely to go in May and June, when you will find many of our rare wild flowers, not easily to be found elsewhere, except in their native dwellings (habitats, the botanist would say).

I saw one very pretty thing, which was new. It is one of Mr. Nuttall's

California plants, with a crimson, jewel-shaped, blossom — Diplacus puniceus, Mr. Carter called it. . . .

From the notices you have repeatedly given of flowers at the Conservatory, I perceive you have not lost your taste for them, as I presume you have not your former interest in the oldest one of the best collections accessible to the public, where you imbibed, or, at least, fostered, that taste.

Yours,

T. N. Y.[39]

Nuttall took advantage of his prolonged stay in Cambridge to put out a new edition of his *Ornithology* of the land birds with the firm of Charles Little and James Brown, formed in 1837. Additions to the first edition amounted to about a hundred and fifty pages and came from various sources: alterations that had appeared in the Appendix to the *Water Birds* were incorporated into the text; many of Dr. Richardson's published observations on his second expedition to the far North and Audubon's of his trip along the Texas coast in the spring of 1837 were added and also items that various acquaintances imparted orally; but most of the supplemental material was the fruit of Nuttall's and Townsend's trek over the Oregon Trail and their months in Oregon, where they studied intently the habits of many species little known or unknown, and of Nuttall's observations on the California coast.

James Brown's fine collection of ornithological books probably furnished Nuttall with expensive up-to-date texts that he needed, such as Richardson's *Fauna Boreali-Americana* and Audubon's *Ornithological Biography*.[40] Nuttall used his own accounts of the western birds quoted in the fourth and fifth volumes of Audubon's text, sometimes giving them a little additional polishing. The meticulousness of his records appears in the descriptions which are handled with great assurance and smoothness and give vivid impressions of the birds as zestful individuals abounding in vitality and ecstatic joy.

The information that Townsend met with a male mourning warbler on the Schuylkill in May 1839 suggests that Nuttall had been collecting items for a new edition of the *Ornithology* before he arrived in Cambridge.[41] Dr. Thomas Brewer, Audubon's young Boston friend, and James Elliott Cabot (1821–1903), a senior at Harvard, were especially communicative. The latter showed Nuttall a nest of the golden-winged warbler sent from White Sulphur Springs by his brother, Dr. Samuel Cabot, Harvard College 1836.[42] Both Cabots maintained their interest in natural history: Samuel after accompanying John Lloyd Stephens on the second of his two expeditions which first clearly revealed the Mayan antiquities of Central America, wrote on the "Birds of Yucatan"; James Elliott Cabot wrote the narrative of Louis Agassiz's tour to Lake Superior.

Current ornithological observations of Nuttall disclose some of his local activities. His description of the nest of a purple finch in a fir tree in Professor Farrar's garden suggests that he was once again a dinner guest of the hospitable Mrs. Farrar. Although Professor Farrar's failing health had forced his retirement in 1833, he lived on in his delightful home on Professors' Row (Kirkland Street) for a score of years. The migratory season offered opportunity for last checks on some of the species discussed in the concluding pages of the volume. On a birding excursion to Spot Pond in Medford on May 8, Gambel shot specimens of male and female black-and-white Warblers and several male Nashvilles; in West Cambridge (Arlington) about May 17, a northern water thrush and a yellow-throat were observed. Through the spring Gambel watched a flicker's burrow "excavated out of the living trunk of a sassafras about 15 feet from the ground. It was about 8 inches in diameter and 18 inches deep, dug with a shelving inclination, and was continued at intervals for more than 4 weeks before it was completed." [43]

Although Townsend and Audubon had already published most of the new western species, Nuttall was able to add two not yet described: Zonotrichia *querula, a sparrow of the plains which had sung mournfully throughout the first days of the journey from Independence, and a far western sparrow, of which Townsend had secured a single male specimen "near Fort Wallah-Wallah," that Nuttall named for Gambel. Since degraded to a variety, it is known as Gambel's white-crowned sparrow, Zonotrichia leucophrys gambeli (Nuttall). [44] This early recognition of Gambel as an ornithologist was amply warranted within a few years by his pioneering papers on California birds.

As Nuttall was living in Cambridge (perhaps at Willard's Hotel in the Village), he would daily encounter some old friends or acquaintances: Dr. Thaddeus W. Harris, the Harvard librarian, then lecturer in natural history, and other erstwhile colleagues; and old friends like Colonel Metcalf, the University printer, Mrs. Peck, Nat Wyeth, and Joseph E. Worcester. The Winships and the large nursery that Charles M. Hovey had developed on the road to Boston would attract his visits as did the Botanic Garden, where William Carter delighted to welcome him. He would call on Susan Austin and her husband in their familiar old house [45] and on Mrs. Craigie in her elegant mansion. The latter would be in her southeast parlor, bright with window plants and singing birds, in her customary gray silk dress and white muslin turban above her snapping gray eyes. She perhaps had exhorted Nuttall as she did Samuel Longfellow, Harvard College 1839, brother of the poet who lived in the Craigie House from mid-1837, "Be good; I want you to be good." A year later she died of cancer, resolutely refusing any medical attendance. In Boston Nuttall saw Benjamin D. Greene and probably the Bootts as well as the Lowells and may have attended meetings of the Boston Society of Natural History and the American Academy of Arts and Sciences.

During their long stay in Cambridge, Nuttall and Gambel became acquainted with Edward Tuckerman, perennial graduate student at Harvard, who considered the lad "very smart and capable" and headed for "distinction worthy of a disciple of Nuttall." [46] They doubtless visited Tuckerman in the rambling old house (ca. 1710) of Royal Morse in Holmes Place in his spacious room with its three large study tables, one for botany, one for Coleridge, and one for Greek drama. Expecting to go to Europe the next spring, he solicited Nuttall's promise of a package of rare plants which he could use as gifts for various botanists whom he hoped to meet; the "long promised" package arrived in ample time. The next winter Gambel wrote to Tuckerman of the expedition he was about to undertake over the Santa Fe Trail to California to collect for Nuttall. [47]

It appears that Nuttall was not in a mood to hurry back to Philadelphia to work on the *Compositae*. Wanderlust assailed him with the complication of spring fever, abetted by an enthusiastic companion. He took Gambel on two excursions to Maine, repeating parts of his route of 1824. In April they took ship for Portland, a rough passage, and proceeded leisurely on foot into the interior as far as Paris; fine tourmaline crystals and beryl were still being uncovered there, and Gambel had learned that striking specimens commanded a good price. Their second trip was to Bath and the Kennebec where, "we got some very fine minerals." [48] Dr. Ezekiel Holmes had corresponded with Nuttall after meeting him in 1824. Soon afterwards, Holmes had moved to the Kennebec valley, which Vaughans, Hallowells, and Gardiners had made a center of culture. He alternately practiced medicine and taught chemistry and natural history at the Gardiner Lyceum and Colby College. In 1840 he was serving in the State Legislature and presumably living in Winthrop. Later he headed the Natural History Survey of Maine. Nuttall may have renewed the acquaintance during these visits to Maine. He took back to Cambridge by early June "an *Empetrum* (*rubrum?*)" and an Arenaria "very close to groenlandica but at a less elevation," both of which excited Tuckerman.[49]

Nuttall perhaps was already contemplating doing the proposed supplement to Michaux's *Sylva* for he made some observations of trees: he noted that the dwarf juniper (*J. horizontalis*) was not uncommon in the vicinity of Portland and observed on the Little Androscoggin River near Paris the largest white pines of his experience, which "seem to emulate in elevation the vast Firs of Oregon."[50]

The last proofreading for the new edition of the *Ornithology* probably awaited Nuttall's attention in Cambridge; the volume was on sale by the end of June.[51] On June 29, Gambel wrote to his mother briefly about the Maine excursions. He expected to be "back home in a few weeks at farthest having been gone 4 months instead of 2 as we expected. . . . We intend returning to Philadelphia without going through Long Island sound, but will go to Springfield on the Connecticut River from there to Albany and thence down the Hudson to N. Y. where we will stay a few days and then go to Phil.ª" The travelers were back by early August.

In March 1841, in his nineteenth year, Gambel set out for the far West as a collector for Nuttall. He had acquired a broad field knowledge of natural history by the apprentice system and was enthusiastically attached to the study of birds and mineralogy. At Independence, Missouri, he joined a caravan of Santa Fe traders setting out in the first part of May. The party suffered the usual trials of clashes with bands of marauding Indians and the heat and thirst of the desert-crossing between the Arkansas River and the Cimarron — stimulants to a rapid trip. After spending July and August collecting and exploring the rough terrain about the Rio Grande, Gambel was able to attach himself to the prosperous and experienced Rowland-Workman party which left northern New Mexico on September 1 and reached California early in November. In January 1842, he wrote to Nuttall from Pueblo Los Angeles that he planned to collect through the summer and return home by ship. However in the autumn he was still in California where he and some companions, after having serious trouble with local Indians, appealed for help to the commander of the Pacific fleet of the United States Navy, which was patrolling the Spanish coast. Commodore T. Ap-Catesby Jones, being in need of a clerk or secretary, offered the post to Gambel, who assumed it on November 15. This gave him an opportunity to collect for two years around scattered harbors of the west coasts of North and South America and on the Sandwich Islands.[52]

THE SYLVA. Hooker promptly reviewed the first volume of Torrey and Gray's *Flora of North America* after it was completed in June 1840. In mentioning the contributors, whose assistance was acknowledged in the Preface of the *Flora*, he wrote:

We are anxious that the names of these individuals who have so ably promoted the cause of American Botany should be recorded in the pages of our Journal. At the head of them, justly stands Mr. Nuttall, to whom the authors are indebted (independently of the immense mass of information derived from his valuable publications, which are known wherever Botany is studied) for a nearly complete series of the plants collected during his recent journey across the Rocky Mountains to Oregon and California, accompanied with manuscript descriptions of his new genera and species and also for many plants obtained during his travels in Arkansas in the year 1819.[53]

The names of eighty other contributors or herbaria were enumerated as providing specimens of species described in the work.

Indications appear in several letters that the collaboration between Nuttall and Torrey and Gray was not happy and would not continue. Torrey wrote to Darlington that Nuttall had described his plants up to the Compositae and that he felt quite sure he would continue or, at any rate, furnish them with specimens. However, he regarded Nuttall as a queer fish.[54] On July 6, 1840, Benjamin D. Greene wrote to Hooker: "Nuttall, who has . . . been here during the printing of a second edition of his work on our birds, seems not quite satisfied with the treatment of his genera and species [in Torrey and Gray's *Flora*] & has some other subjects of complaint — how far he has reason I have not yet had an opportunity to judge." [55]

Nuttall's dissatisfaction with Torrey's and Gray's editing of his species — both the far western species that were being newly described and the species which he had already published — was due to changes made in his work in Volume I. In the few selected cases cited here as illustrations time has proved that Nuttall's diagnoses and conclusions were accurate and that his critics were in error. Torrey and Gray reduced Nuttall's *Anemone *globosa* of the Rockies to a variety of an arctic and eastern species; his good species *Geranium incisum* was made a variety of one of Hooker's species, and his good species *Wisteria macrostachys* was also reduced to a variety; his *Euonymus *occidentalis* (western wahoo) was placed in synonymy with the common burning-bush of the east; a southern species of lupine, published in the *Genera* in 1818, was degraded to a variety of Willdenow's *L. villosus*; his good *Oenothera cruciata* was reduced to a variety of *Oe. biennis* L.; the western service berry that Wyeth collected was made a variety of the eastern; and his new genus *Collomia* was reduced to *Gilia*. Two good, new species of *Oxalis* were discarded: one was judged to be O. *corniculata,* a cosmopolitan weed, and so lost to Nuttall; the other, O. *pilosa* Nutt., was retrieved about sixty years later. Any one of these changes would have been annoying and arguments over them distressing to Nuttall — although not to Gray, who throughout his life loved debate.[56] Nuttall found highly disturbing the cumulative effect of very many alterations made by persons far less experienced and informed than himself. If either of the editors had been able to grasp the distinctness of the western flora, a fundamental difficulty between the two camps would have been overcome. As it was, Nuttall had had enough of such editing.

After a long respite from plant taxonomy, Nuttall plunged into study of his many new species of *Compositae,* writing on August 5 to Darlington to request the loan of Hooker's *Flora.*[57] His work was so expeditious that a great part of it must have already been done. His paper was read in two parts to the American Philosophical Society on October 2 and December 18, 1840. The committee on his paper commented, "In this paper, Mr. Nuttall makes a large addition to the Flora of North America, consisting of fifty new genera, with numerous species." Published the next year in the *Transactions*, it filled one hundred and seventy large pages.[58] The full title of Nuttall's paper is "Descriptions of New Species and Genera of Plants in the Natural Order of the Compositae, Collected in a Tour across the Continent to the Pacific, a Residence in Oregon, and a Visit to the Sandwich

Islands and Upper California, during the Years 1834 and 1835."
Long as it is, it is not completely accurate, for Nuttall's tour extended
well into 1836, he made two visits to the Sandwich Islands, and
species from other regions are included: at least eleven from Arkansas,
seven from the southeast, one from Massachusetts, three from the
sources of the Missouri, one from Fayal, and also miscellaneous collections of others in the United States, Peru, and Chili. Of the
sixty-four new genera recognized by Nuttall, five were named for
persons — Curzonia, *Rafinesquia,* Riddellia, Stylesia, and Tuckerman-
nia. Most of the specific names — about 300 — were descriptive; only
Baldwin, Boykin, Hooker, Pursh, Say, Schweinitz, and Torrey were
honored by specific names and in all these cases, with the exception
of Say, the person recognized either had collected the specimen described or had previously given it an invalid name. Scores of new
combinations were introduced.

Through the winter and early spring Nuttall, concentrated his
attention on a new project. William Maclure during a visit to Paris
had purchased the engraved copper plates — some done by Redouté —
which had been made for François André Michaux's fine work on the
sylva of North America, *Histoire des arbres forestiers de l'Amérique
septentrionale* (Paris 1810–1813).[59] The plates were used at New
Harmony to print a new edition of the work; unfortunately very inferior paper was used, and the edition was "poor" otherwise. Moreover the text needed modernizing because many new species of
North American trees had become known since the last visit of
Michaux *fils* to the United States. An Appendix was therefore proposed, and suggestions for possible authors were bandied about among
naturalists for a number of years. H. B. Croom had undertaken the
preparation of such a supplement but had not made a start on it. The
year following his death, Dr. Samuel G. Morton sounded out Charles
Pickering on the project, who suggested Dr. Bridges as a possibility,
remarking that Nuttall "was never fond of trees." [60] After William
Maclure died in March 1840, his brother and executor, Alexander
Maclure, presented the plates to Dr. Morton, who evidently persuaded Nuttall to prepare the long-talked-of Appendix. Many years
later J. Jay Smith, Sr., brother-in-law of Morton, wrote:

It was a singular circumstance, and a happy one it has proved for advancing science, that Mr. Nuttall arrived in this country the very year
that the younger Michaux left it. From that time he devoted his talents

to Botany, and after visiting a large portion of the United States, with an aptitude for observation, a quickness of eye, tact in discrimination, and tenacity of memory, rarely possessed by one man, he published his extended and most happily executed botanical work, the "Genera of North American plants." In 1834 he crossed the Rocky mountains and explored the territory of Oregon and Upper California. With his peculiar qualifications, he prepared the supplement to Michaux's Sylva, in three handsome volumes.[61]

On February 18, 1841, William Darlington again received a request from Nuttall for the loan of Hooker's flora of North America: "I am now engaged in making additions to Michaux's Sylva, of w$^h$ Dobson is issuing a new Edition. I am therefore very anxious to know what Hooker has given about the forest trees of Oregon."[62] Besides adding all the woody plants published since Michaux fils's work, Nuttall was including unpublished western trees and shrubs thereby swelling the text with many new species of willows, some alders, an oak, an ash, the California laurel (*Umbellularia californica), Taxus *brevifolia, Abies lasiocarpa (Hook.) Nutt., and Larix *occidentalis.

Nuttall was not only compiling the text but he was also supervising drawings for the lithographic plates — each species was to be figured in color as in the original work. Nuttall's notations on the original drawings show that Gambel did a few (pls. 3, 47, 100); other artists were J. B. Butler, J. T. French, E. D. Long, and G. West.[63] The preparation of the drawings was slow, but by midspring Nuttall had completed the text for the new arboreal species known to him. The plates were made by T. Sinclair's lithography, and the coloring was done by Alexander Lawson's daughters, one of whom, Malvina (1806?–1884), recorded her recollections of Nuttall. "Nuttall himself was the least attractive of the Genus Homo I ever met. I could never imagine any Englishman so dirty and disorderly in his dress and appearance. . . . I have heard young men who studied with him speak of him with great respect . . . but I thought his manners rough and abrupt."[64] One wonders if Nuttall appeared in the leather clothing he used on western expeditions.

Intriguing items of Nuttall's text are the frequent references to the size of specimen trees of various species in English gardens in which measurements are given for the year 1837, such as the statement that the original Abies fraseri, introduced by Fraser, had reached a height of fifteen feet in the Hammersmith Nursery and had produced cones for two or three years by 1837. Repetitions of this date raise the question as to whether he was in England during that year. However, although not specifically stated, the statistics were obviously secured from John C. Loudon's *Arboretum et Fruticetum Britannicum* (1838). Nuttall did not make a visit to England after 1833; although on his return from the west coast he expressed the intention of going, his work was an obstacle and, after Jonas Nuttall's death, he abandoned the idea.

Some references occur in the *Sylva* to localities that he was not otherwise known to have visited; for example we learn that he climbed Roan Mountain and Table Top in the southern Appalachians and other details of his many travels. For the *Sylva,* as for his writings generally, Nuttall consulted his field journals; his daily records were probably the basis of some aspects of the excellent memory with which he was credited by contemporaries.

Nostalgic references to his friends and his favorite haunts are abundant. His "late friend David Landreth" found *Chionanthus virginicus* Willd. (fringe tree) on the Brandywine near West Chester and an old specimen of it twenty feet high and thirty-two inches in diameter was in Bartrams' Garden; Mr. C. Wistar and Caspar Wistar, Jr., of Germantown had tables and cabinets made from a single white oak; near Franklin Furnace there were red cedars fifty to sixty feet in height and two feet in diameter, and huge specimens one hundred and forty years old stood in Germantown on the estate formerly of Mr. Shoemaker. The text is strongly autobiographical. An especially touching passage centers on *Campsis radicans* (trumpet creeper, ordinarily a vine).

In the Bartram Garden (Kingsessing) there is one of these trees probably a century old, with a thick, short, and nearly erect stem, its summit spreading out into an independent, airy bower. A familiar retiring-place for three generations of the family, it scarcely presents any sign of decay, being only stunted by the thinness of the soil in which it grows. May the venerable groves and splendid and curious trees of this patriarchal residence long survive the waning existence of its present proprietors! But I fear the love of change and of gain will, at no distant date, turn these remarks and references into a matter of mere historical recollection in place of existing facts.

The *Sylva* was dedicated to the late William Maclure and F. André Michaux. When the text and plates were finally finished they were left with Judah Dobson, who was to publish them in three volumes.

At this period, the *Journal* of the Academy of Natural Sciences was languishing. When Nuttall and Say had both been in Philadelphia, the Academy's *Journal* came out regularly; when both were elsewhere its publication lapsed (1819 and 1820) or became erratic (nothing appeared in 1826, 1828, 1831–1833, 1835–1836). In 1826 Pickering wrote of the great deficiency of papers for the *Journal*. Two of Nuttall's papers in plant taxonomy supplied almost three-fifths of the text of Part I of Volume VII (1834); almost one-fourth of Part II (1837) and a half of Part I of Volume VIII (1839) consisted of reports on zoological collections that Nuttall and Townsend brought back from the far West. After the unpleasantness which arose over Nuttall's material cluttering the hall of the Academy, he presented no more of his work to them for ten years. After Part II of Volume VIII came out in 1842, there were no further issues until 1847. However to a considerable extent the *Proceedings*, which were started in March 1841, served in lieu of the *Journal*.

In the autumn of 1840, Gray had gone to Philadelphia to study Nuttall's specimens of *Compositae* and also those in the Academy's Herbarium, for he was compiling the text on that family for the *Flora of North America*. After his return from Europe, his correspondence with Hooker naturally became more frequent and confiding. In January he wrote to Hooker:

Have you ever received any more of Nuttall's plants, or has Boott? He is selling them to different persons for 10 dollars pr. hundred. . . . He has a considerable number of Oregon and California Compositae which Douglas did not get. . . . Nuttall ought to send all these to you, but his *amor pecuniae* is rather strong.[65] I know you would desire to have them, even Nuttallian specimens,[66] and reproach myself that I did not bespeak some of them when I ordered for Webb. He has given us a portion, not very many; others I have studied at Philadelphia. I cant afford to buy them. My friend Mr. Carey at New York has just desired me to ask Nuttall to put up a set for him. I know with considerable accuracy what plants (Compositae) are desiderata with you; and I will take the liberty of writing at once to Nuttall and of asking for such in your name. I shall ask for about 100 Compositae, and will extend the order to other plants if you desire it. He has however distributed nothing beyond Compositae. Pray let me know at once if I have done rightly in this.[67]

Hooker answered promptly that Gray had "done quite right in ordering the Compositae." [68] A few months later Gray wrote that Nuttall "begs you to receive them [118 specimens] as a present;" [69] Nuttall actually wrote to Gray that he did "not wish to be held up as a huckster to Sir Wm. J. Hooker, and I therefore wish you to send him the specimens in *Compositae* I sent you, as a present from myself." [70]

This little unpleasantness was but a side issue of a more serious dispute which broke out after Gray read the proof of the first part of Nuttall's paper on his new western *Compositae*. During Gray's November visit at the Academy, he had pointed out to Nuttall that some of the genera that Nuttall was setting up as new had already been published under other names. When Gray later found that one or two of his suggestions had been used with no acknowledgement of assistance, he promptly wrote to Nuttall and demanded that recognition be given him. This was the source of bitter exchanges between the two extending through the spring for, when Gray found that Nuttall seemed to view the matter as of little consequence, he brought up old differences and exhumed hitherto concealed grievances of Torrey.[71] The letters show a curious lack of understanding by each of the complaints of the other. Gray had the first and last words of the argument, which started in March and concluded with a letter drafted on June 4.[72] In Nuttall's last letter, sent the end of April, a quasi apology is appended in a postscript: "If I have used any harsh or improper expressions, I hope you will excuse them & attribute them to an undue excitement." In the body of the letter he had written a paragraph of present interest which, although crossed out with double lines, is readable.

From circumstances over w$^h$ I have *no control*, I am obliged to use the utmost economy to live. I have sold everything I am able to keep out of debt, and I therefore, tho' reluctantly, desire Dr. T., to return me the dried plants sent to him when done with, as, having given away one set (to the Acad. of Nat. Sci.) it is as much as I owe a country that never patronized or assisted me in any thing, and to explore which I have sacrificed much property and spent nearly my whole life. On returning them with my manuscripts, I will, if desired, send back 3 or 4 numbers of your Flora for w$^h$ I have now no further use.

Nuttall's attitude belittled Gray's crusade, but he was deeply disturbed by the unpleasantness.[73]

Early in April Nuttall received an invitation to go to Washington to assist with sorting advance shipments of botanical specimens that had arrived from the United States Exploring Expedition. He left

Philadelphia on May 6 for two months' work for the National Institution for the Promotion of Science of which Dr. Henry King had been appointed curator. The collections were installed in the Great Hall of the Patent Office where John Kirk Townsend was already at work on the bird skins.[74] Nuttall reported that there were about 50,000 plant specimens; of them all he was most intrigued by some odd species of the *Ranunculaceae* from Tierra del Fuego and an *Amaryllis* (?) from Rio de Janeiro.[75]

He was back in Philadelphia for the July thirteenth meeting of the Academy, but the last half of July and throughout September he was absent. In midsummer he may have visited the Carrs at the Bartram Garden and the Charles Jones Wisters at Grumblethorpe in Germantown. It was evidently his hostess at the latter household who remarked that "in one respect he was the exemplar of the hero of romance: he always came and went without baggage." C. J. Wister, Jr., calling Nuttall "a man of very simple ways" placed him among his father's "more particular friends" and stressed his intimate knowledge of the plants at Grumblethorpe.[76] The old stone house, built by C. J. Wister, Sr.'s, grandfather, was backed by a large semiformal box-bordered garden planted with unusual species.[77] Nuttall probably stayed also for a time at George Carpenter's estate, Phil-Ellena in Germantown; with 350 improved acres, it became the largest, most opulent, and beautiful place anywhere near Philadelphia. Being an ardent mineralogist, Carpenter constructed a museum in his new home to display his immense and valuable collection. He was the custodian of Nuttall's collection also.

Toward the end of the summer Nuttall seems to have lingered in his favorite mineralogical area in and about Franklin Furnace. On the last day of August he wrote to Dr. George Engelmann in St. Louis from Edenville, Orange County, New York. Although Nuttall had never met Engelmann, he had given William Gambel a letter of introduction to him when Gambel set out in the early spring for St. Louis en route to the West Coast. "Excuse me for enquiring if you have heard any thing of the Santa Fe expedition in wh Mr. Gambel went, or any thing concerning him. If you can find a moment to spare to tell me any thing about him, I shall be exceedingly obliged." [78]

The news of the death of his Aunt Frances on August 17 was not unexpected, for she had been ill for a year. Sadder news was the death of his mother in Long Preston on September 18, in her eighty-first year. Loath though Nuttall was to go back to England, of necessity he started winding up his American affairs of which fresh work for the *Sylva* was the most involved and perplexing because numerous new southern Floridian species collected by Dr. John Loomis Blodgett (1809–1853) of Key West had suddenly come into his hands from Torrey. On October 14, he wrote to Darlington:

In a very few weeks (some time next month) I am about to sail for England. An estate has devolved upon me of considerable importance, by the death of some near relations and I shall (I hear!) be obliged to live mostly in England, but shall then, however, have ample leisure in the retirement of a country house to pursue studies w^h ever must continue to interest me. I shall in England also have the advantage of herbaria of all sorts. . . . If I could spare time I would come over and see you before I go, but this unfortunate Sylva has plunged me into such a labyrinth of employment that I hardly have time to eat. Think of 35 new trees from E. Fla., and a host of all kinds of things w^h to be consistent, I must publish to the disappointment, no doubt, of the public who want nothing to read but amusement or for profit. The figures, however, I hope will be good and that is my only consolation respecting the undertaking, and to botanists at least they must be usefull.

Yours in haste
Truly
Tho^s Nuttall [79]

The occasion of the letter was an idea advanced by Darlington on which Nuttall commented: "Your suggestion about a new Edition of the Genera of N. Am. plants is very flattering & I intend to give it a proper consideration. I agree with you about the utility of such a work, but doubt my ability to render such a publication sufficiently interesting."

Early in November Nuttall wrote to Engelmann that he expected to leave the United States on December 1. He was concerned about the transmission of plants that Gambel had sent from Santa Fe by a "party returning to St. Louis in October." He asked Engelmann to make sure that a makeshift agent in St. Louis (a customer of Carpenter) forwarded the expected packages to him in Liverpool. Unfortunately the collection of plants never arrived in St. Louis.

During 1841, Nuttall's last year as an active member of the Academy of Natural Sciences, his name appears in the Minutes several times. As usual since his return from California, he was elected to the Botanical Committee. At the first meeting of the year he gave through Townsend a specimen of the yellow-billed magpie of California, *Pica nuttalli* (Audubon); and on March 2, Gambel donated two western bird skins received from Nuttall — Gairdner's woodpecker of the Columbia River, *Dryobates pubescens gairdneri* (Audubon), and the tricolor red-wing of California, *Agelaius tricolor* (Audubon). Haldeman described a new freshwater shell he got in Oregon. He was among the twenty members who presented the Academy with a portrait of William Hembel by John Neagle, and he also contributed to a fund for bookcases for the Hall. At the October 12th meeting Dr. Morton commenced a paper on "Descriptions of Some New Species of Organic Remains of the Cretaceous Group of the United States; with a Tabular View of the Fossils Hitherto Discovered in This Formation." [80] References to a few fossils that Lewis and Clark got at the Great Bend of the Missouri, which Morton had identified as Cretaceous, and to some additional species, "for the most part in fragments" that Mr. Nuttall secured, evidently roused Nuttall to present a paper with Conrad two weeks later on "Fossil Shells of the Cretaceous" from the Mandan country, 1500 miles up the Missouri. This paper was not published; we suppose that in it Nuttall emphasized his early paper describing such deposits on the Missouri, to which Morton had made no allusion. Toward the end of the year, he had a likeness drawn by a local artist, M. S. Parker, and copies made for distribution to his friends.[81]

At some time during the autumn Nuttall wrote to Gambel's good friend, James B. Carlin, telling of his inheritance, which the youth quoted in part when writing to Gambel almost two years later: "There is a fine house land & income, & I am desired to lose no time in going over to Liverpool. I . . . [plan] to depart on the 20th of Nov." Nuttall reported to Carlin that he had received a long letter from Gambel written at Santa Fé on July 14, giving an account of his trek to the southwest and of promising possibilities in continuing his journey to California.[82]

Nuttall read the last paper on his western species to the American Philosophical Society on December 3, 1841. It dealt with members of three families of the subclass *Sympetalae* — *Lobeliaceae, Campanulaceae,* and *Ericaceae* — and made only twenty-one printed pages.[83] Nine of the species discussed were from the Hawaiian Islands. Many of the plants were known in eastern North America, the interest lying in the disrupted distribution of the species. No great number of new species was presented but the number of new genera and new combinations was relatively large. No person was given recognition in the nomenclature. Quantities of Nuttall's collection of *Sympetalae* were still unpublished even though he had already described many of the largest family, the *Compositae*. Several years later some of his *Scrophulariaceae* were described by George Bentham for De Candolle's *Prodromus*, but he himself made no effort to publish more than a few scattered species, notably specimens allied to some species in Gambel's far-western collection.

Delay followed delay in Nuttall's efforts to leave his work on the *Sylva* in good order. The completed text "described one hundred and nine American trees including a large number of West Indian species" found on islands off the Florida Coast.[84] An impressionistic account of his wanderings over North America which concludes the Preface to the *Sylva* was probably the last composition of the American phase of Nuttall's life, which had covered a span of almost thirty-four years. The brief narrative, pouring out a prose poem on primeval American scenes, is so inspired by intense emotion that it becomes a moving lamentation. There can be no doubt that Nuttall left his "New World" reluctantly to face an unwelcome future.

He attended the Academy meeting on Tuesday, December 28, and was probably aboard the packet *Thomas P. Cope* when it sailed the next day from Philadelphia for Liverpool.

# CHAPTER 20

# REPATRIATION

The harmonies of Nature . . . make us dwell with delight upon
that which best deserves our recollection. — Thomas Nuttall, *Ornithology*, 1840.

MANORIAL LIFE. Nuttall returned to England in 1842 at the beginning of his fifty-seventh year with a heavy heart, for all his interests
and enthusiasm centered in the natural history of America. His
mother's death in September had dissolved his closest link with England. Unhappily the conditions of 1824 which had moved him to
agree to accept his uncle's estate had so completely changed as to
make his sacrifice of little if any value: Elizabeth Nuttall Dixon's
two surviving children had reached an age of self-sufficiency; Frances
(1817–1868) was perhaps already married to John Merson, and
Francis (1819–1915), the next heir, was becoming established in the
manufacture of glass. However, Nuttall had no alternative to accept-
ing the inheritance. From 1824, with provision for the distant future
assured, he had expended his funds freely to increase his field knowledge of the United States and the country to the south and west.
While he was at Harvard, almost yearly leaves of absence of three
months or more enabled him to go to unfamiliar areas to observe and
collect; these travels, often extensive, must have consumed a large
part of his very modest salary. When the chance arose of reaching the
Rockies and Oregon, he exchanged his salary for unforeseeable expenses. Later, while he studied and described his western collections
and prepared the supplement to Michaux's *Sylva*, he used his savings
and probably royalties from the *Ornithology* for living expenses.[1]
During Nuttall's last eight years in North America the only considerable sum he received was the honorarium for the Lowell Institute

lectures. In consequence of the imbalance of income and outgo, which was intensified by the prolonged depression, he was financially unable to renounce his inheritance and remain in America.[2]

Repatriation proved to be a major ordeal. The English scene with its own species of plants and animals had become alien. During the first year or so after his return, he suffered nostalgia to such an extent that his health was impaired. He did not feel equal in the autumn to making an expected visit to Sir William Jackson Hooker, who had been appointed Director of the Royal Gardens at Kew in March 1841.[3] Although he wrote to Sir William that he was better, he wrote at the same time to James Carlin that he was "far from being in good health" (Carlin's phrasing).[4] On December 12, 1842, evidently in answer to a letter, he wrote to Edward Tuckerman: "You talk of English country life. I prefer the wilds of America a thousand times to all domestic arrangements. I love to be free as the air. I care nothing for privation — it is not worth a thought."[5]

The household at Nutgrove was presided over by Thomas's sister Elizabeth; during the long illness of her Aunt Frances, she doubtless had assumed full responsibility for its supervision. The heavy and elaborate furnishings and general atmosphere of the house were as different from Nuttall's American habitats as the chaffinches, wagtails, and rooks were from his American bird friends. He never became reconciled to the household; it was Elizabeth's home rather than his.

Jonas's will, signed in 1829 and probated in 1838, gave his three trustees detailed instructions to ensure the maintenance of his manor with the care and in the style to which he himself had been accustomed, with a "proper Gardener" to tend the grounds and greenhouses and an experienced husbandman to manage and cultivate the home farm. In addition to numerous legacies, small annuities were established for both of Thomas's sisters and for another niece of Jonas, Frances (Dixon), wife of Dr. James Threlfall of Liverpool. Exacting stipulations swelled the document to eleven legal-sized parchment sheets: "The Wesleyan Methodist Minister who . . . shall come to preach at the Chapel . . . shall for ever be accommodated with the best or second best Bed in my . . . Mansion House and entertained at the family Table." Any heir to the estate not already bearing Jonas's family name was required to take the surname "Nuttall in addition to his family name and quarter the arms of Nuttall with his own family arms." The requirement of the greatest significance to Thomas, and aimed at him, was that the incumbent be in residence nine months of each year "unless prevented by illness or unavoidable accident." Jonas left cash and securities, farms adjoining Nutgrove, property in Liverpool and its suburbs and on the Isle of Man.[6] The taxes on the estate were high, and one may assume that Frances Nuttall's recent enlargement of the Nutgrove School and Chapel did not leave any appreciable accumulation of liquid resources.

A brick wall surrounded the manor grounds. A gatehouse stood just inside the wall on the driveway to the house, which continued on to the carriage house and stable. A large expanse of lawn before the house was diversified by garden plots, shrubs, and trees and a sundial.[7] An elaborate conservatory with a curved front facade was ornamented by four columns in the form of draped feminine figures charmingly depicting the seasons: Spring bearing a garland of flowers; Summer, grapes and other fruits; Autumn, a sheaf of wheat; and Winter cuddling a lamb in protective arms. Only the front part of the interior was devoted to exotic plants; two rear rooms displayed Jonas's collections of objects of art and natural history.[8] Greenhouses were placed back with the other service buildings. The home farm lay outside the walls, contiguous with leased farms belonging to Nutgrove; it raised a large crop of gooseberries for market. It is illuminating that Thomas commented in the *Genera*, "Scarcely any of the American species of *Ribes* produce fruit in England."[9]

In mid-August Nuttall received a visit from Edward Tuckerman who was about to sail from Liverpool after more than a year's stay in Europe.[10] In late June he had attended Sotheby's auction sale of A. B. Lambert's immense herbarium at his London residence, 26 Lower Grosvenor Street.[11] Tuckerman enumerated his very important purchases to Torrey after his return home:

At Lambert's Sale I acquired one half of his old American Herb^m This was disposed in 2 Cabinets — the first contains all Pursh's plants — and the 2^d all the rest (Fraser, Bradbury, Lewis & Clark[,] Nuttall etc) This last I bought I purchased also a bundle marked in the Catal. only "American Plants," which seems to consist entirely of Pursh's plants & contains his Crataegi, Junci, Carices, etc. I also acquired the ms of Ph's originally proposed work (vide his pref.) a "Synopsis secundum Persoonium," a ms map of his Routes; a Catalogue of the plants he gathered in the W. I., & another printed Catal. of a Russian Bot. Gard. by him. . . . besides M^r Lamberts own presentation copy of his Flora, with Don's notes [?] on the unlabelled bundles of Ph's Can^a plants.[12]

It would be most gratifying to know whether Tuckerman showed any part of these collections to Nuttall. Pursh had probably shown him very few of the specimens of Lewis and Clark. Tuckerman, after gloating over these valuable Americana for many years, finally donated all the botanical specimens to the Academy of Natural Sciences in Philadelphia in 1856.[13] The Gray Herbarium at Harvard would probably have received them, as it did the oil painting of Nuttall that Tuckerman secured at the auction sale of Mrs. Craigie's lares and penates,[14] but for the fact that at the time Tuckerman was acutely annoyed with Asa Gray, who was not answering his letters.

In his *London Journal of Botany*, Sir William J. Hooker published news concerning Nuttall, garnered largely from a long letter from Nuttall late in October 1842. "We may congratulate English botanists on the return to this country of Mr. Nuttall . . . with his noble collection of American Plants . . . the unpublished ones will engage Mr. Nuttall's attention in this, his native country." [15] In the same issue Hooker announced Asa Gray's appointment "to the chair of Botany at Harvard University, formerly occupied by Mr. Nuttall: and a more competent successor to so accomplished a Botanist could not anywhere have been selected." Actually Gray was the first incumbent of the new Fisher Professorship of Natural History; Nuttall did not hold a professorship.

Nuttall's letter to Hooker contained other matters of interest.

Sutton (n.<sup>r</sup> Prescot) Oct<sup>br</sup> 29<sup>th</sup> 1842

Dear Sir

I thank you sincerely for the kind inquiries you make concerning my health w.<sup>h</sup> is, for the present, much better than I had expected, still I think I shall now have to defer my visit to London untill [*sic*] the spring, w.<sup>h</sup> is a disappointment, as I hoped to have had the pleasure of seeing you earlier.

Not having heard from Torrey and Gray since my arrival in England, I imagine they have not gone on far in their publication. For my own part I have not yet taken out my collections from their packages, but mean to go on and arrange them this winter in a cabinet w.<sup>h</sup> I have only just got made for them. . . .[16]

Torrey and Gray, finally comprehending the untimeliness of their project, did not carry their *Flora of North America* beyond the second volume.

Hooker, writing to Asa Gray about the plants collected by the Wilkes Expedition, commented, "Except you or Torrey undertake the publication there is no competent person in America now that Nuttall is away."[17] Gray, on the contrary, became very much concerned lest Nuttall describe the plants for he thought him "extremely unfit for such an undertaking." He heard "indirectly" that Nuttall was planning to return to the United States to work on the collection. Continuing rumors aroused such apprehension in Gray that he mentioned them more than once to Hooker in the winter of 1843 to 1844, and to other correspondents.[18] Continuous adverse comments of Gray concerning Nuttall's character and abilities that reached Charles Wilkins Short aroused keen resentment. In 1856, Gray wrote to Short in reply to a protest:

As to Nuttall, he is a truthful man, no doubt, and an interesting one. If I ever spoke disrespectfully of him (as I may have) I was to blame. His Genera was an admirable work for its day, and much the best thing he ever did. His later works and memoirs fell off in character, sound judgement, and conscientiousness — very much indeed, and there are things about them that would tempt one who followed closely after him to compare him with Rafinesque; but it would not be just. If Nuttall had kept up to the promise of *Genera N. Amer. Plants* he would have been the great expounder of American Plants.[19]

All of Nuttall's later work was at the frontiers of taxonomic investigation, where errors were inevitable — the publications of De Candolle, Hooker, and Gray were full of them. No one but Gray has recorded the opinion that Nuttall's work "fell off"; in point of fact his conscientiousness grew to such a degree that hesitation in ultimate decisions delayed the publication of most of his Arkansas collections for fifteen to twenty years. His increasingly incomparable field knowledge of North American plants rendered his judgment more cautious, not less sound.

A letter that Gambel wrote at Pueblo Los Angeles in the early part of 1842 and a manuscript describing eleven species of southwestern birds (four of them new) reached Nuttall after a great delay. Gambel had tagged a small Californian woodpecker to be named for Nuttall, now *Dendrocopos nuttallii* (Gambel), and the handsome desert quail became *Lophortyx gambelii* Nutt. After reflection Nuttall sent the paper to the Academy of Natural Sciences, where it was read, approved by a committee of Cassin, Haldeman, and Phillips on April 25, 1843, and published in the *Proceedings*.[20] In August Gambel was elected a member of the Academy. Nuttall was distressed because the letter from Gambel gave no address to which he could send a reply; however, since Gambel had expressed an intention of returning on the *Alert* at the end of the summer and Nuttall was anxious to make financial arrangements to cover his passage and expenses, he wrote through James Brown to Bryant and Sturgis concerning payment for Gambel's passage to Boston and to Wright Boott and George Carpenter to have advances made to him when he arrived in Boston and Philadelphia. Nuttall was also giving some financial assistance to William's mother during his absence.[21] He did not know of Gambel's taking a clerkship with Commodore Jones of the Pacific fleet until he received a belated letter written from the Bay of Mazatlan on February 27, 1843. Answering this letter on July 2, Nuttall urged his protégé to bring his collections to Nutgrove where his journal might be prepared for publication, the new species of birds and plants studied and described, and specimens sold to advantage.[22]

The first pleasurable botanical interlude for Nuttall in his exile was the visit he paid to Hooker in June 1843. The Hookers occupied "West Park," a very large house in extensive grounds on the Thames about a half mile downstream from Kew Gardens. Here were housed Hooker's tremendous herbarium and his library. Lady Hooker rejoiced in her domestic pets — cows, pigs, and poultry — and Sir William's father enjoyed the garden walks. The family fully appreciated their country life after so many years in Glasgow.[23] Nuttall took to Kew for a neighbor, Mrs. C. R. Sherbourne of Hurst House, Prescot, a flowering branch of a plant from Sierra Leone to be pictured in the *Botanical Magazine* and the offer of a plant for Hooker.[24] Nuttall wrote to Gambel ". . . I have just returned from a visit to London to Sir Wm. J. Hooker who for 3 or 4 days at his house . . . assisted me in comparing my specimens with his *stupendous herbarium*! His uniform kindness, frankness, and honor I shall never forget." On June 30, Hooker wrote to Gray: "Nuttall has been spending some days very happily with me. He seems to have no Books and the hours and hours he spent in going over my Books was quite remarkable."[25] To his closest botanical friend, George Bentham, Hooker wrote that "as of yore" he found Nuttall "very pleasant."[26]

After returning home from Kew, Nuttall sent a package of *Carices* to Francis Boott, including specimens for Hooker of the most advanced fruits he had of the curious new parasitic genus *Pholisma* Nutt., collected at San Diego.[27]

Nuttall was preparing to go to Bolton Lodge near Lancaster, the home of Henry B. Fielding (1805–1851), the possessor of a fine and large herbarium, who invited him to meet Dr. George Gardner (1812–1849), his collaborator on *Sertum Plantarum* (1844). Perhaps the ever-thoughtful Hooker prompted the invitation: Fielding was the nearest phanerogamic taxonomist to Nutgrove. In any case Fielding would be interested in meeting Nuttall for, when he bought the herbarium of John D. Prescott of St. Petersburg, he had acquired hundreds of plants that Nuttall had collected.[28] On at least one later occasion Nuttall consulted Fielding's herbarium.

In midsummer Nuttall spent two or three weeks in his "native hills" of Yorkshire.[29] With his interest in fossils, he probably visited the Victoria Cave, discovered in limestone cliffs rising to the north of Settle in the year of Victoria's accession to the throne. Excavation of the floor of the cave had revealed earlier occupants of the region in bones of the hyena, elephant, hippopotamus, ox, badger, horse, pig, goat, reindeer, sheep, grizzly, and brown bears, bone and flint weapons of the Stone Age, and coins, combs, brooches, bracelets, and rings of the Romans.

Early in 1844 Nuttall went to Manchester to see John Windsor, and they had a long botanical session. Windsor had his heart set on securing recognition for one of his earliest botanical friends, the late Thomas Williams Simmonds, M.D., of Settle, who like Windsor had attended Giggleswick Grammar School. Windsor wanted a genus named in honor of Simmonds and turned to Nuttall to supply the means. Nuttall gladly shifted the name of a new Californian genus to hold in remembrance the brilliant young naturalist who died in Trinidad in 1804. *Simmondsia californica* Nutt. is a low evergreen shrub of the *Buxaceae* that he had found "covering the sides of barren hills . . . in the vicinity of San Diego." He promptly wrote a description and sent it with a flowering specimen to Hooker who published it in his *London Journal of Botany*.[30]

During most of the year Nuttall devoted the greatest part of his leisure to horticulture. In the greenhouse he periodically started seed culled from his herbarium specimens and was successful in securing seedlings of many former floral friends to transplant to the garden where they were a source of enjoyment year after year. He evidently was growing orchids that especially pleased him and examined horticultural collections in the area, reporting rare items or new species to Hooker: "I lately saw the fine Orchidaceous collection of Mr.

Clowes of Manchester. . . . Mr. Blackburne of Hale Hall . . . has a remarkable Palm which fruits and grows almost past all management. . . . I hope Mr. B. will not abandon it, or if he does he will surely let you know previously." [31] Nuttall sent Hooker a South American *Chrysanthemum* that he had raised from a cutting got at Mr. Blackburne's and a purple flowered *Abronia* that he himself raised from seeds of specimens collected on the seashore at San Diego. [32] Attractive species Hooker had promptly figured and published in the *Botanical Magazine*. Since plants of the northwestern *Cornus nuttallii* Aud. were among Nuttall's successful nurslings, he may have sent as seedlings the very plants that now form one of the most magnificent displays at Kew each spring. Their flowering is called to the attention of visitors to the Garden at each of the entrances; as they have a very long blooming period, this one species makes Nuttall's name familiar to thousands of plant enthusiasts. Audubon painted a flowering branch of it as the perch of band-tailed pigeons in Plate 367 of *Birds of America*.

At the Liverpool Botanic Garden, Henry Shepherd had succeeded his uncle as the second director. To him Nuttall gave the pressed ferns that he had collected in the White Mountains of New Hampshire, the far West and the Sandwich Islands [33] and probably donated rare seedlings for the Garden from time to time. In May 1844, Shepherd showed him some herbarium specimens that he had recently purchased from a Mr. Gordon just returned from the Missouri River and the Platte. These included many of Nuttall's "old favorite acquaintances" of which he no longer had specimens. He was eager to buy some but was unable to locate Mr. Gordon although he alerted Hooker to the search. [34] The Earl of Derby, who inquired of Nuttall whether the elusive traveler had any zoological specimens, was also disappointed. [35] Hooker thoughtfully sent Nuttall some western American plants of Nuttall's authorship from his own herbarium before the end of the summer. [36] As Nuttall worked on his herbarium from the far West during the autumn of 1844 and the following winter, he selected as full a set of duplicates as was possible for Hooker.

In 1845, James Brown was in England on business for his publishing firm. July 17 was memorable through his arrival at Nutgrove for a visit. Brown recorded the event in his diary:

Went to Prescott, to see Mr. Nuttall at Nutgrove. Found him beautifully situated on his estates, and pleased to see me. Went over his grounds, and saw his tenantry, who are mostly old men who have occupied under his uncle for many years. They are small farmers, occupying from thirty to sixty acres; and the rents seemed to me low, but they pay all taxes, and those are monstrous. For sixty acres of good grass and grain land the net rental to Mr. Nuttall was only £ 70.

In the morning went to Knowesly Park, the seat of Earl Derby, with Mr. Nuttall, — a delightful walk through wheat and bean fields — beans in full bloom. Innumerable private ways are kept open in England, through fields, parks, &c. One might almost travel over the whole country, without setting his foot on a carriage-way. Earl Derby's seat is surrounded by an immense grove of fine oaks, the whole ranged by deer, and covered with hares and other game. His fruits are of the finest varieties, and the gardens of great extent. . . . He has also a fine and very extensive aviary, and many rare quadrupeds.

Returned to Mr. Nuttall's, and after dinner visited his orchards and gooseberry plantations. One of the last covered six acres and every bush seemed crowded with fruit to its greatest capacity. We supposed there were two hundred barrels of fruit nearly fit to be gathered.

July 19th At twelve o'clock was under way for Boston in the Cambria steamer.[37]

Of six trips to England, this was the only one that Brown made alone and presumably the only occasion on which he stayed at Nutgrove. When this widely loved man died prematurely in 1855 (a year before his friend Nathaniel Wyeth), many glowing obituaries recorded his engaging qualities of mind and heart: "sagacious, liberal, penetrating and wise, he saw far and he saw truly. His knowledge of men was instinctive and he rarely or never made a mistake in his estimate of them."[38] A fine oil portrait of Nuttall at a youthful period was given by Brown's widow to the Boston Society of Natural History.[39]

In August Nuttall made his third consecutive summer visit to Craven, which on this occasion he referred to as "a ramble." "Near Settle Mr Tatham showed me *Aspidium Lonchitis* and *A. rigidum* [*Dryopteris villarsii*]. I also ascended Pennyghent [sic] but had not time to excursion for the rarer plants said to grow on it."[40] Although there are no further statements of such visits, it is reasonable to suppose that they recurred during the next few summers. He obviously got great enjoyment from his returns to these most familiar, unchanging scenes.

About the time he got back to Nutgrove, Nuttall had the satisfaction of receiving a letter from Gambel mailed in Boston on July 31,

1845. His chief collection of plants had been entrusted to a whaling vessel bound for New Bedford, and he was not yet aware of its fate.[41] Nuttall's reply on September 8 stressed the advantages of bringing his collections to England; Geyer, he wrote, had arrived from North America, and Sir William had assisted him in arranging his specimens for sale at £2 for 100. Nuttall stated that the publication of his *Sylva* was held up and suggested that Gambel look into the matter. (The first volume had come out in two parts: pages 1–56 in 1842 and pages 57–136 in 1843.) Dobson had died but arrangements had been made for another firm to continue the printing. Whether due to Gambel's activity or to the natural course of events, the second volume of Nuttall's Supplement finally was issued in 1846, and the third and last, printed by a third company, appeared in 1849.[42] The plates of the publication were not admired in England — Hooker commented that they would be a disgrace to the very Indians of the country![43] England was far advanced in the art of illustration whereas the best American efforts were comparatively crude: Francis Boott constantly found it necessary to apologize for them.

On August 19, 1845, soon after his arrival in Philadelphia, Gambel presented a short paper to the Academy that described five western birds.[44] In the course of the winter a letter from Carpenter informed Nuttall that Gambel was about to study medicine. Nuttall wrote to Gambel in March expressing pleasure that he was preparing for a profession, and said he "had thought of visiting America last autumn but . . . I shall I think certainly do so this fall."[45] However he did not make the trip until the autumn of 1847.

VISIT TO THE UNITED STATES, 1847–1848. The chief source of information about Nuttall's activities after 1841 is the letters that he wrote to Sir William Jackson Hooker. Nothing is available there between December 9, 1845, and October 14, 1847, but we have a letter that Nuttall wrote to Gambel in March 1846. It is evident that Gambel's collection of about 350 species of plants was received in England after this letter was written and that thereafter Nuttall was preoccupied with preparing technical descriptions of selected specimens and formulating his report. Those of his own unpublished western specimens that were related to Gambel's were searched out for publication, and the plants were studied comparatively for reciprocal enlightenment. About two-fifths of the hundred plants included in his paper were his own although it was entitled "Descriptions of Plants Collected by William Gambel, M.D., in the Rocky Mountains and Upper California." [46] To assure himself that the genus to which certain *Compositae* belonged was not Cassini's *Hymenoxys* (as interpreted by Hooker and by Torrey and Gray in the case of a species that Nuttall placed in "Ptilomeris"), he examined examples of that genus in Henry Fielding's herbarium in Lancaster.[47] The paper itself testifies that it was prepared in a leisurely manner: it is too long and deliberate in treatment to have been done in a very few weeks crowded with interruptions, although some last checks and additions may have been made in Philadelphia.

On October 14, 1847, Nuttall wrote to Hooker, evidently very hurriedly: "I have taken rather a sudden resolution to visit the U. Stats [*sic*] again for a few months and shall now sail on the 19th of this month. . . . I was very sorry to have missed the desired opportunity of seeing your son Doctor Hooker on his visit to Lancashire." [48] Nuttall sailed on the steamship *Caledonia*, a Cunarder (the British and North American Royal Mail Steam Packet Company), as one of one hundred and ten passengers, in notable contrast to his ten previous crossings. The ship put in at Halifax, at that time the regular schedule for Cunarders, and arrived in Boston on November 5.[49]

The traveler spent about seven weeks in the United States before going to Philadelphia, but no records for this period have been found. Part of the time at least he would have stayed in Belmont with his very hospitable friend James Brown, who, when he had been in England earlier in the year, probably had urged Nuttall to make the trip. If he lingered thereabouts he would certainly have seen Nat Wyeth, prosperously reestablished in the ice business. At the old Cooper-Austin house on Love Lane, Susan Austin now lived alone save for a faithful housekeeper, for her husband died early in 1847. She continued to live there until her death in the 1880s, keeping her life-mask of Nuttall in the living room. There are some who still remember her "picturesque figure in her hoopskirt, red shawl, and little black bonnet" and her willful nature. She always furnished a home gratis to some student who was struggling to finance his education at Harvard.[50] Nuttall's friend, Joseph E. Worcester, had bought some of the Craigie land and built a new house; the Henry Wadsworth Longfellows owned the Craigie house.

Some of Nuttall's erstwhile colleagues probably received calls from him, especially the entomologist Thaddeus William Harris, who was still Librarian of the College Library. His botanical friends in Boston, Benjamin D. Greene and the Bootts he would have seen, associated as they were with Sir William and Francis Boott, and possibly he attended a meeting or two of the Boston Society of Natural History and the American Academy of Arts and Science where he would see other old acquaintances including former students.

The earliest indication we have of Nuttall's arrival in Philadelphia is his attendance at the December 28th meeting of the Academy of Natural Sciences, which chanced to be the annual business meeting.[51] S. G. Morton, one of the Vice-Presidents, presided. George Carpenter, still Treasurer of the Academy, attended; it is likely that Nuttall was staying with him and that they came together. Dr. Joseph Carson was another former associate among the thirty members present. The report of the Recording Secretary showed that not a single paper of the thirty-three contributed in the previous two years had been botanical. (Actually no report on plants had been printed in the *Journal* since Nuttall's two 1834 papers!) Nuttall was absent from two meetings in mid-January and on February 8, achieving a seventy percent record for attendance for the ten meetings held during his visit in the city. He probably also attended one or more of the biweekly meetings of the American Philosophical Society.

Nuttall wanted to take living plants back to England, and to this end he made a journey to North Carolina in mid-January, probably taking Gambel as a companion.[52] He planned to stop in Washington on his way south to see the collection of plants in the greenhouse and probably did so; when William D. Brackenridge, in charge of the gardens, wrote to Torry in mid-March he commented that Nuttall was "off again for Old England."[53]

Nuttall must have been very busy during his weeks in Philadelphia. He still had very good friends in the area like Charles Pickering, Charles Jones Wister of Grumblethorpe, and Isaac Lea and endless acquaintances, some of whom, like George Ord, he had known for a long period. There was no spot thereabouts dearer to him than Bartram's Garden where the friendly Carrs would surely insist on his once more occupying "Nuttall's room."

On February 1, Nuttall read his paper on Gambel's plants to the Academy and two weeks later read a supplement to the first paper.

Both parts were referred to a committee of Dr. Bridges, Dr. Zantzinger, and Gambel and, in accordance with their recommendation, were published in the *Proceedings* of the Society pending the final publication in the *Journal*.[54] Of the thirteen new genera included, only one was named for a person, Gambelia, based on a shrubby member of the *Scrophulariaceae* with large and brilliant blossoms, from Catalina Island; but, since it differs from *Antirrhinum* only in being shrubby, it has been reduced to *A. speciosum* (Nutt.) Gray. The specific names that Nuttall selected were also descriptive except in two cases: *Quercus gambelii* and Trifolium gambeli. An *Eriogonum* which Nuttall gave as *E. tenellum* in the *Proceedings* became E. nuttallii Gambel in the *Journal*.[55]

Drawings of six of Gambel's new species were made for illustrations in the *Journal* by Margaretta Hare Morris (1797–1867) of Germantown, a lady long active in the study of insects of economic significance, who had probably been acquainted with Nuttall for many years. She and her botanically-inclined sister, Elizabeth Carrington Morris (1795–1865), had been living with their widowed mother in Germantown since 1812. Their home, later known as the Morris-Littell House, stood on the grounds of the old Witt garden of historic interest. Mrs. Morris and her daughters were among the subscribers to the evening course of lectures on mineralogy and geology given at the Germantown Academy in the winter of 1820–1821 by Charles Jones Wister, and they doubtless attended a course of botanical lectures said to have been given there by Nuttall. Margaretta, by raising insects, worked out and published the life cycles of some destructive species. Nuttall was on the committee to judge her first paper, on the life history of the Hessian fly, read to the American Philosophical Society on October 2, 1840, through the courtesy of a member.[56]

Since Nuttall was returning to England on the *Britannia*, due to sail from Boston on March 12, he left Philadelphia in the first week of March, in order to have time to make some last visits in the Boston area. Dr. Darlington, who was engaged in compiling a valuable account of John Bartram and Humphry Marshall from documents available to him, gave Nuttall the commission of delivering to Hooker and Boott daguerrotype likenesses of himself.[57] Nuttall wrote to Short that he visited New York City, but we do not know the time or the length of stay.[58]

# REPATRIATION

To John Amory Lowell, Nuttall took from Gambel a carefully selected set of duplicates of his plants. Asa Gray had just written this piece of botanical gossip to Torrey, and that Lowell would advance $200 toward Fendler's expenses, when he was surprised by a call from his former associate. He gave a hasty account of this event in pencil on the back of his letter:

Friday evening

Dear Doctor

Nuttall came up to the garden this afternoon . . . staid [*sic*] half an hour — seemed wonderfully pleased and tickled — & what is more — he offered to subscribe $100 in advance to Send Fendler back to Santa Fe! (He had seen my specimens at Mr. Lowell's) — What do you think of that for *Nuttall* in his old age!! Dont it beat all? He is to leave an order on Carpenter at Philad[a] payable in May. I hope he wont forget it.

A. G.[59]

Gray asked Nuttall to go to Lancaster to see Henry Fielding and encourage him to subscribe *in advance* to the fund for sending Fendler back to Santa Fe. Fielding, having seen a notice of the proposed expedition in Hooker's *Journal of Botany*, had ordered a set of any specimens that might be collected.[60]

As the *Britannia* sailed a day ahead of the originally scheduled time, Nuttall embarked that evening. At Halifax he sent back a letter to Carpenter.

Off Halifax, March 13, 1848

Dear Friend

I take this final opportunity previous to embarking on the wide Atlantic to tell you of my whereabouts. I had, as you will observe, only about 3 days in Boston as we sailed on the eleventh in place of the 12th. I was delighted with my visit to old friends in Cambridge and Boston.

I wish you would desire Gambel as soon as an opportunity offers to send me on about a dozen of the Bulletins [*Proceedings*] of the Acad. Nat. Sciences w[h] contains my paper w[h] you will perhaps ship at the same time with my minerals.[61] I have given an order on you next May, on the receipt of my dividend, to pay over to the order of Professor Gray of Cambridge 100 dollars, w[h] please charge to my account as usual.

Over leaf can you forward to Dr. Short the note addressed to him. I do not know now whether he do not live in St. Louis

Yours truly
Tho[s] Nuttall [62]

Family stories of the Trustees standing by at Nutgrove with watches in hand to check the exact time of Nuttall's arrival, to ensure that there was no infringement of the requirements of the will, are probably apocryphal but they entertain the family to this day.

Nuttall was wroth over the treatment his plants received in going through customs at Liverpool. Not only his own packages, but also a small one that he was delivering for George Ticknor to Charles Lyell, the geologist, were "unceremoniously torn open at the side." He wrote to Lyell, "If you think proper to show your package and its scandalous condition to any superior officer in London, it would be well for the credit of the country for I think such insolence deserves reproof. . . . My own treatment, . . . I esteem as nothing to the insult offered to you!" [63]

Early in June Nuttall wrote to Hooker, sending him a copy "of the abridgement of my century of plants" (the paper on Gambel's plants as published in the *Proceedings*). Hooker promptly published a report of his activities in his *London Journal of Botany* and in a later issue under "Notices of Books" he commented on the paper in some detail: "Many new genera and a great number of new species are given. . . . One . . . a shrub four or five feet high with . . . white flowers, about the size of large apple blossoms . . . constitutes a new genus in the present work, and has the name of *Crossosoma* Nutt." [64] *Crossosoma californica* established a new family of the *Rosales*.

During the enforced idleness of the sea voyages, Nuttall may have reviewed with himself his travels into botanically unexplored areas of North America and the hundreds of American plant species and scores of genera of which he was the author. He had been the first naturalist in Michigan, Wisconsin, Arkansas, the Indian Territory (Oklahoma), and present Wyoming as well as in great tracts of botanically unknown country from central New York southward to the Red River and westward to the Pacific. Hardly a botanist or horticulturist of his acquaintance had missed recognition in his nomenclature. On the other hand, he himself was honored in specific names by an appreciable number of contemporary workers beginning with Pursh's *Viola nuttallii* late in 1813. Ten years later Augustin Pyramus de Candolle named the first of numerous species for him. Other Europeans who named species "nuttallii" or "nuttallianus" included Roemer and Schultes, Schultes, Alexander Braun, Chamisso and Schlechtendal, Dietrich, Lehmann, Spach, Steudel, Planchon, Shuttleworth, Sweet,

Hooker, and Bentham. Americans had fewer new plants to publish but Nuttall was recognized by specific names given by Torrey, Eddy, Rafinesque, Croom, Audubon, Darlington, Pickering, Englemann, Torrey and Gray, and Gray. After four futile efforts to establish a genus "Nuttallia," the fifth — a rosaceous shrub of Oregon — had every promise of durability.

During the next two years Nuttall gave considerable attention to his minerals that Carpenter sent on to him.[65] In 1860 the collection was sold at auction in London during two half-days; the catalogue shows 485 lots, each consisting of from one to thirteen minerals, totaling over 3000 specimens. Due to gifts or exchanges, all the continents except Africa were represented, but the cabinet, overwhelmingly North American, was largely collected by Nuttall. Many of the specimens were of superb quality. Those bought by the Geological Society of London were later given to the British Museum, which had bid in more than a tenth of the lots at the sale. A study of the Nuttallian mineralogical specimens there recalls many events in the collector's career: "calcareous mudstone" from "Erie, N.Y. [sic!]," his 1810 pedestrian tour on the south shore of Lake Erie; "a beautiful specimen of purple fluorspar" from Shawneetown on the Ohio, his association with John Bradbury during the following winter in St. Louis; Derbyshire fluorite and dogtooth spar (calcite), his protracted stay in England during the War of 1812; the frequency of North Carolina specimens, his several visits to that state. The predominance of the unique minerals of Franklin Furnace and the area emphasizes his many long visits there with Dr. Fowler and other friends that he made in nearby Orange County, New York; specimens from eastern and northern New England, his removal from Philadelphia to Cambridge. The appearance of superior specimens from Dufton, Alston Moor, and unnamed spots in Cumberland is assurance that Nuttall never regretted the purchases he made on a rainy day in Kendal, Westmorland, in 1824, during his second visit home. Nova Scotia minerals recall his friendships with Francis Alger and Charles T. Jackson. Lava from the Azores and the Sandwich Islands, ores from Cornwall, specimens obtained by exchange with various friends or correspondents, all affirm a dedicated life gladdened by durable satisfactions. Bitumen from California, perhaps collected especially for him at the La Brea pit in Los Angeles by William Gambel, may have formed the last accession to his cabinet.

During the winter of 1848–1849, Hooker evidently heard from Gray that duplicates of Gambel's plants were in Boston and inquired from Nuttall about getting some. Nuttall explained that the specimens were given by Gambel to John A. Lowell and that he had "written to Gambell [sic] a good while since for an additional set of his plants wʰ I intended for you, but he has not yet sent them. . . . I intend very soon to look over my set and I shall then at all events lay you out all the duplicates possible." [66]

Domestic changes had been taking place in Nuttall's family circle. In April 1846, Francis Dixon, who was making a success in the manufacture of glass bottles, married Elizabeth Browne at St. Mary's Church, Birkenhead, and brought his bride to live at "Close House," about a mile from Nutgrove. Their youngest daughter, Florence (d. 1954), who like her father lived into her nineties, recalled her mother's sympathy with Nuttall in the restrictions placed on him, which she believed hastened his death, and her mother's statements that he frequently sought sanctuary in her home, for the atmosphere at Nutgrove was very uncongenial to him "as his sister was a great Methodist and there were always parsons staying there and he hated them." [67] Nuttall and the Francis Dixons were Anglicans and presumably attended Christ Church in Eccleston.

Some of the Booths were living near Nutgrove about this time: Susannah Booth, the elder of Thomas's sisters, who was still living in Long Preston when her younger son was christened "Jonas Thomas" at the Church of St. Mary on January 25, 1829, by 1853 was living at or near Nutgrove; William, twelve years older than Jonas Thomas, had already settled in Nuttall's area. By 1849, Jonas was staying either with William or at Nutgrove and was unemployed, although he was twenty years old. His uncle's excursions in the wilds of North America of which he had heard from childhood struck his fancy and stirred in him a desire to travel in remote places as a collector. He was always happy to listen to stories of his uncle's adventures and possibly this was the subject of conversation while Jonas made his pleasing ink profile of Nuttall. Jonas's interest in natural history seems to have been casual and his ideas of the ease with which knowledge of the subject could be picked up exceedingly hopeful. However he had "an excellent disposition" and an enthusiasm for travel which Nuttall felt inclined to encourage.[68] Next best to going on an expedition himself was to have a representative in the field.

# CHAPTER 21

# HORTICULTURAL PURSUITS

Old age hath yet his honor and his toil;
Death closes all: but something ere the end,
Some work of noble note, may yet be done. . . .
— Tennyson, "Ulysses."

RHODODENDRONS. On March 17, 1849, Nuttall wrote to Sir William that he was very glad to hear of his son's extraordinary success in the Himalaya Mountains.[1] At that time Dr. Joseph Dalton Hooker had been almost two years in India collecting seeds and plants for the Kew Gardens. Joseph was exploring in Sikkim, a small British dependency lying between the independent states of Nepal and Bhutan. It was a relatively accessible section of mountainous country, north of Darjeeling and about three hundred and fifty miles from Calcutta. There he found many species of *Rhododendron* of great magnificence in size and hue. He was making colored drawings and sending them to his father, who promptly published them in Parts as he received them. Nuttall became a fascinated subscriber to *Illustrations of Sikkim Rhododendrons*. He commented to Hooker: "Some of them by their extraordinary *parasitic* habit half seem to indicate something different from the ordinary character of the genus. I should like a small particle of the seed . . . if any has been sent to England. . . . It is . . . much the most splendid flowering genus of the whole Ericaceae."[2]

The splendor of the Himalayan rhododendrons aroused an aspiration in Nuttall to acquire some new species of his own for cultivation and study. Going to an exotic place as a collector was just the sort of employment for which his nephew Jonas Thomas Booth or, as he preferred to be called, Thomas J. Booth was yearning. He was as interested in botany as in any occupation. Eager to get advice and information that would facilitate such an undertaking, Nuttall went to Kew in mid-May. No one in England could have been more helpful to him than Hooker, who was in correspondence with botanists and botanical collectors around the world. Nuttall learned that all the rhododendrons that had been shipped to England from India, beginning with the Nepalese R. *arboreum* Sm., which Wallich sent in 1818, had been collected in high altitudes in the great arc of Himalayan ridges, forbidding terrain for a complete greenhorn. Evidently Sir William suggested that young Booth should come to Kew to be briefed on methods of protecting and shipping living plants and handling dried specimens in the conditions he would encounter. Jonas made the trip promptly and returned with letters of introduction to Dr. Joseph D. Hooker and Hugh Falconer, Superintendent of the Garden of the East India Company in Calcutta.[3]

Nuttall attempted to get Jonas a letter of introduction to the Earl of Dalhousie, Governor-General of India, from the Earl of Derby but since the latter did not enjoy the acqaintance of Dalhousie it was impossible for him to accede to the request; however he supplied letters to Mr. Blyth of Calcutta and to another correspondent who had been "exceedingly obliging and useful" to him.[4] Moreover he asked that Jonas procure for him birds of the hill region, especially game birds, and to allow him to place his name on the list of purchasers of any botanical treasures that Jonas might secure. Although Jonas's special objectives were rhododendrons and orchids, he was to collect seeds, living plants, and dried specimens of any horticulturally promising plants; he was also to keep a journal with observations on site, altitude, terrain, soil, associated plants, and other data for each plant collected.

Sir William, from personal observation, and Lord Derby, relying on local hearsay gleaned by his head gardener, Jennings, confided to each other that their views of Booth's chances of success were equally pessimistic. Although the Earl did not expect the expedition to be very productive, especially zoologically, he thought it "just as well to seize the chance."[5] Nuttall thought the lad had "sufficient resolution" for the task but recognized that his glaring inexperience rendered success doubtful; however it gave Jonas an occupation, introduced him to the work of a collector, and might yield some gratifying horticultural prizes.[6]

# HORTICULTURAL PURSUITS

On June 30, Jonas Booth sailed from Liverpool for Calcutta on the *Glendarah*[7] and arrived in the autumn, a favorable time as the monsoon was coming to an end. A letter which he wrote to Francis and Elizabeth Dixon is extant.

Calcutta, Nov[er] 15th 49

My dear Cousins,

. . . Everything has turned out different to what I had expected and there will be many difficulties in exploring the country about Darjeeling. The Rajah of Sikkim is very mutch opposed to Europeans and as jelous as the Chinese, his immediate neighbours. . . .

We are proceeding up the country in about three weeks, by Dack [?] in Palanquins, it will be very tiresome for you cannot lay down in them. With what little experiance I have had I am quite sick of them, I almost dread it.

Altogether it will be a very expensive affair. The parties to whom I have had letters have been very kind to me. . . .

Your Affectionate Cousin
Tho[s] Jonas Booth[8]

On January 22, 1850, Nuttall received a letter from Booth telling of the forcible detention of Dr. Joseph D. Hooker and his companion, Dr. Archibald Campbell, the Superintendent of Darjeeling, by the Dewan (Prime Minister) of the Maharaja of Sikkim, and the ordering of British troops into that province to force their release. Since this crisis suspended all travel to Sikkim, the high country most easy of approach, Booth was doubly fortunate in having the advice of Hugh Falconer. Although on leave and not due back at the Garden in Calcutta until the first of the year, he was in India and available for consultation with Booth through Sir William's letter of introduction. Falconer recommended that he go to Gauhati in the Brahmaputra valley of Assam whence he might reach mountain ranges of suitable altitude for rhododendrons. He assured the youth that a large number of orchids were also available in the forests of Assam.[9]

A letter sent from Calcutta on January 11, by Mr. Blyth to the Earl of Derby, contained the information that Booth had started for Assam some days before.[10] This northeastern province of India that had been wrested from Burma was ceded to the British in 1826. The mighty Brahmaputra River, entering from Tibet and flowing west across most of Assam before turning south to join the mouths of the Ganges, formed with its tributaries the main means of travel. Its valley, averaging fifty miles in width, was flanked on the north by the foothills of

Nutgrove. Dec.r 4th 1853

Dear Sir,

I cannot express sufficiently how greatly I am obliged to you for your fine present of Don's Gardener's Dictionary a standard work wh: came to me in safety by the Railway.

How am I ever in any way to repay you for the present I do not know but that always be happy to do for you any thing in my power

Jonas My sister and all our rela-tives here are well wh I hope is the case with your family

wishing you a happy Christmass
I remain yours truly & obliged
Ths. Nuttall.

Nuttall's handwriting; a personal note written in 1853 by Nuttall to a friend in Craven. Courtesy of Professor Raymond Adams, University of North Carolina.

great ridges from the snow-covered heights of the Himalayas, made accessible by numerous feeders of the Brahmaputra flowing generally southward through high valleys. Gauhati was the administrative head-quarters for Assam. The Commissioner and Agent of the Governor-General, Major-General Francis Jenkins (1793–1855), to whom Falconer supplied a letter of introduction for Booth, was highly plant conscious. The introduction of tea growing in Assam is credited to him; he maintained a large herbarium of native plants and encouraged the Government Apothecary of the District, Charles J. Simons, to collect in outlying areas. The latter discovered in Assam the beautiful *Begonia rex*, now one of the most popular of houseplants. From Jenkins, Booth received invaluable assistance in general advice and in suggestions of routes where he might advantageously achieve his goals, and Simons initiated him in field work.[11] Booth reached some rich horticultural areas.

By mid-December Booth was not far from the eastern boundary of Bhutan in the Balipara Frontier Tract, drained by the Bhareli River and its tributaries, and had discovered a wealth of rhododen-drons in the "Oola" (Yola) mountains, the range separating the Tenga and Dirang Rivers. Here he reached altitudes estimated up to ten thousand feet, encountering in prolonged ascents and descents, snow, ice, and tropical vegetation in temperatures ranging from 7°F to 94°F in the shade. The village that Booth called "Rupa" (Roophrye or Rupraigya) is on the upper waters of the Tenga, a type locality. From this area Booth moved eastward across the Bhareli into the Aka and the Dupha Hills where in April or May he got more species of *Rhododendron* including "the incomparable *R. nuttallii*" which was in full bloom in a marsh on the "Papu River" (Papoo).[12]

Although Booth had arrived in India at a favorable time, toward the end of the wet season, his abysmal ignorance of the country and the mischance barring Sikkim caused such a delay in reaching collecting grounds that the early rains of the monsoon caught him "in the interior of Assam," resulting in great privations and suffering. The "worst trial" was being almost "bled to death by myriads of Leaches." These short, hairlike bloodsuckers, dropping in multitudes from the saturated foliage and quickly attaching themselves to any animal surface, are one of the curses of the Indian hill country dur-ing the rains. Booth sent Nuttall dried specimens, seeds, and some living orchids and miscellaneous plants. He returned to Calcutta to wait out the balance of the monsoon so that he might make another excursion into the mountains of Assam; he had hopes of reaching the high mountains toward Tibet: [13] the anoxia of high altitudes had induced in him the exhilaration that creates a dedicated mountaineer.[14] At the end of the next dry season, he shipped a second harvest, having been "to the frontier of Assam [the Bhutan border] beyond which he was not allowed to travel by the Rajah of the district." [15] On this expedition, passing through the Darrang District from Gomera to the southeast corner of Bhutan, he collected, among many plants, *Talauma rabaniana* Hook. f. and Thoms. and *Agapetes buxifolia* Nutt. (*Bot. Mag.*, t. 5012).[16] He arrived home in June 1851, with still more plants and seeds of many species as well as herbarium specimens.

Hooker received a report of the results of Booth's trip from Lord Derby: "I am glad to hear from him [his head gardener] that your information about Mr. Booth is not quite correct  I mean Nuttall's nephew  He has not been unsuccessfull but has brought over new orchids & the seeds of a few new Rhododendra." [17]

All seeds and living plants as they arrived at Nutgrove were planted with expedition and nurtured with care. Although it took a few years to bring any of the species of *Rhododendron* to blossoming, Booth had prepared dried flowering specimens and fruits which enabled Nuttall to write descriptions of the new species for publication. Some, naturally enough, had already been collected and figured by Joseph Hooker or others; to check such identities as thoroughly as possible, Nuttall occasionally wrote to Sir William for the leaf or flower of some described species for direct comparison with one of Booth's. As his study neared completion, he journeyed to Kew to see Joseph Hooker's living species and herbarium specimens.[18]

On September 29, 1853, he wrote to Hooker that the descriptions of his new species of rhododendron were now "made out more or less completely" and inquired about their publication in his *Journal of Botany*.[19] The paper appeared that year, with some modifications by Hooker, under the title "Descriptions and Observations on Some Species of Rhododendron, Collected in Assam and Bootan by Thomas J. Booth," [20] notwithstanding Booth's statement that he was not allowed to enter Bhutan. Despite his care, among the score or more of species Nuttall published, there were forms already described by Joseph D. Hooker, Wallich, Wight, Don, and Smith. Eleven were named for persons. Personal friends thus recognized were Booth, John Windsor, Henry Shepherd, Isaiah W. N. Keys, William Wilson, and the late Dr. James Kendrick of Warrington.[21] A species was named in honor of Karl L. Blume (1796–1862) of Leyden and one in memory of Sir James Edward Smith. A fine scarlet-flowered form was "dedicated to Dr. Joseph Dalton Hooker, who has contributed so eminently to the illustrations of the Rhododendrons of North India." Another with "magnificent large white flowers deliciously scented" was "named in honor of Major Jenkins of the East India Service, who has done so much for the botany of that country." On March 5, 1858, Nuttall wrote to Hooker that he planned to name a species in honor of William Anderson, but he did not achieve this.[22]

In the spring of 1854, young rhododendrons that Nuttall had raised in his greenhouses from Booth's seed were offered for sale. Some specimens had been purchased earlier by enthusiasts in the Liverpool area but the bulk of the plants were sold to E. G. Henderson and Son (Wellington Nursery), Wellington Road, St. John's Wood, London. In a special section of their 1856 catalog entitled "New Rhododendrons of Assam and Bhotan," they state "we are now prepared to supply strong plants at the following prices [ranging from 10 s. to 63 s. dependent on size]" of the species "described in the *Journal of Botany* by Thomas Nuttall, Esq. of Rainhill, the well-known Botanist and Traveller. . . . Among these brilliant discoveries from the Bhotan Alps, are the most wonderful-sized flowers, delicious fragrance, and distinct colours of any that are known to exist in this gorgeous tribe of plants."

The only disappointing feature of the Asian rhododendrons was that the choicest species of all, *R. nuttallii* Booth, obtained in a relatively low valley, proved too tender for England's climate and so was restricted to greenhouse culture. However it succeeded admirably in southern Europe.[23] Describing it in the *Botanical Magazine*, Sir William ranked it as "the finest of all the Rhododendrons, the flowers being nearly six inches across." Henderson described the flower as fragrant and lilylike, snow-white with a rosy tinge on the outside of the corolla, and rich gold at the base of the interior, in clusters exceeding a foot in diameter, the leaves a foot long. This species has proved especially useful in the production of horticultural hybrids.

At the exhibitions held by the Royal Horticultural Society in London during the mid 1850s, specimens of the Nuttallian rhododendrons shown by the Wellington Nursery and by private growers were creating a sensation in horticultural circles. In 1856 Nuttall's neighbors, Mr. Fairie of Mosely Hill, who had a notable collection of orchids, was planning to send R. *falconeri* Hook. f. and R. *hookeri* Nutt. to the spring Horticultural Exhibit,[24] whereas Miss Willis of Hurst House, Prescot, who also had two species in blossom, intended to send flowering branches to Sir William for picturing in the *Botanical Magazine*;[25] all four specimens were from Booth's collections. As early as 1855, a plate of R. *keysii* Nutt. (t. 4875) had appeared, and R. *hookeri* Nutt. (t. 4926) was figured in 1856. Others followed as the species slower to mature came into bloom toward the end of the decade.

Long before blossoming rhododendrons were available, Nuttall had in flower some herbaceous plants that Booth had been able to send or bring to England in growing condition: among them different species of orchids of the large genus *Dendrobium*, some, at least, already known, and two fine begonias. *Begonia xanthina* Hook., a yellow-flowered species from the shady forests of "Bhutan," and *B. rubro-venia* Hook. were the first of Booth's collection to be figured in the *Botanical Magazine* (t. 4683 and 4689, 1852). Hooker continued to depict the plants as they came into flower: some, although already known from a different district, had never been pictured; others were new species like the rose-colored *Primula mollis* Nutt. (t. 4798, 1854). Among the last to mature were evergreen shrubs of *Vaccinoideae* raised from seed that Booth collected in the higher mountains. Nuttall did not forget his American friends: Buist exhibited his yellow-flowered *Begonia* from Assam at a show of the Philadelphia Horticultural Society in 1854.[26]

Nuttall's project for vicarious collecting in far places in his old age proved to be psychologically sound. Through the years that the Asian plants were developing to the stage of flowering and fruiting, they furnished keen anticipation, stimulation, and diversion as well as unceasing enjoyment. Rhododendrons planted on the grounds at Nutgrove adapted themselves so well to that alien clime that a hundred years after their planting some have attained the form of trees suggestive of towering growth in their native land.

LAST YEARS. Although Nuttall's trip to Kew in May 1849 was to acquire information for launching Jonas Booth as a botanical collector in India, the highlight of his visit was meeting George Bentham

(1800–1884), one of the foremost botanists in Britain and Hooker's intimate friend. As early as 1837 Bentham had acceded to Augustin Pyramus de Candolle's request that he write up the *Scrophulariaceae* for the *Prodromus*; he received the bulky packages of specimens from Alphonse de Candolle in June 1843, and the monograph was published in 1846.[27] Nuttall had discovered and named many American species of that beautiful family; Bentham named one of his Californian discoveries seen in Hooker's herbarium *Antirrhinum nuttallianum*. After returning home Nuttall wrote to Hooker, "I must say that I was delighted to have made the acquaintance of such a man as Bentham."[28] The latter described Nuttall in his diary on May 18, 1849: "Nuttall came — a hale active man of sixty-five (though he looks older) and none the worse for the singular life he has led — wandering so long in the wilds of Arkansas the Rocky Mountains and California, often quite alone and before there were even such facilities as may now be found."[29]

Another celebrity whom Nuttall met during the same visit at Kew was Richard Spruce (1817–1893), a productive bryologist of the North Riding of Yorkshire who was on the point of setting out to collect in the Amazon basin for Hooker, Bentham, and others. Nuttall saw him again shortly afterwards, the night before he sailed, "at a new and rather interesting natural history club, that meet monthly, I think, in each others houses in Liverpool."[30] A companion on the voyage was to be Herbert Wallace going out to join his brother, Alfred Russel Wallace (1823–1913), already exploring on the Amazon. Spruce collected 7000 species of flowering plants in South America and recorded his experiences of fifteen years there in *Notes of a Botanist on the Amazon and Andes*.

A few months later Nuttall became a corresponding member of the club, the Literary and Philosophical Society of Liverpool, which had been organized by William Roscoe, William Rathbone, Dr. Traill, and their friends probably as early as 1810. In 1844 a struggling local Society of Natural History had fused with it. The Reverend Henry Hugh Higgins (1814–1893), later Nuttall's neighbor at Rainhill, an ardent zoologist, perhaps prevailed on him to join this group. Higgins reported that the members "were often surprised to find the professor equally at home whether the subject under discussion was botanical or zoological; indeed, his memory for the names of natural objects was alike envied and admired."[31]

The sensitive Boott had written Hooker years before that Nuttall "apparently has no disposition to call on us tho' he owes me one for . . . getting the Council [of the Linnean Society] to admit him a free Fellow in ack.$^{t}$ of his Services in the Cause of Science. But this is *inter nos*. . . . Tell Nuttall we shall be glad to see him." [32] Hooker no doubt gave Nuttall a hint of Boott's attitude, for, before he left London in 1849, he called at 24 Gower Street. Boott wrote to Hooker on May 25: "I was very glad to see Nuttall who came & drank tea with us. I tried to induce him to give us his notes on Oregon. . . . I wish he saw Lord Derby occasionally for his intelligence would be an acquisition as his knowledge of Birds is great & his account of the American ones always interesting." [33]

At the end of the year Boott was suffering great distress over the shocking news from Boston that Dr. Samuel Parkman, well-known as a philanthropist, had been barbarously murdered, and that Professor John White Webster was being held for the crime. Boott's sensibilities were assailed on both sides; he sought relief in writing of it to Hooker:

Dr. P. had been a great benefactor of the [Harvard] Medical College & the Wife of Dr. Webster is the halfsister of Mrs. Prescott, the mother of the Historian, so that the misery under the present circumstances, is widely spread in the first circles in Boston. . . .

Parkman who wrote the Californian Trail is engaged to a Daughter of Dr. Bigelow. He is the son of the only surviving Brother of the murdered man, a clergyman of Boston. . . . The Boston murder is without parallel in crime & misery and Webster is the colleague of our friend Gray. . . . Dr. Parkman was uncle of Mr. Sturgis — the partner of Mr. Bates & the Barings [of London], & allied to many of the first families of Boston. . . .

Tuckerman by the bye is a Nephew of poor D.$^{r}$ Parkman. His mother was Dr. P's sister.[34]

It appeared that Dr. Parkman, who for a long time had held a mortgage on Webster's mineralogical collection as security for a series of loans, discovered that Webster had sold the minerals (to Robert Gould Shaw, a relative of Parkman!); incensed by such dishonesty, he insisted on the payment of the mortgage. Webster, who lived very extravagantly, did not have the money and had exhausted his credit. He lured Parkman to his laboratory-lecture room at the Harvard Medical School where parts of the victim's body were found some days after his unaccountable disappearance.[35] Although the evidence convinced every member of the jury, Webster maintained his innocence, which his wife and daughters did not doubt. While he awaited the fulfillment of the death sentence he asked to see George Putnam, Harvard College 1826, the minister of the First Church of Roxbury, who thereafter visited him regularly; finally Webster told Putnam that he wished to confess to the murder. Putnam knew something of Webster through Nuttall's excessive discomfiture over his double-dealing in 1823. Later Nuttall had established sufficiently amicable relations with Webster to contribute to his periodical and to the Harvard mineralogical collection in his charge. Nuttall was capable of hot outbursts of temper when he considered himself wronged, but it is noticeable that he soon recovered his equanimity and did not nurse resentment; he was "remarkable for a truly philosophical and conciliatory spirit." [36]

In 1850 news arrived of William Gambel's death in California. Six months after he received his medical degree at the University of Pennsylvania, he married Catherine M. Towson, a friend from childhood. Faced with the difficulties of establishing a practice in Philadelphia, Gambel could not resist the enticements of the Far West when they were manifoldly enhanced by the discovery of gold in California. In the spring of 1849, he shipped his medical books and instruments to San Francisco, resigned from his office as Recording Secretary of the Academy, and set off for Independence, leaving Philadelphia on April 5, with Isaac Jones Wistar (1827–1905), who later became famous.[37] They had arranged to travel the Oregon Trail with a group of inexperienced and unchastened youths; with no recognized leader and no regulations, dogged by accidents and serious illnesses, the youths were perilous companions. On June 2, Gambel left them to join a larger party under a Captain Boone, moving slowly with an ox train for, he explained, he preferred to travel more leisurely — an understandable choice for a naturalist. Wistar regretted losing him, for he found Gambel congenial and an interesting conversationalist although not an eager worker at camp chores.[38]

In this year the Oregon Trail had suddenly become a thoroughfare, crowded with caravans of mule teams and ox teams, loaded with goods, headed for the gold diggings. The trail to California took off southwestward from the Snake River valley beyond Fort Hall and followed the Humboldt River valley across Nevada where ever worsening conditions were encountered. Paucity of grass and water became increasingly acute as the season advanced; draft animals died and wagons, bogged down hopelessly in the sand, were abandoned as their owners struggled desperately to save themselves. Gambel met the most exhausting conditions of the late season. After the gruelling crossing of the Humboldt desert, where the party lost most of their cattle and had to leave many wagons, the brigade was caught by snow in the Sierras. Gambel was among the few of his party who got across the range. Well down the western slope he encountered some placer miners suffering from typhoid fever; in treating them in his debilitated condition, he contracted the disease and died on December 13, 1849.[39]

During the three and a half years that Gambel had been back in Philadelphia he had continued his reports on "Birds Observed in Upper California," which were published in the *Proceedings* of the Academy of Natural Sciences in parts as they were presented.[40] His summarizing ornithological article was "the first paper of note on California ornithology and forms the basis of all subsequent work"; it consisted of an annotated list of one hundred and seventy-six species, several first described by the author.[41] The names of three western birds honor Gambel — *Lophortyx gambelii* Nutt., Gambel's quail; *Parus gambeli* Ridgway, the mountain chickadee; and *Zonotrichia leucophrys gambelii* (Nutt.), a variety of the white-crowned sparrow. Still another western variety of the white-crowned is named for Nuttall. Gambel discovered and named two species of rodents of western California, the kangaroo rat (*Dipodomys agilis agilis*) and the parasitic mouse (*Peromyscus californicus*),[42] and Baird named in his honor the variety *Peromyscus maniculatus gambeli*. "In the short space of eight years Gambel demonstrated that he was possessed of remarkable ability both as an explorer and field naturalist and as a student of natural history." [43]

Nuttall evidently received from Dr. Darlington a copy of his *Memorials of John Bartram and Humphry Marshall* for, on January 29, 1850, he wrote to Hooker:

Our friend . . . seems to employ the close of his useful life in the pleasant reminiscences of the past . . . and gleaned from sources w[h] were fast passing into oblivion. I wish he would not forget my kind old friend the late venerable W[m] Bartram, the first who penetrated the wilds of Florida, and collected many curious plants w[h] have been but recently described and published. There is a collection of his things now in the Banksian herbarium, that well deserve to be examined by the Am[n] botanist.[44]

As Darlington was in England in 1851, looking up his ancestral home about forty miles south of Liverpool, it is very likely that he visited Nuttall.[45]

On the edge of spring in 1850, Nuttall gave a note to his friend Frederick Taylor introducing him to Dr. Wilson, president of the Academy of Natural Sciences of Philadelphia, as one interested in natural history.[46] A few weeks later he acknowledged receiving a "small parcel" of Fendler's plants from Elias Durand; as there was nothing new among the specimens, he suggested that his $100 subscription be filled with plants from Panama. He added that he was soon to receive a large collection of Assam plants, dried and living, and asked if Durand knew of anyone in America likely to be interested.[47]

The next spring Nuttall answered an inquiry of Thaddeus W. Harris who was preparing a paper on historical aspects of the use of various cucurbits as food.

Nutgrove nr. Prescot<br>May 29<sup>th</sup> 1851

Dear Sir,

It gave me great pleasure to hear from you after such a long absence, and also to find you still at old Cambridge, as usual. But as to an answer to the interesting question you put to me, at this distance of time, I am unable to say satisfactorily what Cucurbitaceous plant it actually was w<sup>h</sup> the Indians of the Missouri cultivated tho' I think it not identic with our summer squash. A smaller kind of the common oval pumpkin is much used by the Kansas and Osages of the Missouri and Platte; these we frequently purchased of the natives in the journey I made across the continent in 1834 They are cut into long strips and dried for portable provision in the summer. These strips are woven or platted into matts [sic], and carried thus on horseback, were a very convenient fresh and sweet provision relished by us all.

The Indians of California and in fact all the natives we met with west of the central mountains are unacquainted with the cultivation of this, or indeed, *any other vegetable* as they live a roaming nomadic life, and in such hostility likewise to each other that they know no abiding place, neither homes, town, or scarcely any fixed country, for fear of being hunted to extermination.

Of wild roots, principally bulbous, they make great use; but of Cucurbitaceous edible we never met any indigenous in the whole cours [sic] of our protracted journey. . . .

I consider my assertion of the warted squash as being cultivated by the Arikarees and Mandans, the natives I alude [sic] to, as now too doubtfull [sic] for quotation, and, indeed, I now think, that from the time of year when I visited those natives (August to October) [June to October] that it must rather have been the common oval pumpkin w.[h] I afterwards saw also among the Osages on the Arkansaw.

Hoping you are in the enjoyment of good health, as I am, at present, tho' hastening to that goal from whence no traveller returns,

I remain

Yours truly and obliged

Thos.[s] Nuttall

Pray how is my old friend M.[r] Worcester I suppose still labouring under the loss of sight. Your father, no doubt is numbered with the shadows that have been. Perhaps you can find time before long, to tell me a little about old times and old acquaintances, for I begin to live now much on old remembrances, reviewing what is past, before the scene for ever closes with me, as with all that is human.[48]

In May 1851, Queen Victoria opened the Great Exhibition, the first "World's Fair." Uniquely housed at Hyde Park in "the Crystal Palace," a gigantic prefabricated conservatory designed by Joseph Paxton, the gifted gardener of the Duke of Devonshire, the exhibition was tremendously successful.[49] The display of plants was especially fine, extending even to full-grown trees within the conservatory. Late in the summer Nuttall went to London to see the exhibition. Equally important to him was studying the species of orchids and rhododendrons at Kew, for Booth had arrived back from India in June with a good collection of living plants. On September 12, 1851, he wrote briefly to Hooker: "I have just arrived (after a rather fatiguing journey) at home, and my nephew about to start early tomorrow I have taken the opportunity to send you some plants chiefly orchids, w.[h] appear to be wanting in your collection. My nephews [sic] other plants are too small for safe removal." [50]

For the next two years Nuttall was enjoyably occupied with caring for the miscellaneous eastern plants, raising quantities of seedlings and studying the dried specimens in preparation for publication of the new species. In the autumn of 1853 he sent to Kew a box of miscellaneous living plants including twelve species of rhododendrons; some of these individuals may be in the magnificent and extensive *Rhododendron* grove in the Kew Gardens.

During 1853 Nutgrove received a visit from Isaac Lea, Philadelphia publisher, conchologist, and mineralogist, who had published some of the new molluscan shells Nuttall took back to Philadelphia from diverse places.[51] The two had a long common background of friends and interests centering in the Academy and the American Philosophical Society.

April of the next year brought a visit from Charles Pickering, which was briefly described in a secondhand report by Elias Durand: [52]

They spent several hours together, conversing about old acquaintances, walking through his conservatories, and looking over his collection of living Rhododendrons. [Pickering] perceived a change that he could scarcely account for, namely, — that he who had been accustomed to roam thousands of miles all over North America, should now attach importance to a single visit to Ireland, and further, should have never visited the continent of Europe, close at hand.[53]

Certain conclusions were drawn by Durand from other information that he gathered, which in general appear accurate.

It does not appear that the bequest of the Nutgrove estate had placed Mr. Nuttall in a position of affluence. The estate was, it is said, incumbered with annuities, and burdened with a heavy income tax. He had, moreover, a numerous family of relatives to support. By his old American friends, who visited him at his English abode, he was found living in the fashion of a plain farmer, working on his grounds and nurseries among his men, like one of them, and eating at the same table with them. He used to say that it was difficult, in England, to enjoy the benefits of a moderate fortune, for the government took good care to exact the superfluous.[54]

Eating with the men in the large kitchen spared him some sittings with the visiting ministers.

Constant occupation with horticulture brought to Nuttall the delightful seasonal return in his garden of the flowers of old favorites from America. These stimulated such pleasant memories that early in 1849 he wrote Charles Wilkins Short to enlist his aid in obtaining more of such plants:

If this spring you could collect for me a few seeds of my old favorite Collinsia verna [Nutt.] which has never yet been seen in England, and Synandra [hispidula], Dracocephalum cordatum [Meehania cordata (Nutt.) Britt.] I should be exceedingly pleased to see them growing in my garden as a reminiscence of past times so pleasing when yet young and healthy I saw them first growing in my favorite land of the West! . . . These things sent to our friend George W. Carpenter, Druggist, Market Street, Philadelphia, will be directly transmitted by him to me as soon as they arrive.[55]

Short made continuous attempts to supply Nuttall with viable seed of *Collinsia verna* but, despite all precautions, no germination resulted from several shipments. In the spring of 1854, Nuttall appealed for advice to Hooker, who was constantly receiving shipments of seeds and plants from remote places.[56] Hooker made suggestions for transmitting the seed, which Nuttall forwarded to Short with happy results. In February 1856, Nuttall informed Hooker that he had "at last succeeded in raising from seeds sent me last June from D̲ Short, Lexington Kentucky the beautiful *Collinsia verna* w̲ I have been trying this 10 years to introduce to our gardens; when in flower I shall have great pleasure in sending it to you." In a few months the little American annual, first described by Nuttall in 1817, was pictured in the *Botanical Magazine* (t. 4927, 1856).[57]

In the summers of 1849 and 1850, during vacations at Long Preston, Nuttall visited an "old friend and admirer," Richard Clapham (d. 1856) of Austwick Hall, Clapham, a few miles west of Settle, and in 1853 Jonas Booth also visited there. Nuttall sent the first volume of his *Sylva* to Booth's host and a reprint of his paper on the rhododendrons. Years later Clapham's son, Thomas Richard, recalled "how intensely interested" he was in accounts by both these visitors of their travels in far countries, little dreaming that he himself would make three visits to North America and go "round the Horn." [58]

On April 10, 1856, Thomas Jonas Booth sailed from London for New Zealand, where he intended to settle. Nuttall felt that he was parting with him for the last time but in two or three years he was back in Lancashire.[59]

Nuttall always maintained that writing books was unprofitable for him. This was without a doubt true of his last volumes that formed the Appendix to Michaux's *Sylva of North America*, which three different publishers brought out piecemeal, sporadically, and half-heartedly over a span of seven years.[60] He evidently had no copyright to his part of the work so that it was republished by others a number of times. For the first reissue in 1852, John Jay Smith (1789–1881) of Germantown, librarian and horticulturalist, edited the text and prepared a preface and later published a set in which Nuttall's material was bound in two volumes instead of three.[61] In the winter of 1855 to 1856, the letterpress type of an edition was burned in storage [62] and Smith, planning another edition, inquired of William Darlington concerning the likelihood of Nuttall's contributing further facts or remarks. In replying Darlington stated that he did not know what arrangements Nuttall "made with Judah Dobson, – for whom he furnished the Appendix, as I understood; but I suspect he never got much – if anything – from that quarter, for his labors." On July 8, 1856, Darlington wrote a letter to Nuttall for Smith to enclose with his, saying that Smith "will be happy to avail himself of any facts or remarks, which you may wish to contribute, in further illustration of your valuable and highly interesting portion of the work. Mr. Smith desires me to assure you, that his object is to give increased value to the splendid Production, without much prospect of remuneration." [63]

From 1855–1858 inclusive John Windsor was publishing in the *Phytologist* a series of papers on the flora of Craven in which he credits two specific sites to Nuttall. The papers were published in book form for private circulation as *Flora Cravoniensis* in 1873.

During the winter of 1856–1857, Nuttall suffered severely from rheumatic pains in his arms; although the return of warmer weather brought considerable recovery, he had become "more feeble and slow" and could no longer write with facility. In June he wrote to Hooker:

My days of journeying are at an end. I have seen the last I must see of America. My walking and botanizing are almost over, and now I am content to be at rest. Old age has overtaken me, and I must be content to submit to the laws of nature, wh none can evade.

You seem on the contrary as active and vigorous as ever, and long may you continue is the wish of

Yours truly,
Thos Nuttall [64]

In the autumn of 1857 George Barrell Emerson called on Nuttall bringing a request from Hooker that he have a daguerreotype made. This likeness, promptly made in Liverpool, shows him aged much beyond his years.[65] By this time Nuttall was very confined; rheumatism prevented his walking more than a mile at a time. He was very much pleased by Emerson's visit and the talk of old acquaintances in Boston and Cambridge.[66]

In March 1858, after another winter in the cold northern house, he was obliged to employ an amanuensis to write a note to Hooker, as he did again in early June. But in the interim he wrote briefly himself and again later in June. His last note to Hooker was written on September 6, 1858.[67] All these missives were concerned with

Asian plants he was sending to Hooker that had just come into flower with him; some were new, others were known, but rare. Among those pictured in the *Botanical Magazine* in 1857 and later were more rhododendrons (t. 5002, 5008); *Corallobotrys acuminata* Klotzsch (t. 5010); Gaultheria discolor Nutt. [*Diplycosia discolor* (Nutt.) C. B. Clarke] (t. 5034); Hydrangea cyanema Nutt. (*H. robusta* Hook. f. and Thoms.) (t. 5038); *Polygonatum punctatum* Royle (t. 5061); *Thyrsacanthus indicus* Nees (t. 5062); and Epigynium leucobotrys Nutt. (*Vaccinium serratum* Wight var. *leucobotrys* Nutt.) (t. 5103). During this period some of Nuttall's species, supplied from other sources, were depicted, such as *Sabatia campestris* Nutt. (t. 5015) of Arkansas by way of Germany and *Aesculus californica* Nutt. (t. 5077) from an English garden.

In May 1859, *Rhododendron nuttallii* Booth came into flower at Kew and was promptly figured and later published by Hooker (t. 5146) with a comment on the gratification the reproduction gave to Nuttall: "we know that but a little before his lamented death one of the last sources of pleasure he derived from the vegetable creation — which he had so long and so successfully studied — was the information of his namesake having for the first time flowered at Kew, and the sight of the large drawing," which, Hooker observed, "does no justice to the plant itself."

Dr. Windsor says that Nuttall succumbed on September 10, 1859, to an attack of chronic bronchitis; the death certificate, witnessed by Thomas J. Booth, gave "acute gastritis" of six months' duration and bronchitis for two weeks.[68]

# CHAPTER 22

# POSTSCRIPT

Mr. Nuttall . . . has left a name which will last as long as flowers are loved — J. Jay Smith.

The entailed property passed to Francis Dixon, but Thomas Nuttall left his personal possessions to Thomas Jonas Booth. His collection of minerals, his herbarium, and living plants had market value. The minerals were sold at auction in London on March 15 and 16, 1860, by J. C. Stevens after being advertised weekly in the *Athenaeum* from mid-February.[1] A copy of the catalog is available at the Geological Society of London.

In correspondence which Higgins had with Sir William in the autumn of 1859, concerning the sale of the herbarium, he stated that Nuttall had valued it at £100.[2] However it was sold by Stevens for £30 to the Banksian Department of the British Museum on July 11, 1860. It contained "5759 species including types of North American plants"[3] described in Nuttall's publications. Many species had not been published.

In 1862 Booth was operating "Rainhill Nursery, near Prescott," built around the collection of living plants that he had inherited from Nuttall. By 1878 he had again left England.[4]

Some possessions of Nuttall handed down in the Booth family are probably still in existence, such as a desk, the powderhorn that Nuttall took up the Missouri in 1811, and a copy of Henry J. Brooke's *Familiar Introduction to Crystallography* (London, 1823), presented to Nuttall by Henry Heuland in 1824.[5] But it seems that the most precious personal items, the field journals that gave his various routes of travel and the sites of his hundreds of new species, were destroyed less than a score of years ago when the household of Samuel Rishworth Booth was broken up.[6] Two exceptions were Nuttall's journal of the early part of his 1810 expedition and a little diary of a visit to the Lake Country in 1824, which must have been overlooked and left at Nutgrove; these were evidently appropriated by Francis Dixon's son, Frederick R. Dixon-Nuttall (1852–1929), who remembered Thomas Nuttall as a very quiet old man who could tell most interesting tales of his adventures; these two notebooks came into the possession of *his* son, William F. Dixon-Nuttall.

While working at London Herbaria (1905–1906), Dr. Willis L. Jepson of the University of California made a trip to St. Helens to see Francis Dixon-Nuttall, who received him cordially but knew nothing about his uncle's notebooks. He perhaps had never known they existed, and it seems that no reference was made to the Booth branch of the family. Jepson returned to London "filled with pleasant memories of that beautiful and quiet English countryside which is associated with the name of the botanist who of all the early botanical explorers in California makes the strongest appeal to our scientific understanding and to our intellectual sympathies."[7]

On the death of Francis Dixon-Nuttall in 1915, Nutgrove passed into the hands of his youngest daughter, Florence (Dixon-Nuttall) Sykes, a resident of Belfast. After the Trust was dissolved in 1937, Nutgrove was sold. The building has been marred by exterior and interior changes through years of use as a home for wayward girls (St. Agnes Home) and for its present use as an old people's home for the district of St. Helens.

The Reverend Henry Hugh Higgins who lived "only a few hundred yards" from Nuttall in the last six years of his life and saw him frequently,[8] described "this truly good and distinguished man" as he appeared in his last years:

Retiring in disposition, his intercourse, even with his friends, was not characterized by an abundant flow of conversational remarks, yet on certain occasions, chiefly when by some incident reminded of his early explorations in the wilds of America, he would kindle with animation and speak fluently and even eloquently. I remember bringing to him a little wild flower, with the name of which I was at that time unacquainted. "Ah!" said he "I have not seen that plant for more than thirty years; it is *Chrysosplenium oppositifolium*"; and he then related how he had found it in America, and went on to name a large number of other flowers found in similar situations, though, as he said, he had not seen any of them for more than a quarter of a century. Thus even up to the time of his last illness his memory was as fresh and vigorous as it had been in the prime of life.

Nor was he less remarkable for a truly philosophical and conciliatory spirit. Being himself a member of the Church of England, he appreciated that which was good wherever he might find it. Circumstances very frequently brought into contact with him the ministers and members of a Primitive Methodist chapel; with their peculiarities Mr. Nuttall was far from sympathising, yet he recognized them as striving to do good amongst the very poor and illiterate population of the neighbourhood, and both treated them and spoke of them with uniform consideration and kindness.

His charity, too, was self-denying. Possessing an ample income he was frugal almost to excess, scarcely allowing himself the comforts and lesser luxuries required by his advanced years; whilst at the same time the stream of his liberality towards those whom he considered to be deserving of it was never stinted.[9]

His rector, R. P. Crockett, who considered Nuttall "an intimate and dear friend," stressed "his brilliant abilities coupled with worldly prosperity . . . his beautiful character . . . meek, and kind, and lovely . . . his self denying principles, his Christian charity and sympathy, his intellectual greatness, and child-like humility." [10]

When Charles Wilkins Short heard of Nuttall's death, he wrote to Gray reiterating previous remonstrances for his unfair criticisms of Nuttall and concluded, "I hope that we may be favoured with a full and *just* biographical Memoir of him." [11] To Engelmann he wrote:

The Veteran Nuttall, I perceive, is dead! Do not American Botanists owe him a large debt of gratitude for his early, long-continued and arduous labours in their cause? To him we owe in a main degree our earliest knowledge of the Botany of the vast region west of the Mississippi, which has of late yielded so large a field of discovery. These, however, have been mainly effected by Government appropriations, and under the protection of Government troops; whereas Nuttall's travels and explorations were made by his own unaided and unprotected person, and that, at a time when far greater danger attended his labours. Surely a monument should be erected to his memory, and I respectfully suggest such an expression to M$^r$ Shaw, for his St. Louis Kew! [12]

The granite obelisk in the Missouri Botanical Garden resulted from Short's suggestion.

Nuttall's reputation has grown with elapsed time. Charles Sprague Sargent in his compendious *Silva of North America* commended his explorations made in the face of dangers and hardships, and ranked him as "one of the most indefatigable and judicious of the botanists who have studied the North American flora. Among his numerous publications are some of the most valuable contributions in the field of North American botany; his work on North American birds is still an authority on the subject." [13]

Nuttall's manifold advancements of the natural history of North America are truly unique in accomplishment and in their spirit of complete dedication.

# BIOGRAPHICAL SKETCHES OF
# THOMAS NUTTALL

1. Elias Durand, "Biographical Notice of the Late Thomas Nuttall," APS *Proceedings*, VII (1860), 297–315.
2. Thomas Meehan, "Biographical Sketch of the Late Thomas Nuttall," *The Gardeners Monthly*, II (1860), 21–23.
3. Thomas Jonas Booth, "Mr. Thomas Nuttall, the Naturalist," *The Settle Chronicle and North Ribblesdale Advertiser*, January 1 and February 1, 1861. Reprinted by F. W. Pennell as "An English Obituary Account of Thomas Nuttall," *Bartonia*, XIX (1938), 51–54.
4. Francis W. Pennell, "Travels and Scientific Collections of Thomas Nuttall," *Bartonia*, XVIII (1936), 1–51.
5. Jeannette E. Graustein, "Nuttall's Travels into the Old Northwest," *Chronica Botanica*, XIV (1951), 1–88.
6. ——— "Audubon and Nuttall," *Scientific Monthly*, LXXIV (1952), 84–90.
7. ——— "Nuttall in 1815," *Rhodora*, LVI (1954a), 253–257.
8. ——— "The Date of Pursh's Flora Americae Septentrionalis," *Rhodora*, LVI (1954b), 275.
9. ——— "Nuttall's Quarrel with Pursh," *Rhodora*, LVIII (1956a), 20–22.
10. ——— "Manuel Lisa and Thomas Nuttall," Missouri Historical Society *Bulletin*, XII (1956b), 249–252.
11. ——— "Harvard's Only Massachusetts Professor of Natural History," *Harvard Alumni Bulletin*, LXI (1958), 242–243, 257–258.
12. ——— "Natural History at Harvard," Cambridge Historical Society *Proceedings*, XXXVIII (1961a), 69–86.
13. ——— "The Eminent Benjamin Smith Barton," *Pennsylvania Magazine of History and Biography*, LXXXV (1961b), 423–438.
14. ——— "Early Scientists in the White Mountains," *Appalachia*, new series, XXX (1964), 44–63.
15. Richard G. Beidleman, "Some Biographical Sidelights on Thomas Nuttall, 1786–1859," APS *Proceedings*, CIV (1960), 86–100.

# NOTES

The following abbreviations are used in the notes. Citations by author's name alone can be identified from the preceding list of Biographical Sketches.

*AJS*  *American Journal of Science and the Arts* ("Silliman's Journal").

ANS  Academy of Natural Sciences of Philadelphia.

APS  American Philosophical Society.

*Ark. J.*  Nuttall, *A Journal of Travels into the Arkansa Territory* (Philadelphia, Pennsylvania: Thomas H. Palmer, 1821). Reprinted, *EWT*, XIII.

*Bot. Mag.*  (Curtis's) *Botanical Magazine*.

BMNH  British Museum of Natural History.

*EWT*  R. G. Thwaites, *Early Western Travels, 1748–1846* (Cleveland, Ohio: Arthur H. Clark Company, 1904–1907).

*Gen.*  Nuttall, *The Genera of North American Plants and a Catalogue of the Species, to the Year 1817* (Philadelphia, Pennsylvania: 1818).

HSP  Historical Society of Pennsylvania.

*J.*  *Journal.*

JKT  J. K. Townsend, *Narrative of a Journey Across the Rocky Mountains* (Philadelphia, Pennsylvania: Henry Perkins, 1839). Reprinted, *EWT*, XXI.

Kew  Royal Botanical Gardens, Kew, England.

LCP  Library Company of Philadelphia.

MoBG  Missouri Botanical Garden, St. Louis, Missouri.

MSPA  Papers of the Massachusetts Society for Promoting Agriculture, in the Harvard University Archives, Cambridge, Massachusetts (as distinguished from the files of the Society).

NJW  Nathaniel Jarvis Wyeth, "Correspondence and Journals," F. G. Young, ed., *Sources of the History of Oregon*, I, pts. 3–6 (1899).

NYBG  New York Botanic Garden.

*O.*  Nuttall, *A Manual of the Ornithology of the United States and Canada*, I, *Land Birds* (Cambridge, Massachusetts: Hilliard & Brown, 1832); II, *Water Birds* (Boston, Massachusetts: Hilliard, Gray & Company, 1834).

Peck  Collection of papers concerning William Dandridge Peck (UA
Papers  I 15.1003 and HUG 1677) in the Harvard University Archives, Cambridge, Massachusetts.

*Sylva*  Nuttall, *North American Sylva*.

T. Corr.  John Torrey's Correspondence at the New York Botanic Garden.

## CHAPTER 1. NUTTALL'S AMERICAN RECORD

1. "Probably few naturalists have ever excelled Nuttall in aptitude for observations, in quickness of eye, tact in discrimination, and tenacity of memory." Asa Gray, "The Longevity of Trees," *North American Review*, LIX (1844), 193.

2. Samuel Eliot Morison, *Three Centuries of Harvard* (Cambridge, Massachusetts: Harvard University Press, 1936), 217.

3. Nuttall's *Sylva*, Preface.

4. Durand, 313.

## CHAPTER 2. YOUTH IN ENGLAND

1. Limestone made rich pasturage and supplied quarries as a secondary industry.

2. In *Doomsday Book* (1086) the parish and village were called "Prestune."

3. Embsay Priory, established in 1120 by William and Cecilia Meschines, was moved to Bolton thirty years later by their daughter, Alice de Romelly. J. S. Fletcher, *The Cistercians in Yorkshire* (London, 1919).

4. Graustein (1951) shows a photograph of the parish record of the marriage. Margaret Hardacre was christened on June 26, 1761, and buried September 21, 1841. Her parents, both members of the parish, were married on January 29, 1750. Margaret was the sixth child and fourth daughter; the eldest child was named for his father. Several marriage records of this period bear the signatures of Richard Hardacre or Richard Hardacre Junior as witness. (Not everyone in the village was able to sign his name.)

5. P. A. Whittle, *Blackburn As It Is* (Preston, 1852), 194.

6. Elizabeth, born about 1794, was named for her aunt, one of the witnesses of Margaret's wedding. Neither Susan nor Elizabeth was christened in Long Preston.

7. Booth.

8. This list of nine men, found at Bolton Abbey, was recorded in an anonymous, typed "History of Long Preston" loaned by Thomas ("Tot") Lord, of Settle, to the writer. Mr. Lord, the only person whom the writer encountered in upper Ribblesdale who knew of Thomas Nuttall, has a museum of Roman antiquities and fossil remains procured locally and has accumulated many manuscript and printed records pertaining to the area. A Craven Legion roll (ms.) of males of arms-bearing age, compiled about 1795–1805, when invasion by Napoleon was feared, lists fifteen Hardacres living within the parish of Long Preston; four were Richards. An Ann King (1751–1801), buried in the parish church at Long Preston, married a Richard Hardacre. Kings were established at Whiteholme in the nearby parish of Sladeburne from 1595. In his *Ornithology* (II, 45), Nuttall gives information received from a Mr. King of Wigglesworth (two miles west of Long Preston).

9. Nathaniel Hawthorne's description of a village church near Liverpool. *English Note-books*, I (1853), 24.

10. Various features of the previous Saxon church have been exposed during restorations: the foundations of a semicircular apse with characteristic herringbone masonry and monumental slabs of great antiquity. Lord's "History of Long Preston" (see note 8).

11. Nuttall, *Ark. J.*, 123.

12. *Sylva*, I (1859), 161.

13. *O.*, I, 142; 223; 649; II, 186.

14. Information concerning Jonas's career is given in Whittle, *Blackburn As It Is* (Preston, 1852), 192, which states that Jonas was a native of Blackburn. Nuttall is a widespread name in Lancashire. Whittle says erroneously that Thomas began his apprenticeship before Jonas left Blackburn.

15. Known dates of publications by Hemenway and Nuttall are: one in 1797, eight in 1798, and the last two in 1799; Hemenway published at least one title independently in 1799. A. J. Hawkes, *Lancaster Printed Books . . . to Year 1800* (Wigan, 1925), xxvi, 16–17.

16. Liverpool Directories of 1800 list Jonas as already established in that city; addresses of his various printing firms appear regularly for almost two decades.

17. W. Moss, *The Liverpool Guide* (4th ed., 1807). Benjamin Silliman in *A Journal of Travels in England, Holland and Scotland* [1805–1806] (New Haven, 3d ed., 1820) tells of visiting St. George's Dock in 1805 to see a Guinea slave ship.

18. The Picton Library, Liverpool, has an incomplete collection of works from the press of Jonas Nuttall.

19. Information that Charles Pickering gave to Durand.

20. William Jaggard, *Liverpool Literature* (1905), 4.

21. It is probable that on his arrival in the city Thomas attended the "ancient Church of St. Nicholas, cut off by warehouses from its original position on the river bank."

22. Booth says that this respite from work occurred when Thomas was "about the age of 17," which would place it in 1803; however he also said that the pair climbed Penyghent and Arncliffe Clouder. Windsor in *Flora Craveniensis* (Manchester, 1873) states that he was on Arncliffe Clouder in June 1805, probably the correct date.

23. *Gen.*, I, 70.

24. A youth who had the initiative to get to North America must surely have been able to arrange to visit occasionally, if not frequently, such a botanical Utopia as this.

25. Dr. John W. Francis of New York City, who visited the garden in 1815, wrote enthusiastically about the palms in his "Journal." Francis Papers, New York City Public Library.

26. Based on 1808 catalog of the Garden.

27. There is a copy of one of Bullock's "Companions" in the New York Public Library.

28. Silliman, *Journal of Travels.*

29. DNB.

30. Durand's suggestion, p. 297, that "a hope to improve his position in the world" brought Thomas to the United States (an idea widely adopted) was completely fallacious for in England he would have shared in his uncle's prestige, and his financial prospects were excellent. Moreover it was entirely out of character for, throughout his life, Nuttall showed a complete indifference to money beyond what was needed for the simplest living and the travel necessary for accomplishing the work he had undertaken. Nuttall's close friend, Charles Pickering, was doubtless responsible for the statement in Meehan that "probably in no event of his life did pecuniary considerations influence him."

31. Giggleswick Grammar School, still flourishing on the outskirts of the little village just across the Ribble from Settle, is said to have been in existence as early as 1499. It was one of the schools to which Edward VI gave financial assistance. Its best-known graduate was William Paley whose *Evidences of Christianity* (1794) and *Natural Theology* . . . *Collected from the Appearances of Nature* (1802) formed a part of the curriculum of English schools and American academies and colleges through the first half of the nineteenth century. Paley's father was headmaster for fifty-four years. E. A. Bell, *A History of Giggleswick School* (Leeds, England: 1912).

32. Nuttall to Hooker, April 27, 1844, LXIII, 338, Kew.

33. Durand, 297.

34. *Liverpool Courier*, March 16, 1808. Nuttall named the ship in the *Sylva*.

## CHAPTER 3. TRANSPORTATION

1. *Aurora General Advertiser* under "Commercial Intelligence, Port of Philadelphia."

2. Durand's conclusion, 299, that this anecdote showed that Nuttall "was totally ignorant" of the first principles of botany is very strange for it actually is evidence to the contrary, *Smilax* being one of the few monocots with net-veined leaves.

3. Booth.

4. The Hon. John Davis (1761–1847) of Boston, appointed Comptroller of the Treasury by President Washington in 1795, was actively interested in natural history. During his brief residence in Philadelphia, Davis saw a good deal of Barton. On November 14, 1795, he wrote to Jeremy Belknap (1744–1798), the historian: "Your letter to Dr. Barton procured me an agreeable and valuable acquaintance. I frequently visit him at his Bachelor's Hall . . . surrounded with books, bottles of insects, the bones of the mammoth, and other evidences of his ruling passion. . . . I observed several folio volumes, handsomely bound in red morocco, and lettered on the back, "Herbarium Americanum." . . . it was a work I had not before seen, and asked leave to look into it. I found it to be a collection made by himself of plants and flowers nicely pressed & preserved and pasted on the leaves of the volumes with a short description under each specimen of the habitation of the plant, time of flowering, peculiar properties, etc. . . . already extended to 50 volumes." "Belknap's Correspondence," Massachusetts Historical Society *Collections*, 6th ser., IV (1891), 603. This awkward and expensive method of handling his herbarium was abandoned by Barton, C. Earle Smith, Jr., "A Century of Botany in America," *Bartonia*, XXVIII (1954–1956), 10.

5. *Aurora General Advertiser*, Tuesday, April 26, 1808.

6. Meehan, 21.

7. Booth.

8. The supposition that Nuttall worked for D. Heartt in 1808–1809, is based on two facts. At a time when Nuttall was on the publication committee of the ANS, Heartt printed vol. I, pt. I (1817) of their *Journal*. In 1816 he printed Nuttall's *Genera*, of which tradition reports that Nuttall set much of the type, a privilege that a printer would be unlikely to grant to a stranger.

9. Durand, 298.

10. The facts and quotations about Peale's Museum are from Charles Coleman Sellers, *Charles Willson Peale* (APS, 1947), II, 8–10, 224–252.

11. Peale called it a mammoth. Rembrandt Peale published a number of papers on it — Tilloch's *Philosophical Magazine*, XIV (1802), 162–164, 228–229; XV (1803), 325–327 — and two small books.

12. The Philadelphia Botanical Society, founded in 1806, changed its name the next year to the Philadelphia Linnaean Society. After the ANS was formed, the Linnaean Society faded and disappeared. The quotation is from Barton's *Discourse on Some of the Principal Desiderata in Natural History*, etc. (Philadelphia, 1807), which can be found in C. C. Sellers, *Charles Willson Peale*, II, 246.

13. Carl August Pursch, *Flora* (*Botanische Zeitung*), X (1827), 491–496.

14. In the Preface to his *Flora*, Frederick Pursh gives dates known to be erroneous: he went on the southern trip for Barton in 1806, not 1805; on the northern trip in 1807, not 1806; to Hosack's garden in 1809, not 1807.

15. David Landreth, Jr., "Capt. Mayne Reid's The Plant Hunters," *Horticulturist*, n. s., XIII (1858), 254–257.

16. It is probable that Nuttall talked with Lyon in London in 1812 (see p. 85).

17. S. P. Stetson, "American Garden Books, Transplanted and Native, Before 1807." *William and Mary Quarterly*, ser. 3, III (1946), 362.

18. Jefferson to M'Mahon, January 6, 1807. E. M. Betts, *Thomas Jefferson's Garden Book* (APS, 1944), 337, 344. Lewis's seeds prospered, *ibid.*, 344–347, 372–373.

19. In the Preface to his *Flora*, Pursh implies that Lewis made arrangements directly with him in the autumn. (The time that he says their meeting occurred is impossible, but it could have been in May 1807. Pursh was very weak on the dates of events.) M'Mahon wrote to Jefferson that Lewis requested him to employ Pursh after his return from a collecting excursion he was about to make for Barton. Betts, *ibid.*, 417–418.

20. R. G. Thwaites, *Original Journals of the Lewis and Clark Expedition* (New York: Dodd, Mead, 1904) VI, 151–152.

21. Lewis had become acquainted with Barton in 1802–1803 when, through Jefferson's arrangements, he consulted him as well as Drs. Rush and Wistar to ascertain what special observations were desirable in his fields of interest. Betts, *Thomas Jefferson's Garden Book* (APS, 1944), 282. On October 21, 1809, Elliott wrote to Mühlenberg, "With regard to Gov.ʳ Lewis's work I understand from D.ʳ Barton that in consequence of a dispute between Gov. Lewis and himself the work was suspended and no person could be engaged to conduct the Scientific part of it — Dr. B. complained much of ill usage, and seemed pa[rticularly] displeased with M'Mahon. Since I returned home I heard from Wilson the ornithologist a very different story — Wilson says the Botanical part is progressing under the care of a German named Bursch or Brutch [Pursh] and is nearly compleated." Photostats of Elliott–Mühlenberg Correspondence, Gray Herbarium, Harvard University, Cambridge, Massachusetts (originals at HSP).

22. The only contemporary statement found concerning the fate of the drawings and descriptions that Pursh prepared for Lewis is in the Preface of his *Flora* where he says that he "transmitted all the drawings prepared for the work" to General Clark. In many cases Pursh's pieces of the plants that were

in A. B. Lambert's herbarium can be fitted to the places where they were severed from Lewis's specimens. *Fide* Joseph Ewan.

23. There is a discrepancy between Cleaveland's statement and Benjamin Waterhouse's that Cleaveland attended his course in Natural History for it contained four lectures on geology and mineralogy at the time that he was a student and would have been well illustrated by specimens.

24. Peck lived in Kittery, Maine, from about 1784 to 1800. Hooker recorded having heard Peck make this statement in England. "On the Botany of America," *AJS*, IX (1825), 273.

25. "Index Florae Lancastriensis" [1791], APS *Transactions*, III (1793), 157–184; "Supplementum Indices Florae Lancastriensis" [1796], *ibid.*, IV (1799), 235–242; "Kurze Bemerkungen über die in der Gegend von Lancaster . . . Arten der Gattungen *Juglans, Fraxinus* und *Quercus* . . ." *Ges. Nat. Freunde* N. Schr., III (1801), 387–402; "Ueber die . . . Weiden . . . ," *ibid.*, IV (1806), 62–69.

26. W. P. and J. P. Cutler, *Life, Journals and Correspondence of Manasseh Cutler, LL.D.* (Cincinnati, 1888), II, 291.

27. F. A. Michaux, *Histoire des Arbres forestiers de L'Amérique Septentrionalis* (Paris, 1810–1813), II, 155.

28. On December 17, 1810, Mühlenberg wrote Elliott that Enslen was "past recovery from consumption." Mühlenberg–Elliott Correspondence, Gray Herbarium.

29. On November 8, 1809, Mühlenberg wrote to Elliott that Kinn had sent his entire herbarium of 827 plants to him to be named. Later Nuttall exchanged specimens with Kinn.

30. Curtis to Torrey, December 11, 1835, T. Corr.

31. Kuhn carried a living plant of *Kuhnia eupatorioides* L. to Linnaeus. Gray's *Manual of Botany*, 8th ed. (New York: American Book Company, 1950), 1371.

32. James Greenway to B. S. Barton, January 31, 1793, Delafield Collection of Barton Papers. Copy at ANS.

33. *Genera plantarum secundum ordines naturales disposita*, etc. (Paris, 1789).

## CHAPTER 4. INITIATION TO AMERICAN FLORA

1. The quotation as well as the date of departure are from a letter Nuttall wrote to Barton from Lewes. All extant letters that Nuttall wrote to Barton as well as miscellaneous Barton papers belonged to General John Ross Delafield of Montgomery Place, New York; copies of the letters used in Pennell's paper are at ANS. The Lewes letter was published in full with notes by Robert R. Tatnall as "Nuttall's Plant Collections in Southern Delaware," *Bartonia*, XX (1938–1939), 1–6.

2. O., I, 615–616.

3. There is no evidence that Nuttall had access to Barton's herbarium as Pursh did.

4. The Rodneys are an outstanding Delaware family: Caesar of Dover was a signer of the Declaration of Independence; two of the four Rodneys who were taxpayers in Lewes about this time — Daniel and Caleb — were Governors of Delaware, and Daniel served as a judge and in Congress.

5. Nuttall incorrectly named *Utricularia inflata* as U. ceratophylla in his *Gen.*, I, 12.

6. Nuttall called this plant, "common around Lewistown in Delaware," Martynia proboscidea.

7. He observed the Sabbath scrupulously on both trips of 1809.

8. Nuttall to Barton, June 16, 1809, ANS.

9. John T. Scharf, *History of Delaware* (Philadelphia, 1888), II, 1335.

10. Nuttall to Barton, June 16, 1809, ANS.

11. William S. Taber found it in Selbyville, about seven miles south of Dagsboro, near the Maryland line. Frank Morton Jones, "Description of the Cypress Swamps in Delaware and Maryland States," *Delaware History*, III (1949), 123–137.

12. Although he did not mention the species in his letter to Barton, in the *Genera* (II, 75) Nuttall referred his *Lobelia* \*paludosa to deep sphagnose swamps from Sussex County, Delaware, to Georgia. The eighth edition of Gray's *Manual* suggests that the attribution to Delaware may have been an error for it does not now occur north of southeastern Georgia.

13. Booth's account of this trip reads: ". . . in the summer of 1808[!], by desire of Professor Barton, he made an excursion to the mountainous part [!] of Delaware, Sussex County, and by the assistance of Michaux's Flora acquired a knowledge of most of the curious plants which he met with in walks, and found no inconsiderable number of those species which had hitherto been supposed alone indigenous to Carolina and Virginia."

14. Nuttall evidently went to Bethlehem, fifty-five miles from Philadelphia, by stagecoach and made much of the rest of the long trip on foot. Heller's Inn was about twenty-four miles beyond Bethlehem on the way to the Water Gap where the Delaware River breaks through the Blue Mountain. Joshua Gilpin, "Journey to Bethlehem," *Pa. Mag. Hist. Biog.*, XLVI (1922), 15–38.

15. Some species listed in his letter to Barton from Wilkes-Barre, additional to those mentioned were: three unidentified species of *Trillium, Populus tremuloides* Michx., Corylus rostrata Ait. (*C. cornuta* Marsh.), *Ribes* sp., mountain ash, *Acer saccharinum* L. a garden *Epilobium*, two species of *Bartonia* (?), *Lonicera* sp. (?), and two species of *Viburnum*.

16. In *Ark. J.*, 179, Nuttall says, "No marine plants appear in this vicinity, as at Onondago, where we meet with Salicornia of the sea marshes."

17. Owasco, the St. Lawrence, and the Falls of the Genesee are mentioned in "The Geology of the Mississippi Valley," ANS *Journal*, II (1821), *passim*.

18. Species listed in his letter additional to those mentioned beyond, were: *Potentilla* (either *argentea* or *anserina*), Hippophaë [*Shepherdia canadensis* (L.) Nutt.], *Dodecatheon Meadia, Hyposcymus niger, Linnaea borealis,* and *Artemesia pontica*.

19. In his letter Nuttall says "Valisneria grows in Buffalo creek." The two other species are mentioned in *Gen.* I, 14, 138–139.

20. The species enumerated here were omitted from his letter but appear in the *Genera*, not in all cases under their present names.

21. *Gen.*, II, 60.

22. In 1779, a village of the Seneca Indians on the site of Canandaigua was destroyed by Gen. John Sullivan; about ten years later, New Englanders started settling there.

23. Booth.

24. On January 13, 1810, Jefferson wrote to M'Mahon: "Before you re-

ceive this you will probably have seen General Clarke [*sic*], . . . The papers relating to the expedition . . . had been delivered to Gen. Clarke, & were to be carried by him to Philadelphia, & measures to be taken for immediate publication. . . ." Betts, *Thomas Jefferson's Garden Book*, 431.

25. Elliott Coues, *History of the Lewis and Clark Expedition* (New York: Francis P. Harper, 1893), I, lxxxiii, lxxxiv; II, 409.

26. Pennell (1936), 7.

27. Mühlenberg to Elliott, December 17, 1810, Gray Herbarium, Harvard University, Cambridge, Massachusetts. James Boyd, *History of the Pennsylvania Horticultural Society* (Philadelphia: Pennsylvania Horticultural Society, 1929), 434.

28. In a statement dictated shortly before his death Barton said that he had furnished Nuttall with "a special passport from the president of the United States." For a detailed account of Barton's efforts to get a passport for Nuttall, see Beidleman, 87-88.

29. Nuttall probably received only the $20 in cash and $80 in notes given him when he left Philadelphia. Graustein (1951), 73.

30. "Terms of Agreement, dated April 7, 1810, between Barton and Nuttall," Pennell (1936), 45-46.

31. Graustein (1961b).

32. Nuttall to George Putnam, August 30, 1823, courtesy of Miss Elizabeth Putnam.

33. "List of articles belonging to me which Mr. Th. Nuttall has in his possession." Pennell (1936), 49.

34. "Directions for Mr. Thomas Nuttall." *Ibid.*, 46-48.

35. See the comments on Nuttall's taxonomic training, p. 121.

## CHAPTER 5. WEST WITH THE ASTORIANS

1. The basic account in this section relies on the diary of Nuttall that details the trip from its start in Philadelphia as far as the southern part of Lake Huron, with some additional dated entries at Fox River and the portage to the Wisconsin as well as miscellaneous undated memoranda made subsequently. Graustein (1951).

2. Mühlenberg, writing about the collector Barton had sent to the West, shows no personal knowledge of Nuttall. Mühlenberg–Elliott Correspondence, August 27, 1810, Gray Herbarium, Harvard University, Cambridge, Massachusetts.

3. Delafield Collection of Barton Papers, April 22, 1810, copy at ANS; Graustein (1956b).

4. Many of the statements in this chapter concerning geology, ores, and minerals occur in Nuttall, "Observations on the Geological Structure of the Valley of the Mississippi," ANS *Journal*, II (1821), 14-52.

5. Nuttall wrote to Barton that he took "Fowler's Solution" for the ague.

6. During the days of severe illness he may have studied the Latin descriptions in Michaux's *Flora*, for about this time he began to use Latin phrases in his plant analyses.

7. Graustein (1951), 39. The special significance of Nuttall's record was brought to the writer's notice by Dr. George W. White.

8. Some of the species mentioned in this chapter are not referred to in the diary, but Nuttall located all on the 1810 route. For example the *Euonymus,*

omitted from the diary, is given in *Gen.*, I, 155, "in shady fir swamps betwixt Franklin and Waterford, Pennsylvania."

9. Graustein (1951), 73.

10. Richard came from France to the United States at the beginning of the French Revolution. In 1798 he was sent to Detroit as a missionary and served in Congress in 1823. He died in 1832, aged 68. — J. E. Worcester, *American Almanac*, II (1834).

11. The proposed objective in northern Saskatchewan is still a wilderness of streams, lakes, and tremendous swamps.

12. Pennell (1936), 46–48. At this time the Peaks of Otter in the Blue Ridge were thought to be the most lofty in North America.

13. Beidleman, 87, n. 5.

14. Graustein (1951), 64, n. 225.

15. Nuttall, "Observations on the Geological Structure of the Valley of the Mississippi," ANS *Journal*, II (1821), 19–20.

16. H. R. Schoolcraft, *Narrative Journal of Travels in the Year 1820*, ed. by M. L. Williams (East Lansing, Michigan: Michigan State College Press, 1955), 78.

17. Washington Irving's *Astoria*, inaccurate though it occasionally is, is the chief source of information about the expedition.

18. "The coast of Lake Superior I was then prevented from examining by the sinister regulations of the company of the northwestern fur-traders." Nuttall, ANS *Journal*, II (1821), 16.

19. *Ibid.*, 20.

20. This species was listed under this name by Nuttall in the catalog of plants from the Missouri (1813) that Nuttall drew up for Fraser's Nursery in London to which he sold plants and seeds. In 1818 Nuttall stated, "Mr. Pursh . . . had never seen a flowering specimen except in my herbarium," yet had marked it *v. v.* (seen living). *Gen.* II, 92.

21. Although all of Nuttall's "great calcareous platform" was of Paleozoic origin, various exposures on which he commented belonged to periods varying from the Cambrian through the Mississippian (Lower Carboniferous). I am indebted to Dr. George W. White for calling these points to my attention.

22. In his "Directions for Mr. Thomas Nuttall," Barton wrote, "Here [at Chicago], as well as at Detroit, be sure to inquire for Mr. Dixon, to whom I have given you a letter." Barton probably meant Robert Dickson, the prominent Indian trader whom Nuttall encountered here.

23. Nuttall, ANS *Journal*, II (1821), 18.

24. Charless, an Irishman active in the Rebellion of 1794, fled to France and then to America. After working several years as a printer in Philadelphia, he went to Kentucky. Following negotiations with Governor Meriwether Lewis, he moved to St. Louis where he did the territorial printing. The first issue of the *Missouri Gazette* (or *Louisiana Gazette*) appeared on July 26, 1808. W. H. Lyon, "Joseph Charless, Father of Missouri Journalism," *Missouri Historical Society Bulletin*, XVII (1961), 130–145.

25. Manuel Lisa (1772–1820), a Spaniard born in New Orleans, went to St. Louis about 1790. He gave the Chouteaus keen competition until he became one of their partners in the Missouri Fur Company for a period. A full account of him is given in W. B. Douglas's "Manuel Lisa," *Missouri Historical Society Collections*, III (1911), 233–268, 367–406.

26. Sources for Bradbury's Missouri experiences are John Bradbury, *Travels*

*in the Interior of America in the Years 1809, 1810 and 1811* (2d ed., London, 1819), in *EWT*, V, and H. W. Rickett, "John Bradbury's Explorations in Missouri Territory," APS *Proceedings*, XC (1950), 59–89. Less concerned with the Missouri period is R. H. True's "A Sketch of John Bradbury, Including his Unpublished Correspondence with Thomas Jefferson," APS *Proceedings*, LXVIII (1929), 135–150.

27. Rickett, "John Bradbury's Explorations . . . ," APS *Proceedings*, XC (1950), Letter 13.

28. *Ibid.*, Letter 16.

29. Nuttall, "Observations on the Geological Structure of the Valley of the Mississippi," ANS *Journal*, II (1821), 32. The purple fluorite of Lot 276 in the sale of Nuttall's minerals in London in 1860 (31480, "Register of Collection of Minerals," BMNH) is probably one of these specimens.

30. Eggleston's typed paper on Nuttall deposited at ANS gives November as the time of the trip.

31. Dr. George W. White informs me that the Missourian galena dates from the Cambrian and the Dubuque from the Ordovician.

32. A specimen of this *Mentzelia* that A. B. Lambert raised from Nuttall's seeds and sent to *Bot. Mag.* under the name that Nuttall had given it in Fraser's catalog secured the authorship of the species to Nuttall. *Bot. Mag.*, XLII (September, 1815), t. 1760.

33. Graustein (1951), 71–72.

34. Lambert sent a specimen raised at Boyton from Nuttall's seeds to Sims, the editor, *Bot. Mag.*, XLI (April, 1815), t. 1724.

35. *O.*, I, 546.

36. *O.*, II, 367. This observation was doubtless copied from a field journal.

37. Sources for UP THE MISSOURI and AT THE MANDAN POST are Bradbury, *Travels*, in *EWT*, V, and H. M. Brackenridge, *Journal of a Voyage up the River Missouri, Performed in 1811* (2d ed., Baltimore, 1816), in *EWT*, VI. Washington Irving relied on these two records for this portion of *Astoria* (Chapters 13 to 22).

38. St. Charles lies on the Missouri River twenty miles overland from St. Louis.

39. Bradbury's account of Colter's story was retold in Brackenridge, *Views of Louisiana* (2d ed., Baltimore, 1817) and with some variations by Thomas James (1782–1847), *Three Years Among the Indians and Mexicans*, ed. by Walter B. Douglas (St. Louis, 1916).

40. The party wintered on the beautiful northeastern tributary of the Snake River, since known as Henry's Fork.

41. Fort Osage was abandoned when Fort Leavenworth was established in 1827.

42. "This species of bat was first noted by Mr. Nuttall, at Council Bluffs on the Missouri; and Mr. Say, in *Long's Expedition* describes an individual captured in the same neighborhood." John Richardson, *Fauna Boreali-Americana*, I (1829), 1.

43. The examples of the Missouri Valley flora included here and in the next chapter were selected from *Gen.*

44. Brackenridge, *Views of Louisiana*, etc., (Pittsburgh, 1814), 240.

45. Brackenridge says Lisa's boat overtook Hunt's party on June 2, but Bradbury gives the date as June 3. The latter was ahead of the calendar for he dated the last Sunday in July as July 29, whereas in 1811 it fell on July 28.

46. *EWT*, VI, 102. This account Irving expanded in his inimitable fashion to an imaginative description of Nuttall that has been widely quoted and given too much credence, see pp. 325–326.

47. Fort Mandan of the Missouri Fur Company was at a different location from the Fort Mandan of the Lewis and Clark Expedition, which lay to the east of the Missouri and some miles downstream.

48. The Chief was unhappy: his stories of the great number of the whites and of their ingenious inventions and varied possessions had branded him as a colossal liar since the savages could not conceive of a people more numerous or prosperous than themselves. *EWT*, VI, 137.

49. Brackenridge continued to travel. In 1817–1818, he went to South America on the Frigate *Congress* as secretary of the United States Commission sent to study the political situation. He accompanied the surgeon on board, William Baldwin, a botanist, on exploring trips into the country around Rio de Janeiro and Buenos Aires. H. M. Brackenridge, *Voyage to South America* (Baltimore, 1819). From 1822 to 1832, he served as Judge of the western district of Florida and, 1840–1841, as Congressman from the Pittsburgh area. Nuttall might have seen him again in West Florida or in Washington.

50. The trails mentioned are shown in Thwaites, *Original Journals of the Lewis and Clark Expedition* (New York: Atlas, Maps 12 and 11).

51. There is an error here as the course of the Missouri gets only a few miles north of 48°. However this statement shows that Nuttall went up the river 100 miles beyond the Mandan post, which he always located as 1500 miles up the Missouri.

52. Durand is followed here; the incident as told by Meehan differs in details.

53. T. Say, "Observations on some Species of Zoophytes, Shells, etc., Principally Fossil," *AJS*, II (1820), 42.

54. Elliott Coues, *History of the Lewis and Clark Expedition* (New York: Francis P. Harper, 1893), II, 405–406, n. 23.

55. U. P. Hedrick, *History of Horticulture in America to 1860* (New York: Oxford University Press, 1950), 8. See pp. 391–392 for Nuttall's recollections of Mandan's cucurbits.

56. In December 1804, at Fort Mandan Lewis and Clark received friendly calls from clerks of the Hudson Bay and North West Companies from their posts of the Assiniboine. Thwaites, *Original Journals of the Lewis and Clark Expedition*, I, 205, 237–238.

57. *Missouri Gazette*, October 26, 1811.

58. Rickett, "John Bradbury's Explorations in Missouri Territory," APS *Proceedings*, XC (1950), Letter 20.

59. *EWT*, V, 204.

60. On December 26, 1811, Roscoe wrote to Bradbury's son that the Committee was very dissatisfied with his father's resignation, for his salary had been paid to the end of the year but the quantity of plants received was inadequate. (The full shipment had perhaps not yet arrived; the impending war was affecting shipping.) The son responded with apologies and the suggestion that he would send his father's herbarium to Roscoe. Rickett, APS *Proceedings*, XC (1950), Letters 22 and 23.

61. Nuttall's 1811 visit at New Madrid appears as a chance entry at the end of his first 1810 field journal. Graustein (1951), 72.

62. *O.*, II, 37.

63. Robert Porter Allen in letter to author. A low point of 14 whoopers was reached in 1938; in November 1965, a count of 44 was announced by the Interior Department.

64. Barton wrote, "Previous to his departure he transmitted to me a number of dried specimens and seeds which he had collected. . . . At the same time he sent me a ms. book in which he has given pretty full descriptions of . . . Bartonia superba and B. polypetala." Pennell (1936), 50.

## CHAPTER 6. ENGLAND, 1812–1815

1. Information concerning Nuttall's family has come from many sources that were made available to me: statements of collateral descendants in the Dixon-Nuttall and Booth lines; family records, letters, printed matter, and an old sampler with birth dates; observations in Long Preston, Settle, and the Pennines and of Nutgrove in its sadly altered state and Nutgrove Chapel; inspection of parish records of christenings, marriages, and deaths, church plaques, gravestones and probated wills; relevant clippings in a scrapbook at St. Helen's Library and other clipped articles; miscellaneous old records of Ribblesdale belonging to Thomas Lord of Settle; and T. C. Barker and J. R. Harris, *A Merseyside Town in the Industrial Revolution: an Economic Study of St. Helens 1750–1900* (Liverpool, England: University Press of Liverpool, 1954), 174, 356–358.

2. Rev. John W. Seller, "Thatto Heath Methodism," *Methodist Recorder* (London), February 19, 1903.

3. *Gen.*, II, 52–53.

4. *Ibid.*, 240.

5. Through the courtesy of Dr. H. Stansfield, the writer saw Nuttall's specimens at the Liverpool Museum. However, many herbarium specimens have been destroyed through the years.

6. *Bot. Mag.*, XLI (1815), t. 1706 and text. Also see pp. 84, 88–92.

7. *Gen.*, I, 237.

8. *Ark. J.*, 16.

9. Graustein (1951), *passim*.

10. Reprinted in *Pittonia*, II (1890), 116–119.

11. At ANS there is a copy of the catalog endorsed "By T. Nuttall" in his handwriting. It had been folded and mailed to "Z. Collins Esq., Philadelphia."

12. Ker, a man of several names (Bellenden, Gawler), was the first editor of the *Botanical Register* (1812–1847). He did some taxonomic analyses for *Bot. Mag.*

13. October 23, 1838, to Torrey. T. Corr. Fraser became bankrupt.

14. Brown observed and named the nucleus of the plant cell but is most widely known for his discovery of Brownian movement.

15. A. T. Gage, *History of the Linnean Society of London* (London: Taylor and Francis, 1938).

16. This paper was never published by the Linnean Society despite Pursh's incomplete citations of it as in their *Transactions*, XI, in his *Flora Americae Septentrionalis*.

17. Ms. Minutes, Linnean Society.

18. Pursh said that he grew plants brought from America in the garden of G. Anderson, Esq. *Flora Americae Septentrionalis* (London, 1814), II, 611.

19. As Sir James immediately suspected, this Hosackia was invalid; the present *Hosackia* was named by David Douglas.

20. Ms. Minutes.

21. Pursh reached Cambridge by a circuitous route. In 1810, he left Hosack's Garden to go to the West Indies for his health. The ship on which he returned the next year put in at Wiscasset, Maine, whence he made his way southward, calling on Peck en route.

22. Advertisement in *London Courier*, May 26, 1812.

23. On February 28, 1817, Nuttall wrote C. W. Short that "Mr. Lyons [*sic*] met with Robinia abundantly around Nashville, Tennessee." This information *could* have come through Landreth. Photostat from Filson Club, Louisville, Kentucky.

24. On April 20, 1813, Mühlenberg wrote to William Baldwin that Lyon "has returned from England." W. Darlington, *Reliquiae Baldwinianae* (Philadelphia, 1843).

25. When he published the *Gen.*, Nuttall reintroduced most of the names he had applied in "Fraser's Catalogue" (overlooking a few) but presented no case for his own names except where he considered Pursh's names inappropriate. Later his attitude changed, and, just before leaving for Oregon in 1834, he started a crusade to reestablish his 1813 names and continued it after his return to Philadelphia.

26. Graustein (1956a).

27. On May 17, 1813, Mühlenberg wrote to Elliott, "D. Barton . . . mentions that another American Genus belonging to the Icosandria is named after him." Gray Herbarium, Harvard University, Cambridge, Massachusetts.

28. Pennell (1936), 50, note 111.

29. F. Pursh, *Flora Americae Septentrionalis*, I, 327–328.

30. *Gen.*, I, 298. Nuttall said that A. B. Lambert could support his statement. No *Mentzelia* was found among the Lewis and Clark specimens. — Thomas Meehan, "The Plants of Lewis and Clark's Expedition Across the Continent, 1804–1806," ANS *Proceedings*, L (1898), 12–49. One wonders how Pursh accounted to Lambert, Nuttall, *et al.*, for his possession of Lewis and Clark plants. In the Preface to his *Flora* he says that he was asked "to describe and figure" those plants of the herbarium which he thought were new (page x) and that he inserted "the descriptions of those plants" in his Flora (page xi).

31. *Gen.*, I, 298.

32. Pickering wrote to Schweinitz, August 2, 1831, "of the discovery of Dr. B. S. Barton's herbarium . . . in Mr. Vaughan's garret [APS], where it has been baking these ten years. . . . with labels bearing *the names of those persons who sent them to Dr. Barton!* . . . I did not before suspect that Pursh was such an inveterate pirate." Schweinitz Corr., III, 242, ANS.

33. This undated note Lambert added onto a letter that he had received from Lisbon which he forwarded to Nuttall, who either sent it or gave it to Z. Collins. Collins Corr., ANS.

34. Nuttall stated that Pursh described his Amellus spinulosus [*Aplopappus spinulosus* (Pursh) DC] "from the specimen which I gave to Mr. Lambert." ANS *Journal*, new series, I (1848), 177. In Fraser's catalog, Nuttall called it "Sideranthus spinulosus."

35. "Very obligingly communicated" could impishly refer to data on Nuttall's labels accompanying the herbarium specimens given to Lambert.

36. *Viola nuttallii* Pursh, a yellow violet not in Lewis's or Bradbury's collection, was the first species of scores honoring Nuttall.

37. H. W. Rickett, "John Bradbury's Explorations in Missouri Territory," APS *Proceedings*, XC (1950), 59–89, Letter 24.

38. It would seem that Banks donated his share to Lambert, for none of Bradbury's plants have been reported at BMNH.

39. Pursh, *Flora Americae Septentrionalis* (London, 1814), 490.

40. W. Bullock, *Six Months Residence and Travel in Mexico* (London, 1824).

41. Ms. Minutes, Linnean Society.

42. Ms. Correspondence of Sir James Edward Smith, VI, 150, Linnean Society.

43. Graustein (1954b), 275.

44. Asa Gray, "The Flora of North America," *AJS*, 3d ser., XXIV (1882), 321.

45. For example, among many filchings pointed out by Stephen Elliott in *Sketch of the Botany of South Carolina and Georgia* (Charleston, 1821–1824) are: "collected in Carolina by Mr. Fraser" (I, 189), "found by Mr. Lyon in . . . Georgia" (I, 220), "collected in the bogs of Georgia by Mr. Enslen" (I, 439).

46. Torrey and Gray, *Flora of North America*, I (1838), 51.

47. Ms. Correspondence of Sir James Edward Smith, VI, 146, 155, 156, Linnean Society.

48. Nuttall always believed that this collection, which he presented to the ANS before he left for Oregon in 1834, was made by Masson. I am indebted to Joseph Ewan for the information that the collector is named as David James Niven (1774?–1826) by Mia C. Karsten, *J. S. Afr. Bot.*, XXVI (1960), 11–12; this attribution rests on information that C. Earle Smith, Jr., obtained from Sir George Taylor, Royal Botanical Gardens, Kew. See Chapter 16, n. 66.

49. Ms. Minutes, Linnean Society.

50. William Kirby, "A Century of Insects, Including Several New Genera," Linnean Society *Transactions*, XII (1817), 375–453.

51. T. Say, "Descriptions of Coleopterous Insects," ANS *Journal*, III (1824), 300–301.

52. "During the winter and spring of 1817 and 1818, a class of fifty young ladies was organized in Charleston . . . for the study of botany under a Mr. Whitlow [frequently so spelled in America]. It was reported that many of them made flattering progress." — Wm. M. and M. S. C. Smallwood, *Natural History and the American Mind* (New York, New York: Columbia University Press, 1941), 105.

53. David Landreth, Jr., "Capt. Mayne Reid's The Plant Hunters," *Horticulturalist*, n. s. XIII (1858), 256.

54. Baldwin to Darlington, February 19, 1817 — W. Darlington, *Reliquiae Baldwinianae* (Philadelphia, 1843).

55. The sailing date is mentioned by Nuttall in a letter written to Lambert on January 26, 1816. — Lambert Correspondence, Letter 96, Kew; printed in full, Graustein (1954a).

## CHAPTER 7. SOUTHERN EXPEDITIONS

1. Graustein (1954a), 255. The Philadelphia *United States Gazette* reported on Monday, July 10, the arrival of the British brig *Sceptre*, seventy

days from London. Although Nuttall's name does not appear on the passenger list, only this sailing suits the known facts.

2. Collins Correspondence, Letter 237, ANS. As this is a Eurasian as well as American species, Nuttall had perhaps recently seen it while botanizing in England.

3. Rafinesque, *American Monthly Magazine and Critical Review*, II (1818), 175.

4. Dr. James McBride wrote to Collins on October 15, 1816, that Pursh was extremely in error regarding the southern plants — Collins Correspondence, Letter 245, ANS.

5. David Landreth, Jr., "Capt. Mayne Reid's The Plant Hunters," *Horticulturalist*, n. s. XIII (1858), 256–257.

6. Graustein (1954a), 255.

7. Baldwin's letter of February 19, 1817, to Darlington. W. Darlington, *Reliquiae Baldwinianae* (Philadelphia, 1843).

8. Although no authority is available, it seems that Nuttall must have been subsidized, at least to some extent, by Jonas.

9. The main facts concerning the 1815–1816 expedition are in Nuttall's January 26, 1816, letter to Lambert. Graustein (1954a). Unless otherwise stated, quotations are from this source; species that Nuttall collected not mentioned in the letter were selected from *Gen.*, which usually gives habitats and locations.

10. Now *P. virginica* Spreng.

11. Honoring Aloysius Enslen, "an assiduous and practical botanist, patronised in his researches in the United States by Prince Lichtenstein of Austria, and to whom Mr Pursh was frequently indebted for many of the rarer plants of the Southern States." *Gen.*, I, 164–165.

12. Nuttall sailed twice from New Orleans (1811, 1820) but he wrote to W. J. Hooker on June 11, 1854, that he had never been ashore in the West Indies although he had once had a view of the shore of Cuba — Hooker Corr., LXIV, 297, Kew.

13. Letters of Baldwin to Mühlenberg, January 28, May 26, September 19, 1812. Darlington, *Reliquiae Baldwinianae* (Philadelphia, 1843).

14. Letter of Baldwin to F. A. Mühlenberg, April 23, 1816, *ibid.*

15. Letter of Baldwin to Lambert, September 2, 1817, *ibid.*

16. Nuttall, "Observations on the Genus Eriogonum, and the Natural Order Polygoneae of Jussieu," ANS *Journal*, I (1817), 31.

17. Further evidence that Nuttall habitually kept field journals.

18. *Gen.*, I, 278.

19. The schooner *Hazard* arrived at Philadelphia on February 12 from Wilmington, North Carolina (7 days). *Political and Commercial Register*, Philadelphia.

20. Collins Correspondence, no. 242, ANS; Pennell (1936), 49–51.

21. Dr. John W. Francis to Hosack, February 14–15, 1816 — Francis Papers, New York Public Library.

22. *Ibid.*

23. *Ibid.* Francis believed that Pursh had stolen the Lewis and Clark plants from Barton, who, he supposed, obtained them similarly.

24. Rafinesque, *A Life of Travels* (Philadelphia, 1836). Reissued in *Chronica Botanica*, 1944.

25. Collins Correspondence, 169, October 2, 1816, ANS.

26. *Gen.*, II, 35.

27. *Sylva*, I, 41.

28. Daniel Drake, *Pioneer Life in Kentucky*, ed. by his son, Charles D. Drake (Cincinnati, 1870).

29. *Gen.*, II, 49, 29.

30. P. A. Davies, "Charles Wilkins Short, 1794–1863, Botanist and Physician," The Filson Club *History Quarterly*, XIX (1945), 131–155, 208–249; S. D. Gross, "Obituary Notice of Charles Wilkins Short, M. D.," APS *Proceedings*, X (1865–1868), 171–186.

31. In 1810, Barton gave Nuttall a letter of introduction to Governor W. H. Harrison of Indiana Territory which he had no opportunity of delivering. Pennell (1936), 7.

32. *Gen.*, I, 10.

33. R. Harlan, "Description of the Fossil Bones of the Megalonyx discovered in White Cave . . . Kentucky," ANS *Journal*, VI, pt. II (1830), 269–288; Nuttall, ANS *Journal*, II (1821), 28 note.

34. Possibly one of Nuttall's interests hereabouts was the fossil-containing caves near the Green River.

35. *Gen.*, II, 109, 33, 158.

36. *Gen.*, II, 18.

37. *O.*, II, 25.

38. Nuttall to Short, February 28, 1817, The Filson Club, Louisville, Kentucky, photostat. The fact that Nuttall cannot be trusted implicitly on state boundaries complicates an attempt to establish his route on this trip.

39. Nuttall, ANS *Journal*, II (1821), 26. The chalk cliffs that Nuttall found so similar in appearance are distant in geological time.

40. *Gen.*, I, 95.

41. *Gen.*, I, 301, 160.

42. Collins Correspondence, 169, October 2, 1816, ANS.

43. Lyon died in Asheville and was buried there; money for a headstone was sent over from Britain. While in North Carolina on a botanical excursion in 1842, Asa Gray located the grave, which has since suffered two removals. Asheville *Citizen Times*, August 7, 1939.

44. Lot 182 of Nuttall's mineralogical collection, sold in 1860, contained a specimen of gold from North Carolina; however it is known that he collected specimens of gold in Rutherford County, North Carolina in 1839. See p. 343.

45. *Gen.*, I, 235.

46. *Gen.*, II, 5.

47. *Gen.*, I, 275.

48. Quarrying of this outcrop of pink granite was being started in the spring of 1959, but Nuttall's *Diamorpha pusilla* was collected by the writer near the outer edge. Nuttall wrote to Short, February 28, 1817, The Filson Club, Louisville, Kentucky, photostat: "look narrowly for the *Sedum pusillum* of Michaux wh (notwithstanding the various assertions of Mr Pursh . . .) has never yet been anywhere found but upon *The Flat Rock* nr Cambden [*sic*] in S. Carol. not upon flat rocks as P. asserts and who seems very plainly to confound this sps with the S. pulchellum so common around Harper's-Ferry, Virgia &c."

49. Nuttall, ANS *Journal*, II (1821), 31.

50. *Gen.*, II, 217.

51. *DAB*; H. W. Ravenel, *Botanical Gazette*, VIII (1883), 249–253.

52. Baldwin to John Le Conte, November 16, 1816, Torrey Collection of Autographed Letters, 14, ANS.

53. Collins Correspondence, 168, ANS.

54. Ms. Correspondence of Sir J. E. Smith, VI, 168, Linnean Society.

55. The writer is indebted to Dr. R. L. Stuckey for this information from a letter Drake wrote to Short on January 10, 1817. The Filson Club, Louisville, Kentucky.

56. Relf's Philadelphia *Gazette and Daily Advertiser*, January 20, January 30, and February 14, 1817.

## CHAPTER 8. PUBLICATION

1. Short's answer of March 31, states that Nuttall's letter "was handed to me this morning by Dr. Rodgers. . . ." The Filson Club, Louisville, Kentucky, photostatic copy.

2. The most useful sources of information about the Academy of Natural Sciences are the manuscript Minutes and the ANS *Journals*.

3. On April 1, 1817, Nuttall presented "a horn of the Antelope Americanus" to the Academy. Ms. Minutes.

4. T. Say, "Descriptions of Several New Species of North American Insects," ANS *Journal*, I (1817), 19–23.

5. T. Say, "New North American Neuropterous Insects," ANS *Journal*, VIII (1839–1842), 36; "New species of Hymenoptera," Boston Society of Natural History *Journal*, I (1837), 382–383.

6. The trip to New York is mentioned in a letter of Collins to Rafinesque, November 19, 1817, APS.

7. Rafinesque to Collins, July 21, 1817, APS. The *Allium* was in synonymy with Aiton's *A. tricoccum*.

8. Dr. W. C. Stüve to Elliott, October 20, 1817, Stephen Elliott Papers, Gray Herbarium, Harvard University, Cambridge, Massachusetts.

9. Elliott in the Preface of his *Sketch*.

10. This rare edition was issued for and by Eaton's students at Williams College. H. G. Good, "Amos Eaton (1776–1842), Scientist and Teacher of Science," *Scientific Monthly*, LIII (1940), 464–469.

11. "An Account of Two New Genera of Plants, and of a Species of Tillaea and Limosella," ANS *Journal*, I (1817), 111–123.

12. "Description of Collinsia, a New Genus of Plants," ANS *Journal*, I (1817), 189–192.

13. Collins Correspondence, 248 and 127, ANS.

14. John Vaughan was Librarian of the APS; his "garret" was the top floor of the Society's building.

15. A. Hunter Dupree, *Asa Gray* (Cambridge, Massachusetts: Harvard University Press, 1959), 398, credits Torrey and Gray's *Flora of North America* as the source of such a shift, but it had already been established twenty years before by Nuttall's *Genera*.

16. G. S. Hillard, *Life, Letters and Journals of George Ticknor*, I (Boston, Massachusetts: Houghton Mifflin Company, 1919), 16.

17. J. E. Agan, "Corréa da Serra," *Pennsylvania Magazine of History and Biography*, XLIX (1925), 1–43.

18. Bartonia and *Collinsia* had already been published.

19. Wister believed that the genus was named for his father. Letter of C. J. Wister, May 28, 1894, Torrey's Autograph Collection, ANS.

20. *Ibid.* But Asa Gray with characteristic faith in his own assumptions says, "We trust that . . . such obvious corrections as of Wisteria to Wistaria may prevail. We may assume that the error was typographical; for Dr. Wistar was at the time too well known in Philadelphia for Nuttall to have been ignorant of the orthography of the name." "Botanical Nomenclature," *AJS* third series, XXVI (1868), 417–437, p. 432.

21. Baldwin did not become a member of the Linnean Society. The only American naturalists of his generation elected as Foreign Members were Jacob Bigelow in 1819, Thomas Say in 1829, and Richard Harlan. Foreign membership became limited to fifty in 1818.

22. Baldwin to Collins, Collins Correspondence, 198, ANS.

23. Baldwin to Darlington, September 3, 1818, Gray Herbarium, Harvard University, Cambridge, Massachusetts.

24. Rafinesque, "Review of Nuttall's Genera," *American Monthly Magazine and Critical Review*, IV (1818–1819), 184–196.

25. "Letters from the Collection of Dr. Charles W. Short," ed. by W. C. Coker, Elisha Mitchell Scientific Society *Journal*, LVII (1941), 148.

26. C. Cushing, "Botany of the United States," *North American Review*, XIII (1821), 116–118 and *passim*.

27. J. Bronowski, "The Creative Process," *Scientific American*, CXC (1958), 64.

28. Boott to Hooker, April 18, 1819, Kew.

29. W. J. Hooker, "On the Botany of America," *AJS*, IX (1825), 278; reprinted from Brewster's *Edinburgh Journal of Science*, II (1825), 122–123.

30. Collins Correspondence, 280, ANS.

31. W. Cooper, July 7, 1822, T. Corr.

32. C. L. Shear and N. E. Stevens, "Correspondence of Schweinitz and Torrey," Torrey Botanical Club *Memoirs*, XVI (1921), April 19, 1821.

33. *AJS*, V (1822), 49, 78.

34. James, *Narrative of Long's Expedition*, Thwaites, *EWT*, XVI, 171.

35. Elliott, *Sketch of the Botany of South Carolina and Georgia* (1824), II, 67.

36. Torrey, *Flora of the Northern and Middle Sections of the United States* (New York, 1824), Preface.

37. Curtis to Torrey, May 5, 1834, T. Corr.

38. E. L. Greene, "Botanical Literature, Old and New," *Pittonia*, II (1889–1890), 93.

39. M. L. Fernald, "Some Early Botanists of the American Philosophical Society," APS *Proceedings*, LXXXVI (1942), 65.

40. Darlington, *Reliquiae Baldwinianae* (Philadelphia, 1843), Baldwin to Darlington, August 14, 1818.

41. J. W. Harshberger, *Botanists of Philadelphia* (Philadelphia, 1899), 151–159.

42. Nuttall, "Collections toward a Flora of the Territory of Arkansas," APS *Transactions*, new ser., V (1837), 152.

43. Daniel Parker Correspondence, Box 24, HSP.

44. *Ibid.*, Box 38.

45. Jefferson Papers, Coolidge Collection, Massachusetts Historical Society, Boston, Massachusetts. That Jefferson about that time considered Nuttall's nationality a barrier to his appointment on the faculty of the University of

Virginia appears in correspondence between him and Thomas Cooper. On June 21, 1819, Cooper wrote, "Correa da Serra recommends Thomas Nuttal [*sic*] as botanist," to which Jefferson responded on July 11 that he was "interested in Thomas Nuttal, if a native." *The Jefferson Papers of the University of Virginia* (Charlottesville, Virginia: University of Virginia Library, 1950), nos. 1702 and 1716. In 1827, after the University of Virginia was a reality, a vacancy in the professorship of natural history brought Nuttall's name again under consideration. *Letters and other writings of James Madison* (Philadelphia, 1865), III, 570–571.

46. Nuttall recorded that Dunbar and Hunter found *Maclura* near the Washita. *Gen.*, II, 234.

47. A memorandum by Collins listing the donors includes Reuben Haines and omits Maclure; in Nuttall's dedication the reverse is the case. Collins Correspondence, 173, ANS.

## CHAPTER 9. JOURNEY TO THE SOUTHWEST

1. The events of this chapter were recorded by Nuttall in *A Journal of Travels into the Arkansa Territory during the year 1819*, etc. (Philadelphia, 1821), reprinted in R. G. Thwaites, *EWT*, XIII. Letters of Nuttall to Collins give additional facts. For a detailed account of the expedition from Fort Smith to the Red River and return, with an enumeration of the plants Nuttall collected, see S. W. Geiser, "Thomas Nuttall's Botanical Collecting Trip to the Red River," *Field and Laboratory*, XXIV (1956), 43–60. The quotation is from *Ark. J.*, 2.

2. *Ark. J.*, 18.

3. *Ibid.*, 32.

4. *Ibid.*, 36.

5. The writer understands that the fifty dollars was borrowed for investing in a flatboat and cargo that he could sell at a profit down the river.

6. It is of interest that Haines is included here and Maclure omitted.

7. Did Nuttall intend to name *Tilia* rather than *Populus*? In *Ark. J.*, 28, he wrote that at Le Tart's rapids he was "particularly gratified in finding the *Tilia heterophylla*," and he makes a similar statement in the *Sylva*, I, 90–92. Dr. R. L. Stuckey informed me that a Nuttallian specimen of the *Tilia* in the ANS herbarium is marked "Ohio."

8. Collins Correspondence, 170, ANS.

9. *Ark. J.*, 37.

10. *Ibid.*, 57–58.

11. *Ibid.*, 63.

12. Nuttall published this species as *Draba *brachycarpa* in Torrey and Gray's *Flora* (1838), I, 108.

13. Dobson was evidently distributing the *Genera* for Nuttall.

14. Collins Correspondence, 171, ANS.

15. Nuttall, "Observations on the Geological Structure of the Valley of the Mississippi," ANS *Journal*, II (1821), 14–52.

16. Collins Correspondence, 172, May 12, 1819, ANS.

17. *Ibid.*

18. *Ark. J.*, 141.

19. For this information the writer is indebted to the generosity of Dr. Samuel Wood Geiser who loaned her his files on both Russell and Bradford.

Another classmate of Russell, Henry McMurtrie, who joined the Academy in 1833, became a friend of Nuttall.

20. *Ark. J.*, 152. (Secretary of War John C. Calhoun ordered General Andrew Jackson, Commanding-General of the Southern Division, U. S. A., to cause the removal of all white settlers who should be found in Arkansas Territory west of a line connecting the sources of the Kiamichi and Poteau rivers. *Fide*, Dr. S. W. Geiser.)

21. *Ibid.*, 157–159.

22. *O.*, I, 275–276.

23. *Ark. J.*, 159–161.

24. A passage in the *Sylva*, I, 35, gives another example of Nuttall's troublesome tendency to date events one year too early: "In the summer of 1818, on my journey . . . on the plains of the Red River near its confluence with the Kamesha I had the satisfaction of discovering this curious Elm [*Ulmus *crassifolia*]."

25. *Ark. J.*, 177–181.

26. *Ibid.*, 181–190.

27. *Ark. J.*, 208–209.

28. *Ibid.*, 211.

29. Collins Correspondence, 172, May 12, 1819, ANS.

30. *Ark. J.*, 219–220.

31. *Journal of John James Audubon*, Howard Corning, ed. (Boston: Club of Odd Volumes, 1929), I, 70.

32. Here Audubon tutored his "lovely Miss Pirrie of Oakley" in 1821. Francis H. Herrick, *Audubon the Naturalist*, 2d ed. (New York: Appleton, 1938).

33. *Ark. J.*, 239.

34. *Ibid.*, 244–245. "New-Orleans is a dreadful place in the eyes of a New-England man. They keep Sunday as we in Boston keep the 4th of July, or any other day of merriment and frolic." John B. Wyeth, *A Short History of a Long Journey*, Thwaites, *EWT*, XXI, 94.

35. See Chapter 7, note 12.

36. Schiller, "Die Ideale."

## CHAPTER 10. PHILADELPHIA, 1820–1822

1. As the paper was not printed until early in 1821, additions *might* have been made to the original version, but Nuttall's known activities after his arrival in Philadelphia leave inadequate time for a trip to Richmond thereafter. Information that Nuttall furnished by early 1825, for Dr. Robinson's *Catalogue of American Minerals*, included personal observations at sites in Virginia and Maryland that must have been made on his way north from Richmond. The ANS Minutes for May 15, 1821, state that Collins presented a large fossil striated culm found in the Richmond coal mines by Mr. Nuttall.

2. ANS Ms. Minutes.

3. Landreth placed these lectures "nearly simultaneously with the publication of his Genera," that is, in the summer of 1818, a large part of which Nuttall spent continuously in Germantown. The writer assumes that Landreth was mistaken in the year. Landreth, "Capt. Mayne Reid's The Plant Hunters," *Horticulturist*, n. s., XIII (1858). Advertisements in Philadelphia newspapers

show that the first meeting was held in the room of the Medical Society in the Masonic Hall; the second, in the Hall of the Academy.

4. "An Account of Two North American Species of Rottboellia, Discovered on the Seacoast of the State of Georgia," *AJS*, I (1819), 355–359 and "An Account of Two North American Species of Cyperus Discovered in the State of Georgia: to Which is Added Four Species of Kyllingia, Found on the Brazilian Coast, and on the Rio de la Plata in South America," APS *Transactions*, new ser., II (1825), 167–171.

5. On February 6, 1819, Darlington wrote to Baldwin: "I understand Nuttall has gone somewhere in the direction of the . . . Missouri; & it struck me that he had heard of the expedition, & was determined to anticipate it — so as to leave you nothing to do but to 'corroborate' his discoveries!" Baldwin's answer on February 25, read in part: "I understood in Philadelphia that Nuttall had gone to Washington and it instantly occurred to me that his intention was to 'corroborate' me. I shall not be the least astonished if he falls in with the expedition *accidentally*, and attempts to *billet* himself upon it. He is accustomed to this kind of management." Baldwin–Darlington Correspondence, Gray Herbarium, Harvard University, Cambridge, Massachusetts.

6. *Narrative of the Long Expedition*, Thwaites, *EWT*, XVII, 218, note 84.

7. ANS *Journal*, III (1824), 31; *Boston Journal of Natural History*, I (1834–1837), 295, 170.

8. C. A. LeSueur, "A New Genus and Several New Species of Fish," and "Two New Species of Exocetus," ANS *Journal*, II (1821), 2–11.

9. This statement indicates an absence from North America of approximately three years (1812–1815).

10. Jacob Bigelow, "Review of Nuttall's Journal of Travels into the Arkansas Territory," *North American Review*, XVI (1823), 59–75. Shortly before writing this review Bigelow had met Nuttall and held a long conversation with him (*vide post*).

11. Volume 295, pp. 576–577, 597–598, September 14 and 21, 1822.

12. Letter to author from Dr. George W. White, University of Illinois.

13. "A Description of Some New Species of Plants, Recently Introduced into the Gardens of Philadelphia, from the Arkansa Territory," ANS *Journal*, II, part I (1821), 114–123; and "Descriptions of Rare Plants Recently Introduced into the Gardens of Philadelphia," *ibid.*, 179–182.

14. The section of Nuttall's paper containing *Callirhoë* was read to the Academy on March 5, 1822, and was published soon after near the end of vol. II, pt. I. (The last paper of pt. I was read on March 19; the first of pt. II, on May 14.) Although in his paper Nuttall stated that "Dick has dedicated the genus" to him, it is not to be assumed that the fascicle of W. P. C. Barton's *Flora of North America* in which Dick's "Nuttallia" appeared, II, 74 (1822), had already been published; in fact it strongly suggests that Nuttall was giving advance publicity to a future publication. Nuttall saw both Dick and Barton frequently and would hear promptly of the decision. Moreover Asa Gray, who restored *Callirhoë* as a genus in 1849 after reducing it to *Malva* in 1838, did not doubt that *Callirhoë* had priority; through Torrey, he would know. Misjudgment of this complex situation by E. L. Greene in 1891 caused the loss of a genus honoring Nuttall.

15. The paper, read thirteen years later, was published without plates.

16. E. James, "Catalogue of Plants Collected during a Journey to and from

the Rocky Mountains during the Summer of 1820," APS *Transactions*, II (1825), 172–190.

17. "Observations on the Geological Structure of the Valley of the Mississippi," ANS *Journal*, II (1821), 14–52. The January 1821 issue of the *Journal* was the first following the presentation of the paper the previous May. See ANS Minutes for May 1820 and January 30, 1821.

18. *Ibid.*, 14–15.

19. *Ibid.*, 34–35.

20. Charles Keyes, "A Century of Iowa Geology," Iowa Academy of Science *Proceedings*, XXVI (1919), 408.

21. C. Keyes, "Early Geological Work of Thomas Nuttall," *Popular Science Monthly*, LXXXIV (1914), 184.

22. Dr. George W. White, head of the Department of Geology at the University of Illinois, informs me that his notes on Nuttall's 1821 paper read: ". . . a confused mass of excellent material! It reminds me of the first draft of an eager, and able, but undisciplined, student's thesis which, after brutal 'licking into shape' by a strict committee turns out to be a fine report."

23. Published in Boston, 1821. Webster married a daughter of Thomas Hickling, the American vice-consul at St. Michael.

24. "After attending a lecture by the late Mr. Nuttall, he entered the Mineralogical class, formed under the guidance of that distinguished Naturalist, and went into the study with the greatest enthusiasm." T. Meehan, 220. "Nuttall was a simple hearted enthusiast, whose devotion to natural science was unconquerable, and whose frank and genial character won him admiration and esteem. The friendship of such a man naturally developed young Carpenter's taste for natural history, and in a short time his studies were bent in that direction." — Stephen N. Winslow, *Biographies of Successful Philadelphia Merchants* (Philadelphia, 1864), 125.

25. The main facts of Torrey's life are found in A. D. Rodgers, III, *John Torrey* (Princeton, New Jersey: Princeton University Press, 1942).

26. Collins Correspondence, 213, July 9, 1818, ANS.

27. T. Corr., February 13, 1821. Mr. Tot Lord, of Settle, England, loaned the writer a scrapbook containing excerpts from the diary of William Lodge Paley, a Dalesman who taught at Long Preston for a few years before 1812, when he went to teach at Giggleswick School. Of interest were several comments concerning a bookish Mr. Hardacre of Bendyate (Long Preston), an affluent gentleman, and a statement that Paley used a "nightgown" only on cold nights!

28. T. Corr. Quaker Bridge is still a favorite botanical site in the pine barrens.

29. C. L. Shear and N. E. Stevens, "Correspondence of Schweinitz and Torrey," Torrey Botanical Club *Memoirs*, XVI (1921), March 22, 1821.

30. Nuttall to Torrey, August 2, 1821, Yale University Library. The letter is quoted in full by R. G. Beidleman, "Some Biographical Sidelights on Thomas Nuttall," APS *Proceedings*, CIV (1960), 89.

31. *Recollections of John Jay Smith*, Elizabeth P. Smith, ed. (Philadelphia, Pennsylvania: J. P. Lippincott Co., 1892), 191.

32. Originally named *American Journal of Science*, the second volume became *American Journal of Science and the Arts*, the title that it bore until 1880 when it reverted to the original name, which is used in this work. It was commonly called "Silliman's Journal."

33. Vanuxem is credited with holding the earliest professorship of geology in the United States: College of South Carolina, 1819–1826.

34. *New York Medical and Physical Journal*, I (1822), 194–204; *AJS*, V (1822), 239–248.

35. "More than 140 minerals . . . have been found in the district, 32 of which were first found there and 30 are not known elsewhere in the world" Charles Palache, *The Minerals of Franklin and Sterling Hill, New Jersey* (U.S.G.S.P.P. 180, 1935), 3.

36. It is probable that Torrey gave Nuttall this information.

37. *AJS*, V (1822), 239–248, 336–344, 366; VI (1823), 168–171, 171–173, 356–361.

38. T. Corr., April 12, 1823.

39. Serpentine is considered to be both a rock and a mineral; the rock is now sometimes called "serpentinite."

40. Boston, Massachusetts, Public Library, July 24, 1823.

41. "Observations on the Serpentine Rocks of Hoboken, New Jersey," *AJS*, IV (1822), 16–23. C. U. Shepard published "fowlerite" (later regarded as a variety of rhodonite) in 1832, but he afterwards stated that Nuttall originated the name in the 1820s.

42. New York Lyceum of Natural History *Annals*, I (1824), 92–93; S. Robinson, *Catalogue of American Minerals* (Boston, 1825), Appendix, 289.

43. "A Catalogue of a Collection of Plants made in East-Florida . . . by [N.] A. Ware, Esq.," *AJS*, V (1822), 286–304.

44. Shear and Stevens, "Correspondence of Schweinitz and Torrey," Torrey Botanical Club *Memoirs*, XVI (1921), May 3, 1822.

45. *Ibid.*, May 15, 1822.

46. *Ibid.*, July 21, 1822.

47. Minutes, New York College of Physicians and Surgeons, May 7, 1822 (D, 145), Columbia University Archives.

48. T. Corr., July 7, 1822.

49. *Ibid.*, March 31, 1822.

50. Benjamin Say, brother of Thomas, and John P. Wetherill of Philadelphia and the Academy.

51. Robert Hare (1781–1858), a fellow student and good friend of Silliman at the University of Pennsylvania in 1803–1804, became professor of chemistry there in 1818.

52. HSP.

53. "Localities of Minerals Communicated by Dr. William Meade," *AJS*, VII (1824), 49–54.

54. T. Corr., July 12, 1822.

55. Nuttall was elected to the short-lived American Geological Society (1819–1826) in September 1822. Beidleman, 90, 91, and notes 25 and 27.

56. Silliman, *Remarks Made on a Short Tour between Hartford and Quebec in the Autumn of 1819* (New Haven, 1820), 350–352; Carl A. Pursch, "Nekrolog von Friedrich Pursh," Reichenbach's *Botanische Zeitung*, X (1827), 491–496.

57. T. Corr., September 9, 1822.

58. The wanderings of Nuttall's mineralogical collection will appear in chronological order.

59. T. Corr.

## CHAPTER 11. HARVARD

Important sources of information for chapters of the Harvard period are certain records of the Massachusetts Society for Promoting Agriculture (UA I 15.999) and two collections of papers concerning William Dandridge Peck (UA I 15.1003 and HUG 1677), all deposited in the Harvard Archives, Cambridge, Massachusetts. They will be referred to respectively as MSPA and Peck Papers. Other papers of the Society (Files of MSPA), consulted through the kindness of Richard Saltonstall, President, were especially helpful.

1. Josiah Quincy, *History of Harvard University* (Boston, 1860), II, 267.

2. Samuel Atkins Eliot, *A Sketch of the History of Harvard College* (Boston, 1848), 180; Quincy, *History of Harvard University* (Boston, 1860), II, 542–543. Gifts from the Lowell family, which includes the Higginsons and S. P. Gardner, equaled the maximum single donation, a bequest of $2000.

3. "It was principally with a view to draw this learned and indefatigable labourer of natural history from his retreat that the subscription for a Professorship of Natural History at Cambridge was commenced." John Lowell, "Obituary of William D. Peck," Massachusetts Historical Society *Collections*, 2d ser., X (1823), 163–170; Graustein (1958).

4. Peck's diaries and expense accounts of his European tour and photostats of letters of continental scientists (Rose–Troup Mss., Linnean Society) are in Peck Papers. Letters from Peck to Smith are in Smith's ms. correspondence (XXIII, 24, 25, and 27) Linnean Society. A letter to Peck from Smith and one from Banks are in the Autograph Collection at the Gray Herbarium. A letter from Peck to Kirby acknowledging one from him, is printed in John Freeman, *Life of Rev. William Kirby* . . . (London, 1852), 246–247.

5. Kirby, "Strepsiptera, a new order of Insects proposed," Linnean Society *Transactions*, XI (1815), 86–122; Pursh, *Flora Americae Septentrionalis*; Peck, American Academy of Arts and Sciences *Memoirs*, II, pt. 2 (1804), 46–57; and Storer, Boston Society of Natural History *Journal*, II (1838–1839), 506–510.

6. MSPA Minutes, 41.

7. William Coolidge Lane, "Dr. Benjamin Waterhouse and Harvard University," Cambridge Historical Society *Proceedings*, IV (1909). Waterhouse received a guinea from each student electing his course. Graustein (1961a).

8. M. I. J. Gozzoldi, ed., "Letters to Mrs. William Jenks, 1806–1813" (written by Susannah Hill *et al.*), Cambridge Historical Society *Proceedings*, IX (1914), 32.

9. Files of MSPA. The recent discovery of the bill was the means of identification of the builder. The erection of Center Church in New Haven (1812–1814) launched Town in architecture; he constructed many public buildings in which his handling of the Greek Revival style was outstanding. However he became more widely known and wealthy through his patent of the Town Truss for covered-bridge construction. DAB.

10. In 1910 when the Gray Herbarium was enlarged, the Garden House was sold and the new owner moved it to the west side of Garden Street.

11. H. B. Weiss and G. M. Ziegler, *Thomas Say, Early American Naturalist* (Springfield, Illinois; Charles C. Thomas, 1931), 111.

12. G. B. Emerson, *Reminiscences of an Old Teacher* (Boston, 1878), 13.

13. Peck Papers.

14. Ralph L. Rusk, *The Letters of Ralph Waldo Emerson* (New York: Columbia University Press, 1939), I, 123.
15. Harvard College Papers, X (1821–1824), 39.
16. MSPA Minutes, 140–142.
17. Harvard College Records, VI (1819–1827), 82.
18. This section is based on Charles Eliot Norton, "Reminiscences of Old Cambridge," Cambridge Historical Society *Records*, I (1905); James Russell Lowell, "Cambridge Thirty Years Ago," *Putnam's Monthly Magazine* (April, 1853), reprinted in *Fireside Travels* (New York: Oxford University Press, 1915); Samuel Eliot Morison, *Three Centuries of Harvard* (Cambridge, Massachusetts: Harvard University Press, 1936); and a lifetime of exposure to Cantabrigiana.
19. Footnote by G. B. Emerson in *Memoir of Samuel J. May*, ed. by T. J. Mumford, G. B. Emerson, and Samuel May (Boston, 1873), 33–35. Farrar's first wife was one of the charming Buckminsters.
20. The class of 1823 was divided into two cliques: "a schism developed between the 'high fellows' . . . and the obedient 'blacks' . . . a 'black' played informer against a 'high fellow' who was expelled; and the rebels swore an oath under the Rebellion Tree that they would leave College until the departed hero was reinstated and the informer deprived of his Commencement part." Morison, *Three Centuries of Harvard* (Cambridge, Massachusetts: Harvard University Press, 1936), 231. One of those expelled, Charles Pickering, M. D. 1826, received his A. B. degree in 1849, the degree of a son of John Quincy Adams was posthumously conferred, and many of the expelled group never received degrees.
21. Files of MSPA.
22. Dwight, *Travels in New England and New York* (New Haven, 1821), I, 452–468.
23. Schweinitz Correspondence, II, 235, ANS.
24. Unless otherwise noted, facts concerning John Lowell, "the Rebel," are from Ferris Greenslet's *The Lowells and Their Seven Worlds* (Boston, Massachusetts: Houghton Mifflin Company, 1946), 87–189 and *passim*.
25. Harvard College Papers, X (1821–1824), 39.
26. The Board of Visitors voted that she be allowed to remain six months after Professor Peck's death and that the house be then leased. However Mrs. Peck stayed on until September. MSPA Minutes, 138, 142.
27. MSPA Minutes, 148.
28. Nuttall's original receipt for $41.66 is in the John Davis Papers, Massachusetts Historical Society. Higginson, finding it missing from his records, had Nuttall sign another receipt.
29. The occurrence of this trip is revealed in Nuttall's papers on two species that were collected, an orchid at "New Ipswich, Massachusetts [!]" and a grass near Bellows Falls, Vermont. The locations of the two towns and other observations of Nuttall (which will appear) suggest the objectives of the tour.
30. Collection of the Shoreham mineral is recorded in the Appendix of Dr. Samuel Robinson's *Catalogue of American Minerals* (Boston, 1825), 279.
31. S. J. Spalding, "Memoir of Henry Coit Perkins," Essex Institute *Historical Collections*, XII (1874), 6–7.
32. General Letter File (1812–1840), ANS.
33. "Observations on the genus Oryzopsis," ANS *Journal*, III (1823), 125–128.

34. Torrey's letter is known only through Nuttall's response of July 24, 1823 (Boston Public Library). Torrey had specimens of the grass from three sources: Cooley and Hitchcock, Bigelow, and Beck. Torrey, *Flora of Northern and Middle Sections of the United States* (New York, 1824).

35. ANS *Journal*, III (1823), 135–139.

36. APS. The last numeral of the year date was marked over when written and is undecipherable. However the address and contents ensure the year as 1823.

37. Waterhouse returned to his home in Cambridge in 1825 after a period of service at nearby United States Hospitals.

38. Orie W. Long, *Literary Pioneers* (Cambridge, Massachusetts: Harvard University Press, 1935), 78.

39. Harris to Storer, November 2, 1836. "Entomological Correspondence of Thaddeus William Harris," edited by S. H. Scudder, Boston Society of Natural History *Occasional Papers*, I (1869). Nuttall introduced other correspondents to Say, who received echinoderms from Storer and insects from Ezekiel Holmes.

40. It is useful to recall the picture of the botanist that Durand composed from the recollections of Nuttall's friends and acquaintances: "Nuttall was naturally shy and reserved in his manners in general society, but not so with those who knew him well. If silent or morose in the presence of those for whom he felt a sort of antipathy yet, when with congenial companions, he was affable and . . . the delight of the company . . . [by] . . . his unaffected manners, and amiability. . . ." Durand, 10.

41. Nuttall–Putnam Correspondence. This and the following letters of Nuttall and George Putnam were generously loaned to me by Miss Elizabeth Putnam of Boston, Massachusetts.

42. Nuttall's letter of November 22, 1823, entitled "Notices of American Spodumen," appeared in ANS *Journal*, III (1824), 284–286.

43. Mrs. Peck was perhaps moving to take charge of a small student house.

44. John Finch, *Travels in the United States of America and Canada* (London, 1833), 132–133. Finch used few year dates; it is possible that the commencement he attended was that of 1824.

45. MPSA, Minutes, October 11, 1823.

46. Nuttall gave these facts orally to George Bowen, who wrote them to Silliman on April 7, 1824, – HSP.

47. Webster to Silliman, Boston Public Library.

48. Harvard College Papers, X (1821–1824), 76.

49. Bowen was appointed professor of chemistry and natural philosophy at the University of Nashville in 1826.

50. T. Corr., April 22, 1824.

51. Boltwood Papers, Detroit Public Library.

52. *Journal Kept by David Douglas* (London: William Wesley & Son, 1914), 24, 25–26.

53. Torrey to Hooker, February 3, 1824, XLIV, 174, Kew.

54. W. H. Keating, *Narrative of an Expedition to the source of St. Peter's River*, . . . (Philadelphia, 1824). Schweinitz in his "Catalogue of Plants" paid "a high and delicate eulogium" to Nuttall – Walter R. Johnson, *Memoir of the late Lewis David von Schweinitz, P. D.* (Philadelphia, 1835).

55. Letter of December 30, 1823, Boltwood Papers, Detroit Public Library.

## CHAPTER 12. ENGLAND, 1824

1. Photostat. Correspondence of A. P. de Candolle, Archives of the Geneva Herbarium, Switzerland.

2. DC., *Rapp. Jard. Genèv* (1821), 44; Rafinesque, *American Monthly Magazine*, II (1819), 357. A third invalid Nuttallia (*Trigonia* Aubl. of the *Malpighiaceae*) appeared in Sprengel, *Neue Entdeck.*, II (1821), 158.

3. Bigelow to Torrey, December 4, 1820, T. Corr.

4. The first volume of De Candolle's *Prodromus* is dated 1824; the preface was written on November 25, 1823. The voluminous work, incomplete at his death, was continued by his son, Alphonse. Volume XVII, the last, was published in 1873.

5. The writer is indebted to Major William F. Dixon-Nuttall for the loan of this diary. Determining the date of it presented a problem, for the first entry is headed merely "Thursday, January 23." The only year that Nuttall visited England when the January date fell on a Thursday was 1812, but, on that trip, it is dubious that he reached England sufficiently early to be there on January 23, and the diary contains descriptions of rock formations in America which he did not see until 1822 and 1823. The content is consistent for 1824, and misdating the day is characteristic of Nuttall.

6. This inn is still in operation.

7. Lady Fleming, a widow, born "à le Fleming," lived until 1861. "Wordsworth's cottage" lay within her vast holdings.

8. There is a copy at HSP, and the writer received a copy from Dr. Frans Verdoorn.

9. A copy of Brooke's book that Henry Heuland gave to Nuttall, handed down in the Booth branch of the family, was loaned to the writer some years ago by Samuel Rishworth Booth. Brooke named heulandite in *Edinburgh Philosophical Journal*, VI (1822), 112.

10. H. J. Brooke, *Annals of Philosophy*, London, 2d ser., VII (1824), 366.

11. The writer is indebted to the Liverpool Museums and Dr. H. Stansfield for the privilege of seeing these specimens.

12. ANS ms. Minutes, January 3, 1837.

13. Boott to Torrey, June 3, 1821, T. Corr.

14. Hooker to Bentham, September 6, 1823, I, 1, Kew.

15. Hooker's life is well documented by his own prolific taxonomic writings, periodicals which he edited and for which he wrote much of the copy, a colossal correspondence carried on with warm interest, and the monuments, living and nonliving, that he has left at the Royal Botanical Gardens at Kew. His son, Sir Joseph Dalton Hooker, wrote "Life and Labours of Sir William Jackson Hooker" for *Annals of Botany*, XVI (1902), ix–ccxxi.

16. Thomas Thomson to Nuttall, February 25, 1828, Torrey's Autograph Collection, 220, ANS. "Some American Minerals," Lyceum of Natural History *Annals*, III (1828–1836), 9–86.

17. Whitfield is a very common name in the Liverpool area: Jonas's farmer was mentioned in his will; a field collector of the Earl of Derby was a Thomas Whitfield.

18. MSPA, Minutes, June 12, 1824. Files of MSPA contain an itemized bill showing that supplies and three and a half days' work on Nuttall's rooms in July 1824, cost a total of $8.26 — File C, Folder XXXII, 62.

19. Boltwood Papers, Detroit Public Library.

20. *Ibid.*

## CHAPTER 13. "VEGETATING AT HARVARD"

The chief sources of facts for the first section of this chapter are Jeremy Belknap, *History of New Hampshire* (Philadelphia, 1784–1792); Edward Tuckerman, "History of the Exploration of the White Hills," chapter ii (34–46) in Thomas Starr King, *The White Hills* (Boston, 1860); F. W. Kilbourne, *Chronicles of the White Mountains* (Boston, Massachusetts: Houghton Mifflin Co., 1916); and Arthur Stanley Pease, "Notes on the Botanical Exploration of the White Mountains," *Appalachia*, XIV (1917), 157–173. See also Graustein (1964).

1. The most complete account of the 1784 ascent is in the Belknap Papers printed in Massachusetts Historical Society *Collections*, ser. 5, II (1877), 386–401.

2. Belknap (Philadelphia, 1784–1792), III, 37.

3. Cutler's accounts of the 1784 and 1804 ascents are in *Life, Journals and Correspondence of Rev. Manasseh Cutler, LL.D.*, published by W. P. Cutler and Julia P. Cutler (Cincinnati, 1888), I, 96–113.

4. Shattuck, "Some Account of an Excursion to the White-Hills of New Hampshire, in the Year 1807" (in a letter to the Editor dated August 28, 1807), *Philadelphia Medical and Physical Journal*, III (1808), 26–35.

5. "July 24, [1809] . . . Colonel Gibbs, of Rhode Island . . . called . . . going to the White Mountains to examine the fossils" W. P. and J. P. Cutler, *Life, Journals and Correspondence of Rev. Manasseh Cutler* (Cincinnati, 1888), II, 341. Maclure was in New England in 1808. Struik, *Yankee Science in the Making* (Boston, Massachusetts: Little, Brown and Company, 1948), 167. His figure of 6266 ft. for Mt. Washington was quoted by John H. Spaulding, *Historical Relics of the White Mountains* (Boston, 1855), 12.

6. O., I, 427; W. B. O. Peabody, *Report on the Fishes, Reptiles and Birds of Massachusetts* (State Survey) 1839.

7. Boott to Hooker, May 29, 1828, Hooker Correspondence, XLIV, 46, Kew.

8. Bigelow, "Some Account of the White Mountains of New Hampshire," *New England Journal of Medicine and Surgery*, V (1816), 321–338.

9. J. Pierce, "Notice of an Excursion Among the White Mountains of New Hampshire and to the Summit of Mount Washington in June, 1823," *AJS*, VIII (1824), 172–181.

10. Frank H. Burt, "White Mountain Album: Excerpts from the Registers of Ethan Allen Crawford," *Appalachia*, XXIII (1941), 304, 306.

11. Bigelow to Torrey, May 17, 1824, T. Corr. Oakes–Robbins Correspondence, April 20, 1829, Gray Herbarium, Harvard University, Cambridge, Massachusetts; Oakes, "Some Mosses of New England," Hovey's *Magazine of Horticulture*, XIII (1847), 172.

12. Frederick Tuckerman, "Gleanings from the Visitors' Albums of Ethan Allen Crawford," *Appalachia*, XIV (1916–1919), 367–383. The writer also examined the original owned by W. C. Wheeler, Bangor, Maine.

13. T. Corr. Barratt, a graduate of Trinity College, Cambridge University, was a correspondent of the Duke of Bedford.

14. Samuel H. Scudder, chapter xii, 344, in C. H. Hitchcock, *Geology of New Hampshire*, I (Concord, 1874–1878).

15. T. Say, *American Entomology*, III (Philadelphia, 1828), pl. 50.

16. C. Pickering's nephew, the astronomer Edward Charles, the son of

his only brother, Edward, was more than any other person the initiator of the Appalachian Mountain Club, founded in 1876.

17. T. Corr. Oakes's herbarium specimens are distinguished by their perfection.

18. F. H. Burt, "White Mountain Album," *Appalachia*, XXIII (1941), 308.

19. T. Corr.

20. Oakes–Robbins Correspondence, April 20, 1829, Gray Herbarium, Harvard University, Cambridge, Massachusetts.

21. T. Corr.

22. Lucy Crawford, *History of the White Mountains*, 3d ed. (Portland, Maine, 1886), 121, 134–135.

23. Oakes–Robbins Correspondence, November 2, 1830, Gray Herbarium, Harvard University, Cambridge, Massachusetts. E. A. Crawford has the posthumous honor of having a northern plant (*Carex crawfordii*) named for him by Merritt L. Fernald who spent most of his life at Gray Herbarium in the Botanic Garden. Gray's *Manual of Botany*, 8th ed. (New York: American Book Company, 1950), 324.

24. E. Tuckerman to Darlington, February 4, 1841, and February 6, 1844, Darlington Papers, New York Historical Society.

25. Augustus C. Hamlin, *History of Mount Mica* (Bangor, 1895). Elijah was an older brother of Hannibal Hamlin (1809–1891), fifteenth Vice-President of the United States during Lincoln's first administration.

26. In Samuel Robinson, *Catalogue of American Minerals with their Localities* (Boston, 1825) this location for fibrolite is credited to Nuttall (p. 278). Nuttall possessed a specimen of staurotide from Lisbon, Maine (Catalog of Auction Sale of Nuttall's minerals, 1860 — Lot 337 — seen at Geological Society of London), but, since he collected minerals again in Maine in 1840 and also exchanged specimens freely, it is not certain that he collected the staurotide in 1824, although Lisbon would be on his route.

27. Robinson, *Catalogue of American Minerals* (Boston, 1825), 304.

28. *Ibid.*, 279.

29. In his *American Entomology*, Say referred to three insects received from Holmes.

30. Torrey and Gray, *Flora of North America* (New York, 1838), I, 113.

31. In Torrey's personal copy of his own *Flora* (1824) at Columbia University he made a penciled memorandum that *Panicum xanthophysum* Gray had been collected by Pickering in the White Mountains and by Nuttall at "Bellows Falls, N. H." [!] and at "Conway, Me." [!] No doubt Nuttall was the source of the geographical errors; he was particularly weak on the boundaries of the New England states. Torrey's memo is our only information as to Nuttall's route from Paris to Mount Washington.

32. Robinson, *Catalogue of American Minerals* (Boston, 1825), 279.

33. From Franconia he may have crossed Vermont and proceeded to Franklin Furnace, getting the Shoreham (Vermont) mineral en route instead of in the spring of 1823.

34. C. U. Shepard to G. W. Benedict, November 18, 1824, Boltwood Papers, Detroit Public Library.

35. Robinson, *Catalogue of American Minerals* (Boston, 1825), 296–299.

36. Darlington Papers, New York Historical Society.

37. Shepard's letter to Benedict told of the find of gadolinite, and Nuttall

reported it tentatively in Robinson, *Catalogue of American Minerals* (Boston, 1825), 282.

38. Shepard wrote on September 1, 1824, from Amherst to Dr. J. W. Webster, asking him to send promised specimens to Nuttall in Cambridge within a fortnight. Boltwood Family Papers, Detroit Public Library.

39. C. U. Shepard, "Miscellaneous Localities of Minerals," *AJS*, IX (1825), 47–48.

40. Boltwood Papers, Detroit Public Library.

41. *Ibid.*

42. *Boston Journal of Philosophy and Arts*, II (1824–1825), 394–395, 610.

43. *Ibid.*, II (1824–1825), 299–300, 395–396, 505–512, 611–614; also III (1825–1826), 103–104.

44. MSPA Minutes, 153, 161.

45. Torrey to Hooker, April 1825, XLIV, 177, Kew.

46. Richardson to Hooker, April 25, 1825, XLIV, 140, Kew.

47. Hooker's Correspondence, XLIV, 95, Kew.

48. Phillipe Mercier, a French merchant who spent some years in both Americas, went to Switzerland for his health and worked in De Candolle's herbarium. He was a Corresponding Member of the Academy of Natural Sciences of Philadelphia from 1812. After his death in 1831, his plants were purchased by Philip Barker Webb for his great herbarium. There, in 1840, Asa Gray noticed Nuttall's contributions to Mercier.

49. Photostat. Correspondence of A. P. de Candolle, Archives of the Geneva, Switzerland, Herbarium.

50. Nuttall, considering the specific name of the *Euphorbia* unsuitable, changed it to "heteranthera" in his paper on his Arkansas collection.

51. W. J. Hooker, "On the Botany of America," reprinted in *AJS*, IX (1825), 276.

52. Dewey to Torrey, November 2, 1825, T. Corr. Of interest here is M. L. Fernald's opinion (oral) that Dewey was the best worker of the time on the Carices of North America, but this was not recognized by his contemporaries.

53. Ethel M. McAllister, *Amos Eaton, Scientist and Educator* (Philadelphia, Pennsylvania: University of Pennsylvania Press, 1941), 218.

54. Hooker Correspondence, XLIV, 177, Kew.

55. Asa Gray, *Scientific Papers* (Boston, Massachusetts: Houghton Mifflin Company, 1889), "The Flora of North America," II, 249.

56. "Some Account of a Collection of Plants Made during a Journey to and from the Rocky Mountains in the Summer of 1820, by Edwin P. James, M.D.," Lyceum of Natural History *Annals*, II (1827–1828), 161–254.

57. ANS *Journal*, V (1825), 132–135, pls. VI, VII.

58. *Ibid.*, 158–159.

59. In the second edition of the College catalog of October 1825, Nuttall's position in the list of faculty members was suddenly elevated from the very end below the tutors, where he had been named only "Curator of the Botanic Garden," to a place just below Professor Bigelow and above Professor Ticknor with the additional attribution of "Lecturer in Botany," and was continued in this position. No light can be shed on this fantastic change.

60. Nuttall–Putnam Correspondence, August 30, 1823, lent by Miss Elizabeth Putnam, Boston, Massachusetts.

61. Gray to Torrey, May 24, 1844, T. Corr.

62. M. L. Fernald wrote, "When I first came to Cambridge in the spring of 1891, Mrs. Gray . . . was full of reminiscences of still earlier days. She had retained Nuttall's trap-door. In the corner of the large living-room and study there hung a stout cord. Whenever Thomas Nuttall heard the garden-gate click or a step on the walk he pulled the rope and the trap-door in the ceiling opened nearly to the floor, with a step-ladder on its upper side. Then Nuttall disappeared and was never at home." "Some Early Botanists of the American Philosophical Society," APS *Proceedings*, LXXXVI (1942), 66.

Obviously neither of the Grays ever knew about the days when the Garden House sheltered boarders. Mrs. Gray, a Bostonian, did not live in Cambridge until 1848.

Another known purveyor of Nuttallian anecdotes was the puckish John Holmes (1812–1899), Harvard College 1832, the younger brother of the "Autocrat," who lived throughout his long life in "the Village." Charles Eliot Norton of Shady Hill wrote of him that "the village traditions, all of which he had inherited *and improved* [italics added], ceased with him." However, Charles Foster Batchelder, Harvard College 1878, an ornithologist on the staff of the Museum of Comparative Zoology, on occasion staged impersonations of Nuttall created by John Holmes; as he became for an appreciable period Harvard's oldest living graduate, he made Nuttall's name as an early Harvard teacher familiar to hosts of graduate students in biology. But he could have had no great confidence in the substantialness of Holmes's whimsical picture for when, as a biographer of Nuttall, I approached him on the subject, he refused to comment.

63. See note 60, above.

64. Russell, "On the Study of Natural History," *Magazine of Horticulture*, VIII (1842), 245.

65. Photostat inserted in Harvard College Papers, 2d ser., III (1828–1829); the original is in the Berg Collection, New York Public Library. Nuttall was on leave during most of the academic year of 1827–1828.

66. *Harvard Reminiscences* (Boston, Massachusetts: Ticknor and Company, 1888), 80–81.

67. "Annual Report of the President of Harvard University to the Board of Overseers, 1826." (Printed) Harvard Archives. In the academic year 1828–1829, Nuttall wrote to Torrey "My students this winter have been so numerous that I have been obliged in some measure to dismantle my Classroom to give them room." Nuttall misdated the letter. Torrey Collection of Autographed Letters, 220, ANS.

68. *O*, I, 282.

69. Hentz taught at Round Hill School in its earliest years.

70. *Boston Journal of Natural History*, II (1838–1839), 1–33, 34–52.

71. Audubon, *American Ornithological Biography*, V (Edinburgh, 1839), 470.

72. *Ibid.*, 233.

73. Six members of the Class of 1833 bceame professors at Harvard.

74. In September 1830, a graduate student at Harvard single-handed saved the famed frigate *Constitution* from demolition "with his school-boy scorn." In his attic room in a historic Cambridge house, Oliver Wendell Holmes, Harvard College 1829, scribbled the spirited protest beginning

"Ay, tear her tattered ensign down!
Long has it waved on high, . . .

Promptly published in the Boston *Daily Advertiser* and reprinted throughout the country, the poem raised such a storm of protest that the old ship still exists as a museum piece in the Charlestown Navy Yard. Such power has one gifted pen. Of such calibre were some of the students among whom Nuttall spent a third of his American years.

75. Shepard's Correspondence, Boltwood Papers, Detroit Public Library.

76. W. S. Tyler, *History of Amherst College* (Springfield, 1873), 622.

77. Edward Hitchcock, *Reminiscences of Amherst College* (Northampton, 1863), 101.

78. T. Corr. On November 4, 1842, J. E. Teschemacher wrote to Torrey that Shepard's work was "unanimously distrusted by the mineralogists of the Boston area." One of his recent papers, Teschemacher called "a schoolboy production . . . full of Errors from beginning to end." The writer found that Shepard's mineralogical judgment had always been highly regarded at the British Museum of Natural History.

79. William Meade to Silliman, January 3, 1827, Gratz Collection, HSP.

80. William M. and Mabel S. C. Smallwood, *Natural History and the American Mind* (New York, New York: Columbia University Press, 1941), 307.

81. *U. S. Review and Literary Gazette*, II (1827), 441–442.

82. *AJS*, XIII (1828), 99–106.

83. Harvard College Papers, ser. 2, I, 242.

84. M. Halsey Thomas, the Archivist of Princeton University, found no record in the Trustees' Minutes that Professor Halsey sought to resign his professorship before 1829 and no reference to Nuttall.

85. Harvard College Papers, ser. 2, II, 51.


## CHAPTER 14. RECREATION

1. Herzog Bernard Karl zu Sachsen-Weimar-Eisenbach, *Reise durch Nord-Amerika* (Weimar, 1828).

2. *Strelitzia reginae* (bird-of-paradise flower) is said to have been first cultivated in the United States by John Lowell. Justin Winsor, *Memorial History of Boston* (Boston, 1880–1881), IV, 621.

3. Cooper to Torrey, September 30, 1829, T. Corr.

4. Daniel Drake, *Pioneer Life in Kentucky*, ed. by his son, Charles D. Drake (Cincinnati 1870).

5. Oakes–Robbins Correspondence, November 2, 1830, Gray Herbarium, Harvard University, Cambridge, Massachusetts.

6. "By R. Haynes Esqr I long since sent a paper for publication on birds." Nuttall to Morton, April 15, 1831, S. G. Morton Papers, APS.

7. Maximilian, Prince of Wied, *Travels in the Interior of North America, 1832–1834*, in Thwaites, *EWT*, XXII, 49. In the spring of 1834, Maximilian, returning down the Missouri River, again missed meeting Nuttall, who had left Independence in Wyeth's party about three weeks before Maximilian arrived there.

8. H. Martineau, *Retrospect of Western Travel* (London, 1838), II, 97.

9. On February 24, 1831, I. P. Hearsey, M.D. 1827, wrote to Torrey: "When I was a Pupil in the office of Dr. Bigelow, he and your Friend Mr. Nuttall often expressed their opinion that many Medical Plants might be cultivated in this country with some benefit to Science. . . ." T. Corr.

10. Oakes to Torrey, April 3, 1828. T. Corr.

11. This was the observation of Susan Quincy, the eldest of the daughters of Josiah Quincy, who succeeded Kirkland as president of Harvard. M. A. DeWolfe Howe, ed., *The Articulate Sisters* (Cambridge, Massachusetts: Harvard University Press, 1946), 37.

12. G. S. Hillard, *A Memoir of James Brown*, privately printed, 1856.

13. The Cooper–Austin House, 1657, the oldest house in Cambridge, now belongs to the New England Society for the Preservation of Antiquities.

14. No one could assess the value of this gate better than the writer, who, whenever she worked at the Gray Herbarium after the hour for the locking of the east gate of the Garden, found it a tedious chore to almost circumambulate the dull garden fence to reach "the Gallows Hill" on which she lived.

15. Barratt to Torrey, January 13, 1831, T. Corr. S. W. Pomeroy was living in Brighton in 1823, but he soon built the "Gannett House" with the pillared portico in "the Village." He interested himself in improving the Common, still scarred as the campsite of the Revolutionary Army, by planting trees.

16. After Mrs. Craigie's death, J. E. Worcester and his bride (Amy Mc-Kean) rented the house and allowed Longfellow to continue occupying his rooms. In 1843 the latter's father-in-law bought the house for the Longfellows, and the Worcesters bought Craigie land to the north.

17. Tuckerman to Gray, May 6 and July 3, 1865, Historic Letter File, Gray Herbarium, Harvard University, Cambridge, Massachusetts. Tuckerman's statement about the acquisition of the painting presents an enigma; he supposedly sailed for Europe with his family on April 18, 1841, and was not back until September 1842, whereas Mrs. Craigie died of cancer on May 6, 1841, and the sale of her personal property occurred in May. No name appears on Elizabeth Shaw Craigie's gravestone in Mount Auburn Cemetery. The altarlike column bears a thought of Voltaire: "As flame ascends, the vital principle aspires to God."

18. T. W. Higginson, *Old Cambridge* (New York, 1899), 51.

19. Photostat of ms. letter, The Filson Club, Louisville, Kentucky.

20. Eliza Ware (Rotch) Farrar, *The Young Lady's Friend* (Boston, 1837), 353. Mrs. Farrar's "ideal gentlewoman she frankly defined as the daughter of a rich man." Cleveland Amory, *The Proper Bostonians* (New York: E. P. Dutton & Co., Inc., 1947), 232.

21. C. T. Jackson, "Notice of the Death of Francis Alger of Boston," Boston Society of Natural History *Proceedings*, X (1864–1866), 2–6.

22. Lt. Edward Winship settled in Cambridge in 1635; descendants are still living thereabouts. The Brighton Winships had a trading route between the west coast of North America, the Sandwich Islands, and China and a monopoly on the shipment of sandalwood from the Islands until the War of 1812 destroyed their business.

23. Charles M. Hovey, "Death of Thomas Nuttall," *Magazine of Horticulture*, XXV (1859), 565–566.

24. Audubon to R. Harlan, August 14, 1832, HSP; Graustein (1952).

25. Audubon, *The Ornithological Biography*, II (Edinburgh, 1834), 422–423. Amory in *The Proper Bostonians*, calls Col. Thomas Handasyd Perkins "the king of the merchant princes."

26. Audubon, *ibid.*, Introduction, xvii.

27. Wilson's work cost about $120; Bonaparte's edition was quoted at $180; Audubon's was priced at $1000.

28. Nuttall had been planning to prepare a second edition of his *Genera* — Pickering to Torrey, October 5, 1828, Torrey Autograph Collection, 175, ANS.

29. Peale's Museum had moved in 1827 to "The Arcade," Chestnut Street near Sixth, Philadelphia, Pennsylvania.

30. Especially frequent are references to John Richardson, *Fauna Boreali-Americana*, II (London, 1831); William Bullock, *Six Months Residence and Travels in Mexico* (London, 1824); Charles Waterton, *Wanderings in South America* (London, 1828); and Juan I. Molina, *Geographical, Natural and Civil History of Chile* (Middletown, Connecticut, 1808). James Brown's fine ornithological library would have been made available to Nuttall.

31. *O.*, I, 213.  32. *Ibid.*, 415, 444.

33. *New England Farmer*, IX (1830), July 23, 1.

34. *O.*, II, 94.  35. *O.*, I, 216.  36. *Ibid.*, 237.

37. *Ibid.*, 387-388.  38. *Ibid.*, 312.  39. *Ibid.*, 634-635.

40. *Ibid.*, 662.  41. *Ibid.*, 603-604.  42. *Ibid.*, 343.

43. *Ibid.*, 62.

44. *Ibid.*, 81. In the 1940s the writer observed nests of the osprey thickly placed at Woodland Beach, Delaware. In the *New Yorker* (April 4, 1964, 36-37) Mr. Gardiner is quoted as saying that his island of over 4000 acres has "the biggest collection of ospreys in the world."

45. *Ibid.*, 122.  46. *Ibid.*, 268.  47. *O.*, I, 19-20.

48. *O.*, II, 515-516.  49. *O.*, I, 322-327.  50. *Ibid.*, 253.

51. American Academy of Arts and Sciences *Memoirs*, new ser., I (1833), 91-106.

52. *Journals of Ralph Waldo Emerson*, ed. by E. W. Emerson and W. E. Forbes (Boston, Massachusetts: Houghton Mifflin Company, 1909), II (February 1, 1832), 459.

53. Oakes, Review, *American Monthly Review*, I (1832), 320-322.

54. Peabody commented on Nuttall's *Ornithology* in his "Review of Audubon's Ornithological *Biography*," I, *North American Review*, XXXIV (1832), 368.

55. Unsigned review of "A Popular Handbook of the Ornithology of the United States and Canada" *Nation*, LIV (1892), 453.

56. D. C. Peattie, "Nuttall, Botanist and Ornithologist," *Nature Magazine*, IX (1927), 37-38.

57. *O.*, II, 216.

58. *Ibid.*, 461-463.

59. One of Nuttall's companions on the trip up the Susquehannah evidently pointed out his error in the date and also recalled to him their observation of chestnut-sided warblers. *O.* (1840), 433.

60. *O.*, II, 160-161. The writer observed young cedar waxwings running similarly over leaves of water lilies on a pond in the Adirondacks.

61. *Ibid.*, 549. Of the species named, only crows visit the Dover cliffs.

62. Maria R. Audubon, *Audubon and his Journals* (London, 1897), I, 445.

63. *O.*, II, 387, 390, 395, 435, 437, 443, 445.

64. *O.*, II, 274, note.

65. *A Popular Handbook of the Ornithology of Eastern North America*, by *Thomas Nuttall*: revised and annotated by Montague Chamberlain. Vol. 1,

The Land Birds; vol. 2, Game and Water Birds (Boston, Massachusetts: Little, Brown and Company). The editions were published in 1891, 1896, and 1903.

66. Charles Foster Batchelder, "An Account of the Nuttall Ornithological Club," Nuttall Ornithological Club *Memoirs*, VIII (1937), 16.

## CHAPTER 15. LEAVES OF ABSENCE

1. The order of the two sentences has been reversed. *Three Centuries of Harvard* (Cambridge, Massachusetts: Harvard University Press, 1936), 217.

2. MPSA. Nuttall was in Cambridge on October 26 and in New York be-before November 9, Schweinitz Correspondence, III, 255.

3. The last meeting in the "Old Hall" on Arch Street between Front and Second, was held on May 2, 1826.

4. Torrey to Schweinitz, April 3, 1828, Schweinitz Correspondence, ANS.

5. Hooker's Correspondence, XLIV, 46, Kew.

6. A. G. Harvey, *Douglas of the Fir* (Cambridge, Massachusetts: Harvard University Press, 1947), 158.

7. Ms Minutes of the Council, Linnean Society, March 17, 1833.

8. Hooker was interested in a possible professorship of botany at London University — B. D. Jackson, *Life of George Bentham* (London, 1906), 60.

9. Hooker's Correspondence, XLIV, 96, Kew.

10. Greene to Hooker, February 7, 1835, LXII, 90, Kew.

11. Hooker's Correspondence, XLIV, 97, Kew.

12. Oakes to Robbins, Gray Herbarium. Oakes–Robbins Correspondence.

13. Wray to Hooker, May 19, 1831, LXI, 208, Kew.

14. Boykin to Torrey, May 25, 1847, T. Corr. Nuttall to Oemler, November 4, 1830, ms. Special Collections, Butler Library, Columbia University, New York.

15. *Sylva* (1857), II, 140.

16. Nuttall, "Some of the Rarer . . . Plants Indigenous to the United States," ANS *Journal*, VII (1834), 106. *Podostemum* *abrotanoides* was reduced to *Podostemum ceratophyllum* f. *abrotanoides* (Nutt.) Fassett; *Rhodora* XLI (1939), 527.

17. Nuttall's sketchy references to his route through Alabama in his report to the Corporation (p. 244), in the *Ornithology*, and in the *Sylva* are not consistent. Although consideration of all known factors, especially the dates available, recommended the route given in the text, the places visited may not be in the proper sequence; Cahaba might have been visited twice.

18. *Sylva*, I (1842–1843), 83–84. The Coosa River does not lie in Bibb County, but the Cahaba River flows through it.

19. ANS Minutes record that on October 5, 1830, Nuttall presented "fossils from Cahawba" and land shells. S. G. Morton had already published one of the shells as "Ostraea falcata." ANS *J*. VI, pt. I (1829), 50–51, pl. I.

20. James B. Sellers, *History of the University of Alabama* (University, Alabama: University of Alabama Press, 1953), I, 44.

21. O., 90, 89, 432, 549. The passage on page 89 is dated February 13 and that on page 432 "about" February 20, both in Tuscaloosa.

22. Nuttall to Woods, November 3, 1831. A copy of this letter was kindly sent to me by the late Mrs. Roy A. Hunt of Pittsburgh, donor of the Hunt Botanical Library, Carnegie Institute of Technology.

23. Nuttall to "Professor Saltonstal," Cambridge, December, 1830. I am

indebted to the Library of the University of Alabama for a copy of this three-page letter.

24. O., I, 322.

25. *Introduction to Botany* (1830), 195; ANS *Journal*, VII (1834), 61–115 *passim*.

26. *Sylva* (1857), II, 39.

27. "Description of a New Species of Sarracenia," AP *Transactions*, new ser., IV (1834), 49–51, pl. I.

28. *Gen.*, II, 217.

29. Harvard College Records, VII, 249.

30. *Ibid.*, VII, 278.

31. Harvard College Papers, ser. 2, V, 143.

32. Greene to Torrey, July 1, 1832, T. Corr.

33. Nuttall, ANS *Journal*, VII, pt. I (1834), 98.

34. T. A. Conrad, "New Marine Shells," ANS *Journal*, VII, pt. II (1837), 239–240; 256–260; 263. Conrad's text is occasionally ambiguous as to the collector of a species.

35. Ms. Minutes, ANS, May 1, 1832. Harlan called it "Arvicola Nuttalli."

36. Nuttall, ANS *Journal*, VII, pt. I (1834), 96.

37. Harvard College Papers, ser. 2, V, 200.

38. No sailing to the Azores at this time was found in Boston papers, but Nuttall must have been aboard the *Harbinger*, reported as "spoken" on October 13, en route from Boston to Fayal, in shipping news in *The Boston Evening Transcript*, November 12.

39. O., II, 323–324.

40. Richard Hakluyt, *Principall Navigations of the English Nation* (Everyman's Library), IV, 360–361.

41. *Sylva* (1859), II, 57; *ibid.* (1842–1843), I, 44–45.

42. T. A. Conrad, "New Marine Shells," ANS *Journal*, pt. II (1837), 247, 260, 262, 265.

43. T. W. Higginson, "Fayal and the Portuguese," *The Atlantic Monthly*, VI (1860), 526–544.

44. O., II, 566.

45. *Ibid.*, 77–78.

46. *Ibid.*, 186.

47. *Ibid.*, 576–577.

48. Harvard College Papers, ser. 2, VI, 15.

## CHAPTER 16. GROWING WANDERLUST

1. On January 13, 1827, Ebenezer Francis was elected Treasurer to replace John Davis.

2. Silliman to Griscom, June 24, 1829, HSP.

3. General Dearborn and Nuttall were elected honorary members of the South Carolina Horticultural Society. *The Boston Evening Transcript*, September 1, 1831.

4. MSPA, Minutes, 166.

5. *Ibid.* (June 13, 1829), 165.

6. "Transformed Produce of an Apple Tree," *New England Farmer*, VIII (September 18, 1829), 65–66.

7. *Ibid.* (October 30), 113.

8. Although Nuttall wrote the analysis from a dried specimen, he later raised a plant from a root sent by Coxe. J. R. Coxe, "Some Observations on the Plant that Produces the Official Jalap," *American Journal of Medical Science*, V (1829–1830), 300–307.

9. Durand, 304–305.

10. This trip occurred in the spring of 1830. (See Chapter 14, THE BIRDS, and quotation to which note 58 refers.) J. McMinn of this area sent Nuttall rare plants as long as he remained in the United States; T. Corr.

11. Nuttall was elected May 13 and resigned on August 9. Thomas T. Bouvé, *Historical Sketch of the Boston Society of Natural History* (Boston, 1880).

12. Perhaps at the close of the last lecture Ralph Waldo Emerson consulted Nuttall about the suitability of the climate of west Florida for his brother Edward who was suffering from tuberculosis. On December 3, 1830, R. W. Emerson wrote to his brother William in New York City: "Grieved are we to hear no better news of Edward than your letter brings today. But why not go to Magnolia [near Tallahassee]. Mr. Nuttall says there is no better climate. . . ." *Letters of Ralph Waldo Emerson*, ed. by Ralph L. Rusk (New York: Columbia University Press, 1939), I, 311. Edward Bliss Emerson died in Puerto Rico in 1834.

13. *The Boston Evening Transcript*, November 11, 29, and December 4, 1830.

14. Bouvé, *Historical Sketch of the Boston Society of Natural Society* (Boston, 1880).

15. Nuttall to S. G. Morton, April 15, 1831, APS, and Pickering to Darlington, October 8, 1831, New York Historical Society.

16. October 15, 1830, LXI, 26, Kew.

17. "Ordinances and Resolutions of the Board of Trustees," University of Alabama (1822–1841), 320, 354; President Woods's letter to the Trustees, December 21, 1831; James B. Sellers, *History of the University of Alabama* (University, Alabama: The University of Alabama Press, 1953), 100. I am indebted to the University of Alabama Library for copies of the official records. For the letter from Nuttall to President Woods, see Chapter 15, note 22.

18. Nuttall to S. G. Morton, APS.

19. Rafinesque to Torrey, T. Corr.

20. *Ibid.*

21. T. Drummond to Hooker, LXI, 78, Kew.

22. *Ibid.*, LXI, 79.

23. B. D. Greene to Hooker, LXI, 122; LXII, 93, Kew.

24. Hooker, *Journal of Botany*, I (1834), 52 ff.

25. Greene to Hooker, September 30, 1832, LXI, 125; July 26, 1853, LXI, 128; February 7, 1835, LXII, 90.

26. The Quincys, giving a large party at their Boston home in 1819, "sent to the Botanic Garden for flowers" M. A. DeWolfe Howe, ed., *The Articulate Sisters* (Cambridge, Massachusetts: Harvard University Press, 1946), 33.

27. Dr. James Jackson, Sr., the first professor of clinical medicine at Harvard (1810–1836) had a tremendous practice. His son died soon after taking his M.D. in 1834.

28. Photostat, Correspondence of A. P. de Candolle, Archives of the Geneva Herbarium.

29. *Ibid.*

30. April 13, 1835, LXII, 16, Kew.

31. "Life of Frederic Tudor," State Street Trust Company Pamphlet (Boston, Massachusetts, January 13, 1947), 88–92.

32. NJW, Letter, December 4, 1831, 6–8. The basic facts concerning Wyeth's expeditions are found in his "Correspondence and Journals," F. G. Young, ed., *Sources of the History of Oregon*, I, pts. 3–6 (1899), referred to as NJW; Washington Irving, *Adventures of Captain Bonneville* (New York, 1837), *passim*; Bernard de Voto, *Across the Wide Missouri* (Boston, Massachusetts: Houghton, Mifflin Company, 1947), *passim*. R. O. Cummings, *American Ice Harvests* (Berkeley, California: University of California Press, 1949), 18–51, gives a full account of Wyeth's connection with the ice business.

33. Wyeth left his affairs in charge of James Brown.

34. J. B. Wyeth's 1832 book was reprinted in *EWT*, XXI, along with J. K. Townsend's *Narrative of a Journey . . . to the Columbia River*.

35. NJW, Letter from Fort Vancouver, January 16, 1833, 53.

36. De Voto, *Across the Wide Missouri* (Boston, Massachusetts: Houghton Mifflin Company, 1947), 80–85.

37. Horace S. Lyman, *History of Oregon* (New York, 1903), III, 145 ff.

38. A. G. Harvey, *Douglas of the Fir* (Cambridge, Massachusetts: Harvard University Press, 1947), *passim*. Douglas's resignation was written on September 9, 1832.

39. NJW, "Journals," June 26, 1833, 202–203. Douglas's eyesight was impaired but he had close views of a nesting pair.

40. *Ibid.*, January 31–February 3, 1833, 181.

41. *Ibid.*, 191.

42. Wyeth's dates of collection of the two *Castillejas* were seen on labels with the specimens in the Herbarium of BMNH.

43. NJW, Letter, 67–68.

44. A full account of the western fur trade and Wyeth's plans was written to Mr. Henry Hall and Messrs. Tucker and Williams from Cambridge, November 8, 1833. NJW Correspondence, 73–78.

45. Baptiste was the son of Francis Payette, chief trader at Fort Nez Percé.

46. NJW Correspondence, Cambridge, November 8, 1833–February 4, 1834, 73–108.

47. An appeal for religious instruction made by Flathead Chiefs to General William Clark in 1831 determined the Methodist Church to finance the mission which Jason Lee was selected to found, largely through the influence of Dr. Wilbur Fisk, President of Wesleyan College, Lee's patron. Lee was working on arrangements to go when he heard of the arrival of Wyeth with two Indian boys in Boston and hastened there to meet him. Daniel Lee and J. H. Frost, *Ten Years in Oregon* (New York, 1844); Cornelius J. Brosnan, *Jason Lee, Prophet of New Oregon, 1803–1845* (New York: The Macmillan Company, 1932).

48. Nuttall, "A Catalogue of a Collection of Plants Made Chiefly in the Valleys of the Rocky Mountains or Northern Andes, Toward the Sources of the Columbia River, by Nathaniel B. [!] Wyeth," ANS *Journal*, VII (1834), 5–60, pls. I–VIII.

49. Asa Gray was appointed the first Fisher Professor of Natural History in 1842. At the time of Gray's taunt, Nuttall had had no salary for seven years

and was forced to watch the pennies in order to keep alive and useful through a severe and protracted financial depression.

50. This portrait of Nuttall was given to the Boston Society of Natural History by Mrs. Brown after her husband's death in 1855. The canvas is roughly comparable in size to those of several of contemporary naturalists which hang in the ANS Library and differs from Isaac Lea's by only one quarter inch in width. The writer suggests that Nuttall may have brought the portrait with him when he moved from Philadelphia. Charles Foster Batchelder secured a copy of this painting for use as the frontispiece of William Brewster's *The Birds of the Cambridge Region* (*Memoir* No. 4, Nuttall Ornithological Club, 1906). He wrote me in 1944 that one of the two known oil paintings of Nuttall was a copy of the other. Since he chose the Boston Society's painting for the illustration, rather than Mrs. Craigie's at Gray Herbarium, he must have considered it to be the original. Neither artist has been identified. See Chapter 14, note 17 and the text to which the note refers.

51. Andrew Jackson Downing raised the seeds for Torrey in his Botanic Garden and Nurseries at Newburgh, N. Y. Downing to Torrey, December 29, 1834, T. Corr.

52. Andrew D. Rodgers III, *John Torrey* (Princeton, New Jersey: Princeton University Press, 1942), 106 ff.

53. Torrey to Hooker, April 7, 1836, LXII, 158, Kew.

54. Wyeth wrote six letters from Philadelphia on February 18, 1834. NJW Correspondence, 113–114.

55. E. Durand, 306–307. Durand names Professor Carson as his informant.

56. Darlington Papers, New York Historical Society.

57. Ms. Minutes, ANS. Rogers, one of four brothers eminent in science, became professor of geology and mineralogy at the University of Pennsylvania (1835–1846) and made geological surveys of New Jersey and Pennsylvania. His brother William Barton Rogers was the first president of the Massachusetts Institute of Technology.

58. *AJS*, XXVI (1834), 209.

59. Downing to Torrey, May 11, 1834, T. Corr. The writer does not know of such a painting. Could this have been a print of the 1825 engraving presumably done for Henry Fisher's reprints of Nuttall's two books? That was drawn by "Derby," not known to be a relative of Nuttall.

60. Some of Say's work, printed posthumously, still dealt with specimens he had received from Nuttall. Say received further material from "Dr. E. Holmes of the Gardiner Lyceum": a "fine species" of aquatic *Coleoptera* and "many other interesting objects of natural history." APS *Transactions*, IV (1834), 454, 440–441.

61. Nuttall, "Collections Toward a Flora of the Territory of Arkansas," APS *Transactions*, new ser., V (1837), 139–203.

62. Nuttall, ANS *Journal*, VII (1834–1837), 61–116, pls. IX–XII. Plates XI and XII were signed "A M MEwen" as were pls. III and IV, which illustrate the paper on Wyeth's plants that immediately precedes this. A Thomas M'Ewen was a member of the Academy.

63. Perhaps Nuttall purposefully avoided mentioning himself as collector since he was more or less committed to publishing his Arkansas plants with the American Philosophical Society.

64. Torrey to Hooker, October 31, 1834, LXI, 203, Kew.

65. *Ibid.*, December 8, 1835, LXII, 157, Kew.

66. Ms. Minutes, March 18, 1834, ANS. For Masson's plants see note 48, Chapter 6.

67. Pickering to Torrey, March 30, 1836, T. Corr.

68. Harvard College Papers, ser. 2, V, 264.

69. NJW, Correspondence, 106.

70. J. K. Townsend, *Narrative of a Journey across the Rocky Mountains* (Philadelphia, 1839), 9–10 (reprinted in *EWT*, XXI). Townsend's published account is the chief source for the events of the following year. As indicated in the Appendix of Abbreviations, Townsend's account is referred to as "JKT."

71. *Ibid.*, 10–22.

72. Three busts — of Linnaeus, Nuttall, and Gray — were dedicated June 22, 1883, by Henry Shaw, donor of the Garden.

73. Dr. Engelmann originated the soubriquet.

## CHAPTER 17. ACROSS THE ROCKIES,
## AROUND THE HORN

1. At Independence, Nuttall and Townsend bought five horses and engaged a man for camp duties. JKT, 20.

2. *Ibid.*, 27–28.

3. *Ibid.*, 35. Townsend's dates are usually used although they do not always agree with Wyeth's or Lee's.

4. O. (1840), 555.

5. JKT, 57–58.

6. *Sylva*, Preface, vi.

7. JKT, 57–58.

8. "Diary of Jason Lee," *Oregon Historical Quarterly*, XVII (1916), 128. Jason Lee (1803–1845), well over six feet, large and athletic, warmhearted, civil, quiet, and firm, with no clerical cant, was liked by everyone. His nephew, Daniel, only three years younger, was also an ordained minister. Cyrus Shepard, a school teacher from Massachusetts, and two lay assistants, Philip Leget Edwards and Courtney M. Walker, engaged at Independence, completed the mission staff.

9. JKT, 63.

10. *Ibid.*, 64.

11. *Sylva*, I (1842–1843), 52.

12. William Sublette was starting a fort on the Laramie. John E. Sunder, *Bill Sublette: Mountain Man* (Norman, Oklahoma: The University of Oklahoma Press, 1959), 134.

13. O. (1840), 667.

14. This fact and the error discussed beyond were thoughtfully called to the writer's attention by Reed C. Rollins.

15. Nuttall, "Descriptions of New Species and Genera of Plants in the Natural Order of the Compositae," APS *Transactions*, new ser., VII (1840), 348, 379, 402. The *Polemonium* was published in "Description of Plants Collected by Mr. William Gambel," ANS *Journal*, new ser., I (1848), 154.

16. JKT, 67.

17. Audubon, *Ornithological Biography*, V, 335; Nuttall, O. (1840), 747. Elliott Coues says Lewis and Clark secured this species. *The History of the Lewis and Clark Expedition* I (New York, 1893), 171, n43.

18. Nuttall's account was quoted in John Bachman, "Different Species of Hares . . . ," ANS *Journal*, VII (1837), 358.

19. A footnote on page 75 of Townsend's Journal acknowledged use of Nuttall's field note-books, but Nuttall was unaware of this.

20. JKT, 75–76.

21. *Sylva*, Preface, vii.

22. NJW, Journal, 235, June 18, 1834.

23. NJW, Correspondence, 134–137. Competition for the decreasing pelts had so reduced profits that early in 1834 the Rocky Mountain Fur Company agreed to abandon the upper Missouri trade, and the American Fur Company agreed to retire from the mountain trade. J. E. Sunder, *Bill Sublette: Mountain Man* (Norman, Oklahoma: The University of Oklahoma Press, 1959).

24. NJW, Correspondence, March 31, 1834, 128.

25. *Ibid.*, June 21, 1834, 135.

26. O. (1840), 397.

27. *Sylva*, I (1842–1843), 69–70.

28. *Ibid.*, II (1846), 28–30.

29. JKT, 104.

30. O. (1840), 497.

31. *Sylva*, I (1842–1843), 78.

32. "We manufactured a magnificent flag from some unbleached sheeting, a little red flannel, and a few blue patches." John A. Wyeth, M.D., "Nathaniel J. Wyeth and the Struggle for Oregon," *Harper's Magazine*, 85 (Nov. 1892), 839. On August 6, 1834, Nat wrote, ". . . drank a bale of liquor and named it Fort Hall in honor of the oldest partner of our concern." *Journal*, 227.

33. JKT, 112–113.

34. Named by the weary sufferers for the member of the party who assured Wyeth that he had crossed the mountains by this route. It would seem that the party was on or near Hyndman Peak (12,078 ft.); they exited from the mountains onto the Camas Prairie on the Camas Branch of the South Fork of the Boise River.

35. The sharp-tailed grouse resembles the female European pheasant and is only three inches shorter.

36. JKT, 152.

37. *Sylva*, II (1846), 7.

38. JKT, 152–153.

39. *Ibid.*, 163.

40. Thomas J. Farnham, *Travels in the Great Western Prairies . . . and in the Oregon Country*, as reprinted in EWT, XXIX, 63–66.

41. *Ibid.*, 66.

42. Gairdner to Hooker, LXII, 82, Kew.

43. Audubon, *Birds of America*, pl. 367.

44. *Sylva*, III (1849), 52.

45. Richardson, *Fauna Boreali-Americana*, III (1831), 221.

46. Audubon, *American Ornithological Biography*, V (Edinburgh, 1839), Introduction.

47. Townsend, "Note on Sylvia Tolmaei," ANS *Journal*, VIII (1839–1842), 159. Audubon, *Birds of America*, pl. 399, figs. 4, 5. The common name for this species is Macgillivray's warbler!

48. Hooker Correspondence, November 15, 1836, LXII, 152, Kew. Audubon wrote to Bachman on February 15, 1840, "I have seen a good deal of

Townsend of late, and am sorry to say have lost much toward him [sic], he has become or perhaps always was Lazy and careless in the extreme and hardly speaks of those *who have befriended him when in* need in suficient words of gratitude." — Howard Corning, ed., *Letters of John James Audubon, 1826–1840* (Boston, Massachusetts: Club of Odd Volumes, 1930), II, 232.

49. NJW, Journal, September 28–October 1, 1834, 234.

50. *Sylva*, I (1842–1843), 58.

51. Kelley and Young were both innocent of the charge.

52. H. J. Kelley, *A Narrative of Events and Difficulties in the Colonization of Oregon* (Boston, 1852), 183–184. John B. Wyeth wrote that Kelley "never stops at superlatives."

53. Isaac Lea, APS *Transactions*, VI (1839), 88. Dr. William K. Emerson of the staff of the American Museum of Natural History kindly supplied the valid names of these two species.

54. Jonathan Winship, Jr., one of the founders of the Massachusetts Horticultural Society, had doubtless told Nuttall of his attempt in 1810 to establish a permanent settlement on the Columbia River, forty miles from the sea. The Winships' *Albatross*, like many other Boston ships, was then engaged in the Northwest trade. The crew had broken ground for a vegetable garden and were erecting a log house when they were savagely repulsed by Chinook Indians, and the plans were regretfully abandoned. Nuttall probably looked for the site — an oak grove — in order to report to his friend the condition of this favorite spot.

55. T. A. Conrad, "New Marine Shells . . . ," ANS *Journal*, VII, pt. II (1837), 227–268, *passim*.

56. J. C. Jones, Sr., Harvard College 1768, was one of many wealthy Boston merchants and shipowners of the period. His son, in Honolulu from 1820 as agent for a Boston firm, was also a shipowner, carrying on a large trade with California.

57. S. E. Morison, "Boston Traders in Hawaiian Islands," Massachusetts Historical Society *Proceedings*, LIV, 22.

58. Conrad, "New Marine Shells . . . ," ANS *Journal*, VII, pt. II (1837), 253, 244, 246.

59. JKT, 196.

60. Gulick had moved with his family from Waimea on the west coast of Kauai during the previous summer.

61. O. (1840), 141.

62. Mrs. Gulick was Fanny Hinckley Thomas; the second child was Orramel Hinckley Gulick.

63. He traced his attraction to biology to his early environment. Addison Gulick, *John Thomas Gulick, Evolutionist and Missionary* (Chicago, Illinois: The University of Chicago Press, 1932), 5. This volume was kindly loaned to me by Mrs. Luther Halsey Gulick.

64. On June 25, 1836, Wyeth started from Fort Hall "for the United States by way of Taos and the Arkansas river and arrived home early in the Autumn of 1836." He left Thing in charge at Fort Williams; Fort Hall was sold to the Hudson's Bay Company in 1837.

65. D. Lee and J. H. Frost, *Ten Years in Oregon* (New York, 1844), 132.

66. A note reprinted under "Miscellaneous Intelligence" in *AJS*, XXXI (1837), 179, reads: "*The Travellers* — Letters have been received from Mr. Nuttall, the botanist, and his companion, John K. Townsend, of Philadelphia,

dated in September of last year [1835], from Fort Vancouver, Columbia River. They were in good health, and would set out for home, either via Santa Fe or England, and may be home in the fall of this year. Last week the Academy of Natural Sciences of Philadelphia received safely from them *via* Cape Horn many large boxes; among Mr. Townsend's collections alone are three hundred birds and fifty quadrupeds, many of which are unknown to naturalists. We eagerly await the return of these gentlemen, in order that their remarkable scientific acquisitions, together with the eventful personal narrative of the travellers, may be given to the public. *Waldie's Circ. Library,* July 12, 1836."

67. *Sylva,* Preface.

68. Because Nuttall listed two species of plants from the San Francisco area — APS *Transactions,* new ser., VII (1841), 374, 399 — the question arises whether he collected them. Since he explicitly stated that he reached California at Monterey, where all foreign ships were required to register before entering other ports, it is reasonable to suppose that the plants were given to him. However his friend Captain Hinckley (with whom he may have sailed) was notoriously defiant of the Spanish regulations.

69. Hubert H. Bancroft, *History of California* (San Francisco, 1884–1890), III, 667–668.

70. *Sylva,* Preface.

71. O. (1840), 326.

72. Audubon, *American Ornithological Biography,* V (Edinburgh, 1839), 425.

73. D. Cleveland, *Botanical Gazette,* VII (1882), 64.

74. T. A. Conrad, "New Marine Shells . . . ," ANS *Journal,* VII, pt. II (1837).

75. J. W. Randall, "Crustacea . . . from the West Coast of North America . . ." [read June 18, 1839] ANS *Journal,* VIII (1839–1842), 106–147. Dr. W. K. Emerson kindly supplied the valid name of this species.

76. Richard Henry Dana, *Two Years Before the Mast,* chap. 30.

77. *Ibid.,* chap. 32.

## CHAPTER 18. BACK IN THE UNITED STATES

1. William Macgillivray (1796–1852) of Edinburgh edited the text of the *Ornithological Biography,* furnishing anatomical facts and drawings for Audubon on a business basis.

2. Howard Corning, ed., *Letters of John James Audubon, 1826–1840* (Boston, Massachusetts: Club of Odd Volumes, 1930), II, 127.

3. *Ibid.,* 130. The skins were of male, female, and immature specimens of about forty species.

4. Robert Buchanan, *Life and Adventures of John James Audubon, the Naturalist* (2d ed., London, 1869), 321.

5. *Ibid.,* 322; Graustein (1952), 88. Since Audubon's arrival in Boston he had gone to Roxbury to see the collection of eggs and bird skins of Thomas Brewer, Harvard College 1836. The dates, based on Audubon's, seeming unreliable, are omitted. Audubon was staying at Dr. Shattuck's, as he did on his return from Labrador in 1833.

6. *Ibid.*

7. William IV made William Jackson Hooker a Knight of the Hanoverian Order (K.H.) in 1836.

8. Greene to Hooker, January 14, 1837, LXII, 94, Kew. The Beechey Expedition visited California in 1827-1828. Hooker and George A. W. Arnott were publishing the plants in a series of papers entitled "Contributions toward a Flora of South America and the Islands of the Pacific," which were finally collected in book form as *Botany of Captain Beechey's Voyage* (London, 1841).

9. Boott to Hooker, LXII, 34, Kew. Jonas Nuttall lived until October 21, 1837, when his property, left in trust, went first to his widow.

10. One donor was the Duke of Bedford, a student of the willows, who exchanged herbarium specimens with Joseph Barratt whose herbarium was later given to Harvard University. In 1846 the Boott house was enlarged into the famed Revere House.

11. Harvard College Papers, 2d ser., VI (1833-1835), 314.

12. Harvard College Papers, 2d ser., VII (1835-1836), 9. Under John Lowell's leadership an additional $10,000 had been subscribed to the Fisher legacy in order to achieve the increased salary subsequently offered. Eventually the money was returned to the donors.

13. Boott to Hooker, February 1, 1836, LXII, 22, Kew.

14. T. Meehan, 21-23.

15. MSPA, Minutes of a special meeting of the Board of Visitors, May 24, 1834, 183.

16. *Ibid.*

17. T. W. Higginson, *Contemporaries* (Boston, Massachusetts: Houghton Mifflin Company, 1899), 199-200.

18. Barratt to Torrey, T. Corr.

19. New York Lyceum of Natural History *Annals*, III (1828-1836), 191-220, 221-238.

20. *Ibid.*, 239-452.

21. T. M. Brewer, "Reminiscences of John James Audubon," *Harper's New Monthly Magazine*, LXI (1880), 666-675.

22. Torrey to Hooker, September 7, 1836, LXII, 160, Kew.

23. Plates 362 and 367 of Audubon's *Birds of America*. Nuttall furnished descriptions for Audubon's text, *Ornithological Biography*, IV (Edinburgh, 1838), *passim.*

24. *Ibid.*, IV (Edinburgh, 1838), Introduction.

25. Boston Society of Natural History *Occasional Papers*, I (1869), 149.

26. "Descriptions of Twelve New Species of Birds," ANS *Journal*, VII (1837), 187-193.

27. R. Harlan, ANS *Journal*, IV (1825), 299-304, and AJS, XXXI (1837), 383-385.

28. *Ibid.*, 382-383. For the valid name of this species the writer is indebted to Charles M. Bogert, chairman and curator, Department of Herpetology, American Museum of Natural History, New York.

29. T. A. Conrad, ANS *Journal*, VII, pt. II (1837), 227-268, pls. 17-20, 73 figs.

30. Isaac Lea, "New Freshwater and Land Shells," APS *Transactions*, new ser., VI (1839), 73-108 *passim*; IX (1846), 3-13, *passim.*

31. J. Bachman, ANS *Journal*, VII, pt. II (1837), 345-348.

32. It is interesting to note that Townsend named none of his new species for Nuttall.

33. Ms. Minutes. On June 4, 11, and 18, 1839, an expanded version which included the *Crustacea* collected by Townsend as well as Nuttall was read.

"Catalogue of the Crustacea Brought by Thomas Nuttall and J. K. Townsend, from the West Coast of North America and the Sandwich Islands with Descriptions of Such Species as Are Apparently New . . . ," ANS *Journal*, VIII (1839), 106–147, pls. III–VII.

34. Gifts to ANS are recorded in ms. Minutes; the articles donated to APS are enumerated in *Transactions*, new ser., V (1837), 481–482.

35. T. Corr.

36. Torrey to Hooker, April 17, 1837, LXII, 162, Kew. The criticism concerning Nuttall's loss of time might have originated with Gray; Torrey appeared very susceptible to Gray's views.

37. Attendance at APS meetings was not fully recorded. The business of the meeting often reveals Nuttall's presence.

38. Washington Irving, *Astoria*, Chapter 17.

39. April 17, 1837, LXII, 162, Kew.

40. May 26, 1837, LXII, 163, Kew.

41. In 1842, when Gray arrived in Cambridge his one thought of William Carter, the gardener for thirty-four years, was to get rid of him. Nuttall, an experienced horticulturist, thought highly of Carter's work. (See his letter to *The Boston Evening Transcript*, Chapter 19).

42. The quotations thus far in this paragraph are from A. Hunter Dupree, *Asa Gray* (Cambridge, Massachusetts: Belknap Press of Harvard University Press, 1959), 30, 32, 129, 55. No more inaccurate word to describe Gray could be found than "unassuming," used by Loren Eiseley in reviewing Dupree's biography in *The New York Times*, October 4, 1959. The experienced biographer Gamaliel Bradford had "glimpses of direct ambition that peep out in his correspondence." *As God Made Them* (Boston, Massachusetts: Houghton Mifflin Company, 1929).

43. September 21, 1859, Historic Letter File, Gray Herbarium, Harvard University, Cambridge, Massachusetts.

44. Gray first encountered the "natural system of classification" late in 1832. On May 8, 1834, Gray wrote to Torrey, "My friend the bearer of this will call upon you for my microscope and my copies of Beck, Eaton and Lindley. I want them very much by the 25th of May when I commence my lectures at Hamilton College." Ethel M. McAllister, *Amos Eaton, Scientist and Educator* (Philadelphia, Pennsylvania: University of Pennsylvania Press, 1941), 252.

45. Eaton to Torrey, November 4, 1835, T. Corr.

46. Short to Gray, June 23, 1836, Gray Herbarium, Harvard University, Cambridge, Massachusetts.

47. McAllister, *Amos Eaton, Scientist and Educator* (Philadelphia, Pennsylvania: University of Pennsylvania Press, 1941), 242.

48. Dupree, *Asa Gray* (Cambridge, Massachusetts: Harvard University Press, 1959), 49, Gray's letter to N. W. Folwell, June 15, 1835.

49. David Lavendar in *Land of Giants* (Garden City, New York: Doubleday and Company, Inc., 1958), 159, called Nuttall "the shy, parsimonious, self-educated curator of Harvard University's Botanical Garden" — an extraordinary choice of adjectives to describe Nuttall, a genius in the breadth and depth of his insight. Gray stressed Nuttall's imagined *amor pecuniae* at a time when he had been unemployed for seven years. See Chapter 19, note 65 and the text to which it refers.

50. "Sketch of Past History," Boston Society of Natural History *Annual*, I (1868), 27–48.

51. Trudeau, "Description of a New Species of Woodpecker," ANS *Journal*, VII (1837), 404–406; O. (1840), 684–685.

52. Asa Gray, "Charles Pickering," American Academy of Arts and Science *Proceedings*, XIII (1877–1878), 441–444, and W. S. W. Ruschenberger, ANS *Proceedings*, XXX (1878), 166–170.

53. Charles's father, Timothy, Jr., settled on part of the large land grants which Timothy, Sr., received in recognition of his services in the Revolutionary War.

54. Pickering to Hooker, May 3, 1835, LXII, 106, Kew.

55. Pickering to T. W. Harris, December 10, 1826, H. B. Weiss and G. M. Ziegler, *Thomas Say, Early American Naturalist* (Springfield, Illinois: Charles C Thomas, 1931), 177.

56. Daniel C. Haskell, *The United States Exploring Expedition, 1838–1842, and Its Publications, 1844–1874* (New York: New York Public Library, 1942).

57. October 19, 1837, LXII, 51, Kew.

58. "On Two New Genera of California Plants," *Annals of Natural History*, I (1838), 136–139. Hooker conducted the *Botanical Magazine* from 1827 on, contributing over 2500 plates and descriptions.

59. Hovey's *Magazine of Horticulture*, V (1839), 315.

60. "On a New Species of Tacca," *American Journal of Pharmacology*, new ser., III (1838), 305–308.

61. H. B. Croom to Torrey, April 30, 1837, HSP.

62. Witmer Stone, "John Kirk Townsend," *Cassinia*, VII (1903).

63. December 29, 1837, T. Corr.

64. October 27, 1838, HSP.

65. J. W. Bailey to Torrey, November 17, 1838, T. Corr.


## CHAPTER 19. LAST YEARS IN AMERICA

1. LXII, 16, Kew.

2. Nuttall wrote to Torrey on October 23, 1838, "Most of my new plants . . . wʰ I gave in Fraser's Catal. . . . were at the time much better known, (actually existing for inspection) than anything in Mühlenberg's *Cat.* wʰ is so carefully published as authority"; T. Corr.

3. Durand wrote to Torrey on December 1, 1838, "Rafinesque says he is ready to publish a supplement to your flora!!!" T. Corr.

4. Darlington to Torrey, March 24, 1838, T. Corr.

5. Torrey's Collection of Autographed Letters, 93, ANS.

6. In September, 1840, John Coffin Jones sent from Boston to the Academy a collection of bird skins from the Sandwich Islands and the Rockies. Ms. Minutes.

7. September 11, 1845, T. Corr.

8. Darlington Papers, New York Historical Society.

9. *Ibid.*, August 17, 1838.

10. T. Corr.

11. HSP.

12. Torrey and Gray were presumably better informed concerning the exact dates of the two malvaceous claimants than anyone except the principals.

Barton's publication, appearing in small monthly installments, was suffering increasing delays in 1822. See Chapter 10, note 14.

13. August 4, 1838, LXII, 165, Kew.

14. Nuttall to Torrey, October 23, 1838; Hooker's letters of November 4, 1836, March 22, 1837, and August 4, 1838, T. Corr.

15. LXII, 102, Kew.

16. On December 12, 1838, Francis Boott wrote, "My generous Hooker — I beg you to consider all Nuttalls plants as your own or if you will make exceptions let it be only in Carex: if there be any species of my favourite genus in the Collection. I owe you so many obligations, that it would delight me to know anything belonging to me could be useful and acceptable . . . put all N's plants in your own Herbarium. My thanks to N. will only be more grateful. . . ." LXII, 46, Kew.

17. William Dawson Hooker died of yellow fever in the West Indies.

18. The corrections of the text formed Part IV of Volume I.

19. The "proposal" was probably for subscribers for Torrey and Gray's *Flora of North America.*

20. HSP.

21. *Ibid.*

22. Mss., Library Company of Philadelphia.

23. Durand to Torrey, August 13, 1838, T. Corr.

24. Torrey to G. Bentham, November 9, 1838, Bentham Correspondence, 3832, Kew.

25. Oakes to Robbins, April 21, 1841, Gray Herbarium, Harvard University, Cambridge, Massachusetts.

26. Gray to Hooker, January 15, 1841, LXIII, 224, Kew.

27. The fullest source of information concerning William Gambel is the Gambel Papers, HSP. His maternal uncle, the donor of the letters, added information concerning the family.

28. Lewis Fenno to Gambel, November 1839, Gambel Papers, HSP.

29. Darlington Papers, New York Historical Society.

30. Henry P. McClellan to Gambel, February 25, 1840, Gambel Papers, HSP.

31. Ferris Greenslet, *The Lowells and Their Seven Worlds* (Boston, Massachusetts: Houghton Mifflin Company, 1946), 233–234.

32. Gambel Papers, HSP. The steamboat from New York ran to Stonington, Connecticut, a whaling port, where connection was made by train to Boston.

33. Greenslet, see note 31 above.

34. *Ibid.,* 187.

35. *The Boston Evening Transcript,* January 25 and February 25, 1840.

36. Gould to Haldeman, S. S. Haldeman Correspondence, ANS.

37. Hooker Correspondence, LXIII, 455, Kew.

38. Obviously Thomas Nuttall.

39. Leading article on editorial page (2), *The Boston Evening Transcript,* April 25, 1840. Nuttall's acquaintance with "old grads" would be astounding had he been a recluse.

40. Brown gave his de luxe volumes on birds to the Boston Athenaeum; the rest of his ornithological library was bequeathed to the Boston Society of Natural History.

41. O. (1840), 460.

42. *Ibid.*, 421, 639, 821–822.

43. *Ibid.*, 664.

44. *Ibid.*, 555, 556.

45. Susan Austin's mother had died in 1838.

46. Tuckerman to Hooker, July 30, 1842, LXIII, 474, Kew.

47. *Ibid.*

48. Gambel to his mother, June 29, 1840, Gambel Papers, HSP.

49. Tuckerman to Torrey, June 8, 1840, T. Corr.

50. *Sylva* (1857), II, 158–159, 176–177.

51. The writer has the page proof of the 1840 edition of the *Ornithology*, obtained some years ago at a Parke–Bernet sale. An accompanying document states that the proof corrections are "in Nuttall's own hand." The ink is of the brown color characteristic of much of his writing; the printer's signs are meagre.

52. Gambel Papers, HSP; Josiah Gregg, *Commerce of the Prairies*, reprinted in *EWT*, XIX, XX, *passim*; H. H. Bancroft, *History of California* (San Francisco, 1884–1890), III, 751–752; IV, 276–278.

53. Hooker, *Journal of Botany*, III (1840), 292–299.

54. Darlington Papers, New York Historical Society.

55. LXIII, 289, Kew.

56. Gamaliel Bradford, *As God Made Them* (Boston, Massachusetts: Houghton Mifflin Company, 1929), 252, says that Gray had an argumentative disposition and was ready to discuss, to debate, even to argue, with much vehemence. Other contemporaries emphasized this characteristic.

57. Darlington Papers, New York Historical Society.

58. APS *Transactions*, new ser., VII (1840), 283–453.

59. S. G. Morton, *A Memoir of William Maclure* (Philadelphia, 1841).

60. January 25, 1838, S. G. Morton Papers, APS.

61. This statement appeared in J. Jay Smith, Preface to the edition of the *North American Sylva*; it is dated Philadelphia, February 1850.

62. HSP. This is the earliest *record* the writer has found that Nuttall was undertaking an appendix to Michaux's *Sylva*.

63. The originals are at the Arnold Arboretum, Boston, Massachusetts.

64. Alexander Lawson, a Scot settled in Philadelphia, engraved the plates for Alexander Wilson's *American Ornithology* and thereafter for many notable zoological works. F. L. Burns, "Miss Lawson's Recollections of Ornithologists," *Auk*, XXXIV (1917), 275–282.

65. On October 7, 1842, Torrey wrote to Hooker (LXIII, 459, Kew) that Nuttall "has become very fond of money." A man without salary for eight years usually has to take some thought for the morrow.

66. "Even Nuttallian specimens" rates comment. This criticism, which Gray frequently made, especially to Torrey (cf. "Nuttall's scraps of western plants," September 15, 1842) came repeatedly to mind during the weeks I studied Nuttall's own herbarium in the British Museum of Natural History, for the words were conspicuously inappropriate. I tried Gray's opinion on various workers in the herbarium and received blank stares and the comment that more specimens like Nuttall's would make life easier. When Nuttall sold specimens, he no doubt divided them as much as possible; his own are of generous proportions and beautifully preserved. George Bentham referred to "Nuttal's well pressed specimens" — Bentham to Gray, December 12, 1841.

67. January 15, 1841, LXIII, 224, Kew.

68. February 27, 1841, Historic Letter File, Gray Herbarium, Harvard University, Cambridge, Massachusetts.

69. May 20, 1841, LXIII, 230, Kew.

70. April 23, 1841, Historic Letter File, Gray Herbarium, Harvard University.

71. See Torrey's letters of October 31, 1834, and December 8, 1835, to Hooker, notes 64, 65 in Chapter 16.

72. Gray's first letter is missing. Drafts of his letters of April 14 and June 4, 1841, and Nuttall's letters of March 27, April 7, and 23 are in the Historic Letter File, Gray Herbarium, Harvard University.

73. For details of this correspondence, see A. Hunter Dupree, "Thomas Nuttall's Controversy with Asa Gray," *Rhodora*, LIV (1952), 293–303.

74. Nuttall to J. K. Townsend, April 7, 1841, HSP; E. Durand to Torrey, T. Corr. In 1843 as a result of controversies between the National Institution and Captain Wilkes, Townsend was discharged.

75. Nuttall to Hooker, October 29, 1842, LXIII, 333, Kew.

76. C. J. Wister, Jr., *Memoir of C. J. Wister* (Germantown, 1866), II, 197–198.

77. Edwin C. Jellett, "Grumblethorpe" in *Germantown History* (Germantown, Pennsylvania, 1915), 99–121.

78. Letter at Missouri Botanic Garden, St. Louis, Missouri. The writer is indebted to Dr. Richard G. Beidleman for a copy of this letter and of Nuttall's letter of November 3 to Engelmann that is quoted later.

79. Mrs. Gray's Scrapbooks, Gray Herbarium, Cambridge, Massachusetts. Blodgett, who lived at Key West from 1838, was born and died in Amherst, Massachusetts.

80. S. G. Morton, ANS Journal, VIII (1839–1842), 207–227. The various facts in this paragraph are from the ms. Minutes of the Academy or from ANS *Proceedings*, I.

81. This picture was published with Meehan's obituary of Nuttall in 1860.

82. J. B. Carlin to Gambel, September 7, 1843, Gambel Papers, HSP.

83. "Descriptions and Notices of New or Rare plants in the Natural Orders Lobeliaceae, Campanulaceae, Vaccinieae, Ericaceae, Collected in a Journey over the Continent of North America, and during a Visit to the Sandwich Islands and Upper California," APS *Transactions*, new ser., VIII (1843), 251–272.

84. Charles Sprague Sargent, *Silva of North America*, I (1891), vi.

## CHAPTER 20. REPATRIATION

1. In addition to receipts for dried and living plants, Nuttall presumably was paid for a few weeks' work of sorting plants of the Wilkes Expedition.

2. Torrey wrote to Hooker on October 7, 1842, that Nuttall did not want to live in northern England so might make some arrangement with the other heirs that would permit his return to America, LXIII, 459, Kew.

3. Nuttall to Hooker, October 29, 1842, LXIII, 333, Kew.

4. Carlin to Gambel, July 4, 1843, Gambel Papers, HSP.

5. Quoted by Frederick Tuckerman (nephew of Edward), "Gleanings from the Visitors' Albums of Ethan Allen Crawford," *Appalachia*, XIV (1916–1919), 374.

6. Jonas Nuttall's will is deposited at Preston, Lancashire.

7. The sundial was long at "Inglehurst," Huyton, the home of Major W. F. Dixon-Nuttall, Francis Dixon's grandson.

8. When the conservatory collapsed near the turn of the century, "the ladies" were removed to the garden at "Ingleholme," near St. Helens, the residence of Francis Dixon-Nuttall's son, Frederick Richard (1852–1929).

9. *Gen.*, I, 140.

10. Tuckerman sailed on the *Caledonia* on August 19, 1842, and arrived in Boston on September 2. He immediately made arrangements to accompany Asa Gray to the White Mountains. Gray wrote to Torrey that they made two ascents of the higher mountains and saw the ocean distinctly.

11. Lambert's library was sold on April 18, 19, and 20; his herbarium on June 27, 28, and 29.

12. November 5, 1842, T. Corr.

13. The donation of "A Collection of Plants from Mr. Tuckerman" was reported at the meeting of May 6, 1856 — ANS *Proceedings*, VIII (1856), ix.

14. See Chapter 14, note 17.

15. *London Journal of Botany*, I (1842), 637.

16. LXIII, 333, Kew.

17. November 10, 1842, Historic Letter File, Gray Herbarium, Harvard University, Cambridge, Massachusetts.

18. January 1, and April 1, 1844, LXIII, 246, 247, Kew; Gray to Darlington, November 29, 1843, Darlington Papers, New York Historical Society. Eventually Torrey and Gray prepared the publications on the *Phanerogamia* collected by the Wilkes Expedition so far as they were done.

19. "Letters from the Collection of Dr. Charles Wilkins Short," W. C. Coker, ed., Elisha Mitchell Scientific Society *Journal*, 57 (1941), 148.

20. Gambel, "Descriptions of Some New and Rare Birds of the Rocky Mountains and California," ANS *Proceedings*, I (1841–1843), 258–262.

21. James Carlin wrote a note, to Gambel's mother, indicating this, December 12, 1844, at the bottom of Gambel's July 15, 1844, letter to her, which she had sent for Carlin to read — Gambel Papers, HSP.

22. Most of the facts in this paragraph (and the quotation in the next) appear in Nuttall's letter to Gambel, July 2, 1843, Gambel Papers, HSP. Nuttall's letters to Gambel are quoted in S. D. McKelvey, *Botanical Exploration of the Trans-Mississippi West, 1790–1850* (Boston, Massachusetts: Arnold Arboretum, 1955), 747–750.

23. Leonard Huxley, *Life and Letters of Sir Joseph Dawson Hooker* (London, 1918), I, 352.

24. Mrs. C. R. Sherbourne to Hooker, XX, 222, 223, 224, Kew. Hurst House and estate is now a clubhouse and golf course. Sherbourne, like Francis Dixon-Nuttall, was a glass manufacturer.

25. Nuttall to Gambel, Gambel Papers, HSP; Hooker to Gray, Historic Letter File, Gray Herbarium, Harvard University, Cambridge, Massachusetts.

26. June 14, 1843, Bentham Correspondence, II, Kew.

27. Nuttall to Hooker, June 27, 1843, LXIII, 335, Kew.

28. *Ibid*. Gardner, a pupil of Hooker at Glasgow, collected in Brazil in 1836 to 1841, and from 1844 was Superintendent of the Botanic Garden, Peradenia, Ceylon. Nuttall sold Prescott a collection in 1830. Fielding bequeathed his herbarium of 70,000 species to Oxford University.

29. Nuttall to Hooker, July 11, 1843, LXIII, 334, Kew.

30. Nuttall to Hooker, April 2 and 27, 1844, LXIII, 339, 338, Kew. *London Journal of Botany*, III (1844), 400–401, pl. 16.

31. Nuttall to Hooker, April 27, 1844, LXIII, 338, Kew.

32. September 24, 1844, LXIII, 346, Kew.

33. The writer is indebted to Dr. Henry Stansfield for a list of the species. In 1836 the Liverpool Garden had been moved from Olive Street to Edge Hill.

34. Nuttall to Hooker, May 31, 1844, LXIII, 342, Kew. Alexander Gordon (fl. 1835–1845), a gardener, collected in the Rocky Mountains and South Carolina for George Charlwood, an English nurseryman. Sir William gave him a letter of introduction to John Torrey on August 26, 1844.

35. Nuttall to Hooker, June 22, 1844, LXIII, 341, Kew.

36. Nuttall to Hooker, September 2, 1844, LXIII, 344, Kew.

37. Quoted by George S. Hillard in *A Memoir of James Brown with Obituary Notices and Tributes of Respect from Public Bodies* (privately printed, Boston, 1856), 41–42.

38. *Ibid., passim.*

39. The Boston Society of Natural History has become the Boston Museum of Science.

40. Nuttall to Hooker, June 22, 1844, XLIII, 341 and September 2, 1845, LXIII, 349, Kew.

41. The plants arrived safely and were sent on to Nuttall in England. However a collection which Gambel had sent four years before from Santa Fe was lost.

42. The second volume of the *Sylva* was brought out by T. Ward and the third by Smith and Wistar. Durand says that Dr. Lambert, "a protégé and pupil of Nuttall," assisted in completing the publishing.

43. Hooker to Gray, May 29, 1844, Historic Letter File, Gray Herbarium, Harvard University, Cambridge, Massachusetts.

44. Gambel, "Descriptions of New and Little Known Birds Collected in Upper California," ANS *Proceedings*, II (1844–1845), 263–266.

45. Nuttall to Gambel, March 12, 1846, Gambel Papers, HSP.

46. ANS *Journal*, new ser., I (1848), 149–189, pls. XXII–XXIV.

47. *Ibid.*, 174. Nuttall failed to place them in the correct genus, *Baeria*, which Fischer and Meyer published in St. Petersburg, 1835.

48. LXIII, 332, Kew.

49. S. N. Dickinson, *Boston Almanac for 1849*, 45.

50. L. D. Saunderson "The Evolution of Cambridge Heights," Cambridge Historical Society *Proceedings*, XXXVIII (1959–1960), 117. The Cooper-Austin House (1657), the oldest in Cambridge, now belongs to the Society for Preservation of New England Antiquities.

51. Ms. Minutes, ANS.

52. Pickering wrote to Brackenridge on January 3, 1848, that Nuttall "proposes to set out very shortly. . . . He will be sure to visit the greenhouse [in D. C.], as his affections are now . . . engaged with living plants. . . ." United States National Museum Library, Smithsonian Institution. Brackenridge, assistant botanist on the Wilkes Expedition, published the fern collection.

53. S. Brackenridge to Torrey, March 14, 1848, T. Corr.

54. ANS *Proceedings*, IV (1848), 7–26; ANS *Journal*, new ser., I (1848), 149–189, Pls. XXII–XXIV.

55. Nuttall evidently sought a permanent association of his name with *Eriogonum*, one of his favorite genera, and in the effort violated the principle of priority, as he so often did.

56. Elizabeth Morris's copy of Nuttall's *Genera* was acquired the month it appeared. Margaretta studied fungal diseases of plants as well as insect enemies. In the late 1850s she was made an honorary member of ANS.

57. Darlington to Gray, September 18, 1848, Historic Letter File, Gray Herbarium, Harvard University, Cambridge, Massachusetts.

58. Nuttall to Short, January 24, 1849, W. C. Coker, ed., "Letters from the Collection of Dr. Charles Wilkins Short," Elisha Mitchell Scientific Society *Journal*, LVII (1941), 98–168.

59. Gray to Torrey, March 10, 1848, T. Corr. Augustus Fendler (1813–1883), a protégé of Engelmann, had gone to Santa Fe in 1846–1847 with a United States military expedition. His collections had been gratifying to the several botanists who subscribed to his expenses. Gray published *Plantae Fendlerianae* in November 1848.

60. Gray to Engelmann, March 15, 1848, Missouri Botanical Gardens, St. Louis, Missouri.

61. "My minerals" refers to Nuttall's main collection which Carpenter had been storing for him. On March 12, 1846, he had written to Gambel: "I have desired Mr. Carpenter to offer my cabinet of minerals for sale" — Gambel Papers, HSP.

62. Dr. Redfield's Correspondence, ANS.

63. Nuttall to Lyell, Autographs of Botanists and Naturalists, APS. The letter is quoted by Beidelman, 99. John Amory Lowell asked Boott to persuade Sir William J. Hooker to give a series of Lowell Lectures, but, as Hooker was harassed by moving to Kew and by family illness, Boott suggested Lyell, who gave a series late in 1841. Two years later, Boott forwarded to Hooker a second invitation from Lowell, but Hooker declined it.

64. *London Journal of Botany*, VII (1848), 391–392.

65. Nuttall to Short, January 24, 1849 and March 13, 1850. W. C. Coker, ed., "Letters from the Collection of Dr. Charles Wilkins Short," Elisha Mitchell Scientific Society *Journal*, LVII (1941).

66. Nuttall to Hooker, March 17, 1849, LXIII, 331, Kew.

67. Florence Dixon-Nuttall Sykes (Mrs. Thomas Sykes of Belfast) to her nephew, Major William F. Dixon-Nuttall, June 6, 1938. Mrs. Sykes inherited Nutgrove on her father's death in 1915 and sold it about 1940.

68. Nuttall to Hooker, January 29, 1850, LXIII, 328, Kew.

## CHAPTER 21. HORTICULTURAL PURSUITS

1. LXIII, 331, Kew.
2. *Ibid.*
3. Nuttall's letter introducing his nephew to Hooker (LXIII, 325, Kew) is dated May 26, 1849, but the letter thanking Hooker for his assistance to Jonas (LXIII, 326) is dated May 11, 1849 — an error for June 11; other records confirm this conclusion (*vide post*).
4. Derby to Hooker, July 4, 1849, XXVII, 163, Kew.
5. Derby to Hooker, July 6, 1849, XXVII, 164, Kew.

6. Nuttall to Hooker, January 29, 1850, LXIII, 328, Kew.

7. Derby to Hooker, July 4, 1849.

8. This letter was kindly made available to me by Thomas Dixon-Nuttall of Liverpool, grandson of Francis Dixon-Nuttall. India was reached by taking ship to Port Said and going overland to Suez, whence a second ship completed the journey.

9. Nuttall to Hooker, January 22, 1850, LXIII, 320, Kew.

10. Derby to Hooker, undated letter, XXIV, 214, Kew.

11. Simons and Booth are named as the collectors of *Inula simonsii* C. B. Clarke (Comp. Ind. 121). I am indebted to I. Henry Burkill, Leatherhead (Surrey), England (distinguished economic botanist, Director of Garden, Strait Settlements, 1912–1925) for this and other very helpful information and also for introductions.

12. For all geographical information about Assam the writer is indebted to letters and a sketch map from F. Ludlow, BMNH, who is acquainted with the area. He also furnished other facts such as that Booth's specimens of *R. nuttallii* at Kew, showing flowers, date his visit to the Papu River as in April or May.

13. Nuttall to Hooker, September 25, 1850, LXIII, 330, Kew; Nuttall to Durand, May 7, 1850, Torrey's Collection of Autographed Letters, ANS.

14. "Rapture of the heights" is discernible in an 1853 letter of Booth. See Chapter 21, note 58.

15. Nuttall to Hooker, April 9, 1851, LXIII, 323, Kew.

16. *Fide* F. Ludlow, BMNH.

17. Lord Derby to Hooker, December 31, 1850 [1851], XXXII, 146, Kew.

18. Nuttall later inquired about two species he failed to see at Kew — September 29, 1853, LXIV, 289, Kew.

19. *Ibid.*

20. Hooker, *Journal of Botany and Kew Garden Miscellany,* V (1853), 353–367.

21. Keys (1818–1890), a bookseller and printer, wrote a flora of Cornwall and Devon; Wilson (1799–1871) of Warrington, a bryologist, described the mosses of the 1839–1843 Antarctic Expedition.

22. Nuttall to Hooker, March 5, 1858, LXIV, 319, Kew.

23. A specimen flowering out of doors in Bavaria was reported in Hovey's *Magazine of Horticulture,* XXV (1859), 227.

24. Nuttall to Hooker, March 22, 1856, LXIV, 305, Kew.

25. Nuttall to Hooker, April 1, 1856, LXIV, 306, Kew.

26. Hovey's *Magazine of Horticulture,* XX (1854), 331–332.

27. A. P. de Candolle, *Prodromus,* X (1846).

28. Nuttall to Hooker, LXIII, 326, Kew. Bentham was the nephew and literary heir of Jeremy Bentham.

29. Bentham's Diaries, Book XII, May 18, 1849, Kew.

30. Nuttall to Hooker, LXIII, 326, Kew.

31. *Proceedings* of the Literary and Philosophical Society of Liverpool, XIV (1859), 2–5.

32. Boott to Hooker, June 6, 1843, LXIII, 56, Kew.

33. LXIII, 103, Kew.

34. LXIII, 107, 108, 111, 129, Kew. Dr. Parkman had given the Boston land on which the Harvard Medical School was built. Mrs. Prescott (mother of William Hickling Prescott) and Mrs. J. W. Webster were half-sisters,

daughters of Thomas Hickling, Vice-Consul at St. Michael, Azores. Francis Parkman wrote *The California and Oregon Trail.*

35. The janitor's suspicions were aroused, and he started a search, encouraged by Jacob Bigelow.

36. H. H. Higgins, see note 31.

37. Isaac Jones Wistar, a great-nephew of the famous Dr. Caspar Wistar, became a General during the Civil War and later a founder and president of the Wistar Museum of Anatomy and Biology of the University of Pennsylvania and President of the American Philosophical Society.

38. I. J. Wistar, *Autobiography* (Philadelphia, 1937), 42–75.

39. Obituary by D. B. Woods, reprinted in *AJS*, 2d ser., XI (1850), 143–144; C. S. Sargent, *Silva of North America* (Boston, Massachusetts: Houghton Mifflin Company, 1891–1902), VIII, 35, based on a letter to Sargent from General Wistar.

40. ANS *Proceedings*, III (1846–1847), 44–48, 110–115, 154–158, 200–205.

41. "Remarks on the Birds Observed in Upper California, With descriptions of New Species," ANS *Journal*, 2d ser., I (1847–1850), 25–56, 215–229. W. Stone, "Ornithological Facts," *Cassinia*, XIV (1910), 1.

42. Gambel, "Description of Two New Californian Quadrupeds," ANS *Proceedings*, IV (1848–1849), 77–78.

43. W. Stone, "Ornithological Facts," *Cassinia*, XIV (1910), 2.

44. January 29, 1850, LXIII, 328, Kew.

45. Darlington Papers, NYHS.

46. Nuttall to Wilson, March 24, 1850, Torrey's Collection of Autographed Letters, ANS.

47. Nuttall to Durand, May 7, 1850, *ibid.*

48. Thaddeus W. Harris Papers, Gray Herbarium, Harvard University, Cambridge, Massachusetts. Harris died in Cambridge on January 16, 1856.

49. The profits were used toward the establishment of the South Kensington Museums.

50. LXIV, 286, Kew.

51. Nuttall to C. W. Short, January 26, 1854: "Letters from the Collection of Dr. Charles Wilkins Short," ed. by W. C. Coker, Elisha Mitchell Scientific Society *Journal*, LVII (1941), 98–168.

52. Probably this was not Pickering's first visit at Nutgrove, for he had been in England in 1843 and 1847 and would have sailed to and from Liverpool for Boston, his headquarters.

53. Elias Durand, APS *Proceedings*, VII (1860). Pickering had called on Hooker, who found Pickering talented, interesting, and agreeable and regretted that his son had not been home to meet him — Hooker to Torrey, August 17, 1854, T. Corr.

54. *Ibid.*, 315. At some time three of the breakfast-room windows at Nutgrove had been bricked up to reduce "the window tax," according to observation of the writer in 1954 when she had the opportunity of examining the house without and within.

55. W. C. Coker, ed., "Letters from the Collection of Dr. Charles Wilkins Short," Elisha Mitchell Scientific Society *Journal*, LVII (1941), 102. This letter was followed by further requests for *Collinsia verna* on March 13, 1850, and January 26, 1854.

56. April 19, 1854, LXIV, 295, Kew. In this letter Nuttall sent some seeds of *Cladrastis lutea* that he had just received from Short.

57. February 12, 1856, LXIV, 303, Kew. This would give great pleasure to Short, who subscribed to the *Botanical Magazine*. Short to Engelmann, January 16, 1849, Missouri Botanical Garden, St. Louis, Missouri.

58. I am indebted to Professor Raymond Adams of the University of North Carolina for the facts in this paragraph, the records of which were attached to an odd volume of Nuttall's *Sylva* which he got from an English bookdealer. Through Dr. Francis Harper's kindness and wide interests I was put in touch with Professor Adams. Among several miscellaneous papers were two pieces of R. Clapham's correspondence: a brief note of Nuttall written on December 4, 1853, thanking him for the gift of Don's "Gardeners' Dictionary," and a letter of December 12, 1853, from Jonas Booth. There was also a letter of September 25, 1878, from Jno. Goodwin of Liverpool answering an inquiry of T. R. Clapham concerning Thomas Nuttall and his family; this stated "Jonas is not in England."

59. April 1, 1856, LXIV, 306, Kew.

60. Vol. I, Judah Dobson, pt. I (1842), 1–56; pt. II (1843), 57–136. Vol. II, T. Ward (Philadelphia, 1846). Vol. III, Smith and Wistar (Philadelphia, 1849).

61. Reissues of Nuttall's *Sylva* in three volumes were printed in 1852, 1853, and 1855 and in two volumes in 1857, 1859, and 1865.

62. The *Horticulturist*, XI (1856), 242.

63. The two letters of Darlington are at the Library Company of Philadelphia, so it would seem that Smith failed to make use of the letter he solicited.

64. June 4, 1857, LXIV, 311, Kew.

65. G. B. Emerson to Hooker, October 7, 1857, LXIV, 101, Kew.

66. Nuttall to Hooker, October 19, 1857, LXIV, 317, Kew.

67. Nuttall to Hooker, LXIV, 319, 323, 325, Kew.

68. The death certificate was examined through the kindness of Geoffrey Dixon-Nuttall. Near the close of his "Biographical Notice of the late Thomas Nuttall," Durand wrote that he "met with an accident that ultimately resulted in his death. In his eagerness to open a case of plants which he had just received from Mr. Booth, he unfortunately overstrained himself, and from the time of his injury he gradually sunk and died. . . ." Durand's "Notice" is found in APS *Proceedings*, VII (1860), 297–315. Nuttall's certified illnesses were of a nature to discredit this alleged cause; moreover his Rector, R. P. Crockett, remarked in detail on his "long and protracted illness," which was obvious in the suspension of his correspondence with Hooker a full year before he died.

## CHAPTER 22. POSTSCRIPT

1. Stevens, London's third oldest auctioneers (dating from 1776), was "blitzed-out" in World War II. The first natural history objects it sold were collections of Captain Cook. B. Partridge, *Going, Going, Gone* (Dutton, 1958).

2. Higgins to Hooker, October 31, XXXIX, 408, Kew.

3. *Historical Collections in Natural History Department of British Museum*, I (1904), 171.

4. *Gardeners' Chronicle* (1862), 406. Jno. Goodwin of Liverpool to T. R. Clapham, Sept. 25, 1878. See Chapter 21, note 58.

5. Information received in letters of June 1948, through October 1949, from Samuel Rishworth Booth of Rainhill, who loaned Brooke's volume to the writer.

6. S. R. Booth never stated that the field journals had been destroyed, but his remarks pointed to it. This was also the impression of Dr. Henry Stansfield who, as Keeper of Botany at the Liverpool Museums, talked with him on more than one occasion.

7. Willis Linn Jepson, "The Overland Journey of Thomas Nuttall," *Madroño*, II (1934), 143–147.

8. When Higgins was in the Americas, a stay in Philadelphia in 1876 permitted a number of visits to the Academy of Natural Sciences where he talked with Nuttall's old friend Isaac Lea. He was presented with an album containing letters of early members of the Academy including "several from my late dear friend and neighbour Professor Nuttall." H. H. Higgins, *Notes by a Field-Naturalist in the Western Tropics* (Liverpool, 1877), 192–193. No trace of the album could be found at the Liverpool Museums.

9. Higgins, Literary and Philosophical Society of Liverpool *Proceedings*, XIV (1859), 2–5.

10. T. J. Booth, "Mr. Thomas Nuttall, the Naturalist," *The Settle Chronicle and North Ribblesdale Advertiser*, January 1 and February 1, 1861. Reprinted in *Bartonia*, XIX (1938), 51–54.

11. October 8, 1859, Historic Letter File, Gray Herbarium, Harvard University, Cambridge, Massachusetts.

12. November 7, 1859, Missouri Botanical Garden, St. Louis, Missouri. The monument that Nuttall most desired was an enduring *Nuttallia*.

13. (Boston, 1891), II, 34.

# INDEX

# INDEX

# INDEX

*mus* (1815), 117; *Flora of North America,* 157

*Bartonia,* 34, 290; decapetala Pursh, 83; superba, 86

Bartram, Ann, 97

Bartram Garden, 19, 20, 22, 24, 97, 355, 358, 373

Bartram, John, 19–20, 29, 88, 194, 374

Bartram, John, Jr., 19, 28; death, 97

Bartram, William, 19–20, 24, 27, 28, 29, 75, 88, 97, 104, 109, 167, 248; *Travels Through North and South Carolina, Georgia, East and West Florida, etc.,* 29; death, 194

Beechey Expedition (California), 319, 327

*Begonia: rex,* 383; *xanthina* Hook., 386; *rubrovenia* Hook., 386

*Belemnites,* 217

Belknap, Reverend Jeremy, 207; *History of New Hampshire,* 208

Bell, Captain John R., 154

Belle Point. *See* Fort Smith

Bentham, George, 291, 334, 361, 367, 377; and De Candolle's *Scrophulariaceae,* 387

*Berberis: aquifolium* Pursh, 91; *nervosa* Pursh, 91

Beryl, 349

Berzelius, Jöns J., 165

Bethune, John McLean, 226; and Nuttall's *Land Birds,* 249

*Betula occidentalis* Hook., 298

Biddle, John, 131

Biddle, Nicholas, 38

Bigelow, Dr. Jacob, 156, 167, 175, 178, 179, 188, 198, 203, 235, 270; *Florula Bostoniensis,* 95, 184, 229, 236, 346; Mt. Washington trip (1816), 208, 210; Boston reputation, 235–236; *American Medical Botany,* 235–236; "The Self-limited character of Disease," 236; and Mt. Auburn Cemetery, 268

Bingham, Reverend Hiram, 310

Binney, Amos, Jr., 209

Birds. *See* Ornithological studies

Blackburne, Mr., 369

Blanding, Dr. William, 285

Blodgett, Dr. John Loomis, 359

Blume, Karl L., 385

Blumenbach, Johann F., 164, 188

Blyth, Mr., 380, 381

Bogy, Charles(?), 138, 145, 148

*Bolophyta,* 297

Bonaparte, Charles Lucien, 244, 256

Bonneville, Capt. Benjamin L. E. de, 281–282, 283

Boone, Captain, 389

Boone, Daniel, 60

Booth, Jonas Thomas, 378, 386, 392, 394, 396; and Himalayan rhododendrons, 379–384; and Nuttall's collections, 397; and Rainhill Nursery, 397

Booth, Samuel Rishworth, 397–398

Booth, Susan. *See* Nuttall, Susan

Booth, Thomas, 81, 198

Booth, William, 378

Boott, Dr. Francis, 174, 232, 255, 319–320, 330, 340, 349, 367, 371, 373, 387–388; and Nuttall's *Genera,* 127, 203; Mt. Washington expedition (1816), 208–210, 218; and London Horticultural Society, 255–256; and Nuttall's herbarium, 271; and Hooker's *Flora Boreali-Americana,* 276–277; and Say, 287; on Torrey's *Flora,* 336

Boott, John Wright, 209, 212, 232, 246, 367

Boott, Mrs. Kirk, 319–320

Boott, William, 320

Boston Athenaeum, 175, 270

*Boston Evening Transcript,* 270–271, 346–347

*Boston Journal of Philosophy and the Arts,* 217

Boston Society of Natural History, 226, 249, 270, 330, 349, 370, 373; and B. D. Greene, 276, 319, 330; and Lowell's herbarium, 345

Botanic Garden, Cambridge, 95, 172–176, 198, 233–243, 269, 320, 321, 334, 346; Nuttall becomes curator, 171; Garden House, 182–183, 224, 237, 275; Garden Committee, 235; and Harvard Corporation, 274–275

*Botanical Magazine* (Curtis), 83, 86–87, 201, 202, 334, 367, 369, 386, 394, 396; Hooker's description of Nuttall's *Rhododendron,* 385

Botanic Garden, Geneva, 127

*Botanische Zeitung* (Reichenbach), 171

Botany in North America. *See* North American botany

Bowditch, Nathaniel, 208, 260; *New Practical Navigator,* 267; and Harvard Corporation, 267

Bowdoin College, 25

Bowen, George T., 168, 189, 192

Boykin, Dr. Samuel, 99, 257, 289, 290; and Nuttall's *Compositae,* 353

Brackenridge, Henry Marie, 56–57, 68–

461

# INDEX

Carolina, Florida, and the Bahamas Islands, 30, 220
Caxton Press, 8, 156
Ceanothus: cuneatus (Hook.) Nutt., 312; thyrsiflorus Esch., 314; *rigidus, 314; *verrucosus, 315
Centaurea americana Nutt., 143, 144, 157
Centrocercus urophasianus, 299
Cercocarpus: ledifolius Nutt., 300; *betuloides, 314
Chamisso, Adalbert von, 376
Channing, Edward Tyrrell, 178
Channing, Dr. Walter, 235
Chapman, Dr. Nathaniel, 119, 162
Chara, 257
Charbonneau, 67
Charles, Joseph, 73; Missouri Gazette, 55
Charlevoix, Pierre, 155
Charlton, Captain, 309
Chelsea Botanic Garden (Guild of Apothecaries), 85, 202, 203
Chimaphila, 126
Chinquapin, 112
Chionanthus virginious (Willd.), 33, 355
Chouteau, Auguste, 54, 58, 140, 145, 293
Chouteau, Pierre, 145
Christian Examiner, 344
Chrysanthemum, 369
Chrysemys picta belli, 323
Chrysopsis: *trichophylla, 102; *alpina, 281
Cimicifugas, 325
Cirsium undulatum (Nutt.) Spreng., 51
Citellus tridecemlineatus pallidus (Allen), 72
Clapham, Richard, 394
Clapham, Thomas Richard, 394
Clark, General William, 61, 140; report of expedition, 38; Agent for Indian Affairs, 55; and Fort Osage, 63; and Pursh, 84–86, 365; and fossils, 360; see also Lewis and Clark Expedition
Clarke, Dr. Adam, 9
Clay, Mr., 343
Clayton, John, 29, 88
Cleaveland, Parker, 25, 95, 191, 192; Elementary Treatise on Mineralogy and Geology, 25
Clematis: hirsutissimus, 198; columbiana (Nutt.) T. & G., 281
Clifford, John D., 108
Clifford, Lord Henry, 5
Cliftonia ligustrina Sims [C. monophylla (Lam.) Sarg.], 259

Clinocardium nuttalli (Conrad), 309
Clintonia borealis (Ait.) Raf., 36, 177
Clowes, Mr., 369
Cogswell, Joseph Green, 178, 188, 191
Colaptes cafer collaris, 297
Colby College, 350
Colden, Cadwallader, 155
Coleoptera, 117, 226, 252
Collins, Zaccheus, 104, 109, 112, 124, 127, 160, 194, 233; friendship with Nuttall, 24, 27, 94; and Academy of Natural Sciences, 96, 115, 117–119, 185–186, 203; as Nuttall's agent, 98; and American Philosophical Society, 103, 119; Nuttall names plants for, 105, 122–123, 289; daughter, 129; and Nuttall's Arkansas trip (1819), 131, 136, 139, 155, 161; and Silliman's Journal, 163–164; herbaria, 271–273
Collinsia, 119; verna Nutt., 45, 105, 393–394; *violacea, 142, 229; heterophylla Graham, 334
*Collomia, 352; linearis, 64
Colter, John, 60–62, 65
Columbia River Fishing and Trading Company, 284
Comandra, 126
Comeawhait, 21
Compositae (Nuttall), 29, 124, 220, 229, 273, 288, 289, 297, 315, 343, 346, 349, 352–353, 361, 372; and Asa Gray, 356–357
Conrad, Solomon White, 118, 289
Conrad, Thomas, 159
Conrad, Timothy A., 261–262, 264, 285, 360; "Description of New Marine Shells from Upper California, Collected by Thomas Nuttall, Esq.," 323
Conradia fuchsioides, 291
Convallaria, 126
Cooper, Dr. Thomas, 115, 130–131
Cooper, William, 127, 160, 168, 233–234; and Nuttall's Land Birds, 249
Corallobotrys acuminata Klotzsch, 396
Corallorhiza: trifida var. verna (Nutt.) Fern., 177, 186; maculata, 187
Coreopsis, 257; *palmata, 51; *rosea, 101; *tinctoria (calliopsis), 144, 157, 202, 238–239, 263
Coriandrum, 143
Cornus: florida, 259, 325; nuttallii Audubon, 305, 325, 369
Cornus nuttallii Audubon, 322
Cornuti, 220
Cornutus, 30

# INDEX

Corréa da Serra, Abbé José Francisco, 95, 130, 136, 140, 180; and American Philosophical Society, 120; and *Genera*, 122, 123; and Nuttall's Arkansas trip, 131, 155; and Academy of Sciences of Lisbon, 152

*Corydalis*, 286

Coulter, Thomas, 280, 319

*Courrier de la Louisiané*, 76

Coues, Elliott, 309

Couthouy, Joseph P., 332; and United States Exploring Expedition, 332

Coville Nursery, London, 102

Coxe, Dr. John Redman, 142, 269

*Coyotes*, 314

Craigie, Andrew, 173, 239

Craigie, Elizabeth Shaw, 239–240, 349, 365

Crantz, Heinrich J. N., 122–123

*Crataegus sanguinea* Pallas, 303

Crawford, Abel, 209

Crawford, Ethan Allen, 209–211, 212–213, 214

Craven District, Yorkshire, 4, 9–10

*Crinum americanum* L., 76

*Crithmum maritimum*, 252

Crockett, R. P., 399

Crooks, Ramsey, 57, 63, 67, 68, 69

Croom, Hardy Bryan, 262, 353, 377; death, 334

*Crossosoma* Nutt., 376; *californica*, 376

*Cruciferae*, 123, 157, 198, 229, 288, 315

*Crustacea*, 226, 309, 315–316, 324, 330

Crystal Palace, 392

*Culmariae*, 81

Cummings, Hilliard and Company, Boston, 216

Cunningham, Edward Linzie, 263

*Cupressus disticha (Taxodium distichum)*, 34

Curzonia, 353

Cutler, Reverend Manasseh, 21, 207–208; "Account of Some of the Vegetable Production Growing in this Part of America, Botanically Arranged" (1785), 26

Curtis, Moses Ashley, 28, 128

Curtis, William, 90–91, 202

Cushing, Caleb, 126, 175, 209, 210, 232; "Botany of the United States," 126; review of *Genera*, 126–127

Cuvier, Georges, 122

Cyanite, 214

*Cyperaceae*, 271, 325

*Cypripedium acaule*, 177

Dabney, Frederick, 263, 264

Dabney, John Bass, 263

Dagsworthy, General John, 34

*Dalea *enneandra*, 54

Dalhousie, Earl of, 380

*Dalibarda repens* L., 36

Dallas, J. H., 115

Dana, James Dwight, 332; and U. S. Exploring Expedition, 332

Dana, Dr. James Freeman, 174, 192; death, 254

Dana, Richard Henry, 2, 316–317

*Danthonia *sericea*, 102

Darlington, Dr. William, 27, 99, 154, 254, 286, 338, 343, 351, 354, 359, 374; and Baldwin, 123–125; Torrey visit, 215; *Flora Cestrica*, 286; *Florula Cestrica*, 286; and *Genera*, 359; *Memorials of John Bartram and Humphry Marshall*, 390

Dartmouth College, 235

Davis, Isaac P., 319

Davis, John, 182, 183

Day, Mary A., 238

Dearborn, General Henry A. S., 246, 268

De Candolle, Augustin Pyramus, 197, 212, 218, 275–276, 289, 324, 366, 376; *Mémoires*, 122; *Prodromus Systematis Naturalis*, 198, 220, 361, 387; *Regni Vegetabilis Systema Naturale*, 198; *Cinquième Mémoire: sur la famille Ombellifères*, 200

*Dendrocopus: villosus auduboni*, 330; *nuttallii* (Gambel), 366

*Dentaria: *maxima*, 37, 198; *heterophylla* Nutt., 45, 198

Derby, Earl of (Lord Stanley), 80, 369, 370, 380, 381, 388

Derby, Elias H., 234

Derby, 201

Desfontaines, René Louiche, 126

*Desmodium pauciflorum* (Nutt.) DC, 108

DeSoto, 137, 141

Dewey, Chester, 160–161, 165, 167, 171, 328, 330; "Caricography," 221

Dexter, Dr. Aaron, 234

*Diamorpha*, 111

*Diapensia lapponica* L., 208

Dick, William, 157, 194

Dickson, Robert, 53

Dickson, James, 84, 88, 90–91

Diell, Reverend John, 310

Dietrich, Albert, 376

*Diodia: virginiana* L., 33; *teres* Walt., 35

# INDEX

# INDEX

# INDEX

# INDEX

# INDEX

Peabody, Andrew Preston, 225, 226
Peabody, William B. O., 250, 330
Peale, Charles Willson, 20–22
Peale, Rembrandt, 21
Peale, Rubens, 21
Peale, Titian R., 21; and Yellowstone Expedition, 131, 154; and United States Exploring Expedition, 332
Pearsall, Robert, 338
Peattie, Donald Culross, 250–251
Peck, Harriet Hilliard, 173, 182, 188, 237, 348
Peck, William Dandridge, 25–26, 85, 95, 270, 275; death, 171, 175, 236, 274–275; Professor of Natural History, Harvard, 172–173; students of, 174–175, 236; White Mountain expedition (1804), 208
Peck, William Dandridge, Jr., 226
Pendleton, William, 229
Pennines, 4–6, 9–10
*Penstemons*, 64, 80; *\*grandiflorus*, 54, 64; *\*albidus*, 64; *\*gracilis*, 64, 71; *angustifolius*, 71; *\*Cobaea*, 144; *\*tubaeflorus*, 144; *\*Digitalis*, 202, *\*pumilus*, 281; *\*micranthus*, 282
Pennsylvania Horticultural Society, 332
*\*Pentachaeta aurea*, 315
*Peplis diandra* Nutt., 220
Perkins, Henry Coit, 184–185, 225
Perkins, Samuel G., 234
Perkins, Thomas Handasyd, 243, 246
*Peromyscus: nuttalli*, 262; *californicus*, 390; *maniculatus gambeli*, 390
*Persea Borbonia* (L.) Spreng., 35
*Petalostemum: \*multiflorum*, 141; *\*gracilis*, 259
*Petrificata Derbiensia*, 81
*Phacelia \*hirsuta*, 141
*Phacoides*, 323
*Phalaenoptilus nuttalli* (Audubon), 298
Philadelphia, 17–18, 26–28; Peale's Museum, 16, 20–22, 244; Port Folio, 16, 235; Nuttall visits (1808), 18–24; Linnaean Society, 22, 40; Nuttall returns (1815), 94–98; Academy of Natural Sciences, 35, 96, 114–115, 242; Medical Society, 40; Horticultural Society, 386
*Philadelphia Journal of the Medical and Physical Sciences*, 162, 208
Philadelphia Library Company, *Botanical Register*, 338
*Philadelphus \*hirsutus*, 109
Phillips, John S., 366
*\*Pholisma*, 367; *arenarium*, 315

*Phlox*, 236; *\*caespitosa*, 281; *\*longifolia*, 282
*Phoradendron flavescens* (Pursh) Nutt., 33, 100
*Photinia arbutifolia* Lindl. (Toyon), 315
*Phrynosoma cornutum*, 323
*Phyllanthus polygonoides* Nutt., 220
*Phyllitis scolopendrium* (L.) Newm. var. *americana* Fern., 37
Physic Garden, 88
*Physostegia: intermedia* (Nutt.) Englem. & Gray, 144; *\*parviflora*, 312
*Phytologist*, 395
*Pica nuttallii* (Aud.), 315, 360
Pickering, Dr. Charles, 120, 210, 234, 236, 322, 356, 377; and Peck, 174; and Wilkes Expedition, 175; White Mountain trips, 211–212; Harvard undergraduate, 225; friendship with Nuttall, 237, 269, 272, 286, 291, 373; and Nuttall's *Land Birds*, 249; and Franklin Institute, 287; at Academy of Natural Sciences of Philadelphia, 288, 325; Nuttall names plant for, 289; and Harris, 318; and Randall, 324; United States Exploring Expedition, 330–331, 332–333; "Geographical Distribution of Plants," 332; *Races of Man and Their Geographical Distribution*, 333; visits Nuttall in England, 393
Pickering, Timothy, 237
*\*Pickeringia*, 314
Pierce, James, 209
Pike, Zebulon, 129; Expedition, 60, 146
Pike's Peak, 154
*Pilularia*, 161
*Pinckneyeas*, 22
*Pinguicula lutea* Walt., 102
Pinkham, Daniel, 211
*Pinus*, 84; *australis*, 101; *pungens* Lambert, 110
Pitcher, Dr. Zina, 288, 289, 290
*Pittosporum*, 264
*Pittsburgh Navigator*, 137
Planchon, Jules Emile, 376
*Plantago \*purpurascens* (*P. virginica* L.), 220
*Platanus \*racemosa*, 314, 322
*Pleea tenuifolia* Michx., 102
*Podostemum*, 258, 289
*Pogonia ophioglossoides* (L.) Ker., 102
*Polanisia graveolens* Raf., 37
Polemoniaceae, 203
*Polemonium \*viscosum*, 297
Pollock, George, 119

475

# INDEX

# INDEX

# INDEX